TEACHER'S EDITION

Common Core

Progress™

Mathematics

4

For additional online resources, access your state-specific Teacher Toolbox.
Go to www.SadlierConnect.com and enter the Teacher's Access Code:

State	Access Code	State	Access Code
Alabama	CCPM01AL4R	Mississippi	CCPM28MS4G
Arizona	CCPM04AZ4N	Missouri	CCPM29MO4M
Arkansas	CCPM05AR43	New Jersey	CCPM34NJ4F
California	CCPM06CA4E	North Carolina	CCPM37NC4C
Colorado	CCPM08CO48	Ohio	CCPM39OH4X
Connecticut	CCPM09CT4Z	Oklahoma	CCPM40OK4B
Florida	CCPM12FL4T	Pennsylvania	CCPM42PA4C
Georgia	CCPM13GA47	South Carolina	CCPM45SC4B
Illinois	CCPM17IL4O	Tennessee	CCPM47TN4S
Kentucky	CCPM21KY4L	Texas	CCPM48TX4H
Louisiana	CCPM22LA4P	Wisconsin	CCPM55WI40
Massachusetts	CCPM25MA42	Other States	CCPMNA2493
Michigan	CCPM26MI4K		

 Sadlier School

TEACHER'S EDITION

Cover: *Series Design:* Studio Montage; *Title design:* Quarasan, Inc.

Photo Credits: Cover: Getty Images/Cameron Davidson: *bottom left.* Used under license from Shutterstock.com: kle555: *top left;* RoboLab: *background;* Vlad 61: *right;* Marty Wakat: *center;* Richard Whitcombe: *right.* Interior: Corbis/Rob Lewine: T12; Ocean: T15 and T17; Dann Tardiff: T09. Used under license from Shutterstock.com/wavebreakmedia: T03. Alamy/Purestock/Lisette Le Bon: 54 *top.* Blend Images/ JGI: 124 *top;* KidStock: 8 *top,* 232 *top;* Somos: 302 *top.* Corbis/Patrick Giardino: 233. Dreamstime.com/ Steve Allen: vi *bottom left;* vi *top right.* Getty Images/ Ming Tang-Evans: 55. Used under license from Shutterstock.com/Ilya Akinshin: vi *bottom right;* Jana Guothova: 8 *bottom,* 54 *bottom,* 124 *bottom,* 232 *bottom,* 302 *bottom;* kle555: vi *center;* Levent Konuk: 9; koosen: vi *top left;* RoboLab: 1, vi *background;* Ilya Ryabokon: vi *top left.* SuperStock/SuperFusion/Ron Chapple Photography: 125; John Warden: 303.

Illustrator Credit: Dave Titus

ꞩ is a registered trademark of William H. Sadlier, Inc.

William H. Sadlier, Inc.
9 Pine Street
New York, NY 10005-4700

Printed in the United States of America.
ISBN: 978-1-4217-3164-3
1 2 3 4 5 6 7 8 9 WEBC 18 17 16 15 14

Common Core State Standards © 2010. National Governors Association Center for Best Practices and Council of Chief State School Officers. All rights reserved.

Contents

Access Your Digital Resources

Get Started

1. Go to www.SadlierConnect.com.

2. Log in

Don't have a username and password? Self register! Teachers click "Get Started!" in the Teacher Registration section.

3. Select your program to begin accessing content.

With one username and password, you now have access to all your Sadlier Mathematics and English Language Arts content.

T3

Contents

continued next page

Contents

continued next page

Contents

Unit 5   Focus on Geometry

Program Overview

Common Core Progress Mathematics is a streamlined, yet comprehensive K-8 supplemental mathematics program that follows the structure of the Common Core State Standards for Mathematics and integrates the Standards for Mathematical Practice into every lesson. The program systematically addresses all of the Common Core State Standards for Mathematics across the Domains: Operations and Algebraic Thinking, Number and Operations in Base Ten, Number and Operations–Fractions, Measurement and Data, and Geometry, which helps prepare students for the rigor of Common Core standardized assessments and enables them to develop key college and career readiness skills.

In *Common Core Progress*, students will:

- Build understanding of key mathematical concepts using multiple representations of a skill.

- Model mathematics with real-world problems to make sense of math and apply their knowledge.

- Share their thinking and reason mathematically while developing academic vocabulary.

- Use higher-level thinking skills and apply levels of Webb's Depth of Knowledge (DOK) with rigorous, cognitively-demanding independent practice items.

- Regularly use the Standards for Mathematical Practice so that they become habits of mind.

With the support of a comprehensive Teacher's Edition, teachers will be able to:

- Scaffold student learning with easy-to-use, comprehensive lesson plans.

- Use student assessment data, both observational and formal, to inform and redirect instruction.

- Understand the progression of Common Core Mathematics requirements across grade levels and tailor instruction to Common Core grade-level standards.

- Support diverse learners, including English language learners, struggling learners, and those needing extended learning opportunities.

- Access online and professional development resources to enhance instruction.

Founded on the Common Core Standards

Sadlier's *Common Core Progress Mathematics* was designed to effectively implement the three instructional shifts (focus, coherence, and rigor) that are necessary to teach the Common Core State Standards (CCSS) and fully addresses the shifts that were reorganized by Student Achievement Partners and the Publisher's Criteria to fall under rigor: fluency, deep understanding, application, and dual intensity.

Shifts in Mathematics Common Core Standards		
Shift	**Requirement**	**How Addressed in *Common Core Progress***
Focus	Class time and energy spent on a deeper focus on the key concepts as prioritized by the standards.	*Common Core Progress* is designed to focus on the major work of the grade per the CCSS.
Coherence	Learning within and across grade levels is carefully connected in order to build students' understanding.	Learning Progression charts that describe how the standards are developed across the grade levels are provided for each unit.
Rigor as Fluency	Students are expected to have speed and accuracy with simple calculations; teachers structure class or homework time for students to memorize through repetition.	Fluency Practice is provided (online) with references to the extra practice included at point of use in the Teacher's Edition.
Rigor as Deep Understanding	Students deeply understand and can operate easily within a math concept before moving on.	The structure of the lesson allows the student to develop a deep understanding of the concept being covered, with the Guided Instruction and Guided Practice portions of the lesson establishing the conceptual understanding.
Rigor as Application	Students use math and choose appropriate concept for application–not only when prompted.	While working independently on the independent practice and the performance tasks, students must determine which skills, strategies, and practices best serve to solve the problems and tasks at hand.
Rigor as Dual Intensity	Students are practicing and understanding with intensity.	As students work through the scaffolded Independent Practice exercises, teachers can gauge student understanding of the concepts by referencing the Common Error Analysis guidance provided in the Teacher's Edition. Through both direct instruction and practice students work toward a deep understanding of the concept.

Flexible Program Use

Common Core Progress fully aligns to the Common Core State Standards, serving as a flexible resource for supporting schools in meeting the full breadth and rigor of these standards. Lessons focus on the key concepts addressed in the Common Core and combine solid content with a pedagogically-sound lesson design that simplifies the instructional process.

Common Core Progress can be used as:

- Supplemental lessons to fill Common Core gaps in a current core Mathematics program.

- Targeted preparation materials for Common Core standardized assessments.

- Support for individual or small group instruction on a particular Common Core standard.

Diverse Grouping Models

The *Common Core Progress* program employs diverse grouping and instructional models to help teachers provide effective instruction in the Common Core State Standards.

Guided Instruction For standard instruction, the program uses **whole-class** instruction to provide direct skill instruction and think-aloud modeling while the students follow along with the teacher, helping students conceptualize skills and concepts through modeling and reasoning.

Guided Practice For scaffolded practice of the standard, students work through problems of increasing complexity, independently or in small groups, as the teacher circulates around the classroom to gauge understanding of the concepts and skill being learned.

Independent Practice For application of the standards, lessons offer independent practice requiring students to use their critical-thinking skills and apply their math knowledge.

Foundational Skill Support and Fluency Practice

Foundational skills lessons and fluency practice are provided in the following ways in *Common Core Progress*.

- A comprehensive Foundational Skills Handbook, located in the back of this guide as well as in the student edition, provides a review of *all* prerequisite mathematics needed to understand the concepts and skills of Grade 4.

- Fluency practice is available online providing students with the opportunity to build their skills of performing calculations and solving problems quickly and accurately in order to meet the grade level fluency expectations specified by the Common Core State Standards.

- Problem-Solving Model offers students a four-step model as an approach to solving problems.

Print Components

Student Worktext

Organized around the Common Core Domains, the standards-based instruction includes clearly-stated models, multiple representations of skills, a focus on the critical areas of each grade level, and connections between topics to meet all Common Core State Standards. ▶

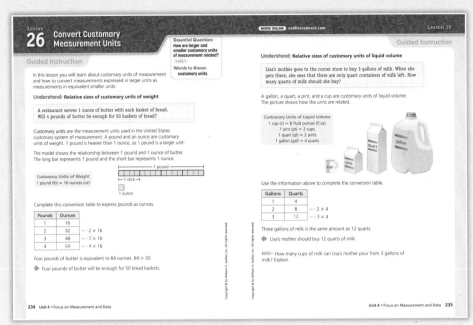

Grade 4 Pages 234–235

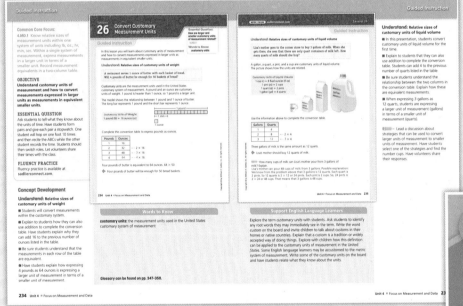

Grade 4 Teacher's Edition Pages 234–235

◀ Teacher's Edition

Teacher-friendly lesson plans with targeted standards instruction and supportive features suitable for both novice and experienced teachers. Supports instruction for all Common Core State Standards!

Progress Monitor

Four comprehensive Benchmark Assessments to identify instructional needs as benchmarked against the grade level's full set of Common Core State Standards. ▶

Grade 4 Progress Monitor

Digital Components

A rich array of online digital components supports program implementation and extends learning.

- **Home Connect Activities** support family member involvement and help create associations with math in real-world situations

- **Student Book Performance Tasks 1 and 2 Resources** allow students to apply their learning and provide teachers with robust evaluation support

- Downloadable **Unit Performance Tasks** provide practice opportunities for Performance Tasks related to the program's instructional units

- **Additional Practice** downloadables offer opportunities to augment program practice

- **Fluency Practice** downloadables provide opportunities for students to improve speed and accuracy with simple calculations

- **Teacher Resources**, such as a professional development training video support teachers in implementing the program

iProgress Monitor (Optional Purchase)

This dynamic online assessment system is available to help monitor student progress on the Common Core standards in real time and customize assignments based on individual needs through it's built-in test generator feature. See page T13 of this guide for more information.

Online State-Specific Teacher Toolbox

Tailored to your state, and to each grade level, K-8, the online State-Specific Teacher Toolbox has everything you need to seamlessly incorporate *Progress* into your core Math programs!

Find answers to critical questions on structure and pacing to assessment to professional development and much more! Learn how *Progress*…

- Relates to your state's Common Core **implementation plan**.
- Aligns with the **structure and pacing** of your state's model curriculum.
- Correlates to your **state's standards**.
- Supports your state's **assessment** plan.
- Helps to implement a **Common Core curriculum**.
- Provides embedded **Professional Development**

Interactive Edition

The Interactive Edition of Common Core Progress is a web-based version of the complete program through **www.SadlierConnect.com**, with access to rich media and an abundance of resources for teachers, students, and parents.

Core Digital Components

Digital **Student Worktext** Digital version of the Student Worktext, accessible online to all students.

Digital **Teacher's Edition** Digital version of the Teacher's Edition, available 24/7 to teachers at home or at school without the need to carry a heavy text! Incorporates links to all online resources as well as iProgress Monitor.

Digital Components

Exclusive to the Interactive Edition!

- **Interactive Whiteboard Tools** provide support for teaching key skills and concepts.

- ***Domain- and Lesson-Specific Videos*** support student learning of Commom Core State Standards.

- **iProgress Monitor** gives students access to:
  - Independent Practice
  - Common Core Reviews
  - Performance Tasks

Plus, access program assessment in a digital format or build your own!

Plus all the Digital Components included with the Print Edition!

Common Core Progress contains many formative and summative assessment opportunities to help teachers gather evidence of students' progress toward mastering the Common Core State Standards and prepare for the new Common Core assessments.

Integrated, Ongoing Assessment Opportunities

Observational Assessment opportunities are a routine part of each Lesson Plan in the Teacher's Edition. Common Errors and Teaching Tips features at point of use help teachers identify student misconceptions and provide strategies for solutions. ▶

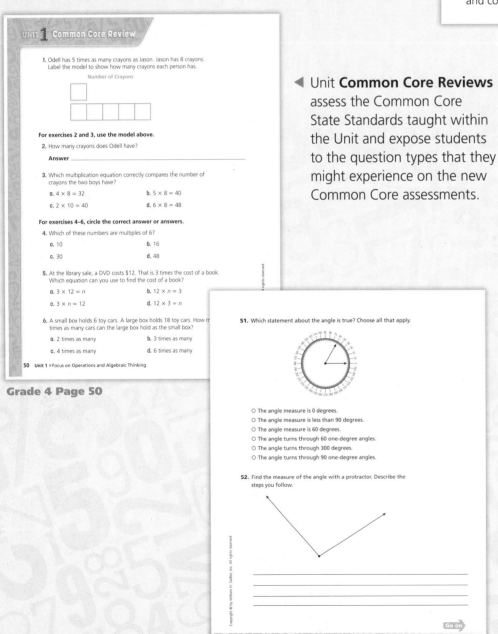

◀ Unit **Common Core Reviews** assess the Common Core State Standards taught within the Unit and expose students to the question types that they might experience on the new Common Core assessments.

Grade 4 Page 50

◀ Benchmark Assessments in **Progress Monitor** (an optional purchase) provide four comprehensive assessments that can be administered periodically throughout the school year to evaluate students' knowledge and skill level relative to the grade level's set of Common Core State Standards.

Grade 4 Progress Monitor Benchmark Assessment

Performance Tasks 1 and 2

provide benchmark Performance Tasks that parallel the tasks in standardized assessments to be used as guided practice opportunities. The tasks assess conceptual understanding of the content standards and show evidence of the Standards for Mathematical Practice through application, modeling, and written arguments. They are also available online at **www.SadlierConnect.com**. These Performance Tasks can also be used for mid-year and end-of-year assessment purposes. These Performance Tasks play a vital role in helping you determine if students are able to integrate the standards being taught and apply them in solving real-world problems. ▶

Grade 4 Pages 226–227

Performance Task 1

A Visit to the Natural History Museum

1. The fourth-grade students go on a field trip to the Natural History Museum. They vote to decide where they will start their visit in the museum.

   a. Seven children vote to start at the Whale Exhibit. Three times as many children vote to start at the Minerals Hall. Draw a diagram to show the comparison.

   Whale Exhibit

   Minerals Hall

   b. Explain how your diagram shows the comparison.

   c. Write an equation to show the comparison.
   w = number of votes for the Whale Exhibit
   m = number of votes for the Minerals Hall

   d. Use your equation and the information given in the problem to find the number of students who vote to start at the Minerals Hall.

226 Performance Task 1

Performance Task 1

Deep-Sea Minerals

2. A scientist will talk about deep-sea minerals. Many students will listen to the scientists. Fifty-four students are already seated. The remaining 32 students are standing in line. The seats are arranged in rows. Each row has 9 seats.

   a. Describe the steps you will take to find how many rows of seats are needed for all the students.

   b. Write an equation that shows how you can find the number of rows of seats the students will need. Use r to represent the unknown number of rows.

   c. Find the number of rows the students will need. Explain how you decided on the final answer.

   d. Check that your answer is reasonable. Use reasoning or mental math. Justify your reasoning.

Performance Task 1 227

Downloadable **Unit Performance Tasks**, available online at **www.SadlierConnect.com**, provide practice opportunities for students to solve real-world problems that integrate the standards within each Domain, connect to the Standards for Mathematical Practice, and often require students explain and justify their solutions.

iProgress Monitor (Optional Purchase)

Augment your assessment resources with customized assignments and test-building power!

- **Independent Practice, Unit Common Core Reviews, and Benchmark Assessment** items can be assigned to individual learners with reports that capture student progress. Includes additional items beyond those in the print program. Items can be accessed according to standard/lesson. Responses are automatically scored and reported in a grade book.

- The **Build a Test** feature enables teachers to customize assignments/assessments by a particular standard with items beyond those provided in the Student Worktext.

Student Worktext

With a full-color, engaging design the Student Worktext, also available in an ebook format, provides students with the opportunity to

- Develop proficiency in mathematics through the integration of the Common Core State Standards and the Standards for Mathematical Practice
- Build conceptual understanding of mathematical content following a gradual release of responsibility model of instruction
- Reason and communicate mathematically
- Develop mathematical arguments and model real world problems

Organized around the Common Core Domains, the lessons in the Student Worktext address all of the Common Core State Standards and focus on the major work of each grade level.

A Unit Introduction That Focuses on Standards

Grade 4 Page 7

Grade 4 Page 8

Home Connect activities for each unit provide families a window into their child's learning and encourage them to take an active role.

Progress Check at the beginning of each unit allows students to focus on the unit's key standards, self-assess before learning, and reflect on progress at the end of the unit.

Grade 4 Page 9

An **Essential Question** sets the focus and identifies the big idea for each unit, enhanced with vivid images featuring engaging and relevant content that helps students make connections between math and the real world.

Gradual Release of Responsibility

Each standard is taught using a gradual release of responsibility instructional model. By gradually decreasing the level of support within each lesson, students can develop the conceptual understanding necessary for solving complex problems and tasks independently.

This gradual release of responsibility instructional model starts with **Guided Instruction**, helping students conceptualize skills and concepts through modeling and reasoning. The Standards for Mathematical Practice (MP) are embedded in all instructional presentations.

Guided Instruction

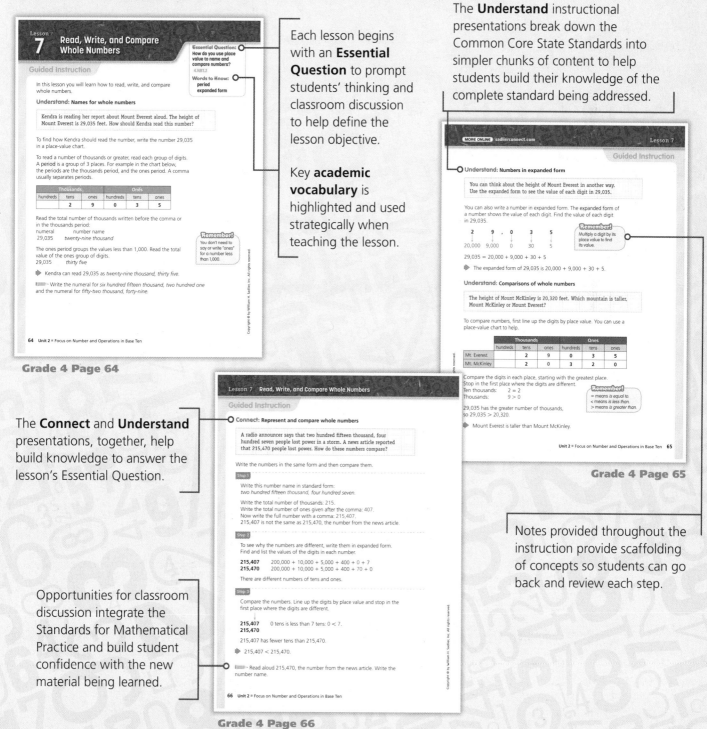

Each lesson begins with an **Essential Question** to prompt students' thinking and classroom discussion to help define the lesson objective.

Key **academic vocabulary** is highlighted and used strategically when teaching the lesson.

Grade 4 Page 64

The **Understand** instructional presentations break down the Common Core State Standards into simpler chunks of content to help students build their knowledge of the complete standard being addressed.

Grade 4 Page 65

Notes provided throughout the instruction provide scaffolding of concepts so students can go back and review each step.

The **Connect** and **Understand** presentations, together, help build knowledge to answer the lesson's Essential Question.

Opportunities for classroom discussion integrate the Standards for Mathematical Practice and build student confidence with the new material being learned.

Grade 4 Page 66

Gradual Release of Responsibility

The structure of the lesson continues the gradual release of responsibility model with **Guided Practice,** which allows the opportunity for students to work through problems with the teacher's supervision and assistance.

Guided Practice

Grade 4 Page 67

MORE ONLINE sadlierconnect.com

Lesson 7

Guided Practice

Fill in the blanks to write the number in a different form.

1. 21,109

   number name: _____-one _____, one _____ nine

2. 492,013

   number name: _____ hundred _____-_____

   thousand, _____

3. sixty-three thousand, eight hundred fifty two

   numeral: ____ ____, ____ ____ ____

4. five hundred fourteen thousand, three hundred three

   numeral: _____

5. 89,780

   expanded form: _____ + 9,000 + _____ + ____

6. 307,326

   expanded form: _____ + _____ + _____ + ____ + ____

Write < , =, or > to compare the numbers.

7. 6,5̲89 ____ 6,9̲28   8. 2̲1,807 ____ 2̲0,931

9. 37,146 ____ 37,146   10. 458,9̲23 ____ 459,8̲23

Think · Pair · Share

MP1 11. Extend the place-value chart on page 64 to show 21,385,604. Be sure to label the millions period. Explain the value of each digit.

Unit 2 ▪ Focus on Number and Ope[...]

Scaffolding is gradually removed as students work through the problems on the page(s). This allows students more independence in applying and developing strategies and skills necessary to solve the problems.

Think-Pair-Share opportunities encourage students to think independently about mathematics and then discuss, model, and explain their reasoning while learning from one another, serving to establish reliance on the Standards for Mathematical Practice.

Think·Pair·Share

Gradual Release of Responsibility

The gradual release of responsibility culminates with **Independent Practice,** which requires students to use their critical-thinking skills, apply their math knowledge, and respond to problems leveled to Webb's Depth of Knowledge. These Independent Practice pages can be used independently at home or in class.

Independent Practice

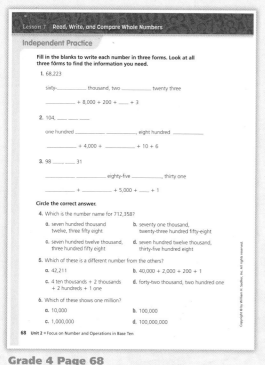

Grade 4 Page 68

As the level of scaffolding decreases and students' knowledge and confidence with the material increases, the exercises become more difficult and require higher-order thinking as well as justification of answers.

Grade 4 Page 69

Students have ample opportunities to model, reason, and justify their answers and apply all of the Standards for Mathematical Practice.

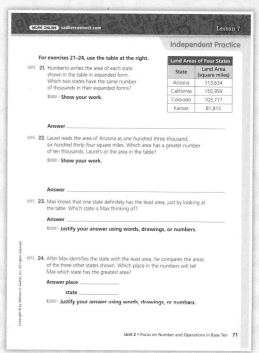

Grade 4 Page 70

Grade 4 Page 71

Built-In Common Core Assessment Practice

Every unit concludes with a **Common Core Review** that provides practice with items similar to those students will encounter on Common Core standardized assessments. Covering all of the standards presented in the unit, the reviews allow teachers to monitor student progress and understanding of each standard.

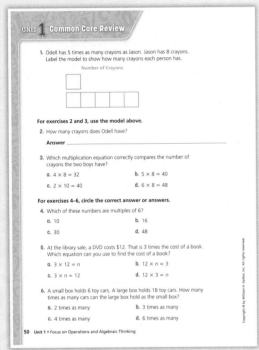

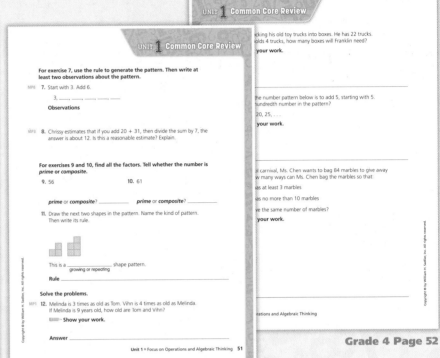

Grade 4 Page 50

Grade 4 Page 51

Grade 4 Page 52

Performance Task 1

A Visit to the Natural History Museum

1. The fourth-grade students go on a field trip to the Natural History Museum. They vote to decide where they will start their visit in the museum.

 a. Seven children vote to start at the Whale Exhibit. Three times as many children vote to start at the Minerals Hall. Draw a diagram to show the comparison.

 Whale Exhibit

 Minerals Hall

 b. Explain how your diagram shows the comparison.

 c. Write an equation to show the comparison.
 w = number of votes for the Whale Exhibit
 m = number of votes for the Minerals Hall

 d. Use your equation and the information given in the problem to find the number of students who vote to start at the Minerals Hall.

226   Performance Task 1

Grade 4 Page 226

Performance Task 2

Building a Neighborhood Playground

1. The children and adults who live in Dan's neighborhood are building a playground. A team of children works together to tear down an old fence and take the boards away to a recycling bin.

 a. The team begins work at 3:30 P.M. Draw a point on the number line to show 3:30 P.M.

 3:00   4:00   5:00   6:00
 P.M.

 b. The team spends $\frac{3}{4}$ hour tearing down the fence. What time does the team finish tearing down the fence? Show how to use the number line above to find what time the team finishes the task.

 c. Next, the team works $1\frac{1}{2}$ hours taking away the boards to a recycling bin. What time does the team finish taking away the boards? Show how to use the number line above to find what time the team finishes this task.

 d. How many minutes does the team spend altogether on the two tasks? Explain the method you used to find your answer.

332   Performance Task 2

Grade 4 Page 332

Performance Tasks provide opportunities for students to demonstrate their understanding of content standards and to show evidence of the Standards for Mathematical Practice through application, modeling, and written arguments.

T18

Teacher's Edition

Teacher-friendly, easy-to-use lesson plans support teachers in providing systematic instruction, practice, and application of Common Core State Standards. The Teacher's Edition is also available in an eBook format.

At-a-Glance Unit Introduction Pages

Unit introduction pages, featuring student self-assessment, a home connection, a planner for understanding key concepts at a glance, and learning progressions provide an at-a-glance reference for busy educators!

Each unit begins with support for student self-assessment and connecting to home. The **Progress Check** provides students with a visual roadmap identifying how the Standards are developed and linked across grade levels, emphasizing coherence.

Home Connect activities for each unit encourage families to take an active role in their child's learning and connect math to real-world situations.

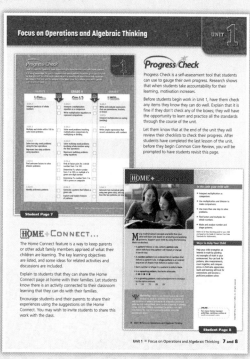

Grade 4 Teacher's Edition Pages 7 and 8

Unit Planner

The **Unit Planner** outlines everything a teacher needs to know to gather unit resources, and identify all lesson objectives, essential questions, and vocabulary.

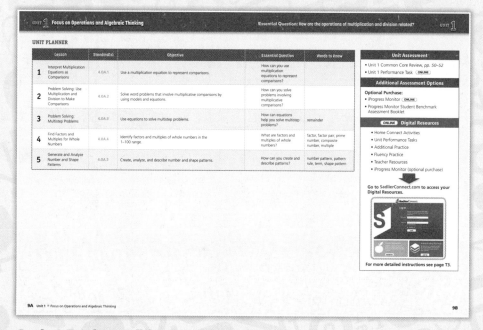

Grade 4 Teacher's Edition Pages 9A and 9B

Learning Progressions

Learning Progressions provide context and background knowledge for the Common Core State Standards by showing what students learned in the previous grade and connections to what they will learn in the next grade, building coherence within and across grade levels.

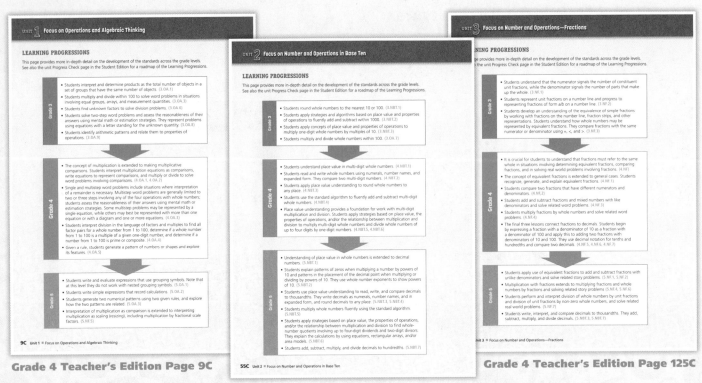

Grade 4 Teacher's Edition Page 9C

Grade 4 Teacher's Edition Page 55C

Grade 4 Teacher's Edition Page 125C

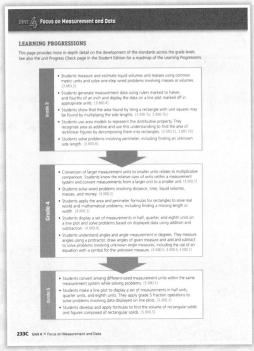

Grade 4 Teacher's Edition Page 233C

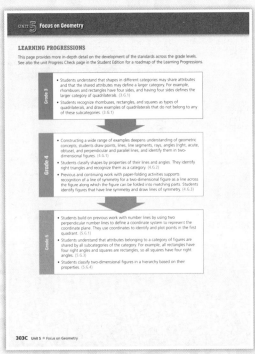

Grade 4 Teacher's Edition Page 303C

On-the-Spot Lesson Support Makes Teachers Common Core Experts!

Lesson plans featuring instruction built around key standards cover ALL Common Core standards.

Guided Instruction

Clearly stated objectives provide the focus for each lesson.

Resources available to support all learners and encourage fluency practice are listed at point-of-use.

The standards are broken down to help students build the concept and gain full understanding.

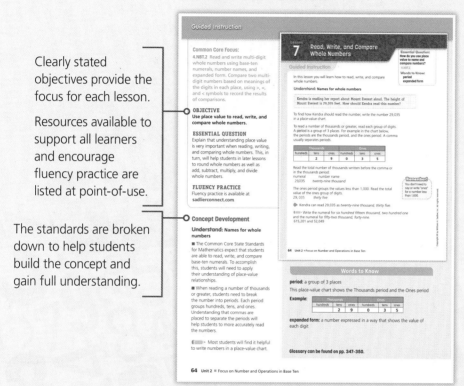

Grade 4 Teacher's Edition Page 64

The Guided Instruction culminates with the **Connect** feature building the students' understanding of the mathematical concept being taught.

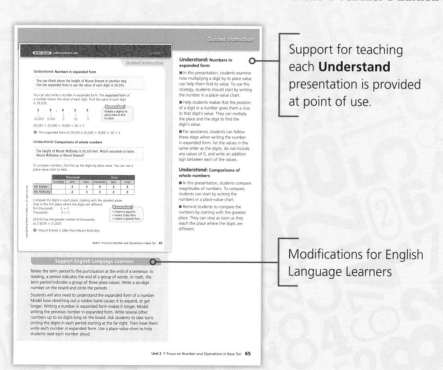

Support for teaching each **Understand** presentation is provided at point of use.

Modifications for English Language Learners

Grade 4 Teacher's Edition Page 65

Grade 4 Teacher's Edition Page 66

Successive Increase of Student Responsibility Leads to Success

Guided Practice

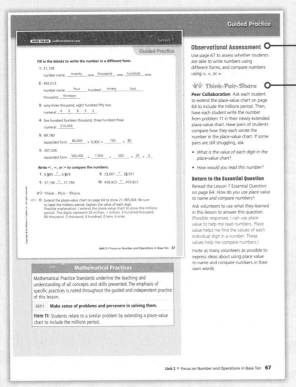

Grade 4 Teacher's Edition Page 67

Observational Assessment
The Guided Practice pages offer teachers an opportunity for formative assessment to gauge student progress.

Think-Pair-Share Support for this peer collaboration activity helps teachers to encourage students to work together.

Grade 4 Teacher's Edition Page 83

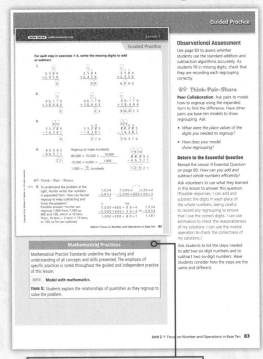

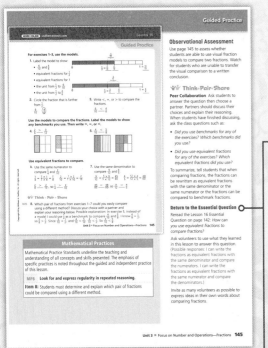

Grade 4 Teacher's Edition Page 145

Return to the Essential Question In order to help solidify understanding, before students begin to work independently, teachers encourage them to return to the Essential Question of the lesson, allowing them to explain what they have learned in their own words.

Mathematical Practices Detailed explanations of the Standards for Mathematical Practice and their application to exercises are detailed throughout the lesson as an at-a-glance reference for teachers.

Scaffolded Practice Make Independent Application of Skills Accessible

Common Core Progress provides ample opportunity for rigorous independent practice allowing students to develop procedural fluency together with conceptual understanding.

Independent Practice

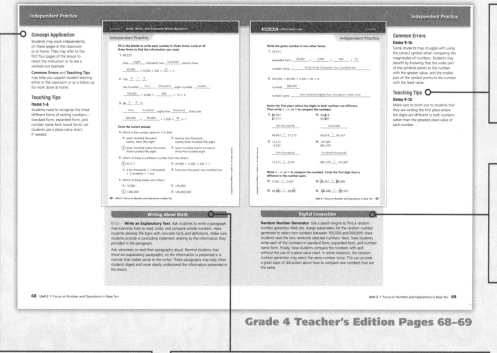

Grade 4 Teacher's Edition Pages 68–69

Teaching Tip Point-of-use teaching strategies and Common Error Analyses provide help to identify potential areas of confusion or misconceptions.

Digital Connections give suggestions for helping students find online resources to enhance their understanding of mathematical concepts.

Concept Application Teachers direct students to work independently on increasingly cognitive demanding exercises and tasks.

Writing About Math Teacher-directed suggestions for helping students to make connections between concepts and integrate ELA skills in their math lessons.

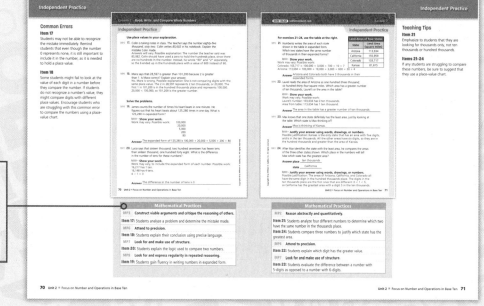

Mathematical Practices Chart The Standards for Mathematical Practice are seamlessly correlated to items throughout the program.

Grade 4 Teacher's Edition Pages 70–71

Assessment Tools Make Grading Simple

Common Core Progress supports busy teachers by offering easy-to-use rubrics for grading and results charts that outline next steps after grading or assessment.

Grade 4 Teacher's Edition Pages 50–51

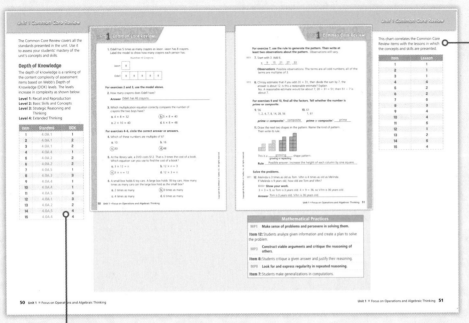

A correlation is provided for each item in the Common Core Review, identifying the lesson in which the concepts or skills are presented providing teachers with a quick reference should students require a review of the concepts.

Each item is identified by the DOK level, allowing teachers to quickly identify the level of understanding of each student.

Grade 4 Teacher's Edition Page 336

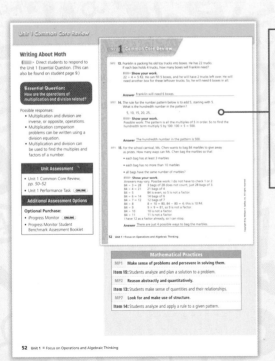

The reviews culminate with higher-order thinking problems and require students to justify their answers in writing.

Additional Assessment options are referenced at point-of-use.

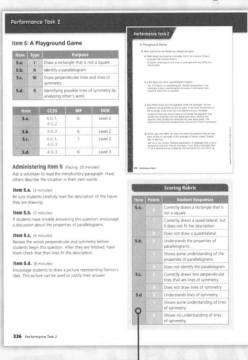

Performance Task Rubrics provide clear and thorough guidance on how to evaluate the assessment.

Grade 4 Teacher's Edition Page 52

Suggested Planning and Pacing Guide

For more specific suggestions on planning and pacing, please see the Teacher Toolbox.

Weeks	Student Worktext	Online Resources to Enrich, Support, and Assess
1-4	Unit 1: Focus on Operations and Algebraic Thinking Lessons 1–5; pp. 7–52	Unit 1 Performance Task; Additional Practice; Fluency Practice; Teacher Resources Optional purchase: iProgress Monitor
5-10	Unit 2: Focus on Number and Operations in Base Ten Lessons 6–13; pp. 53–122	Unit 2 Performance Task; Additional Practice; Fluency Practice; Teacher Resources Optional purchase: iProgress Monitor
11-18	Unit 3: Focus on Number and Operations – Fractions Lessons 14–25; pp. 123–224	Unit 3 Performance Task; Additional Practice; Fluency Practice; Teacher Resources Optional purchase: iProgress Monitor
19	Performance Task 1 pp. 225–230	Performance Task 1
20-27	Unit 4: Focus on Measurement and Data Lessons: 26–33; pp. 231–300	Unit 4 Performance Task; Additional Practice; Fluency Practice; Teacher Resources Optional purchase: iProgress Monitor
28-29	Unit 5: Focus on Geometry Lessons: 34–36; pp. 301–330	Unit 5 Performance Task; Additional Practice; Fluency Practice; Teacher Resources Optional purchase: iProgress Monitor
30	Performance Task 2 pp. 331–336	Performance Task 2

Suggested Pacing

To achieve optimum student results, it is suggested that *Common Core Progress* become an integral part of your math instruction. The multi-part lesson structure provides you with the flexibility you need in order to focus on a particular Common Core State Standard each day.

Suggested Timeline	Day 1	Day 2	Day 3	Day 4	Day 5
Lesson Structure	Guided Instruction	Guided Practice	Independent Practice	Independent Practice	• Additional Practice Online • iProgress Monitor Customized Assignments

Progress Monitor Student Benchmark Assessments, an optional purchase, is a workbook containing four comprehensive Benchmark Assessments that you may administer throughout the school year to track and assess students' mastery of the Common Core State Standards.

The lessons in this book are built upon the progression of the Grade 4 Common Core State Standards for Mathematics (CCSS). These standards identify the mathematical concepts that students need to learn.

Operations and Algebraic Thinking   4.OA

Use the four operations with whole numbers to solve problems.

4.OA.1 Interpret a multiplication equation as a comparison, e.g., interpret $35 = 5 \times 7$ as a statement that 35 is 5 times as many as 7 and 7 times as many as 5. Represent verbal statements of multiplicative comparisons as multiplication equations.

4.OA.2 Multiply or divide to solve word problems involving multiplicative comparison, e.g., by using drawings and equations with a symbol for the unknown number to represent the problem, distinguishing multiplicative comparison from additive comparison.

4.OA.3 Solve multistep word problems posed with whole numbers and having whole-number answers using the four operations, including problems in which remainders must be interpreted. Represent these problems using equations with a letter standing for the unknown quantity. Assess the reasonableness of answers using mental computation and estimation strategies including rounding.

Gain familiarity with factors and multiples.

4.OA.4 Find all factor pairs for a whole number in the range 1–100. Recognize that a whole number is a multiple of each of its factors. Determine whether a given whole number in the range 1–100 is a multiple of a given one-digit number. Determine whether a given whole number in the range 1–100 is prime or composite.

Generate and analyze patterns.

4.OA.5 Generate a number or shape pattern that follows a given rule. Identify apparent features of the pattern that were not explicit in the rule itself. *For example, given the rule "Add 3" and the starting number 1, generate terms in the resulting sequence and observe that the terms appear to alternate between odd and even numbers. Explain informally why the numbers will continue to alternate in this way.*

Number and Operations in Base Ten   4.NBT

Generalize place value understanding for multi-digit whole numbers.

4.NBT.1 Recognize that in a multi-digit whole number, a digit in one place represents ten times what it represents in the place to its right. *For example, recognize that $700 \div 70 = 10$ by applying concepts of place value and division.*

4.NBT.2 Read and write multi-digit whole numbers using base-ten numerals, number names, and expanded form. Compare two multi-digit numbers based on meanings of the digits in each place, using >, =, and < symbols to record the results of comparisons.

4.NBT.3 Use place value understanding to round multi-digit whole numbers to any place.

Use place value understanding and properties of operations to perform multi-digit arithmetic.

4.NBT.4   Fluently add and subtract multi-digit whole numbers using the standard algorithm.

4.NBT.5   Multiply a whole number of up to four digits by a one-digit whole number, and multiply two two-digit numbers, using strategies based on place value and the properties of operations. Illustrate and explain the calculation by using equations, rectangular arrays, and/or area models.

4.NBT.6   Find whole-number quotients and remainders with up to four-digit dividends and one-digit divisors, using strategies based on place value, the properties of operations, and/or the relationship between multiplication and division. Illustrate and explain the calculation by using equations, rectangular arrays, and/or area models.

Number and Operations—Fractions   4.NF

Extend understanding of fraction equivalence and ordering.

4.NF.1   Explain why a fraction a/b is equivalent to a fraction $(n \times a)/(n \times b)$ by using visual fraction models, with attention to how the number and size of the parts differ even though the two fractions themselves are the same size. Use this principle to recognize and generate equivalent fractions.

4.NF.2   Compare two fractions with different numerators and different denominators, e.g., by creating common denominators or numerators, or by comparing to a benchmark fraction such as 1/2. Recognize that comparisons are valid only when the two fractions refer to the same whole. Record the results of comparisons with symbols >, =, or <, and justify the conclusions, e.g., by using a visual fraction model.

Build fractions from unit fractions by applying and extending previous understandings of operations on whole numbers.

4.NF.3   Understand a fraction a/b with $a > 1$ as a sum of fractions $1/b$.

    4.NF.3a   Understand addition and subtraction of fractions as joining and separating parts referring to the same whole.

    4.NF.3b   Decompose a fraction into a sum of fractions with the same denominator in more than one way, recording each decomposition by an equation. Justify decompositions, e.g., by using a visual fraction model. *Examples: 3/8 = 1/8 + 1/8 + 1/8; 3/8 = 1/8 + 2/8; 2 1/8 = 1 + 1 + 1/8 = 8/8 + 8/8 + 1/8.*

    4.NF.3c   Add and subtract mixed numbers with like denominators, e.g., by replacing each mixed number with an equivalent fraction, and/or by using properties of operations and the relationship between addition and subtraction.

    4.NF.3d   Solve word problems involving addition and subtraction of fractions referring to the same whole and having like denominators, e.g., by using visual fraction models and equations to represent the problem.

4.NF.4 Apply and extend previous understandings of multiplication to multiply a fraction by a whole number.

> **4.NF.4a** Understand a fraction a/b as a multiple of $1/b$. *For example, use a visual fraction model to represent 5/4 as the product 5 × (1/4), recording the conclusion by the equation 5/4 = 5 × (1/4).*

> **4.NF.4b** Understand a multiple of a/b as a multiple of $1/b$, and use this understanding to multiply a fraction by a whole number. *For example, use a visual fraction model to express 3 × (2/5) as 6 × (1/5), recognizing this product as 6/5. (In general, n × (a/b) = (n × a)/b.)*

> **4.NF.4c** Solve word problems involving multiplication of a fraction by a whole number, e.g., by using visual fraction models and equations to represent the problem. *For example, if each person at a party will eat 3/8 of a pound of roast beef, and there will be 5 people at the party, how many pounds of roast beef will be needed? Between what two whole numbers does your answer lie?*

Understand decimal notation for fractions, and compare decimal fractions.

4.NF.5 Express a fraction with denominator 10 as an equivalent fraction with denominator 100, and use this technique to add two fractions with respective denominators 10 and 100. *For example, express 3/10 as 30/100, and add 3/10 + 4/100 = 34/100.*

4.NF.6 Use decimal notation for fractions with denominators 10 or 100. *For example, rewrite 0.62 as 62/100; describe a length as 0.62 meters; locate 0.62 on a number line diagram.*

4.NF.7 Compare two decimals to hundredths by reasoning about their size. Recognize that comparisons are valid only when the two decimals refer to the same whole. Record the results of comparisons with the symbols >, =, or <, and justify the conclusions, e.g., by using a visual model.

Measurement and Data   4.MD

Solve problems involving measurement and conversion of measurements from a larger unit to a smaller unit.

4.MD.1 Know relative sizes of measurement units within one system of units including km, m, cm; kg, g; lb, oz.; l, ml; hr, min, sec. Within a single system of measurement, express measurements in a larger unit in terms of a smaller unit. Record measurement equivalents in a two-column table. *For example, know that 1 ft is 12 times as long as 1 in. Express the length of a 4 ft snake as 48 in. Generate a conversion table for feet and inches listing the number pairs (1, 12), (2, 24), (3, 36),…*

4.MD.2 Use the four operations to solve word problems involving distances, intervals of time, liquid volumes, masses of objects, and money, including problems involving simple fractions or decimals, and problems that require expressing measurements given in a larger unit in terms of a smaller unit. Represent measurement quantities using diagrams such as number line diagrams that feature a measurement scale.

4.MD.3   Apply the area and perimeter formulas for rectangles in real world and mathematical problems. *For example, find the width of a rectangular room given the area of the flooring and the length, by viewing the area formula as a multiplication equation with an unknown factor.*

Represent and interpret data.

4.MD.4   Make a line plot to display a data set of measurements in fractions of a unit (1/2, 1/4, 1/8). Solve problems involving addition and subtraction of fractions by using information presented in line plots. *For example, from a line plot find and interpret the difference in length between the longest and shortest specimens in an insect collection.*

Geometric measurement: understand concepts of angle and measure angles.

4.MD.5   Recognize angles as geometric shapes that are formed wherever two rays share a common endpoint, and understand concepts of angle measurement:

     4.MD.5a   An angle is measured with reference to a circle with its center at the common endpoint of the rays, by considering the fraction of the circular arc between the points where the two rays intersect the circle. An angle that turns through 1/360 of a circle is called a "one-degree angle," and can be used to measure angles.

     4.MD.5b   An angle that turns through *n* one-degree angles is said to have an angle measure of *n* degrees.

4.MD.6   Measure angles in whole-number degrees using a protractor. Sketch angles of specified measure.

4.MD.7   Recognize angle measure as additive. When an angle is decomposed into non-overlapping parts, the angle measure of the whole is the sum of the angle measures of the parts. Solve addition and subtraction problems to find unknown angles on a diagram in real world and mathematical problems, e.g., by using an equation with a symbol for the unknown angle measure.

Geometry   4.G

Draw and identify lines and angles, and classify shapes by properties of their lines and angles.

4.G.1   Draw points, lines, line segments, rays, angles (right, acute, obtuse), and perpendicular and parallel lines. Identify these in two-dimensional figures.

4.G.2   Classify two-dimensional figures based on the presence or absence of parallel or perpendicular lines, or the presence or absence of angles of a specified size. Recognize right triangles as a category, and identify right triangles.

4.G.3   Recognize a line of symmetry for a two-dimensional figure as a line across the figure such that the figure can be folded along the line into matching parts. Identify line-symmetric figures and draw lines of symmetry.

The eight Standards for Mathematical Practice identified in the Common Core State Standards set the expectations for the ways students should approach the study of, and practice with, the subject of mathematics. These Mathematical Practices are fully embedded within the instruction and practice, labeled as MP, and encourage students to develop the habit of reliance on the practices when approaching problems.

Mathematical Practices in *Common Core Progress*

Additionally, the emphasis of specific practices is noted throughout the guided and independent practice of the lessons.

1. **Make sense of problems and persevere in solving them.**
   The Guided Instruction provided in the program offers stepped out approaches to solving problems, helping students develop strategies to use when approaching new problems.

2. **Reason abstractly and quantitatively.**
   Concepts are introduced using the Understand and Connect structure to help students break down the components of the standard and develop the reasoning skills necessary for deep conceptual understanding.

3. **Construct viable arguments and critique the reasoning of others.**
   Whether justifying their reasoning in writing or participating in group discussions about a Think-Pair-Share exercise, there are opportunities in every lesson for students to practice the skills of developing and defending mathematical arguments and communicating their ideas clearly.

4. **Model with mathematics.**
   In addition to the models of real world situations presented to the students throughout the program to introduce new concepts, students are encouraged to develop their own models when working through the exercises.

5. **Use appropriate tools strategically.**
   Having a solid understanding of the tools available and practicing with those tools during Guided Instruction and Guided Practice, fosters familiarity and fluency using the tools when working independently.

6. **Attend to precision.**
   Students are encouraged to be precise and accurate during each stage of the problem solving process, from using the correct vocabulary to communicate ideas to attending to the units used to express their answers.

7. **Look for and make use of structure.**
   Presenting concepts and skills in a way that reveals mathematical structures, allows students to seek out these patterns on their own.

8. **Look for and express regularity in repeated reasoning.**
   As students work through cognitively-demanding exercises, they develop an awareness of repeated reasoning which promotes their ability to apply similar reasoning in real world situations.

Progress Check

Look at how the Common Core standards you have learned and will learn connect. It is very important for you to understand the standards from the prior grade level so that you will be able to develop an understanding of operations and algebraic thinking in this unit and be prepared for next year. To practice your skills, go to sadlierconnect.com.

UNIT 1

GRADE 3		GRADE 4		GRADE 5
I Can...	Before Unit 1	**Can I ?**	After Unit 1	**I Will...**
3.OA.1 Interpret products of whole numbers	☐	4.OA.1 Interpret a multiplication equation as a comparison	☐	5.OA.1 Write and evaluate expressions that use parentheses, brackets, or braces
		Write multiplication equations to represent comparisons	☐	5.NF.5 Interpret multiplication as scaling (resizing)
3.OA.3 Multiply and divide within 100 to solve word problems	☐	4.OA.2 Solve word problems involving multiplicative comparisons by multiplying or dividing	☐	5.OA.2 Write simple expressions that record calculations with numbers
3.OA.8 Solve two-step word problems using the four operations	☐	4.OA.3 Solve multistep word problems involving whole numbers using the four operations	☐	
Represent two-step problems using equations	☐	Represent multistep problems using equations	☐	
3.OA.6 Find unknown factors to solve division problems	☐	4.OA.4 Find all factor pairs for a whole number from 1 to 100	☐	
		Determine if a whole number from 1 to 100 is a multiple of a given one-digit number	☐	
		Determine if a number from 1 to 100 is prime or composite	☐	
3.OA.9 Identify arithmetic patterns	☐	4.OA.5 Generate a pattern that follows a given rule	☐	5.OA.3 Generate two numerical patterns using two given rules, and explain how the two patterns are relat...
		Explore and explain features of patterns	☐	

Unit 1 ■ Focus on Operations and Algebraic Thinking

Student Page 7

Progress Check

Progress Check is a self-assessment tool that students can use to gauge their own progress. Research shows that when students take accountability for their learning, motivation increases.

Before students begin work in Unit 1, have them check any items they know they can do well. Explain that it is fine if they don't check any of the boxes; they will have the opportunity to learn and practice all the standards through the course of the unit.

Let them know that at the end of the unit they will review their checklists to check their progress. After students have completed the last lesson of the unit, before they begin Common Core Review, you will be prompted to have students revisit this page.

HOME CONNECT...

The Home Connect feature is a way to keep parents or other adult family members apprised of what their children are learning. The key learning objectives are listed, and some ideas for related activities and discussions are included.

Explain to students that they can share the Home Connect page at home with their families. Let students know there is an activity connected to their classroom learning that they can do with their families.

Encourage students and their parents to share their experiences using the suggestions on the Home Connect. You may wish to invite students to share this work with the class.

HOME CONNECT...

Many mathematical concepts and skills that your child will learn are based on analyzing and applying patterns. Support your child by using the following Math vocabulary:

- A **pattern** follows a rule, called a **pattern rule**, which tells how the pattern will repeat or change in some way.
- A **number pattern** is an ordered list of numbers that follows a pattern rule. A **shape pattern** is an ordered sequence of shapes that follows a pattern rule.
- Each number or shape in a pattern is called a **term**.
- In a **repeating pattern**, the terms alternate.
  ○ ■ ○ ■ ○ ■
- In a **growing pattern**, each subsequent term increases by the same amount.
  5   10   15   20   25

Activity: Patterns are everywhere in the world around us. Look for patterns in the environment and use them to make a pattern book of number and shape patterns. For each pattern, show several repeating or growing terms. Ask your child to determine the pattern rule, and then follow the rule to extend each pattern using the appropriate terms.

8   Unit 1 ■ Focus on Operations and Algebraic Thinking

In this unit your child will:

- Interpret multiplication as comparison.
- Use multiplication and division to make comparisons.
- Use more than one step to solve problems.
- Find factors and multiples for whole numbers.
- Make and analyze number and shape patterns.

NOTE: All of these learning goals for your child are based on the Grade 4 Common Core State Standards for Mathematics.

Ways to Help Your Child

Help your child strengthen an interest in math by pointing out examples of math in your environment. You can look for patterns, take measurements, count together, and compare prices. A child who appreciates math and learning will look for connections and become a proficient problem solver.

ONLINE
For more Home Connect activities, continue online at sadlierconnect.com

Student Page 8

UNIT PLANNER

	Lesson	Standard(s)	Objective
1	Interpret Multiplication Equations as Comparisons	4.OA.1	Use a multiplication equation to represent comparisons.
2	Problem Solving: Use Multiplication and Division to Make Comparisons	4.OA.2	Solve word problems that involve multiplicative comparisons by using models and equations.
3	Problem Solving: Multistep Problems	4.OA.3	Use equations to solve multistep problems.
4	Find Factors and Multiples for Whole Numbers	4.OA.4	Identify factors and multiples of whole numbers in the 1–100 range.
5	Generate and Analyze Number and Shape Patterns	4.OA.5	Create, analyze, and describe number and shape patterns.

Essential Question	Words to Know
How can you use multiplication equations to represent comparisons?	
How can you solve problems involving multiplicative comparisons?	
How can equations help you solve multistep problems?	remainder
What are factors and multiples of whole numbers?	factor, factor pair, prime number, composite number, multiple
How can you create and describe patterns?	number pattern, pattern rule, term, shape pattern

Unit Assessment

- Unit 1 Common Core Review, *pp. 50–52*
- Unit 1 Performance Task ONLINE

Additional Assessment Options

Optional Purchase:
- iProgress Monitor ONLINE
- Progress Monitor Student Benchmark Assessment Booklet

ONLINE Digital Resources

- Home Connect Activities
- Unit Performance Tasks
- Additional Practice
- Fluency Practice
- Teacher Resources
- iProgress Monitor (optional purchase)

Go to SadlierConnect.com to access your Digital Resources.

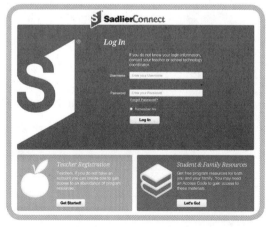

For more detailed instructions see page T3.

LEARNING PROGRESSIONS

This page provides more in-depth detail on the development of the standards across the grade levels. See also the unit Progress Check page in the Student Edition for a roadmap of the Learning Progressions.

Grade 3

- Students interpret and determine products as the total number of objects in a set of groups that have the same number of objects. (3.OA.1)
- Students multiply and divide within 100 to solve word problems in situations involving equal groups, arrays, and measurement quantities. (3.OA.3)
- Students find unknown factors to solve division problems. (3.OA.6)
- Students solve two-step word problems and assess the reasonableness of their answers using mental math or estimation strategies. They represent problems using equations with a letter standing for the unknown quantity. (3.OA.8)
- Students identify arithmetic patterns and relate them to properties of operations. (3.OA.9)

Grade 4

- The concept of multiplication is extended to making multiplicative comparisons. Students interpret multiplication equations as comparisons, write equations to represent comparisons, and multiply or divide to solve word problems involving comparisons. (4.OA.1, 4.OA.2)
- Single and multistep word problems include situations where interpretation of a remainder is necessary. Multistep word problems are generally limited to two or three steps involving any of the four operations with whole numbers; students assess the reasonableness of their answers using mental math or estimation strategies. Some multistep problems may be represented by a single equation, while others may best be represented with more than one equation or with a diagram and one or more equations. (4.OA.3)
- Students interpret division in the language of factors and multiples to find all factor pairs for a whole number from 1 to 100, determine if a whole number from 1 to 100 is a multiple of a given one-digit number, and determine if a number from 1 to 100 is prime or composite. (4.OA.4)
- Given a rule, students generate a pattern of numbers or shapes and explore its features. (4.OA.5)

Grade 5

- Students write and evaluate expressions that use grouping symbols. Note that at this level they do not work with nested grouping symbols. (5.OA.1)
- Students write simple expressions that record calculations. (5.OA.2)
- Students generate two numerical patterns using two given rules, and explore how the two patterns are related. (5.OA.3)
- Interpretation of multiplication as comparison is extended to interpreting multiplication as scaling (resizing), including multiplication by fractional scale factors. (5.NF.5)

Focus on Operations and Algebraic Thinking

Essential Question:
How are the operations of multiplication and division related?

Unit 1 ■ Focus on Operations and Algebraic Thinking 9

Essential Question:
How are the operations of multiplication and division related?

As students become involved with the Essential Question, they will use their knowledge of multiplication and division as inverse operations to build a stronger understanding of their relationship. They will use this knowledge to identify factors and multiples, complete word problems, and develop and identify number patterns.

Conversation Starters

Have students discuss the photograph. Ask questions such as: *What plants and animals do you see in the photo? What can you tell about these fish from looking at the photo? Why do you think these fish have stripes?*

Ask students to look at the fish in the bottom left corner of the page. *Look closely at this fish. Assume the stripes go all the way around the fish. How can you determine how many stripes it has?* (I could count the stripes from top to bottom.)

Now have students look at the entire school of fish. *Suppose you know each fish in the school has 8 stripes. How can you determine the total number of stripes in the school of fish?* (I could count how many fish are in the school and then I could multiply that number by 8 because each fish has 8 stripes.)

Let students work in pairs to discuss how to count the fish. Lead them to see that their understanding of multiplication is helpful in finding the total number of stripes in the school of fish.

Activity

Materials: paper, pencil

Explain to students that they can also determine the number of fish in a school from the total number of stripes in the school and the total number of stripes on one fish. Tell students there are a total of 65 stripes in the school of fish and 5 stripes on each fish. Have students draw a picture to show how they can determine how many fish are in the school and write a mathematical equation representing their picture.

Have a whole-class discussion to share students' methods. Students should have shown that they split the 65 stripes into groups of 5. They should recognize that this represents a division equation. Use the answers to this question and to the conversation starter to spark the idea that multiplication and division are inverse operations.

Common Core Focus:

4.OA.1 Interpret a multiplication equation as a comparison. Represent verbal statements of multiplicative comparisons as multiplication equations.

OBJECTIVE

Use a multiplication equation to represent comparisons.

ESSENTIAL QUESTION

Review with students what they know about multiplication in terms of equal groups. In this lesson students will use multiplication to compare the size of quantities. Sentences such as, *This shirt costs 3 times as much as that shirt,* and *I have 4 times as many pencils as I have pens,* involve comparisons.

PREREQUISITE SKILLS

Use Item A on page 337 of the Foundational Skills Handbook to review interpreting products of whole numbers.

FLUENCY PRACTICE

Fluency practice is available at **sadlierconnect.com**.

Concept Development

Understand: How a multiplication equation represents two comparisons

■ In this presentation, students will apply their prior experience of interpreting arrays to interpret comparisons as multiplication equations.

■ Relate the circled rows and columns to students' previous understanding of arrays. Note that an array with 5 columns and 3 rows can be interpreted as 5 groups of 3 dots or as 3 groups of 5 dots.

✏️ Have students write a multiplication equation in terms of groups: number of groups × number in each group = number in all.

Interpret Multiplication Equations as Comparisons

Essential Question:
How can you use multiplication equations to represent comparisons?
4.OA.1

Guided Instruction

In this lesson you will learn about how a multiplication equation can represent comparisons.

Understand: How a multiplication equation represents two comparisons

The array below represents the multiplication equation $15 = 3 \times 5$.

A multiplication equation shows that:
factor × factor = product
$3 \times 5 = 15$
$5 \times 3 = 15$

Use the array to help you explain why the equation $15 = 3 \times 5$ represents these two comparison statements:

"15 is 5 times as many as 3."   "15 is 3 times as many as 5."

➡ There are 3 dots in each column. There are 5 times that many dots in all five columns.
So, the array represents "15 is 5 times as many as 3."

There are 5 dots in each row. There are 3 times that many dots in all three rows.
So, the array represents "15 is 3 times as many as 5."

✏ Jamie has 7 times as many pictures as Mary. Mary has 8 pictures. Write a multiplication equation that represents the comparison for this situation.
$7 \times 8 = 56$

Support English Language Learners

Use specific examples to clarify the meanings of comparative forms of adjectives. For example, show three books of different heights. Describe the heights using comparison terms, such as tall, taller, tallest, or short, shorter, shortest. Explain that words that end with –er and –est can be used to compare quantities, sizes, and measurements.

Draw examples of situations such as the following: two lines of different lengths, two items of different sizes, and two people of different ages. Have them describe each example using the terms longer/shorter, larger/ smaller/ and older/younger. Have students use comparative statements such as 3 times longer, 4 times larger, and 2 times as old to further describe the examples.

Lesson 1

Guided Instruction

Connect: Multiplication equations and comparisons

> Daniel is growing plants in science class. His shortest plant is 4 inches tall. His tallest plant is 20 inches tall.
>
> Write a multiplication equation comparing the heights of Daniel's tallest and shortest plants.

Step 1

A comparison statement for this situation will be of the form:

height of tallest plant = unknown number × height of shortest plant

We know the heights of the tallest and shortest plants. We do not know the unknown number.

Step 2

Draw a model and use it to find the unknown information.

First represent 4 inches, the height of the shortest plant. Copy that model until you get 20 inches, the height of the tallest plant. You need 5 copies.

The height of the tallest plant is 5 times the height of the shortest plant.

Heights of Daniel's Plants

```
            4
            4
  20 {      4
            4
   4        4
shortest  tallest
 plant     plant
```

Step 3

Write a multiplication equation to represent the comparisons.

➤ 20 = 5 × 4 ⟵ 20 inches is 5 times as much as 4 inches.

This equation shows that the height of the tallest plant is 5 times the height of the shortest plant.

✏ What other multiplication equation represents the comparison between Daniel's shortest and tallest plants?
20 = 4 × 5

Unit 1 ■ Focus on Operations and Algebraic Thinking **11**

Connect: Multiplication equations and comparisons Use this page to strengthen students' understanding of how to find the factor that multiplies one known quantity resulting in another known quantity.

■ Students' ability to translate a verbal statement as a mathematical equation is critical. Guide students through Steps 1, 2, and 3 as they use the relationship between quantities in a real-world situation to formulate equations.

■ In Step 2, provide connecting cubes to students who need to use concrete manipulatives to represent the relationship between the heights of the tallest and shortest plants. Make sure students understand that each connecting cube represents 1 inch, therefore 4 cubes represents the height of Daniel's shortest plant. Have students count by 4s until they reach 20. Ask how many groups of 4 they need to count in order to reach 20. Relate the concrete model to the model shown on the page.

✏ Ask students to verbally restate the solution, 20 = 5 × 4, as a comparison between the number of shortest plants it takes to equal the height of the tallest plant. Discuss how the multiplication 20 = 4 × 5, can be interpreted as 20 is 4 times as many as 5 copies.

Math-to-Statistics Connection

Current Events It is common to hear statistics reported in terms of multiplicative comparisons. For example, there are 2 times as many girls than boys in an afterschool club.

Have students research two similar items or events and then use multiplication to compare them. For example, students might compare and find that the cost of a name-brand item is three times the cost of a similar generic item. Brainstorm with students a list of ideas for multiplicative comparisons such as the number of rainy days to sunny days, the number of teachers to students, or the number of school days to the number of non-school days. Since students will be multiplying by whole numbers, most of the comparisons will be close estimates rather than exact comparisons.

Guided Practice

Observational Assessment

Use pages 12–13 to assess whether students are able to write verbal statements of multiplicative comparisons as multiplication equations. Take note of those students who may not understand that the total number of objects always represents the product. The factors are represented by the number of objects in one group and the number of times it takes that group to equal the product.

Guided Practice

Complete exercises 1 and 2. Use the model at the right.

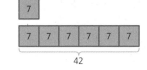

1. Complete the comparison statement to represent the model.

   12 is __4__ times as many as 3.

2. Complete the multiplication equation to represent the model.

   12 = __4__ × 3

Complete exercises 3 and 4. Use the model at the right.

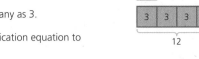

3. Complete the comparison statement to represent the model.

   __42__ is __6__ times as many as __7__.

4. Write a multiplication equation to represent the model.

   42 = 6 × 7 or 42 = 7 × 6

Solve the problem.

5. Lian has a new camera. She printed out 3 pictures for her album. Lian took 9 times as many pictures as she printed out. Write a multiplication equation comparing the number of pictures Lian took to the number she printed out.

   27 = 9 × 3

   ▸ **Complete the model below to justify your answer.**

   Lian's Pictures

Math-to-Math Connection

Converting Measurements Students can use multiplicative comparisons to convert familiar measurements. Using statements such as *1 foot is 12 times the length of 1 inch* and *1 meter is 10 times the length of 1 decimeter* may strengthen students' understanding of knowing when to multiply to convert measurements.

Lesson 1

Guided Practice

Use the model. Represent the comparison as a multiplication equation.

6. There are 7 girls and 35 boys on the team. Label the model to show the size of each equal group.

   Count the number of equal groups that make up the total number of boys. Use the information to complete the following sentence.

   There are __5__ times as many boys as girls.

   Compare the numbers of boys and girls. Write a multiplication equation.

   $$\frac{35}{\text{boys}} = \frac{5}{} \times \frac{7}{\text{girls}}$$

Students on the Team

girls | 7

boys | 7 7 7 7 7

Make a model to help you solve the problem.

7. Katie scored 6 points in the first basketball game of the season. In the second game, she scored 3 times as many points as she scored in the first game. Write a statement in words comparing the numbers of points Katie scored in the two games. Then, write an equation to represent the comparison.

   Show your work.
   Katie scored 3 times as many points in the second game as in the first game.
   $18 = 3 \times 6$

   first game | 6

   second game | 6 6 6

Think • Pair • Share

MP7 8. Use a diagram or model to help you explain why 4 times as many as 3 is the same amount as 3 times as many as 4.
Possible answer: In a 3 by 4 array, there are 3 dots in each column, and there are 4 times this many in the whole array, so the total number is 4 times as many as 3. There are 4 dots in each row, and there are 3 times as many in the whole array, so the total number is 3 times as many as 4.

Unit 1 ■ Focus on Operations and Algebraic Thinking **13**

Think•Pair•Share

Peer Collaboration Have pairs of students present their models and discuss similarities and differences. Students who need additional support can refer to page 10. Ask:

- *How does each model represent a different multiplication equation?*

- *How can the models be used to express the total number of objects in equal groups?*

Make sure students understand how two different comparison statements can interpret the same quantity.

Return to the Essential Question

Reread the Lesson 1 Essential Question on page 10: *How can you use multiplication equations to represent comparisons?*

Ask volunteers to use what they learned in this lesson to answer this question. (Possible responses: A comparison statement, such as *Plant A is 3 times as tall as Plant B* can be written as a multiplication equation because there are 3 equal groups and each group represents the height of Plant B.)

Mathematical Practices

Mathematical Practice Standards underline the teaching and understanding of all concepts and skills presented. The emphasis of specific practices is noted throughout the guided and independent practice of this lesson.

| MP7 | **Look for and make use of structure.** |

Item 8: Students evaluate the structure and meaning of multiplicative comparisons.

Independent Practice

Concept Application

Students may work independently on these pages in the classroom or at home. They may refer to the first four pages of the lesson to revisit the instruction or to see a worked-out example.

Common Errors and **Teaching Tips** may help you support student learning either in the classroom or as a follow-up for work done at home.

Common Errors

Items 1–3

Students may multiply the number in each group by the total number of groups shown in the model. Point out that each row of the model represents one group. For example, in exercise 1, there are 8 in the first group. The second group has 2 times as many as the first group.

Teaching Tips

Item 7

Help students identify what is known and what they need to find in order to solve the problem. Students should realize that one factor is identified by the phrase *4 times the amount*.

Item 8

Some students may benefit from restating the problem as a single sentence before writing the equation. For example, students might say: *Ramon needs to read 8 times as many as 6 pages.*

Independent Practice

Write a multiplication equation to represent the comparison shown in the model.

1. $2 \times 8 = 16$

8	
8	8

2. $6 \times 3 = 18$

3	3	3	3	3	3
3					

3. $3 \times 7 = 21$

7	7	7
7		

In exercises 4–6, complete the comparison statement that is represented by the equation. The factors may be in either order.

4. $72 = 9 \times 8$

   $\underline{72}$ is $\underline{9}$ times as many as $\underline{8}$.

5. $49 = 7 \times 7$

   $\underline{49}$ is $\underline{7}$ times as many as $\underline{7}$.

6. $36 = 4 \times 9$

   $\underline{36}$ is $\underline{4}$ times as many as $\underline{9}$.

In exercises 7 and 8, solve the problem.

7. A sweater costs \$40. This is 4 times the amount of money that Beth has. Write a multiplication equation to represent the comparison between the price of the sweater and the amount Beth has.

   Answer $40 = 4 \times 10$ or $40 = 10 \times 4$

   ◗ **Draw a model to justify your answer.**

   Money Amounts

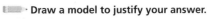

   cost of sweater: 10 10 10 10

   Beth's money: 10

8. Ramon has read 6 pages in his book. He needs to read 8 times as many pages to finish the book. Write a multiplication equation to represent the comparison between the number of pages Ramon has read and the number he has to read to finish the book.

   Answer $48 = 8 \times 6$ or $48 = 6 \times 8$

   ◗ **Draw a model to justify your answer.**

   Pages

   pages left: 6 6 6 6 6 6 6 6

   pages read: 6

Writing About Math

◗ **Compare and Contrast** Have students write a paragraph to compare and contrast the concept of writing multiplication equations to represent equal groups to the concept of writing multiplication equations to represent comparisons. Students should support their work with examples.

Independent Practice

For exercises 9 and 10, use the model at the right to write a multiplication equation.

9. A large paint set has 2 times as many colors as a small set. A small paint set has 12 colors.

   Write a multiplication equation for the comparison.

   $24 = \underline{\ 2 \times 12\ }$

Paint Sets

large | 12 | 12
small | 12

10. Hassan lives 9 blocks from school. Jada lives 36 blocks from school. Complete the following sentence.

    Jada lives __4__ times as far from school than Hassan does.

    Write a multiplication equation for the comparison.

    $\underline{\ 4\ } \times \underline{\ 9\ } = \underline{\ 36\ }$

Blocks from School

Hassan | 9
Jada | 9 | 9 | 9 | 9

11. The tree in Derrick's front yard is 8 times as old as the tree in his backyard. The tree in the front yard is 72 years old. Label the model to show the age of each tree.

Derrick's Trees

front | 9 | 9 | 9 | 9 | 9 | 9 | 9 | 9

backyard | 9

For exercises 12–14, use the model above.

12. How old is the tree in Derrick's backyard?

    Answer 9 years old

13. How old is the tree in Derrick's front yard?

    a. 8 years   b. 9 years

    c. 10 years   (d.) 72 years

14. Which multiplication equation correctly compares the ages of the two trees?

    a. $10 \times 8 = 80$ (b.) $8 \times 9 = 72$

    c. $6 \times 12 = 72$ d. $9 \times 9 = 81$

Common Errors

Item 11

If students use the incorrect factor to label the model, guide them to find the missing factor. The length of the longer model is 72. There are 8 parts, so the longer model is 8 times longer than one part.

Teaching Tips

Item 14

Discuss with students how to eliminate two out of four answer choices by identifying what the factors of the multiplication equation represent.

Digital Connection

Random Number Generator Use a search engine to find a Web site with a random number generator. Assign parameters for the random number generator to select two numbers between 1 and 10. Have students write two comparison statements using these numbers. When applicable, challenge students not only to use the two numbers as factors, but to use one number as a product. For example, if the numbers 5 and 10 are selected. The comparison statement *10 is 2 times as many as 5* could be written. After students have written the comparison statement, have them write the comparison as a multiplication equation.

Independent Practice

Common Errors

Item 18

Students may not recognize that 8 is a factor in both problems. Explain that the problem asks if the same model can also represent 8 × 2 = 16 if each 4 in the model is replaced with 2.

Teaching Tips

Item 15

Point out that this problem has two parts. Students should provide a situation and a corresponding equation.

Independent Practice

MP4 15. Give an example of a situation in which you would need to compare two amounts using multiplication. What multiplication equation shows the relationship between the numbers in your example?
Possible answer: If you get $20 for allowance each week, and you used to get $10, then your allowance is twice as much as it was before. $20 = 2 × $10.

MP7 16. In a multiplication equation, is it always important to know which amount represents the number of groups and which represents the size of each group? Give one example.
No, it is not always important. Possible answer: For example, you may need to set up 100 chairs for a school assembly. It may not matter if you use 5 rows of 20 chairs or 20 rows of 5 chairs, as long as you have 100 chairs altogether.

Solve the problems.

MP4 17. Last year, Ben's family went on vacation for 12 days. This year, the family is traveling for 5 times as many days as last year. Use your own method to find how long the family's trip will be.

> **Show your work.**

12

Work may vary. Students may multiply or use repeated addition to find 5 × 12.

12	12	12	12	12

Answer The family's trip will be 60 days long.

MP3 18. Nina draws the model at the right to represent the relationship 8 times as many as 4 is 32. Nina thinks she can label the model to represent 8 × 2 = 16. Is Nina correct?

4

4	4	4	4	4	4	4	4

> **Show your work.**

The same model can show 8 × 2 = 16, since the number of equal groups is also 8. Just the "4" labels for each part should be changed to "2," since the size of each part is 2.
8 × 4 = 32

Answer Yes, Nina is correct.

16   Unit 1 ▪ Focus on Operations and Algebraic Thinking

Mathematical Practices

MP3	**Construct viable arguments and critique the reasoning of others.**
Item 18: Students analyze a problem situation and share their reasoning.	
MP4	**Model with mathematics.**
Item 15: Students relate mathematics to everyday problems.	
Item 17: Students use models to explain the relationship of quantities.	
MP7	**Look for and make use of structure.**
Item 16: Students evaluate the structure of a multiplication equation.	

MORE ONLINE sadlierconnect.com

Lesson 1

Independent Practice

Solve the problems.

MP6 **19.** One plant is 12 inches tall and another is 3 inches tall. Sam says "The height of the tall plant is 4 times as much as the height of the short plant." Meg says "The height of the tall plant is 9 inches more than the height of the small plant." Who is correct?

Answer Both Sam and Meg are correct.

Justify your answer using words, drawings, or numbers.
Possible justification: Sam is correct because $12 = 4 \times 3$, so 12 inches is 4 times as much as 3 inches. Meg is also correct because $12 = 3 + 9$, so 12 inches is 9 inches more than 3 inches.

MP5 **20.** Huey walks neighborhood dogs to earn extra money. He walks 2 dogs each week. Huey says that he can walk 4 times *more* dogs each week. Is this the same as saying that Huey can walk 4 times *as many* dogs each week?

Answer No, it is not the same.

Justify your answer using words, drawings, or numbers.
Possible justification: "4 times more dogs" means adding 8 dogs to the 2 dogs that Huey already walks, for a total of 10 dogs.

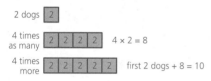

2 dogs [2]
4 times as many [2][2][2][2] $4 \times 2 = 8$
4 times more [2][2][2][2][2] first 2 dogs + 8 = 10

MP4 **21.** A summer camp has 5 cabins. There are 10 single beds in each cabin. So there are 10 times as many beds as cabins. If 55 campers sign up for camp, how many more beds will be needed?

Show your work.
$10 \times 5 = 50$; 50 beds. $55 - 50 = 5$

Answer Five more beds will be needed.

Common Errors
Item 19
Students may be inclined to think multiplication is required in both comparisons. Point out that the first comparison includes the words *times as much as* (multiplication) while the second comparison includes the words *more than* (addition).

Item 20
The phrases *4 times more dogs* and *4 times as many dogs* may be difficult for some students to understand. Have students circle the phrase *4 times more* in the problem. Explain that this means they should add 4 times as many dogs to the 2 dogs Huey already walks.

Teaching Tips
Item 21
Guide students to understand that they will use a multiplicative comparison to find the number of beds and subtract to find the difference between the number of campers and the number of beds.

Mathematical Practices

MP4	**Model with mathematics.**

Item 21: Students relate mathematics to everyday problems.

MP5	**Use appropriate tools strategically.**

Item 20: Students use tools carefully and strategically to justify a solution.

MP6	**Attend to precision.**

Item 19: Students formulate full explanations for two comparisons.

Common Core Focus:

4.OA.2 Multiply or divide to solve word problems involving multiplicative comparison.

OBJECTIVE

Solve word problems that involve multiplicative comparisons by using models and equations.

ESSENTIAL QUESTION

In Lesson 1, students learned how to use multiplication equations to represent comparisons. In this lesson, students will solve problems that involve multiplicative comparisons. It is important for students to understand that a multiplicative comparison involves two quantities in which one is described as a multiple of the other.

FLUENCY PRACTICE

Fluency practice is available at **sadlierconnect.com**.

Concept Development

Understand: Comparison with an unknown product

■ Students will learn how to interpret a comparison word problem as a multiplication equation in order to solve the problem.

■ Lead students to use multiplication instead of repeated addition to find the cost.

Understand: Comparison can involve addition

■ Discuss how comparison phrases such as *times as many, times more,* and *times as much,* indicate multiplication, and comparison phrases such as *how much more* or *how many more* indicate addition.

◖▭▸ Be sure students understand the difference between the two comparison statements. Ask students to tell how to distinguish between multiplicative and additive comparisons.

Lesson 2 Problem Solving: **Use Multiplication and Division to Make Comparisons**

Essential Question:
How can you solve problems involving multiplicative comparisons?
4.OA.2

Guided Instruction

In this lesson you will learn how to solve problems involving multiplicative comparison.

Understand: Comparison with an unknown product

> A board game costs $9. An electronic game costs 6 times as much as the board game. How much does the electronic game cost?

You can start by making a model of the problem, like the one shown at the right. Use a ■ for the unknown amount.

Next, write and solve a multiplication equation to find the cost of the electronic game.

Game Prices

board game $9

electronic game $9 $9 $9 $9 $9 $9 ■

6 times as much as $9 = cost of electronic game

$6 \times \$9 = ■$ ← Multiply to find the unknown product.

$6 \times \$9 = \$54$

▸ The electronic game costs $54.

Understand: Comparisons can involve addition

> A board game costs $9. An electronic game costs $54. How much more does the electronic game cost than the board game?

A model of this problem is shown at the right.

Write and solve an equation.

$54
$9 | ■

$\$9 + ■ = \$54$ ← $9 *plus* unknown amount equals $54.

$\$54 - \$9 = ■$ ← Write an equivalent subtraction equation.

$\$54 - \$9 = \$45$

▸ The electronic game cost $45 more than the board game.

◖▭▸ Compare these statements: $54 is 6 *times as much as* $9.
$54 is *$45 more than* $9.
Times as much as means you multiply, and more than means you use addition.

18 Unit 1 ■ Focus on Operations and Algebraic Thinking

Support English Language Learners

It is important for students to be able to translate words into symbols and symbols into words to gain an understanding of mathematical language.

Provide students with the words and phrases below.
addition: *more than, greater than, plus, added to, the sum of*
multiplication: *times more, times as much, times greater*
equal: *is, is equal to*

Present addition and multiplication equations. Have students read each equation aloud using different phrases to represent the operations.

For example, 12 = 4 × 3. Have students read aloud the equation, "twelve equals four times three." Then have students read the equation as a comparison statement, "twelve is four times as much as three."

MORE ONLINE sadlierconnect.com   Lesson 2

Guided Instruction

Understand: Comparison with an unknown factor

> Tyler waits 21 minutes for the school bus. Tyler's waiting time is 3 times as long as Grace's waiting time. How long does Grace wait for the bus?

To find how long Grace waits for the bus, first model the problem. Then write and solve an equation. Use g to represent the unknown quantity, Grace's waiting time.

Waiting Times

21 minutes

Tyler | g | g | g |

Grace | g |

Grace's waiting time is the amount being multiplied, or the size of each group in the model.

Write a multiplication equation for the comparison.

21 = 3 times as long as Grace's waiting time

$21 = 3 \times g$

Write and solve a related division equation to find g, the unknown factor.

$21 \div 3 = g$

$7 = g$

Remember!
Multiplication and division are opposite, or *inverse*, operations.

➤ Grace waits 7 minutes for the bus.

✏️ Find how many minutes more Tyler waited than Grace waited.
$21 - 7 = 14$. Tyler waited 14 minutes more than Grace waited.

Understand: Comparison with an unknown factor

■ Students learn to use a symbol or letter for the unknown number in a comparison equation. Guide students to see that the letter stands for *what number* and that using a letter makes it easier to represent the situation with an equation. Help students to remember the meaning of the unknown factor. For this problem, students can write g = *Grace's wait time*.

■ Have students explain why it is best to avoid using the letter *o* to represent an unknown number, since it can be easily confused with the number 0. Relate that the letter *l* is commonly written in cursive or italics to distinguish it from the number 1.

■ Remind students that the product and the factors of multiplication are the quotient, dividend, and divisor of the related division. Discuss how the multiplication and division equations in the presentation are related.

✏️ Ask students to explain how this problem is different from the problem at the top of the page. Listen for students to express that the phrase *3 times as long* is comparing the length of one wait time to another and *how many more* is asking about the difference between the two wait times.

Math-to-Science Connection

Mixtures The term *mixture* means a combination of different substances. Trail mix is a popular snack consisting of a mixture of such things as nuts, cereal, and dried fruits. Have students work in small groups to create their own recipe for trail mix. The recipe should have at least four different ingredients and include 1 cup of their favorite dried fruit. The remaining ingredients should be listed as a multiplicative comparison. For example, the recipe might include statements such as *twice as much cereal as raisins,* or *three times more nuts than cereal.* Recipes should also include the total amounts of each ingredient based on the multiplicative comparisons.

Guided Instruction

Connect: What you know about comparison and multiplication Use this page to strengthen students' understanding of using unknown factors to solve problems that involve comparison.

■ There can be two types of missing factors: group size and number of groups. Previously, students were given the number of groups and asked to find the group size. Now, students are given the group size and asked to find the number of groups.

■ Discuss how to check a solution by replacing the unknown factor in an equation with the solution. If the value of the unknown factor is correct, the equation will be true.

✏ Ask students to identify whether the problem is a multiplicative comparison problem or an additive comparison problem. Discuss how multiplication and related division can be used to solve the problem.

Lesson 2 Problem Solving: **Use Multiplication and Division to Make Comparisons**

Guided Instruction

Connect: What you know about comparison and multiplication

> There are 32 students in an art contest. Only 4 prizes will be given. How many times the number of prizes is the number of students?

To solve, make a model and write an equation.

Step 1

Make a model to help you understand the situation.

You need to find the factor that you must multiply 4 by to get 32.

Art Contest

32

students | f groups of 4

prizes | 4

Step 2

Write an equation. Use f to represent the unknown factor.

32 is an unknown factor times as many as 4

$32 = f \times 4$

Step 3

Write a related division equation to find f.

$32 \div 4 = f$
$8 = f$

Remember!
factor × factor = product
product ÷ factor = factor

➡ There are 8 times as many students as prizes.

✏ In another contest, there are 42 students. There are 7 times as many students as prizes. How many prizes are there?
Let p represent the number of prizes. Then, $42 = 7 \times p$.
This means $p = 42 \div 7 = 6$. There are 6 prizes.

20 Unit 1 ■ Focus on Operations and Algebraic Thinking

Math-to-Math Connection

Multiplicative Comparison and Fractions A strong understanding of multiplicative comparison problems with whole numbers is needed for students to be successful with solving word problems that involve multiplying whole numbers and fractions and multiplying two fractions. Multiplicative comparison problems that involve fractions often use phrases such as, *half as much* and *one-fourth as many*. Notice that the word "times" is not part of the phrases, so recognizing comparison situations is essential in correctly translating and solving these types of problems.

Lesson 2

Guided Practice

Use the model at the right to solve the problem.

1. An adult cat weighs 8 pounds, and is 4 times heavier than a kitten. How much does the kitten weigh?

   Cat's Weights

   8 pounds

   adult cat | 2 | 2 | 2 | 2 |

   kitten | 2 |

   a. Identify the numbers given in the problem.

   the greater amount, or product: __8__ pounds

   the factor telling the number of groups in 8: __4__

   b. What do you need to find? Describe the unknown factor. Possible answers:
   the kitten's weight, the size of each group, the amount being multiplied

   c. Write a letter to represent the unknown factor.
   Answers will vary. Possible answer: k

   Use this same letter for exercises d and e below.

   d. Write a multiplication equation for the comparison.
   $8 = \underline{4} \times \underline{k}$

   e. Write a related division equation to find the unknown factor.
   $\underline{8} \div \underline{4} = \underline{k}$

   f. Use your division equation to solve, and label the model above with your answer. Then complete the following sentence.
   The kitten weighs __2__ pounds.

   g. How do you know that your answer is correct?
   Possible answer: 2 is correct because $4 \times 2 = 8$, the weight of the adult cat.

☆ Think ▪ Pair ▪ Share

MP3　2. Why is it helpful to represent a multiplicative comparison problem with both a multiplication equation and a division equation? Explain.
Possible explanation: Writing both kinds of equations can help you better understand what you need to find. Also, after you solve one equation, you can replace the letter in the other equation with your answer to check if it is correct.

Unit 1 ▪ Focus on Operations and Algebraic Thinking　**21**

Observational Assessment

Use page 21 to assess whether students are able to represent the unknown factor, and then use multiplication and related division to solve for the unknown. Watch for students who are unable to describe the unknown factor.

☆ Think▪Pair▪Share

Peer Collaboration Ask pairs of students to write a multiplicative comparison problem. After pairs solve their problem, ask:

- *Do you think it is better to find an unknown factor using a multiplication equation or a division equation?*

- *How is it possible to check your answer using a related equation with the opposite operation? Explain.*

Return to the Essential Question

Reread the Lesson 2 Essential Question on page 18: *How can you solve problems involving multiplicative comparisons?*

Ask volunteers to use what they learned in this lesson to answer this question. (Possible response: I can solve a multiplicative comparison problem by making a model, identifying and representing the unknown factor, writing a multiplication equation for the comparison, and finally writing and solving a related division equation to find the unknown factor.)

If students have difficulty answering the Essential Question, revisit the steps shown on page 20 with them.

Mathematical Practices

Mathematical Practice Standards underline the teaching and understanding of all concepts and skills presented. The emphasis of specific practices is noted throughout the guided and independent practice of this lesson.

MP3	**Construct viable arguments and critique the reasoning of others.**

Item 2: Students justify their conclusion as to why it is helpful to represent multiplicative comparison problems with both a multiplication equation and a division equation.

Concept Application

Students may work independently on these pages in the classroom or at home. They may refer to the first four pages of the lesson to revisit the instruction or to see a worked-out example.

Common Errors and **Teaching Tips** may help you support student learning either in the classroom or as a follow-up for work done at home.

Common Errors

Items 1–2

Students may use the same order of values when translating a multiplication equation to the related division equation. Have students write the multiplication facts before completing the division equations. Point out that the answer for the multiplication equation is used to begin the related division equation.

Teaching Tips

Items 4–7

Point out that any of the equations a.–d. may be a matching equation for more than one of the exercises 4–7. One or more equations may not match any of the problems.

Alert students that the value of y will be different for each situation. Students may benefit by highlighting words in each problem that will help them find the matching equation.

Lesson 2 Problem Solving: Use Multiplication and Division to Make Comparisons

Independent Practice

Write an equation you can use to solve for *u*, the unknown number. Then solve.

1. $2 \times u = 8$

   $\underline{8} \div \underline{2} = u$

   $\underline{4} = u$

2. $u \times 7 = 49$

   $\underline{49 \div 7} = u$

   $\underline{7} = u$

3. $9 \times 10 = u$

   $\underline{9 \times 10} = u$

   $\underline{90} = u$

Describe the unknown number, *y*, in each problem. Then write the letter of the matching equation.

a. $6 \div 3 = y$ b. $6 - 3 = y$

c. $6 \times 3 = y$ d. $6 + 3 = y$

4. A fruit salad has 6 strawberries and 3 times as many blueberries. How many blueberries are there?

   y is Possible answers: the number of blueberries, the product, the greater number being compared

   Matching equation: c

5. Diego orders 3 books online. The store mails him 6 books instead. How many more books does Diego have than he ordered?

   y is Possible answers: the number of extra books, the difference of books mailed and books ordered

   Matching equation: b

6. A rectangular sign is 6 feet long. This is 3 times as long as the width of the sign. What is the width of the sign?

   y is Possible answers: the sign width, the group size, the amount multiplied, the lesser number being compared

   Matching equation: a

7. Emma's soccer team scores 3 goals. The winning team scores 6 goals. How many times as many goals does the winning team score as Emma's team?

   y is Possible answers: the number of times the lesser number is multiplied, the multiplier

   Matching equation: a

Writing About Math

Write Narratives Ask students to write a narrative based on real or unreal experiences or events. Have students include more than one multiplicative comparison in their narratives. For example, a student may write about Paul Bunyan and describe his height as being 10 times the height of an average adult.

Allow students to be as creative as possible, but encourage them to include descriptive details and clear event sequences. Let volunteers read their narratives aloud for the class to discuss.

Independent Practice

Write an equation with a letter for the unknown number. Then solve the problem. You can use the model to help.

8. Caleb's family has a car that is 3 years old. They also have a minivan that is 5 times as old as the car. How old is the minivan?

Equation _____ 3 × 5 = m _____

Answer _____ The minivan is 15 years old. _____

Automobile Ages

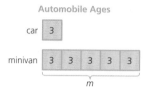

9. Houston gets about 48 inches of rain a year. Winslow gets about 8 inches of rain a year. How many times as much rain does Houston get as Winslow?

Equation _____ r × 8 = 48 or 48 ÷ 8 = r _____

Answer _____ Houston gets 6 times as much rain as Winslow. _____

Annual Rainfall in Inches

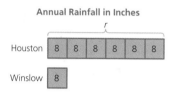

10. Aliyah needs to bake 24 muffins. This is 4 times as many muffins as her muffin pan holds. How many muffins does Aliyah's pan hold?

Equation _____ 4 × p = 24 or 24 ÷ 4 = p _____

Answer _____ Aliyah's pan holds 6 muffins. _____

Aliyah's Muffins

24

muffins needed | p | p | p | p |

muffins in 1 pan | p |

Circle the correct answer.

11. Jin has a muffin pan that holds 12 muffins. He lends the pan to Aliyah, who needs to bake 24 muffins. How many times as many muffins are needed as Jin's pan can hold?

(a.) 2 times as many   b. 3 times as many

c. 4 times as many   d. 6 times as many

Teaching Tips

Items 8–10
Remind students to use the given letter from the model when writing the equations.

Items 9–10
Ask students to identify whether the unknown factor represents the group size (problem 10) or number of groups (problem 9). Encourage students to use the given models to help them write and solve the equations.

Digital Connection

Internet Resources Use a search engine on a news media Web site to find articles that cite facts using comparison language. Comparisons are often used when reporting statistics. For example, a school planted three times as many trees on Arbor Day this year as they planted last year. Once students find an article, have them create a multiplicative comparison or additive comparison problem that can be answered using the data in the article.

These articles will help students to get a sense of how mathematical language is used every day.

Independent Practice

Common Errors

Item 12

Students may have difficulty setting up the model, erroneously using 8 to represent the group size and using 9 to represent the number of groups. In this case, the solution is the same, but that is not always the case. Remind students to read carefully and highlight important words before drawing their models.

Teaching Tips

Item 15

If students are struggling, remind them to revisit the types of comparison problems they have solved in this lesson. Students can use the examples in the lesson to justify that there are counterexamples to Serena's thinking.

Independent Practice

Draw a model and write an equation to represent each problem. Then solve.

MP1 **12.** Dmitri has saved $9 to buy a skateboard. The one he wants costs 8 times as much as his savings. How much does the skateboard cost?

· **Show your work.**

$$8 \times \$9 = s$$
$$\$72 = s$$

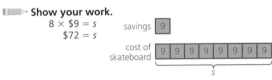

savings | 9

cost of skateboard | 9 9 9 9 9 9 9 9

s

Answer The skateboard costs $72.

MP2 **13.** An office building has 40 floors. It is 5 times as tall as the apartment building across the street. How many floors does the apartment building have?

· **Show your work.**

$$40 = 5 \times a$$
$$40 \div 5 = a$$
$$8 = a$$

40 { a a a a a

a

office building   apartment building

Answer The apartment building has 8 floors.

Answer each question in a complete sentence.

MP6 **14.** The deep end of a pool is 12 feet deep. The shallow end is 3 feet deep. Noah solved the equation $12 \div 3 = p$ to find that the deep end is 4 times as deep as the shallow end. Explain how Noah can check his answer.
Possible explanation: Since Noah divided to solve the problem, he can multiply to check if $p = 4 \times 3 = 12$, so $12 \div 3 = 4$. Noah's answer is correct.

MP3 **15.** Serena says that all multiplicative comparison problems are solved by multiplying the given numbers. Do you agree? Explain your answer.
Possible answer: This is only true when the comparison problem asks you to find a product, or the greater number being compared. But to find an unknown factor, you divide instead of multiplying.

Mathematical Practices

MP1	**Make sense of problems and persevere in solving them.**

Item 12: Students analyze given information and their relationship to solve the problem.

Item 17: Students analyze given information, relationships, and goals to make a plan for solving the problem.

MP2	**Reason abstractly and quantitatively.**

Item 13: Students create a representation of the problem and use it to write an equation.

 **MORE ONLINE** sadlierconnect.com

Lesson 2

Independent Practice

Solve the problems.

MP4 **16.** Eli collects stamps. He has 63 stamps from the United States. He also has 7 stamps from Canada. How many times as many U.S. stamps does Eli have as Canadian stamps?

⬛ **Show your work.**

U.S. stamps
63
s groups of 7

Canadian stamps
7

$63 = s \times 7$
$63 \div 7 = s$
$9 = s$

Answer Eli has 9 times as many U.S. stamps as Canadian stamps.

MP1 **17.** Olivia says that she used the computer for 9 hours this week. She thinks her brother Jack used it for 3 times as long as she did. Jack says he used it for 12 more hours than Olivia. Who counts a greater number of hours for Jack?

Answer Olivia counts a greater number of hours for Jack.

⬛ **Justify your answer using words, drawings, or numbers.**
Possible justification:

Olivia's count

Olivia   9

Jack   9 9 9
        27

Olivia says Jack used the computer for $3 \times 9 = 27$ hours. Jack says he used the computer for $9 + 12 = 21$ hours. Since $27 > 21$, Olivia thinks Jack spent more time on the computer than he said he did.

MP4 **18.** Olivia and Jack's father says that they used the computer for 30 hours altogether. He tells them that Jack used the computer for 2 times as long as Olivia. If this is true, did Olivia use the computer for 9 hours?

Answer No. Olivia used the computer for 10 hours, not 9. Jack used the computer for 20 hours.

⬛ **Justify your answer using words, drawings, or numbers.**
Possible justification:

Father's count

Olivia   h
                    }10 + 20 = 30
Jack   h h
        20

h = Olivia's hours
$2 \times h$ = Jack's hours
$3 \times h$ = their combined hours
$3 \times h = 30$
$30 \div 3 = h$
$10 = h$

Unit 1 ▪ Focus on Operations and Algebraic Thinking **25**

Common Errors

Item 16

Students might be uncertain whether this problem is a multiplicative comparison problem or an additive comparison problem. Have students locate the words *times as many* in the problem, and circle them. Remind them that *times* means multiply.

Teaching Tips

Items 17–18

Point out that these are multistep problems and that students will need to interpret their mathematical results within the context of the problem.

Mathematical Practices

MP3	**Construct viable arguments and critique the reasoning of others.**

Item 15: Students evaluate the thinking of other students.

MP4	**Model with mathematics.**

Item 16: Students write and solve an equation to represent a situation.

Item 18: Students support their answers mathematically within the context of the problem.

MP6	**Attend to precision.**

Item 14: Students explain how to check an answer.

Common Core Focus:

4.OA.3 Solve multistep word problems posed with whole numbers and having whole-number answers using the four operations, including problems in which remainders must be interpreted. Represent these problems using equations with a letter standing for the unknown quantity. Assess the reasonableness of answers using mental computation and estimation strategies including rounding.

OBJECTIVE

Use equations to solve multistep problems.

ESSENTIAL QUESTION

Students will solve multistep problems that require more than one step to solve. Writing an equation to represent a multistep problem is an important strategy that is used to solve many real-world problems.

FLUENCY PRACTICE

Fluency practice is available at **sadlierconnect.com**.

Concept Development

Understand: Equations to solve multistep problems

■ Students are expected to solve multistep word problems with whole numbers. This presentation walks students through the solution and a check for reasonableness of the answer.

■ Guide students to develop a plan for problem solving. This presentation first represents the problem as a word equation. This helps students think through the problem first, and then think about the quantities.

■ In the expression for the total number of people, discuss why 30 is multiplied by 2. Point out that in the problem, there are two classes of 30 students.

Lesson 3
Problem Solving: Multistep Problems

Essential Question: How can equations help you solve multistep problems?
4.OA.3

Words to Know: remainder

Guided Instruction

In this lesson you will learn how to use equations to solve problems with more than one step.

Understand: Equations to solve multistep problems

> The fourth graders are having a picnic. Two classes of 30 students each, 2 teachers, and 2 parents will be there. If 8 people sit at each table, how many tables are needed for all the people at the picnic?

To find the number of tables needed, you divide the total number of people by the number of people who can sit at each table. To solve this problem, first write a statement or a word equation.

$$\text{number of tables needed} = \text{total number of people} \div \text{number who can sit at each table}$$

Next, think about the three quantities in the equation: The number of tables needed is unknown. You can use t to represent this number. The total number of people is the number of students in the two classes plus the number of adults: $2 \times 30 + 2 + 2$ The number of people at each table is 8.

Use this information to rewrite an equation.

$$t = (2 \times 30 + 2 + 2) \div 8$$

2 groups of 30 students plus 2 teachers and 2 parents

Use parentheses to show that the total number of people is calculated *before* dividing.

Now, solve the equation. Use the order of operations.

$t = (2 \times 30 + 2 + 2) \div 8$	
$t = (60 + 2 + 2) \div 8$	Multiply within the parentheses.
$t = 64 \div 8$	Add within the parentheses.
$t = 8$	Divide.

Check that your answer is reasonable. You can use reasoning and mental math. Eight tables can hold 8×8, or 64 people. There will be 4 adults plus 2×30, or 60 students, which is a total of 64 people. The answer is correct.

➡ Eight picnic tables are needed for all the people at the picnic.

26   Unit 1 ■ Focus on Operations and Algebraic Thinking

Words to Know

remainder: the amount left over after dividing

Example: $52 \div 6 = 8 \text{ R4}$
52 divided by 6 equals 8 remainder 4.
The amount left over after dividing is 4.

Glossary can be found on pp. 347–350.

MORE ONLINE sadlierconnect.com

Lesson 3

Guided Instruction

Understand: The meaning of a remainder

Amanda collects old postcards. She had 71 postcards. Then, she sold 19 of them to another collector. She wants to put the postcards she has left in an album that fits 6 cards on each page. How many pages will Amanda need to hold the postcards she has left?

To find the number of pages Amanda needs, write a word equation for the problem.

number of pages = number of postcards ÷ number that fit on each page

You can use p to represent the unknown number of pages. Use the information from the problem to write the equation.

$$p = (71 - 19) \div 6$$

71 cards she started with minus the 19 she sold

Use parentheses to show that the subtraction is done *before* the division.

Now, solve the equation.

$p = (71 - 19) \div 6$

$p = 52 \div 6$ Subtract within the parentheses.

$p = 52 \div 6 = 8 \text{ R}4$ Divide. Read as, "52 divided by 6 equals 8 remainder 4."

There are 8 groups of 6 in 52 with 4 left over. The amount left over after dividing is called the remainder. The remainder is written with an R before it.

Amanda can fill 8 whole pages. She will need 1 more page for the remaining 4 postcards. So, she needs 9 pages in all.

➡ Amanda will need 9 pages to hold the postcards she has left.

Understand: The meaning of a remainder

■ Mathematically proficient students are able to solve word problems, including problems in which remainders must be interpreted. In this presentation, students will solve a word problem involving division with a remainder and learn how to interpret a remainder.

■ Real-world word problems involving division often require a whole-number quotient. Explain that sometimes the quotient is rounded up or down to the nearest whole number depending on the context of the problem. Be sure students understand why the quotient was rounded up in this problem.

Support English Language Learners

Have students act out simple division problems to help them understand the meaning of *remainder*. Write the equation $10 \div 3$ on the board. Have a group of 10 students model the problem by separating themselves into three equal groups. Explain that the number of students in each group is the quotient, or answer. Write the answer on the board.

Explain that there is one student left over. The student that remains without a group represents the remainder. Write R1 on the board.

Repeat the activity with other students and other simple division problems. Check that the class understands that the student(s) who *remain* without a group represent the *remainder*. Be sure to discuss why some divisions may not include remainders.

Connect: Problem situations and reasonable solutions Use this page to help students strengthen their understanding of how to write an equation for a word problem and how to check the reasonableness of their answers.

■ Mathematically proficient students are able to approximate solutions to simplify a complicated situation and use this approximation to check the reasonableness of their solution.

■ It is important that students carefully read word problems for understanding. Writing a word equation will help students understand the problem situation. Using a model, such as the one shown in Step 2, will help students visualize the information from the problem and help them write the corresponding mathematical equations.

■ This presentation uses rounding as an estimation strategy for determining if the answer is reasonable. Review the rules for rounding numbers with students. Discuss why numbers are rounded to the nearest 10, not the nearest 100, in Step 4. Be sure students understand that rounding is one of many estimation methods.

Connect: Problem situations and reasonable solutions

> On the first night of the school play, 371 tickets were sold. On the second night, 59 fewer tickets were sold than the first night. How many tickets were sold altogether for both nights of the play?

To find how many tickets were sold, write and solve an equation.

Step 1

Write a word equation to represent the problem.
total tickets sold = tickets sold the first night + tickets sold the second night

Step 2

Use the information from the problem to write an equation. You can use a model to help you understand how the quantities are related. Notice that you need to subtract to find the number of tickets sold on the second night.

t	
371	371 − 59

$t =$ 371   + $(371 − 59)$

59 fewer tickets than
on the first night

Step 3

Solve the equation.

$t = 371 + (371 − 59)$
$t = 371 + 312$ Subtract within parentheses.
$t = 683$ Add.

Step 4

Use rounding and estimation to check that the answer is reasonable. 371 is about 370 and 59 is about 60, so the answer should be about:
$370 + (370 − 60) = 370 + 310 = 680$

Remember!
An estimate is a number that is close to an exact amount.

The estimate 680 is close to the actual answer 683. So the answer is reasonable.

A total of 683 tickets were sold altogether for both nights of the play.

Math-to-Statistics Connection

Averages Finding the average of a data set is a two-step process—first finding the sum of the data, and then dividing by the number of pieces of data. Averages are commonly used in schools. Teachers may want to know the average test score or find the average grade for a student. A principal may need to know the average class size or the average number of lunches sold per day.

Have small groups of students decide on a statistical question they want to answer by finding an average. Students can use real data or generate their own. Have groups present their statistical question and answer to the class. Students should explain how they calculated the average and how they checked to determine that their answer is reasonable.

Lesson 3

Guided Practice

For exercises 1–6, follow the steps to solve the problem. Use the model if it helps you.

There are 70 people waiting to tour a museum. The tour guide takes 4 groups with 16 people each. The remaining people will be in the last tour group. How many people are in the last tour group?

Museum Tour Groups

16	16	16	16	p

70

1. Use the following terms to make a word equation for this problem:
   people in first 4 groups, people waiting, people in last group.

   <u>people in last group</u> = <u>people waiting</u> − <u>people in first 4 groups</u>

2. There are <u>70</u> people waiting.

3. Show the number of people in the first four groups.

   <u>4</u> × 16

4. Use p to represent the number of people in the last group. Then write an equation to find how many people are in the last group using the information from the problem.

   $p = \underline{70} - (\underline{4 \times 16})$

5. Solve the equation.

   $p = \underline{70} - (\underline{4 \times 16})$

   $p = \underline{70} - \underline{64}$

   $p = \underline{6}$

6. There are <u>6</u> people in the last tour group.

ᗡᗡ Think • Pair • Share

MP2

7. Molly says that the answer for the problem above is the same as the remainder for 70 ÷ 16. Is Molly correct? You can use the model to help you explain your answer.
   Possible explanation: Molly is correct. The model shows that there are 4 groups of 16 in 70, and 6 people left over. When you subtract 4 groups of 16 from 70, you are left with 6, so 70 ÷ 16 = 4 R6.

Unit 1 ■ Focus on Operations and Algebraic Thinking **29**

Use page 29 to assess whether students are able to write and solve an equation in order to solve a multistep problem.

ᗡᗡ Think•Pair•Share

Peer Collaboration Ask students to answer the question and then separate them into groups. Ask group members to compare their answers. During a class discussion have a volunteer from each group answer the following:

• *What explanation(s) were given?*

• *If more than one explanation was given, how were they alike? How were they different?*

Return to the Essential Question

Reread the Lesson 3 Essential Question on page 26: *How can equations help you solve multistep problems?*

Ask volunteers to use what they learned in this lesson to answer this question. (Possible response: I can use a letter to represent an unknown quantity in a word problem. I can use estimation to check if the answer is reasonable. I can use order of operations to write and solve equations.)

Mathematical Practices

Mathematical Practice Standards underline the teaching and understanding of all concepts and skills presented. The emphasis of specific practices is noted throughout the guided and independent practice of this lesson.

MP2 **Reason abstractly and quantitatively.**

Item 7: Students use a model to help explain their answer.

Independent Practice

Concept Application

Students may work independently on these pages in the classroom or at home. They may refer to the first four pages of the lesson to revisit the instruction or to see a worked-out example.

Common Errors and **Teaching Tips** may help you support student learning either in the classroom or as a follow-up for work done at home.

Common Errors

Item 2

Students may mix up the sum and the addend. Have them relate that the question is asking them to find the sum.

Teaching Tips

Items 1–2

Point out that when students use estimation to check their answer, the equation for the estimate must follow the same order as the original equation. Students will decide which numbers to round, and also whether to round to the nearest 10 or 100.

Independent Practice

Use the steps to model and solve each problem. Then estimate to check your answer. Estimates may vary.

1. Three hikers want to share the weight in their backpacks equally. Their backpacks weigh 32 pounds, 39 pounds, and 22 pounds. How much weight should each hiker carry?

   Write a word equation.

   weight each person carries = total weight ÷ __number of people__

   Use b for the unknown. Use the information from the problem to rewrite the equation.

   $b = ($ _32_ $+$ _39_ $+$ _22_ $) ÷$ _3_

   Solve the equation to find the answer.
   $b = (32 + 39 + 22) ÷ 3$
   $b = 93 ÷ 3$
   $b = 31$

   Answer _31 pounds_

   Use estimation to check your answer.
   $(30 + 40 + 20) ÷ 3 = 90 ÷ 3 = 30$; the answer is reasonable.

2. Jacob has read 39 library books since school began. He plans to read another 2 books a week for the next 12 weeks. At the end of this time, how many books will he have read altogether?

   Write a word equation.

   __total books read__ = books read so far + __books read in the next 12__ weeks

   Use t for the unknown. Substitute the information from the problem.

   $t =$ _39_ $+$ _12 × 2_

   Solve the equation to find the answer.
   $t = 39 + (12 × 2)$
   $t = 39 + 24$
   $t = 63$

   Answer _63 books_

   Use estimation to check your answer.
   $40 + (10 × 2) = 40 + 20 = 60$; the answer is reasonable.

Writing About Math

▸ **Write an Explanatory Text** When solving a problem involving division with remainders, the quotient must be interpreted. Sometimes a problem only needs the remainder as an answer. Sometimes the quotient needs to be rounded up or down to a whole number.

Have students describe at least two situations that involve remainders and how the remainders are used. Students should include a specific problem for each situation. Ask volunteers to read their paragraphs aloud.

Lesson 3

Independent Practice

In exercises 3–5, follow the steps to solve the problem. Use the model at the right if it helps you.

Tina has 6 packs of 8 colored markers to put into party gift bags. She splits the markers equally among 9 gift bags. How many markers can she put in each bag?

Party Gift Bags

g	g	g	g	g	g	g	g	g

m markers

3. Write an equation for this problem.

$g = \underline{6 \times 8 \div 9}$

4. Solve the equation.
$g = 6 \times 8 \div 9$
$g = 48 \div 9$
$g = 5\ R3$

5. Answer the question.

Tina can put __5__ markers in each bag.

6. Is the final answer in exercise 5 the same as the solution to your equation? Explain why or why not.
No. Possible explanation: The solution to the equation is 5 R3, which means that Tina can put 5 markers in each bag, and she will have 3 markers left over. The answer to exercise 5 is just 5 with no remainder because she can put 5 markers in each bag.

Circle the correct answer.

7. Peter practices the piano for 25 minutes 3 times a week. He also has a 55-minute piano lesson every Saturday. How much time does Peter spend playing the piano in one week?

  a. 80 minutes   (b.) 130 minutes

  c. 190 minutes   d. 240 minutes

8. Sixteen teams of 5 students each sign up for a sports tournament. The principal will combine the teams and then divide the students into 10 new teams. How many students will be on each of the new teams?

  a. 7   b. 7 R5

  (c.) 8   d. 10

Unit 1 ■ Focus on Operations and Algebraic Thinking **31**

Teaching Tips

Item 3

If students are struggling to write an equation, have them first write a word equation. For example, *number in each bag = total number of markers ÷ number of bags.*

Item 5

Be sure students realize that they need to interpret the remainder. Some students may benefit from using concrete objects to model the situation. This can help them visualize that each bag contains 5 markers and that there are 3 markers remaining.

Digital Connection

Interactive Whiteboard Use a whiteboard to lead students in a secret number game. Give the first clue: *When you divide 32 by this number, the remainder is 2.* Give another clue: *When you divide 18 by this number, the remainder is 3.* Keep track of the clues. Continue giving clues until a student guesses the secret number. In this instance, the secret number is 5. When an answer is given, go back through the clues to make sure the number fits each clue.

Independent Practice

Common Errors

Item 11

Some students may divide 96 by 2 or multiply 96 by 2. Guide students to understand why they need to divide 96 into 3 equal groups. One group will represent the votes for the radio station and two groups will represent twice the number of votes for the radio station, which is the number of votes for the zoo.

Teaching Tips

Item 10

Students need to develop a plan before attempting to write and solve a division problem. They should first decide if they want to use the remainder or disregard the remainder, and then develop a word problem around the quotient.

Independent Practice

MP6 **9.** Haj solved the equation $w = 718 - (329 + 178)$. She got the solution $w = 567$. Use estimation to check Haj's solution. Do you think her solution is reasonable? Explain.
Possible explanation: If you round the numbers to the nearest hundred you get $700 - (300 + 200) = 700 - 500 = 200$. Haj's answer is much greater than 200, so it is not reasonable.

MP1 **10.** Consider this division problem: $27 \div 4 = 6$ R3. Describe a real-world problem that can be solved by finding $27 \div 4$. Give the solution to your problem. How did you think about the remainder when you found the solution?
Possible answer: Ms. Chang wants to divide the 27 students in her class into groups of 4 to work on a problem. How many groups will there be? There will be 7 groups. The solution 6 R3 means that Ms. Chang can make 6 groups of 4, but she will have 3 students left over. These 3 students can form another group, so I made the answer 7 groups.

Solve the problem.

MP4 **11.** A total of 96 students vote on two choices for a field trip. The zoo gets 2 times as many votes as the radio station. How many students vote to go to the zoo?

Show your work.

Work may vary. Possible work:
$z = (96 \div 3) \times 2$
$z = 32 \times 2$
$z = 64$

Answer 64 students vote to go to the zoo.

Mathematical Practices	
MP1	**Make sense of problems and persevere in solving them.**
Item 10: Students write a word problem similar to other problems that involve interpreting a remainder.	
MP4	**Model with mathematics.**
Item 11: Students draw a model to represent a quantity that is not explicitly given in the problem.	
MP6	**Attend to precision.**
Item 9: Students find and explain an error in another's work.	

Independent Practice

Solve the problems.

MP4 **12.** A soccer team orders 36 new jerseys for games. Half of the jerseys are red and the other half are white. Five of the white jerseys the team receives are the wrong size. How many white jerseys are the correct size?

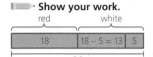

➤ **Show your work.**

red   white

| 18 | 18 − 5 = 13 | 5 |

36

Work may vary. Possible work:
$c = (36 \div 2) − 5$
$c = 18 − 5 = 13$

Answer 13 of the white jerseys are the correct size.

MP7 **13.** There are 29, 15, 31, and 25 people in four groups of volunteers. Colin wants to divide the volunteers into 5 equal teams to clean up different areas of the park. The following equation can be used to find the number of people on each team:

$p = (29 + 15 + 31 + 25) \div 5$

Rewrite this equation so it is easy to solve mentally. Then solve the problem in your head. Explain what you did.

Answer $p = (29 + 31 + 15 + 25) \div 5$; There will be 20 people on each team.

➤ **Justify your answer using words, drawings, or numbers.**
Possible justification: I rearranged the numbers in the parentheses, so I could add them to make 10s. This gave me 100 ÷ 5, which I could divide in my head: $p = (29 + 31 + 15 + 25) \div 5 = (60 + 40) \div 5 = 100 \div 5 = 20$.

MP6 **14.** A water faucet that drips 10 times a minute wastes 3 liters of water in 1 day. If 2 of the faucets in Charlotte's house drip at this rate, how many days will it take to waste 100 liters of water?

Answer It will take about 17 days.

➤ **Justify your answer using words, drawings, or numbers.**
Possible justification: $d = 100 \div (2 \times 3) = 100 \div 6 = 16$ R4. The two faucets together waste 6 liters in 1 day, and 96 liters in 16 days ($16 \times 6 = 96$). The remainder 4 represents 4 liters, and this is more than half of 6 liters ($4 > 3$). So I rounded 16 days up to 17 days.

Unit 1 ■ Focus on Operations and Algebraic Thinking   **33**

Teaching Tips

Item 13
Remind students that the Commutative Property of Addition states that changing the order of the addends does not change the sum.

Item 14
There are multiple units in this problem: minutes, liters, and days. Point out that students can use units as a guide to understanding the problem, setting up an equation, and checking the reasonableness of a solution.

Mathematical Practices	
MP4	**Model with mathematics.**

Item 12: Students draw a model to find a quantity that is not explicitly given in the problem.

MP6	**Attend to precision.**

Item 14: Students use measurement units to guide their solutions.

MP7	**Look for and make use of structure.**

Item 13: Students use the order of operations to evaluate a numerical expression inside parentheses before dividing.

Common Core Focus:

4.0A.4 Find all factor pairs for a whole number in the range 1–100. Recognize that a whole number is a multiple of each of its factors. Determine whether a given whole number in the range 1–100 is a multiple of a given one-digit number. Determine whether a given whole number in the range 1–100 is prime or composite.

OBJECTIVE

Identify factors and multiples of whole numbers in the 1–100 range.

ESSENTIAL QUESTION

In this lesson, students will apply their knowledge of multiplication and division facts to find factors and multiples of whole numbers.

PREREQUISITE SKILLS

Use Item B on page 337 of the Foundational Skills Handbook to review division as an unknown-factor problem.

FLUENCY PRACTICE

Fluency practice is available at **sadlierconnect.com**.

Concept Development

Understand: Factors and factor pairs

■ Explain to students that once they find one factor in a factor pair, they can divide to find the other factor. The divisor and the quotient are a factor pair of the dividend.

Understand: Prime and Composite Numbers

■ The number 1 is neither a prime number nor a composite number because it only has one factor: itself.

■ The number 0 is not a prime number because there are an infinite number of factor pairs equal to 0: itself and any other number. Neither is 0 a composite number because there are no two non-zero factors whose product is 0.

Essential Question:
What are factors and multiples of whole numbers?
4.0A.4

Words to Know:
factor
factor pair
prime number
composite number
multiple

Guided Instruction

Understand: Factors and factor pairs

> Mr. Yoo has 12 student worksheets to display. He wants to display them in rows. He wants the same number of worksheets in each row. How many different ways can Mr. Yoo display the worksheets?

Model all the ways that the 12 worksheets can be displayed in a rectangular array. To do this, find the pairs of factors with a product of 12.

Factors are whole numbers that are multiplied together to make a product. A factor of a number can also be thought of as a number that divides evenly into that number, without a remainder.
The factors of 12 are 1, 2, 3, 4, 6, and 12.

The factor pairs for 12 are: 1 and 12, 2 and 6, 3 and 4.
You can make two arrays for each factor pair.

3×4 4×3 2×6 6×2 1×12 12×1

➡ Mr. Yoo can display the worksheets in 6 different ways.

Understand: Prime and Composite Numbers

> Suppose Mr. Yoo has 13 pieces of student worksheets. In how many ways can Mr. Yoo display the worksheets in equal rows?

The only factor pair for 13 is 1 and 13. So Mr. Yoo can display the worksheets as a 1×13 array or as a 13×1 array.

The number 13 is an example of a prime number. A prime number is a number greater than 1 with only two factors, 1 and the number itself. The number 12 is a composite number. A composite number is a number greater than 1 that has more than two factors.

➡ Mr. Yoo can display the worksheets in 2 different ways.

34 Unit 1 ■ Focus on Operations and Algebraic Thinking

Words to Know

factor: one of the two or more numbers that are multiplied to form a product

Example: factors of 6: 1, 2, 3, and 6

factor pair: two numbers that multiply to give a product

Example: factor pairs of 6: 1 and 6, 2 and 3

prime number: a number greater than 1 with only two factors, 1 and the number itself

Example: 7 and 13 are prime numbers.

Glossary can be found on pp. 347-350.

Lesson 4

Guided Instruction

Understand: Finding factors of a whole number

> Find all the factors of 15. Tell whether 15 is prime or composite.

Remember!
A factor of a whole number divides evenly into the number.

To find the factors of 15, divide 15 by whole numbers, starting with 1. If a number divides into 15 evenly, then both it and the quotient are factors of 15. Keep checking until the factors start to repeat.

Is 15 divisible by 1?	by 2?	by 3?	by 4?
Yes, $15 \div 1 = 15$	No	Yes, $15 \div 3 = 5$	No
1 and 15 are factors.		3 and 5 are factors.	

The next number to check is 5, but you already found that 5 is a factor of 15. You can stop checking. The factors of 15 are 1, 3, 5, and 15.

➡ The factors of 15 are 1, 3, 5, and 15. It is a composite number.

Understand: Finding multiples of a whole number

> Students sign up for a competition in teams of 3. What are some possibilities for the total number of students in the competition?

1 team is $1 \times 3 = 3$ students
2 teams is $2 \times 3 = 6$ students
3 teams is $3 \times 3 = 9$ students
4 teams is $4 \times 3 = 12$ students
5 teams is $5 \times 3 = 15$ students
6 teams is $6 \times 3 = 18$ students

The numbers 3, 6, 9, 12, 15, and 18 are multiples of 3. A multiple of a whole number is the product of that number and another whole number. Notice that 3 is a factor of each of its multiples.

➡ The possible numbers of students are the multiples of 3: 3, 6, 9, 12, 15, 18, 21, 24, and so on.

✏ Find all the factors of 19 and 24. Tell whether each is prime or composite.
The factors of 19 are 1 and 19. It is a prime number. The factors of 24 are 1, 2, 3, 4, 6, 8, 12, and 24. It is a composite number.

Unit 1 ■ Focus on Operations and Algebraic Thinking   35

Understand: Finding factors of a whole number

■ Help students understand that when finding all the factors of a number, they should stop dividing when they see a reversal in the factors pairs. For example, the factor pair 3 and 5 is the same as the factor pair 5 and 3.

■ Model how to find and write the factor pairs in an organized list.

Understand: Finding multiples of a whole number

■ Relate finding multiples of whole numbers to skip counting. Point out that skip counting is actually naming multiples of the beginning number.

■ Some students may benefit by identifying multiples using a multiplication table. Help these students discover patterns in a multiplication table. For example, all the numbers in a column or a row are multiples of each of the two factors at the ends of the table.

✏ Have students share their methods for determining prime and composite numbers.

Words to Know

composite number: a number greater than 1 that has more than two factors

Example: The number 16 is a composite number.
The factors of 16 are 1, 2, 4, 8, and 16.

multiple: the product of a given whole number and another whole number

Example: The multiples of 4 are 4, 8, 12, and so on.

Glossary can be found on pp. 347-350.

Connect: Factors and multiples Use this page to help students strengthen their understanding of how factors and multiples are related.

■ In this presentation, students find the least common multiple of 6 and 8. It is essential that students become fluent in finding factors and multiples. In later grades students will be expected to find the greatest common factor and the least common multiple of greater numbers.

■ Be sure students understand the statement: *In general, a whole number is a multiple of each of its factors.* Point out that the equations $3 \times 8 = 24$ and $4 \times 6 = 24$ show that 24 is a multiple of 3, a multiple of 8, a multiple of 4, and a multiple of 6.

Connect: Factors and multiples

> Juice boxes are sold in packs of 8. Snack bags of crackers are sold in packs of 6. Ms. Leone takes one of each in her lunch. What is the least number of packs of each Ms. Leone can buy to have the same number of juice boxes and bags of crackers?

To solve use multiples of 8 and 6.

Step 1

Use multiples to find the possible numbers of each item Ms. Leone can buy.

There are 8 juice boxes in each pack, so Ms. Leone can only buy juice boxes in multiples of 8. List the first several multiples of 8:

8	16	24	32	40	48	56	64
1×8	2×8	3×8	4×8	5×8	6×8	7×8	8×8

There are 6 bags of crackers in every pack, so Ms. Leone can only buy bags of crackers in multiplies of 6. List the first several multiples of 6:

6	12	18	24	30	36	42	48
1×6	2×6	3×6	4×6	5×6	6×6	7×6	8×6

Step 2

Find the least number that is both a multiple of 8 and a multiple of 6.

The least number that is both a multiple of 8 and a multiple of 6 is 24. Ms. Leone can buy exactly 24 boxes of juice and 24 bags of crackers.

$3 \times 8 = 24$, she must buy 3 packs of juice boxes to get 24 boxes.
$4 \times 6 = 24$, she must buy 4 packs of crackers to get 24 bags.

Notice the connection between factors and multiples:
24 is a multiple of 8 and 8 is a factor of 24.
Similarly, 24 is a multiple of 6 and 6 is a factor of 24.

> In general, a whole number is a multiple of each of its factors.

➡ The least number of packs Ms. Leone can buy is 3 packs of juice boxes and 4 packs of crackers.

Support English Language Learners

Some students struggle distinguishing between *factors* and *factor pair*, and between *prime number* and *composite number*.

Write a composite number, such as 12, on the board. Have students brainstorm a list of numbers that, when multiplied, equal 12. Record the factors in pairs. Explain that each number is a *factor* of 12. Each pair of numbers that work together to equal 12 is called a *factor pair*.

Tell students that numbers that have two or more factor pairs are called *composite numbers*. Students should understand that only the two factors that equal the given product make a factor pair. Repeat the activity using prime numbers. Point out that numbers that have only one factor pair are called *prime numbers*.

Make all the possible arrays for the number. Then, list the factors and circle *prime* or *composite*.

1. 10

Arrays:

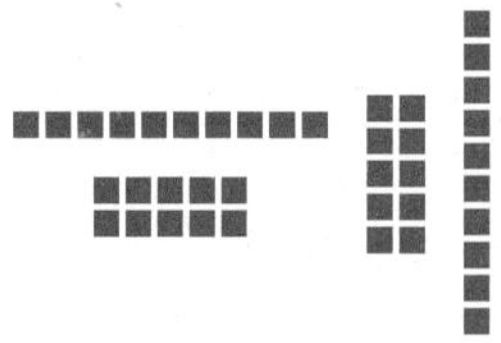

Factors: 1, 2, 5, 10

prime or ***composite*** (circled)

2. Complete this table to find the factors of 35. Use the first two rows as a guide. Some cells in the last column will be empty.

Is 35 divisible by 1?	Yes, 35 ÷ 1 = 35	1 and 35 are factors.
Is 35 divisible by 2?	No	
Is 35 divisible by 3?	No	
Is 35 divisible by 4?	No	
Is 35 divisible by 5?	Yes; 35 ÷ 5 = 7	5 and 7 are factors
Is 35 divisible by 6?	No	

Why don't you need to check 7? I already found that 7 is a factor.

List all the factors. 1, 5, 7, 35

Think • Pair • Share

MP2 **3.** Cole said, "All prime numbers are odd and all composite numbers are even." Do you agree with Cole? Explain.
No, I do not agree. Possible explanation: The number 2 is even, and it is prime because its only factors are 1 and 2. There are lots of odd composite numbers. For example, the number 15 is odd, and it has four factors: 1, 3, 5, and 15.

Mathematical Practices

Mathematical Practice Standards underline the teaching and understanding of all concepts and skills presented. The emphasis of specific practices is noted throughout the guided and independent practice of this lesson.

MP2	**Reason abstractly and quantitatively.**

Item 3: Students use mathematical language to reason about numbers.

Observational Assessment

Use page 37 to assess whether students are able to find all the factors for given whole numbers and to determine whether a given whole number is prime or composite.

Think•Pair•Share

Peer Collaboration Have pairs of students list prime and composite numbers before answering the question. Explain the term *counterexample.* Explain that counterexamples can be used to disprove a statement. Ask:

- *What strategy can you use to find a counterexample?*
- *How many counterexamples are needed to disprove a statement?*

Point out that there may be many counterexamples. Not everyone has to use the same counterexample.

Return to the Essential Question

Reread the Lesson 4 Essential Question on page 34: *What are factors and multiples of whole numbers?*

Ask volunteers to use what they learned in this lesson to answer this question.
(Possible responses: A factor is a whole number that, when multiplied by another whole number, results in a product. The numbers 3 and 4 are factors of 12. A multiple of a whole number is the product of that whole number and another whole number. The multiples of 3 are 3, 6, 9, 12, and so on.)

Concept Application

Students may work independently on these pages in the classroom or at home. They may refer to the first four pages of the lesson to revisit the instruction or to see a worked-out example.

Common Errors and **Teaching Tips** may help you support student learning either in the classroom or as a follow-up for work done at home.

Teaching Tips

Items 1–2

Some students may need to use manipulatives to model the arrays before drawing them.

Items 1–3

Remind students that each factor will be listed only once.

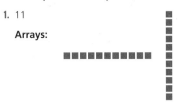

Lesson 4 **Find Factors and Multiples for Whole Numbers**

Independent Practice

Make all the possible arrays for the number. Then, list the factors and circle *prime* or *composite*.

1. 11

Arrays:

Factors: 1, 11

(prime) or *composite*

2. 16

Arrays:

Factors: 1, 2, 4, 8, 16

prime or (composite)

3. Complete this table to find the factors of 18. Use the first two rows as a guide. Some cells in the last column will be empty.

Is 18 divisible by 1?	Yes, 18 ÷ 1 = 18	_1_ and _18_ are factors.
Is 18 divisible by 2?	Yes; 18 ÷ 2 = 9	2 and 9 are factors.
Is 18 divisible by 3?	Yes; 18 ÷ 3 = 6	3 and 6 are factors.
Is 18 divisible by 4?	No	
Is 18 divisible by 5?	No	

Why don't you need to check 6? _I already found that 6 is a factor._

List all the factors. _1, 2, 3, 6, 9, 18_

Math-to-Social Studies Connection

Prime-Number History Eratosthenes, an ancient librarian, is credited with the invention of the algorithm for identifying prime numbers called Eratosthenes' Sieve. Provide each student with a hundreds chart. Have each student cross out the 1 on the hundreds chart. Next, have them leave the number 2, and then cross out the remaining multiples of 2. Repeat the process, leaving and crossing out the multiples of 3, 5, 7, and 11. All the numbers remaining on the hundreds chart represent the prime numbers from 0–100.

Lesson 4

Independent Practice

For exercises 4–7, find all the factors of the number. Show your work. Then circle *prime* or *composite*.

4. 22

5. 23

Factors: 1, 2, 11, 22

prime or *composite*

Factors: 1, 23

prime or *composite*

6. 36

7. 50

Factors: 1, 2, 3, 4, 6, 9, 12, 18, 36

prime or *composite*

Factors: 1, 2, 5, 10, 25, 50

prime or *composite*

For exercises 8 and 9, list the first six multiples of the number.

8. 7

9. 5

Multiples: 7, 14, 21, 28, 35, 42

Multiples: 5, 10, 15, 20, 25, 30

For exercises 10 and 11, circle the correct answer or answers.

10. Which of these numbers are multiples of 9?

a. 9

b. 38

c. 81

d. 84

11. Which of these numbers are prime numbers?

a. 2

b. 19

c. 52

d. 77

12. Mandy says that the factors of 20 are 2, 4, 5, and 10. What mistake did Mandy make?

Mandy forgot to include 1 and 20.

Unit 1 ■ Focus on Operations and Algebraic Thinking **39**

Common Errors

Items 4–7

Some students may mistakenly assume prime numbers are all odd numbers. Have students check whether each number is divisible by 2, 3, 5, 7, and/or 11.

Teaching Tips

Items 8–9

Point out that multiples of a number are products of the multiplication facts for that number. Think: 1 × the number, 2 × the number, 3 × the number, and so on.

Items 10–11

Remind students to circle **all** the correct answer choices for each exercise.

Talking About Math

Report on a Topic Have students work in small groups. Assign half of the groups the topic, *Factors and Multiples*. The rest of the groups will have the topic, *Prime and Composite Numbers*. Ask each group to prepare a presentation with visual models explaining what they have learned about their topic. When the groups are ready have them present their reports and be prepared to answer questions.

Independent Practice

Common Errors

Item 14

Students may misunderstand the phrase *28 is a multiple of* and be unable to correctly answer the problem. Review the definition of the terms *multiple* and *factors*. Ask students to provide examples of multiples and factors before they analyze David's reasoning.

Item 16

Students may misinterpret the question and attempt to find multiples of 42. Remind students that every number is a multiple of each of its factors.

Independent Practice

MP7 13. Lily learns that all numbers that have 0 or 5 as the last digit have 5 as a factor. Explain why this is true.
Possible explanation: All numbers that end with 0 or 5 are multiples of 5, so they are evenly divisible by 5. If you multiply 5 by an even number, the product ends in 0. If you multiply 5 by an odd number, it ends in 5.

MP7 14. David says that finding all the numbers that 28 is a multiple of is the same as finding the factors of 28. Is David correct? Explain.
David is correct. Possible explanation: Think about 7. 28 is a multiple of 7 because $28 = 4 \times 7$, but that means that 4 and 7 is a factor pair for 28, so 7 is a factor of 28. The same reasoning works for any number 28 is a multiple of.

Solve the problems.

MP7 15. Amelia says that 50 must have more factors than 40, since it is a greater number. Is Amelia correct? Find the factors of 50 and 40.

✏️ **Show your work.**
Work may vary. Possible work:

$50 \div 1 = 50$	$40 \div 1 = 40$
$50 \div 2 = 25$	$40 \div 2 = 20$
$50 \div 3 = 16$ R2; not a factor	$40 \div 3 = 13$ R1; not a factor
$50 \div 4 \rightarrow 4 \times 12 = 48$; not a factor	$40 \div 4 = 10$
$50 \div 5 = 10$	$40 \div 5 = 8$
$50 \div 6 \rightarrow 6 \times 8 = 48$; not a factor	$40 \div 6 \rightarrow 6 \times 7 = 42$; not a factor
$50 \div 7 \rightarrow 7 \times 7 = 49$; not a factor	$40 \div 7 \rightarrow 7 \times 6 = 42$; not a factor
$50 \div 8 \rightarrow 8 \times 6 = 48$; not a factor	
$50 \div 9 \rightarrow 9 \times 5 = 45$; not a factor	

Answer No, Amelia is not correct; 50 has 6 factors: 1, 2, 5, 10, 25, and 50. 40 has 8 factors: 1, 2, 4, 5, 8, 10, 20, and 40.

MP7 16. A multiplication table shows that 42 is a multiple of both 6 and 7. What other numbers have 42 as a multiple?

✏️ **Show your work.**
Work may vary. Possible work:

$42 \div 1 = 42$	$42 \div 2 = 21$
$42 \div 3 = 14$	$42 \div 4 \rightarrow 4 \times 10 = 40$; not a factor
$42 \div 5 \rightarrow$ not a factor	$42 \div 6 \rightarrow 7$, given
$42 \div 7 \rightarrow 6$, given	$42 \div 8 \rightarrow 8 \times 5 = 40$; not a factor
$42 \div 9 \rightarrow 9 \times 4 = 36$; not a factor	$42 \div 10 \rightarrow$ not a factor
$42 \div 11 \rightarrow$ not a factor	$42 \div 12 \rightarrow 3$ R6

Answer 42 is also a multiple of 1, 2, 3, 14, 21, and 42.

Mathematical Practices

MP7	**Look for and make use of structure.**

Item 13: Students search for a pattern of factors and multiples.

Item 14: Students evaluate the structure of a problem.

Item 15: Students search for patterns of factors.

Item 16: Students evaluate the structure of the factors of a number.

Lesson 4

Independent Practice

Teaching Tips

Item 19

Be sure students recognize that this is a two-step problem. Students first need to find the multiples of each number. Then they need to find the least common multiple.

Solve the problems.

MP6 **17.** A farmer has 96 apples to sell at the farmers market. She wants to bag the apples before going. How many ways can the farmer bag the apples so that:

- each bag has at least 4 apples

- each bag has no more than 10 apples

- all bags have the same number of apples?

▶ **Show your work.**
Work may vary. Possible work: I do not have to check 1, 2, or 3.

$96 \div 4 = 24$	4 bags of 24 does not count, just 24 bags of 4.
$96 \div 5$	96 is even, so 5 is not a factor.
$96 \div 6 = 16$	16 bags of 6
$96 \div 7$	$7 \times 12 = 84$, $96 - 84 = 12$; this is 13 R5.
$96 \div 8 = 12$	12 bags of 8
$96 \div 9$	$9 \times 10 = 90$, so 9 is not a factor.
$96 \div 10$	10 is not a factor.
$96 \div 11$	11 is not a factor.

I have 12 as a factor already, so I can stop.

Answer There are just 3 possible ways for the farmer to bag the apples.

MP4 **18.** A chef makes 88 ounces of jam. He wants to put the jam in 6-ounce jars. Can he use this size jar if each must be completely filled with jam, without any jam left over? If not, tell what sizes the chef can use.

Answer No, the chef can not use the 6-ounce jars.

▶ **Justify your answer using words, drawings, or numbers.**
Work may vary. Possible justification: To fill the jars completely and use all of the jam, he has to use sizes that are the factors of 88: 1, 2, 4, 8, 11, 22, 44, and 88 ounces. 6 is not a factor of 88, since $88 \div 6 = 14$ R4.

MP1 **19.** Andy set his computer to beep every 6 minutes and to chirp every 10 minutes. His computer just beeped and chirped at the same time. In how many minutes will it next make both sounds at the same time?

Answer The computer will make both sounds at the same time in 30 minutes.

▶ **Justify your answer using words, drawings, or numbers.**
His computer will beep at minute values that are multiples of 6: 6, 12, 18, 24, 30, 36, and so on. It will chirp at minute values that are multiples of 10: 10, 20, 30, 40, 50, 60, and so on. The next time the sounds happen together will be in 30 minutes.

Unit 1 ■ Focus on Operations and Algebraic Thinking **41**

Mathematical Practices

MP1	**Make sense of problems and persevere in solving them.**

Item 19: Students analyze the relationship between numbers and plan a method to solve the problem.

MP4	**Model with mathematics.**

Item 18: Students relate mathematics to solving real-world problems.

MP6	**Attend to precision.**

Item 17: Students carefully formulate and communicate full explanations.

Common Core Focus:

4.OA.5 Generate a number or shape pattern that follows a given rule. Identify apparent features of the pattern that were not explicit in the rule itself.

OBJECTIVE

Create, analyze, and describe number and shape patterns.

ESSENTIAL QUESTION

Have students brainstorm a list of real-world patterns. Explain that sometimes patterns can be used to solve real-world problems. In this lesson, students will learn how to find the terms of a pattern, to identify the pattern rule, and to identify the common features of the terms in a pattern.

FLUENCY PRACTICE

Fluency practice is available at **sadlierconnect.com**.

Concept Development

Understand: Number patterns and pattern rules

■ Students begin to understand how number patterns can be defined by a pattern rule. In this presentation, students practice extending a pattern given the rule and comparing the features of the terms.

■ Encourage a conversation about how each term in the pattern is 5 more, and how this relates to the pattern rule, *add 5*.

▟▆▆▶ Remind students to compare the terms to each other as well as comparing how the terms change. Explain that the terms in the pattern are determined by both the starting number and the pattern rule. Ellipses show that the pattern continues forever.

Essential Question: How can you create and describe patterns? 4.OA.5

Words to Know:
number pattern
pattern rule
term
shape pattern

In this lesson you will learn how to make, analyze, and describe number and shape patterns.

Understand: Number patterns and pattern rules

> Maria is saving money for a new violin. She starts with $10 and saves $5 the first week and each week thereafter. How much money does Maria have each week for the first five weeks?

To find the money amounts, you can make a number pattern. A number pattern is an ordered list of numbers that follow a rule and repeat or change in some way. The pattern rule tells you how the pattern works.

To generate the pattern for Maria's savings, start at 10 and follow the rule *add* 5. Each number in a number pattern is called a term. This pattern tells you that each new term *increases* by 5, so this is a growing pattern.

| +5 | +5 | +5 | +5 | +5 |

| 10 | 15 | 20 | 25 | 30 | 35 |
| 1st term | 2nd term | 3rd term | 4th term | 5th term | 6th term |

➡ For the first five weeks, Maria will have $15, $20, $25, $30, and $35.

▟▆▆▶ Use the same rule to make a new number pattern that starts with 1 instead of 10. How does the pattern compare to Maria's pattern?
Start with 1 and add 5. Number pattern: 1, 6, 11, 16, 21, 26 . . . The terms increase by 5, just as in Maria's pattern. But, because the starting number is 9 less than the starting number in Maria's pattern, all the terms are 9 less than the corresponding terms in Maria's pattern.

Words to Know

number pattern: an ordered list of numbers that follow a rule and repeat or change in some way

pattern rule: tells the term to start with and how to find the next term in a number or shape pattern

term: each number or shape in a number or shape pattern

shape pattern: an ordered sequence of shapes that follow a rule

Glossary can be found on pp. 347–350.

Lesson 5

Guided Instruction

Understand: Growing shape patterns

> Maria uses parallelograms to make a pattern of growing shapes.
>
> 1st   2nd   3rd   4th
>
> What is the rule for Maria's pattern? What are the next two terms?

A shape pattern is an ordered sequence of shapes that follow a rule. Each shape in a shape pattern is called a term. Maria's shape pattern starts with one parallelogram and follows the rule *attach 1 parallelogram to the right side of the previous term.*

➡ Here is Maria's pattern with two more terms.

Understand: Repeating shape patterns

> Start with the first term below and use the following rule to make a pattern: *If the term before is an ✕, make an ◯. If the term before is an ◯, make an ✕.*
>
> ✕
> 1st

➡ Start with ✕ and follow the rule. The pattern goes back and forth, or alternates, between ✕ and ◯. Here are the first eight terms.

✕ ◯ ✕ ◯ ✕ ◯ ✕ ◯
1st   2nd   3rd   4th   5th   6th   7th   8th

In this pattern all the odd-numbered terms are ✕-shapes. All the even-numbered terms are circles.

Unit 1 ■ Focus on Operations and Algebraic Thinking   **43**

Understand: Growing shape patterns

■ In this presentation, students generate growing shape patterns and understand how they relate to number patterns. In growing shape patterns, the pattern rule is represented by a visual change in the shape from one term to the next.

■ Discuss how to find a rule to describe a growing shape pattern. Model how to compare the term to the number of shapes in the term. For example, the first term has one parallelogram, the second term has two parallelograms, the third term has three parallelograms, and so on.

Understand: Repeating shape patterns

■ Help students realize that the repeating pattern rule cannot be that the terms appear as pairs of X and O. There would be no way to complete the pattern when there are an odd number of terms. The pattern rule must explain the change from one term to the next rather than the change from group to group.

■ Students should realize that growing shape patterns increase in size while repeating shape patterns follow a predictable sequence of patterns.

Support English Language Learners

Some students may know the terms *pattern, repeating,* and *growing* in different contexts. Help them make the connection between those contexts and how these terms are used in math.

Discuss how patterns are used to make or repeat the same thing over and over again, as in a drawing or a pattern on a sweater. Students can use colored pencils to draw a repeating color pattern, shape pattern, or number pattern. Have students use their drawings to explain repeating patterns.

Ask what *growing* means. Relate students' answers to the concept of getting bigger or larger. Have students use colored pencils to show a growing shape pattern, color pattern, or number pattern.

Connect: **Making patterns and analyzing terms** Use this page to help students strengthen their understanding of making patterns and analyzing terms.

■ This page addresses the second part of the Common Core State Standard: Identify apparent features of the pattern that were not explicit in the rule itself. In order to identify these types of features, students will need to compare the terms to one another as well as comparing the terms to their unique position within the sequence.

■ For each Observation shown here, ask students to explain the relationship to the pattern 2, 4, 8, 16, 32, 64. Remind students that ellipses (. . .) show that the pattern continues forever.

Connect: **Making patterns and analyzing terms**

> Maria makes a new number pattern. She starts with 2 and uses the rule *multiply by 2*. What are the first six terms for Maria's pattern? Look for other patterns and relationships in the terms and record your observations.

To find the first six terms generate the pattern.

➡ To generate the first six terms, start with 2 and multiply the previous term by 2 to get the next term.

2, 4, 8, 16, 32, 64, . . .

Observation 1: The terms are all even numbers and increase by doubling.

Look at how the terms increase. Subtract each term from the next term to find their difference.

terms	2	4	8	16	32	64
difference		2	4	8	16	32

Observation 2: The difference between each two terms is the same as the lesser term. The same pattern is formed by the differences.

Look for a relationship between each term and its order in the pattern.

Terms

1st term	2	= 2
2nd term	4	$= 2 \times 2$
3rd term	8	$= 2 \times 2 \times 2$
4th term	16	$= 2 \times 2 \times 2 \times 2$
5th term	32	$= 2 \times 2 \times 2 \times 2 \times 2$
6th term	64	$= 2 \times 2 \times 2 \times 2 \times 2 \times 2$

Observation 3: Each term's place in the pattern tells you the number of times 2 is multiplied by itself.

Math-to-History Connection

The Fibonacci Sequence Fibonacci was a talented Italian mathematician of the Middle Ages. He is best known for spreading the Hindu-Arabic numeral system throughout Europe and for the number sequence 0 1 1 2 3 5 8 13 21 ... which is named after him.

Write the sequence on the board and have students discuss how addition might be applied to the first three terms. Students may recognize that the sum of the first two terms is equal to the third term. Ask students whether the sum of the second and third terms is equal to the fourth term, and so on. Have students use the rule to find that the next two terms in the pattern are 34 and 55.

MORE ONLINE sadlierconnect.com
Lesson 5

Guided Practice

Use the rule to write or draw the missing terms in each pattern. Then complete the sentence below each exercise.

1. Start with 1 and follow the rule *add 2*.

1, _3_, 5, _7_, 9, _11_, . . .

All of the terms are ___odd___.
                    even or odd?

2. Start with 50 and follow the rule *subtract 5*.

_50_, 45, _40_, 35, _30_, . . .

All the terms are multiples of _5_.

3. Start with a row of 2 unit squares and follow the rule *add a row of 2 unit squares on top of the shape*.

This is a ___growing___ shape pattern. The height of the shape
          growing or repeating

increases by _1_ unit with each term.

👭 Think • Pair • Share

MP7 4. Create a new pattern by adding the corresponding terms in the patterns from exercises 1 and 2. That is, add 1 and 50 to get the first term, add 3 and 45 to get the second term, and so on. The new pattern starts with 51. Show the pattern. What is the rule for the pattern? Explain why this rule makes sense?
The new pattern is 51, 48, 45, 42, 39, 36. The rule is *subtract 3*. This makes sense because the rule for the first pattern is *add 2* and the rule for the second pattern *subtract 5*. Adding 2 and subtracting 5 is the same as subtracting 3.

Unit 1 ■ Focus on Operations and Algebraic Thinking **45**

Mathematical Practices

Mathematical Practice Standards underline the teaching and understanding of all concepts and skills presented. The emphasis of specific practices is noted throughout the guided and independent practice of this lesson.

MP7 **Look for and make use of structure.**

Item 4: Students evaluate the structure of a number pattern.

Observational Assessment

Use page 45 to assess whether students are able to complete number and shape patterns and to identify relationships in the terms. Note those students who need additional help completing the patterns and check whether they need help with basic math facts.

👭 Think•Pair•Share

Peer Collaboration Have pairs create a three-row, seven-column table. Label the first row Add 2 and fill in the terms from exercise 1. Label the second row Subtract 5 and fill in the terms from exercise 2. Students can add the terms in each column to find and record the terms for the new pattern, Row 3. Ask:

- *What strategy can you use to find the rule for the new pattern?*

- *How is the third rule related to the first two rules?*

Point out that the rule for the new pattern applies both rules from exercises 1 and 2. Be sure that students also understand how to find the rule for the third pattern without using the rules for the first two patterns.

Return to the Essential Question

Reread the Lesson 5 Essential Question on page 42: *How can you create and describe patterns?*

Ask volunteers to use what they learned in this lesson to answer this question. (Possible responses: I can create growing number patterns by completing the same operation on each new term in a sequence. I can create growing shape patterns by making the same change to each new shape in a sequence. Patterns can be described by using rules that tell how a term is different from the previous term.)

Invite as many students as possible to provide a response and list them on the board.

Independent Practice

Concept Application

Students may work independently on these pages in the classroom or at home. They may refer to the first four pages of the lesson to revisit the instruction or to see a worked-out example.

Common Errors and **Teaching Tips** may help you support student learning either in the classroom or as a follow-up for work done at home.

Common Errors

Item 6

Students may mistakenly add terms rather than add the two digits of a single term. Demonstrate how to add the tens digit and the ones digit of the same term to find the new term.

Teaching Tips

Items 1-4

Alert students that not every answer choice will be used, as there are more answer choices than exercises.

Independent Practice

Identify the rule for the pattern. Write the letter of the correct rule.

1. 1, 5, 9, 13, 17, . . . __c__

2. 3, 6, 12, 24, 48, 96, . . . __e__

3. 1, 4, 16, 64, 256, . . . __a__

4. 4, 7, 10, 13, 16, . . . __d__

a. Multiply by 4
b. Add 2
c. Add 4
d. Add 3
e. Multiply by 2

Use the rule to write or draw the missing terms in each pattern.

5. Start with 10 and add 5.
   10, __15__, 20, __25__, 30, __35__, . . .

6. Add the digits in each term in exercise 5 to make a new pattern.
   1, __6__, 2, __7__, 3, __8__, . . .

7. Start with 1 and multiply by 3.
   1, __3__, __9__, __27__, 81, . . .

8. Make a new pattern by finding the differences of consecutive terms for the pattern in exercise 7.
   2, __6__, __18__, __54__, . . .

9. What is the rule for the new pattern in exercise 8?
   Multiply by 3.

10. Start with a triangle and follow this rule: *If the term before is a triangle, make a square. If the term before is a square, make a triangle.*

11. What pattern is shown by the number of sides in the shapes in exercise 10?
    Possible answer: There is a pattern of 3 and 4.

12. The pattern in exercises 10 and 11 are ___repeating___.
    growing or repeating

Talking About Math

Look for Patterns Students will work in small groups to create examples of different types of repeating number and shape patterns, and growing shape patterns. Allow time for groups to share their patterns and have the class name the rule. Ask the class to identify any other patterns in the sequences that are not a result of the rule. For example, *are all of the terms even? Is every fifth shape identical?*

MORE ONLINE sadlierconnect.com

Lesson 5

Independent Practice

For exercises 13–15, use the rule to generate the pattern. Then write at least two observations about the pattern. Observations will vary.

MP7 **13.** Start with 6 and use the rule *add 3*.

6, __9__, __12__, __15__, __18__, __21__, . . .

Observations Possible answers: The terms alternate between even and odd numbers; all of the terms are multiples of 3.

MP2 **14.** Continue the growing pattern of dots. How many dots will be in the bottom row of the 8th term?

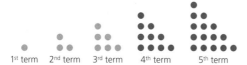

1st term   2nd term   3rd term   4th term   5th term

Answer Eight dots will be in the bottom row of the 8th term.

Observations Possible answers: The number of dots alternates between two odd and two even numbers; the term number is the number of dots in the bottom row; the difference between the number of dots in consecutive terms starts with 2 and increases by 1 with each term; after the first, each term makes a right triangle.

MP6 **15.** Start with 3. Use the rule *multiply by 2 and then subtract 1*.

3, 5, __9__, __17__, __33__, __65__, . . .

Observations Possible answers: All of the terms are odd; the difference between terms doubles with each term; there is a repeating pattern of two prime numbers followed by a composite number (the seventh term is 129).

MP4 **16.** Marley generated this pattern using an addition rule. One term in the pattern is incorrect.

  7, 15, 25, 31, 39, 47, . . .

Which is the incorrect term?

a. 7   **b.** 25   **c.** 39   **d.** 47

➤ **Justify your answer using words, drawings, or numbers.**
Possible justification: The difference between each pair of terms is 8, so the third term is 31 − 8 = 23, not 25.

Unit 1 ■ Focus on Operations and Algebraic Thinking **47**

Teaching Tips

Item 14
Encourage students to look for a pattern between the number of the term and the number of dots in the bottom row.

Item 16
Students must first determine the pattern rule before they can determine the incorrect term.

Mathematical Practices

MP2	**Reason abstractly and quantitatively.**
Item 14: Students represent problems using symbols.	
MP4	**Model with mathematics.**
Item 16: Students interpret a solution in the context of a number pattern.	
MP6	**Attend to precision.**
Item 15: Students calculate accurately and formulate full explanations.	
MP7	**Look for and make use of structure.**
Item 13: Students evaluate and record observations about a number pattern.	

Common Errors

Item 20

Students may double the amount for the second week but not continue the doubling pattern for each of the last four weeks. Show students how to use a table or chart to help organize their thinking.

Teaching Tips

Item 19

To answer the question, students should evaluate whether Haley's number pattern corresponds to the rule. Ensure students understand that the phrase *twice as many* means doubling the term.

Independent Practice

Solve the problems.

MP3 **17.** Tanya said, "If two patterns are generated using the same rule, then they must be the same." Is Tanya correct? Explain.
No, Tanya is not correct. For example, the patterns 1, 4, 7, 10, 13, . . . and 3, 6, 9, 12, 15, . . . both follow the rule *add 3*, but they are different because the starting numbers are different.

MP3 **18.** Michael says that number patterns cannot use subtraction. Do you agree? Give a simple example in your answer.
Possible answers: No, I do not agree. A simple number pattern with subtraction is to start with 555 and subtract 5: 550, 545, 540, 535, 530, 525, and so on is a number pattern.

MP7 **19.** Haley is studying for a spelling bee. Her goal is to learn twice as many words each day as on the previous day. To show her study schedule for the next six days, she makes this number pattern for the number of words.

10, 20, 30, 40, 50, 60

If Haley learns this many words each day, will she meet her goal?

Show your work.
Possible work:
$10 \times 2 = 20$; $20 \times 2 = 40$, not 30; $40 \times 2 = 80$; $80 \times 2 = 160$; $160 \times 2 = 320$

Answer No, Haley's number pattern will not meet her goal. If 10 is the correct starting number, she should use this number pattern as her schedule: 10, 20, 40, 80, 160, 320.

MP8 **20.** Justin's neighbor hired him to mow her lawn each week for 6 weeks. She said she could either give him $10 per week, or she could give him $2 the first week and then double the amount each week. Write a number pattern for Justin's weekly earnings under the second plan. Which plan should Justin choose?

Show your work.
Possible answer: The number pattern 2, 4, 8, 16, 32, 64 shows Justin's weekly earnings for the second plan. With the first plan, he makes a total of $60. With the second plan, he makes more than $60 in the last week.

Answer Justin should choose the second plan.

Mathematical Practices

MP3	**Construct viable arguments and critique the reasoning of others.**

Item 17: Students analyze a problem situation and share their reasoning.

Item 18: Students share their reasoning and explain their approach to the problem.

MP7	**Look for and make use of structure.**

Item 19: Students evaluate the structure of a pattern.

MP8	**Look for and express regularity in repeated reasoning.**

Item 20: Students use patterns to make generalizations.

Independent Practice

Teaching Tips

Item 21

Encourage students to think of the pattern in terms of groups of 3 and multiply by 3 or count by 3s. Think: $3 \times 10 = 30$, $3 \times 20 = 60$, and so on. There are between 30 and 40 groups of 3 in 100. Think: $3 \times 31 = 93$, $3 \times 32 = 96$, and so on. There are 33 whole groups of 3 in 100. One more sticker is needed to equal 100.

Item 23

Students may benefit by labeling the given terms 1, 2, 3, 4, and 5 and look for a relationship between the number of the term and the value of the term.

Return to the

Remind students to return to the Progress Check self-assessment, page 7, to check off additional items they have mastered during the unit.

Solve the problems.

MP7 **21.** A roll of stickers starts with the three shapes shown below. The shapes repeat to make up the entire roll.

1st term   2nd term   3rd term

Which shape will be the hundredth sticker in the roll?

▬▬ Show your work.
Possible answer: 3 full sets of the shapes × 33 = 99. So by the hundredth sticker, the pattern will start over again.

Answer The hundredth sticker in the roll will be a star.

MP8 **22.** Simon said, "If the rule for a pattern is *add 2*, then the terms will either be all even numbers or all odd numbers." Is Simon correct?

Answer Yes, Simon is correct.

▬▬ Justify your answer using words, drawings, or numbers.
Possible justification: Adding 2 skips a number. If a pattern starts with an even number, then adding 2 skips the next number, which is odd, and goes to the next even number. It does this same thing for all the terms. If the pattern starts with an odd number, then, adding 2 skips all the even numbers and goes to the next odd numbers.

MP7 **23.** The rule for the number pattern below is *add 8*, starting with 8.

8, 16, 24, 32, 40, . . .

Find the 50th term of this pattern without finding all the terms in between.

Answer 400 is the 50th term.

▬▬ Justify your answer using words, drawings, or numbers.
Possible justification: The pattern is the multiples of 8. $1 \times 8 = 8$ is the first term, $2 \times 8 = 16$ is the second term, and so on. So to find the fiftieth term, all you need to do is multiply 50 × 8. $50 \times 8 = 400$.

Mathematical Practices

MP7	**Look for and make use of structure.**

Item 21: Students evaluate the structure of a problem and determine the pattern.

Item 23: Students evaluate a number pattern to determine an unknown term.

MP8	**Look for and express regularity in repeated reasoning.**

Item 22: Students evaluate the reasonableness of an answer.

The Common Core Review covers all the standards presented in the unit. Use it to assess your students' mastery of the unit's concepts and skills.

Depth of Knowledge

The depth of knowledge is a ranking of the content complexity of assessment items based on Webb's Depth of Knowledge (DOK) levels. The levels increase in complexity as shown below.

Level 1: Recall and Reproduction
Level 2: Basic Skills and Concepts
Level 3: Strategic Reasoning and Thinking
Level 4: Extended Thinking

Item	Standard	DOK
1	4.OA.1	1
2	4.OA.1	2
3	4.OA.1	2
4	4.OA.4	1
5	4.OA.2	2
6	4.OA.2	2
7	4.OA.5	1
8	4.OA.3	3
9	4.OA.4	1
10	4.OA.4	1
11	4.OA.5	3
12	4.OA.1	3
13	4.OA.2	2
14	4.OA.5	4
15	4.OA.4	4

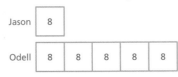

1. Odell has 5 times as many crayons as Jason. Jason has 8 crayons. Label the model to show how many crayons each person has.

Number of Crayons

| Jason | 8 | | | | |

| Odell | 8 | 8 | 8 | 8 | 8 |

For exercises 2 and 3, use the model above.

2. How many crayons does Odell have?

   Answer Odell has 40 crayons.

3. Which multiplication equation correctly compares the number of crayons the two boys have?

   a. $4 \times 8 = 32$ **b.** $5 \times 8 = 40$

   c. $2 \times 10 = 40$ **d.** $6 \times 8 = 48$

For exercises 4–6, circle the correct answer or answers.

4. Which of these numbers are multiples of 6?

   a. 10   **b.** 16

   c. 30   **d.** 48

5. At the library sale, a DVD costs $12. That is 3 times the cost of a book. Which equation can you use to find the cost of a book?

   a. $3 \times 12 = n$ **b.** $12 \times n = 3$

   c. $3 \times n = 12$ **d.** $12 \times 3 = n$

6. A small box holds 6 toy cars. A large box holds 18 toy cars. How many times as many cars can the large box hold as the small box?

   a. 2 times as many   **b.** 3 times as many

   c. 4 times as many   **d.** 6 times as many

For exercise 7, use the rule to generate the pattern. Then write at least two observations about the pattern. Observations will vary.

MP8 **7.** Start with 3. Add 6.

3, _9_, _15_, _21_, _27_, _33_

Observations Possible observations: The terms are all odd numbers; all of the terms are multiples of 3.

MP3 **8.** Chrissy estimates that if you add 20 + 31, then divide the sum by 7, the answer is about 12. Is this a reasonable estimate? Explain.
No. A reasonable estimate would be about 7; 20 + 31 = 51; then 51 ÷ 7 is about 7.

For exercises 9 and 10, find all the factors. Tell whether the number is *prime* or *composite*.

9. 56
1, 2, 4, 7, 8, 14, 28, 56

10. 61
1, 61

prime or *composite*? _composite_   *prime* or *composite*? _prime_

11. Draw the next two shapes in the pattern. Name the kind of pattern. Then write its rule.

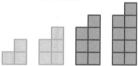

This is a ___growing___ shape pattern.
      growing or repeating

Rule _Possible answer: Increase the height of each column by one square._

Solve the problems.

MP1 **12.** Melinda is 3 times as old as Tom. Vihn is 4 times as old as Melinda. If Melinda is 9 years old, how old are Tom and Vihn?

▸ **Show your work.**
3 × 3 = 9, so Tom is 3 years old. 4 × 9 = 36, so Vihn is 36 years old.

Answer _Tom is 3 years old. Vihn is 36 years old._

Unit 1 ■ Focus on Operations and Algebraic Thinking **51**

This chart correlates the Common Core Review items with the lessons in which the concepts and skills are presented.

Item	Lesson
1	1
2	1
3	1
4	4
5	2
6	2
7	5
8	3
9	4
10	4
11	5
12	1
13	2
14	5
15	4

Mathematical Practices

MP1	**Make sense of problems and persevere in solving them.**

Item 12: Students analyze given information and create a plan to solve the problem.

MP3	**Construct viable arguments and critique the reasoning of others.**

Item 8: Students critique a given answer and justify their reasoning.

MP8	**Look for and express regularity in repeated reasoning.**

Item 7: Students make generalizations in computations.

Writing About Math

✏️ ▸ Direct students to respond to the Unit 1 Essential Question. (This can also be found on student page 9.)

Essential Question:
How are the operations of multiplication and division related?

Possible responses:
- Multiplication and division are inverse, or opposite, operations.
- Multiplication comparison problems can be written using a division equation.
- Multiplication and division can be used to find the multiples and factors of a number.

Unit Assessment

- Unit 1 Common Core Review, *pp. 50–52*
- Unit 1 Performance Task ONLINE

Additional Assessment Options

Optional Purchase:
- iProgress Monitor ONLINE
- Progress Monitor Student Benchmark Assessment Booklet

UNIT **1** Common Core Review

MP2 **13.** Franklin is packing his old toy trucks into boxes. He has 22 trucks. If each box holds 4 trucks, how many boxes will Franklin need?

✏️▸ **Show your work.**
$22 \div 4 = 5$ R2. He can fill 5 boxes, and he will have 2 trucks left over. He will need another box for these leftover trucks. So, he will need 6 boxes in all.

Answer Franklin will need 6 boxes.

MP7 **14.** The rule for the number pattern below is to add 5, starting with 5. What is the hundredth number in the pattern?

5, 10, 15, 20, 25, . . .

✏️▸ **Show your work.**
Possible work: The pattern is all the multiples of 5 in order. So to find the hundredth term multiply 5 by 100: $100 \times 5 = 500$.

Answer The hundredth number in the pattern is 500.

MP1 **15.** For the school carnival, Ms. Chen wants to bag 84 marbles to give away as prizes. How many ways can Ms. Chen bag the marbles so that:

- each bag has at least 3 marbles
- each bag has no more than 10 marbles
- all bags have the same number of marbles?

✏️▸ **Show your work.**
Answers may vary. Possibe work: I do not have to check 1 or 2.
$84 \div 3 = 28$	3 bags of 28 does not count, just 28 bags of 3.
$84 \div 4 = 21$	21 bags of 4
$84 \div 5$	84 is even, so 5 is not a factor.
$84 \div 6 = 14$	14 bags of 6
$84 \div 7 = 12$	12 bags of 7
$84 \div 8$	$8 \times 10 = 80$, $84 - 80 = 4$; this is 10 R4.
$84 \div 9$	$9 \times 9 = 81$, so 9 is not a factor.
$84 \div 10$	10 is not a factor.
$84 \div 11$	11 is not a factor.

I have 12 as a factor already, so I can stop.

Answer There are just 4 possible ways to bag the marbles.

Mathematical Practices

MP1	**Make sense of problems and persevere in solving them.**
Item 15: Students analyze and plan a solution to a problem.	
MP2	**Reason abstractly and quantitatively.**
Item 13: Students make sense of quantities and their relationships.	
MP7	**Look for and make use of structure.**
Item 14: Students analyze and apply a rule to a given pattern.	

Progress Check

UNIT 2

Look at how the Common Core standards you have learned and will learn connect. It is very important for you to understand the standards from the prior grade level so that you will be able to develop an understanding of number and operations in base ten in this unit and be prepared for next year. To practice your skills, go to sadlierconnect.com.

GRADE 3 I Can...	Before Unit 2	GRADE 4 Can I ?	After Unit 2	GRADE 5 I Will...
		4.NBT.1 Understand place value in whole numbers	☐	**5.NBT.1** Understand place value in whole numbers and decimal numbers
				5.NBT.2 Explain patterns of zeros when multiplying by powers of 10
				Use whole number exponents to show powers of 10
		4.NBT.2 Read and write whole numbers using numerals, number names, and expanded form	☐	**5.NBT.3** Read, write, and compare decimals to thousandths
		Compare whole numbers	☐	
3.NBT.1 Round whole numbers to the nearest 10 or 100	☐	**4.NBT.3** Round multi-digit whole numbers to any place	☐	**5.NBT.4** Round decimals to any place
3.NBT.2 Add and subtract whole numbers within 1000	☐	**4.NBT.4** Add and subtract whole numbers within 1,000,000	☐	**5.NBT.7** Add and subtract decimals
3.NBT.3 Multiply one-digit numbers by multiples of 10	☐	**4.NBT.5** Multiply whole numbers by one-digit whole numbers	☐	**5.NBT.5** Multiply whole numbers
3.OA.7 Multiply and divide whole numbers within 100	☐	Multiply two 2-digit numbers		**5.NBT.7** Multiply and divide decimals
		4.NBT.6 Divide whole numbers by one-digit divisors	☐	**5.NBT.6** Divide whole numbers by two-digit divisors

Unit 2 ■ Focus on Number and Operations in Base Ten

Student Page 53

Progress Check

Progress Check is a self-assessment tool that students can use to gauge their own progress. Research shows that when students take accountability for their learning, motivation increases.

Before students begin work in Unit 2, have them check any items they know they can do well. Explain that it is fine if they don't check any of the boxes; they will have the opportunity to learn and practice all the standards through the course of the unit.

Let them know that at the end of the unit they will review their checklists to check their progress. After students have completed the last lesson of the unit, before they begin Common Core Review, you will be prompted to have students revisit this page.

HOME ◆ CONNECT...

Problem solving is an important skill for your child to master. Your child will make use of various problem-solving methods to solve word problems involving addition, subtraction, multiplication, and division. Support your child by using the following problem-solving model:

- **Read** Read the problem with your child. Focus on the facts and the questions. Ask: *What facts do you know? What do you need to find out?*
- **Plan** Outline a plan with your child. Plan how to solve the problem. Ask: *What operation (addition, subtraction, multiplication, or division) will you use? Do you need to use 1 step or 2 steps? Will you draw a picture? How have you solved similar problems?*
- **Solve** Follow the plan to solve the problem with your child. Ask: *Did you answer the question? Did you label your answer?*
- **Check** Test that the solution is reasonable. Ask: *How can you solve the problem a different way? Is the answer the same? How can you estimate to check your answer?*

Conversation Starter: Your child will need to have an understanding of both place value and operations. Practice place value by naming numbers for your child to write. Discuss the place value of each digit in the number. For example, the standard form of *seven thousand six hundred and seventy two* is 7,672. It has seven thousands, six hundreds, seven tens, and two ones.

54 Unit 2 ■ Focus on Number and Operations in Base Ten

In this unit your child will:

- Understand place value of whole numbers.
- Read, write, and compare whole numbers.
- Apply place value understanding to round whole numbers.
- Add and subtract fluently with whole numbers.
- Multiply and divide whole numbers using place value and properties of operations.

NOTE: All of these learning goals for your child are based on the Grade 4 Common Core State Standards for Mathematical Content.

Ways to Help Your Child

Make time to talk with your child's teacher about your child's level of progress. Discuss ways that you can assist with your child's learning at home. If your child needs extra practice, your support can really make a difference.

ONLINE
For more Home Connect activities, continue online at sadlierconnect.com

Student Page 54

HOME ◆ CONNECT...

The Home Connect feature is a way to keep parents or other adult family members apprised of what their children are learning. The key learning objectives are listed, and some ideas for related activities and discussions are included.

Explain to students that they can share the Home Connect page at home with their families. Let students know there is an activity connected to their classroom learning that they can do with their families.

Encourage students and their parents to share their experiences using the suggestions on the Home Connect. You may wish to invite students to share this work with the class.

UNIT PLANNER

	Lesson	Standard(s)	Objective
6	Understand Place Value of Whole Numbers	4.NBT.1	Understand how the place of a digit in a number affects its value.
7	Read, Write, and Compare Whole Numbers	4.NBT.2	Use place value to read, write, and compare whole numbers.
8	Apply Place Value to Round Whole Numbers	4.NBT.3	Understand how to round whole numbers to any place using place value.
9	Add and Subtract Fluently with Whole Numbers	4.NBT.4	Use the standard algorithms for adding and subtracting multi-digit whole numbers using place value.
10	Multiply Whole Numbers: Use Place Value	4.NBT.5	Use place value and patterns to multiply whole numbers.
11	Multiply Whole Numbers: Use Properties of Operations	4.NBT.5	Use the Distributive Property and other properties of operations to multiply whole numbers.
12	Divide Whole Numbers: Use Place Value	4.NBT.6	Find whole-number quotients and remainders using place value and estimation to divide.
13	Divide Whole Numbers: Use Properties of Operations	4.NBT.6	Use properties and the relationship between multiplication and division to divide numbers.

Essential Question: How does understanding place value help you with number relationships and computing efficiently?

UNIT 2

Essential Question	Words to Know
How does the place of a digit in a number affect its value?	
How do you use place value to name and compare numbers?	period, expanded form
How can place value help you round to different places in a whole number?	
How can you add and subtract whole numbers efficiently?	
How can you use place value and patterns to multiply?	partial products
How can you break apart greater factors to multiply?	
How can place value and estimation help you divide?	dividend, divisor, quotient, compatible numbers
How can breaking apart whole numbers make them easier to divide?	

Unit Assessment

- Unit 2 Common Core Review, *pp. 120–122*
- Unit 2 Performance Task ONLINE

Additional Assessment Options

Optional Purchase:

- iProgress Monitor ONLINE
- Progress Monitor Student Benchmark Assessment Booklet

ONLINE   Digital Resources

- Home Connect Activities
- Unit Performance Tasks
- Additional Practice
- Fluency Practice
- Teacher Resources
- iProgress Monitor (optional purchase)

Go to SadlierConnect.com to access your Digital Resources.

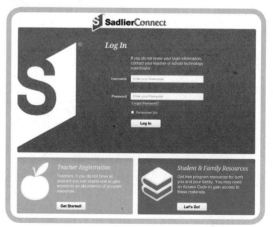

For more detailed instructions see page T3.

55B

LEARNING PROGRESSIONS

This page provides more in-depth detail on the development of the standards across the grade levels. See also the unit Progress Check page in the Student Edition for a roadmap of the Learning Progressions.

Grade 3

- Students round whole numbers to the nearest 10 or 100. (3.NBT.1)
- Students apply strategies and algorithms based on place value and properties of operations to fluently add and subtract within 1000. (3.NBT.2)
- Students apply concepts of place value and properties of operations to multiply one-digit whole numbers by multiples of 10. (3.NBT.3)
- Students multiply and divide whole numbers within 100. (3.OA.7)

Grade 4

- Students understand place value in multi-digit whole numbers. (4.NBT.1)
- Students read and write whole numbers using numerals, number names, and expanded form. They compare two multi-digit numbers. (4.NBT.2)
- Students apply place value understanding to round whole numbers to any place. (4.NBT.3)
- Students use the standard algorithm to fluently add and subtract multi-digit whole numbers. (4.NBT.4)
- Place value understanding provides a foundation for work with multi-digit multiplication and division. Students apply strategies based on place value, the properties of operations, and/or the relationship between multiplication and division to multiply multi-digit whole numbers and divide whole numbers of up to four digits by one-digit numbers. (4.NBT.5, 4.NBT.6)

Grade 5

- Understanding of place value in whole numbers is extended to decimal numbers. (5.NBT.1)
- Students explain patterns of zeros when multiplying a number by powers of 10 and patterns in the placement of the decimal point when multiplying or dividing by powers of 10. They use whole number exponents to show powers of 10. (5.NBT.2)
- Students use place value understanding to read, write, and compare decimals to thousandths. They write decimals as numerals, number names, and in expanded form, and round decimals to any place. (5.NBT.3, 5.NBT.4)
- Students multiply whole numbers fluently using the standard algorithm. (5.NBT.5)
- Students apply strategies based on place value, the properties of operations, and/or the relationship between multiplication and division to find whole-number quotients involving up to four-digit dividends and two-digit divisors. They explain the calculations by using equations, rectangular arrays, and/or area models. (5.NBT.6)
- Students add, subtract, multiply, and divide decimals to hundredths. (5.NBT.7)

Focus on Number and Operations in Base Ten

Essential Question:
How does understanding place value help you with number relationships and computing efficiently?

Unit 2 ■ Focus on Number and Operations in Base Ten 55

Essential Question:
How does understanding place value help you with number relationships and computing efficiently?

As students become involved with the Essential Question, they will use their knowledge of place value to add, subtract, multiply, and divide whole numbers. They will also analyze different strategies to determine more efficient ways of solving multiplication and division problems.

Conversation Starters

Have students discuss the photograph. Ask questions such as: *How is this garden organized? Why do you think the gardener organized the garden in this way? How might an organized garden lead to efficient gardening?*

Ask the students to look at the light purple plants in the lower part of the picture. *Look closely at these plants. How can the gardener tell how many of these plants are in the garden?* (He could count the plants)

Tell students there are 6 light purple plants in one row. *Suppose the gardener plants 6 light purple plants in every row. Throughout his garden he has planted 15 rows of light purple plants. How can you determine the total number of light purple plants in his garden?* (I could multiply 6 by 15 to determine the total number of light purple plants in his garden.)

Let students work in pairs to discuss how to find the total number of other plants in the garden. Lead them to see that their understanding of multiplication is helpful in answering this question.

Activity

Materials: paper, pencil

Explain to students that when solving, we want to solve in the most efficient way possible. Solving efficiently means solving in a way that involves the least amount of time and effort.

Explain that there are 52 small purple plants in each row and that there are 8 rows of small purple plants. Ask students to create another method to solve using place value instead of the multiplication algorithm.

Have a whole-class discussion to share students' methods. Students may have used partial products to break the factor 52 into 50 and 2. They can then multiply each factor by 8 and add the partial products, which equals 416 small purple plants. Point out they get the same answer as when using the multiplication algorithm.

Common Core Focus:

4.NBT.1 Recognize that in a multi-digit whole number, a digit in one place represents ten times what it represents in the place to its right.

OBJECTIVE

Understand how the place of a digit in a number affects its value.

ESSENTIAL QUESTION

Read the Essential Question and ask students to share what they know about place value. Record 735 and 753 on a place-value chart. Lead a discussion about how the place of the digits affects the value of the number. For example, the value of the 5 in the ones place in 735 is less than the value of the 5 in the tens place in 753.

FLUENCY PRACTICE

Fluency practice is available at **sadlierconnect.com**.

Concept Development

Understand: Place value and the value of a digit

■ This presentation provides students with a conceptual picture of place-value relationships in whole numbers. This understanding builds a foundation for rounding and comparing larger numbers and for future work with decimals.

■ Analyzing the top row of the first place-value chart helps students connect their knowledge of patterns to the increasing values in the top row to see a pattern of *multiply by 10*.

✏ Relate 2,000 and 200 to the digits in the number 162,257. Students can use their understanding of relationships in the first place-value chart to find the relationship using division. Students should be able to reason that the value of the digit to the left of a given digit is ten times greater if and only if the digits are the same.

Lesson

6 Understand Place Value of Whole Numbers

Essential Question: How does the place of a digit in a number affect its value?
4.NBT.1

Guided Instruction

In this lesson you will learn about place value relationships in whole numbers.

Understand: Place value and the value of a digit

> Kevin sees the digit 2 twice in the number 162,257. What is the value of each digit 2 in 162,257?

To find the value of each digit 2, use a place-value chart. The value of each digit in a whole number is shown by its place in the number. The value of the digit in each place is ten times greater than its value in the place to the right.

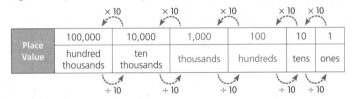

Place Value	100,000	10,000	1,000	100	10	1
	hundred thousands	ten thousands	thousands	hundreds	tens	ones

Use the place-value chart below to find the value of each 2 in 162,257.

hundred thousands	ten thousands	thousands	hundreds	tens	ones
1	6	2	2	5	7

The place-value chart shows 2 in the thousands and hundreds places.

2 thousands = 2 × 1,000 = 2,000
2 hundreds = 2 × 100   = 200

> To find the value of each digit 2, multiply it by its place value.

Then 2,000 is ten times the value of 200, or
2,000 = 10 × 200

▶ In 162,257, the value of the digit 2 in the thousands place is 2,000 and the value of the digit 2 in the hundreds place is 200.

✏ Show the relationship between 2,000 and 200 using division.
2,000 ÷ 200 = 10 or 2,000 ÷ 10 = 200

56 Unit 2 ■ Focus on Number and Operations in Base Ten

Support English Language Learners

The words *number* and *digit* are frequently used throughout this lesson. Some students may struggle with understanding the difference between these two terms. Review the terms with students. A *digit* is a single symbol used to make numbers. A digit is a numeral from 0 to 9. *Numbers* are made up of digits.

Point out that digits make up numbers in the same way that letters make up words. Digits are like the letters of the alphabet and numbers are like words.

Write a list of numbers, varying the number of digits. Have students practice reading each number and counting aloud the number of digits in each number.

Understand: Place value and multiples of 10

> A mistake in a store ad shows the price of a digital notepad as $30. The correct price of the digital notepad is $300. How many times as much as $30 is $300?

To find how many times as much $300 is compared to $30, you can use place value. The value of the hundreds place is 10 times the value of the tens place: $100 = 10 \times 10$.

Remember!
All numbers that end with 0 are multiples of 10.

hundreds	tens	ones
3	0	0
	3	0

$30 = 3$ tens

$300 = 10 \times 3$ tens $= 3$ hundreds

$300 = 10 \times 30$

➡ $300 is ten times as much as $30.

Because 30 and 300 are multiples of 10, you can use a model to find the number of tens in 300.

Use place-value models to show that 300 is the same as 30×10.

$$300 = 3 \times 100$$
$$= 3 \times (10 \times 10)$$
$$= (3 \times 10) \times 10$$
$$= 30 \times 10$$

10×10 10×10 10×10

✏ What number times 30 would move the digit 3 to the thousands place in a place-value chart? Explain your answer.
$100 \times 30 = 3,000$
Possible explanation: I need to move the digit 3 two places to the left. Each place-value is 10 times greater than the place to its right. So, multiplying by 100 will move the 3 to the thousands place in a place-value chart.

Understand: Place value and multiples of 10

■ Students should recall that the product of a given whole number and another whole number is called a *multiple*.

■ As students investigate the product of a two-digit number and 10, have them explain why the product ends with a zero. For example: $25 \times 10 = 250$ because the 2 in 250 represents 2 hundreds, which is 10 times as much as 2 tens, and the 5 represents 5 tens, which is 10 times as much as 5 ones. Therefore, 250 is ten times as much as 25.

✏ If students need additional support, have them refer to a place-value chart on page 56. Have students share different ways to explain the answer by writing equations, using a place-value chart, and drawing a model.

Math-to-History Connection

Egyptian Number System Research with students Egyptian hieroglyphic symbols that were used to keep track of things including time, distance, and money. The Egyptians also used a base-ten system, but they recorded place values vertically rather than horizontally. The number 573 would be written showing five hundreds on top, seven tens in the middle, and three ones in the bottom of a column. Find examples of multi-digit Egyptian numbers and explore a different way of representing place value. Extend the activity by having students use the Egyptian symbols to write the number of the current year.

Connect: Relationships between place values Use this page to help students strengthen their understanding of place value relationships

■ It may be helpful for some students to use a place-value chart when writing the value of each digit for the number 4,444. Remind them that only the values of identical digits can be compared using multiples of 10.

■ This presentation provides the framework for students' learning in future grade levels. In Grade 5, students will recognize that in a multi-digit number, a digit in one place represents $\frac{1}{10}$ of what it represents in the place to its left.

✎ Since multiplication and division are inverse operations, students can use both multiplication and division equations to justify their answers.

Guided Instruction

Connect: Relationships between place values

> Abbie says that if you divide the value of each digit in 4,444 by the value of the digit to the right, the quotient will always be 10. Is Abbie correct?

Use place value.

Step 1

Start with the digits in the tens and the ones places.

4, 4 **4 4**.

$40 \div 4 = 10$.

Step 2

Continue with the digits in the hundreds and in the tens places.

4, **4 4** 4.

$400 \div 40 = 10$.

Step 3

Then continue with the digits in the thousands and in the hundreds places.

4, 4 4 4.

$4{,}000 \div 400 = 10$.

➡ Yes, Abbie is correct. If you divide the value of each digit in Abbie's number by the value of the digit to the right, the quotient will always be 10.

✎ Does this pattern continue for 444,444? Explain.
Yes. Possible explanation: $400{,}000 \div 40{,}000 = 10$.

Math-to-Math Connection

Patterns and Money Have students look for patterns in money by creating a chart and determining how many pennies are in a dime, $1, $10, $100, and $1,000. Other patterns they can find are: how many $100 bills are in $1,000; $10 bills in $1,000; $10 bills in $100; and $1 in $10? Have students write about the patterns that they see.

Lesson 6

Guided Practice

Complete the place-value chart. Write the missing values and place names.

1.

Place Value	100,000	10,000	1,000	100	10	1
	hundred thousands	ten thousands	thousands	hundreds	tens	ones

Complete the sentences for each underlined digit. You can use the place-value chart above to help.

2. 450,32**8**   The digit 8 is in the ____ones____ place.

   Its value is 8 × 1 = __8__.

3. 450,3**2**8   The digit 2 is in the ____tens____ place.

   Its value is __2__ × 10 = 20.

4. 450,**3**28   The digit 3 is in the ____hundreds____ place.

   Its value is 3 × ____100____ = ____300____.

5. 45**0**,328   The digit 0 is in the thousands place.

   It shows that there are ____0 or no____ thousands.

6. 4**5**0,328   The digit 5 is in the ____ten thousands____ place.

   Its value is 5 × ____10,000____ = 50,000.

7. **4**50,328   The digit 4 is in the hundred thousands place.

   Its value is __10__ times the value of ____40,000____.

Think · Pair · Share

MP4 8. Use the place-value chart in exercise 1. Describe the rule for the pattern shown by the place values from right to left, starting with 1. How would you extend the place-value chart to show 1,000,000, or one million? Possible answer: The rule for the pattern is multiply by 10. I would extend the place-value chart by adding the millions place to the left of the hundreds thousands place because 1,000,000 is 10 × 100,000.

Unit 2 ■ Focus on Number and Operations in Base Ten   **59**

Mathematical Practices

Mathematical Practice Standards underline the teaching and understanding of all concepts and skills presented. The emphasis of specific practices is noted throughout the guided and independent practice of this lesson.

MP4	**Model with mathematics.**

Item 8: Students explain the relationships between place values by using a place-value chart.

Observational Assessment

Use page 59 to assess whether students are able to use place value to find the value of a digit. As the amount of scaffolding drops off, note students who need extra help and practice.

Think•Pair•Share

Peer Collaboration Have pairs of students discuss their explanations. Ask them to discuss the following questions:

- *How many possible place values are there when moving to the left on the place-value chart?*

- *How can you find how many times as much 100,000 is than 10?*

To summarize, make sure students understand that each place to the left increases in value by multiples of 10. The value of a given digit is ten times as much as the value of the same digit one place to the right.

Return to the Essential Question

Reread the Lesson 6 Essential Question on page 56: *How does the place of a digit in a number affect its value?*

Ask volunteers to use what they learned in this lesson to answer this question. (Possible responses: The value of a digit in a number is determined by its place in the number. The value of a digit in one place represents ten times the value of the same digit one place to the right.)

Concept Application

Students may work independently on these pages in the classroom or at home. They may refer to the first four pages of the lesson to revisit the instruction or to see a worked-out example.

Common Errors and **Teaching Tips** may help you support student learning either in the classroom or as a follow-up for work done at home.

Common Errors

Items 11–13

Students may mistakenly circle the greater number. Explain that the place value they are supposed to compare is given.

Teaching Tips

Items 7–10

Students may have difficulty identifying place value without a place-value chart. Suggest that they create a place-value chart by using the given chart as a model.

Lesson 6   Understand Place Value of Whole Numbers

Independent Practice

Write 546,893 in the place-value chart. Then name the value of each digit in the number.

hundred thousands	ten thousands	thousands	hundreds	tens	ones
5	4	6	8	9	3

1. __3__ ones = 3

2. __9__ tens = __90__

3. __8__ hundreds = __800__

4. __6__ thousands = __6,000__

5. __4__ ten thousands = __40,000__

6. __5__ hundred thousands = __500,000__

Write the place for the underlined digit. Then write the value of the digit.

7. 7,**4**45   place: __hundreds__

The digit 4 represents __400__.

8. 16,2**3**8   place: __tens__

The digit 3 represents __30__.

9. 4**8**,524   place: __thousands__

The digit 8 represents __8,000__.

10. **4**01,902   place: __hundred thousands__

The digit 4 represents __400,000__.

Compare the values of the digits in the given place. Circle the number whose digit has the greater value.

11. tens   (572)   614

12. thousands   (14,308)   22,563

13. ten thousands   263,450   (275,029)

60   Unit 2 ■ Focus on Number and Operations in Base Ten

Copyright © by William H. Sadlier, Inc. All rights reserved.

Writing About Math

▸ **Write an Opinion Text** Ask students to write a paragraph expressing their opinion about the statement: A place-value chart is useful when comparing the values of different numbers. Have students use specific examples to support their opinions.

Ask volunteers to read their paragraphs aloud. Remind students that these are opinion paragraphs, so there are no right or wrong answers.

60   Unit 2 ■ Focus on Number and Operations in Base Ten

Lesson 6

Independent Practice

For exercises 14–16, use the model at the right.

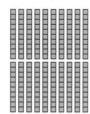

14. The model shows __20__ tens.

15. The model shows __2__ hundreds.

16. There are __10__ times as many tens as hundreds.

**Write the value of the underlined digit.
Then regroup the value.**

17. **3**49 _____300_____ = __30__ tens

18. **2**,158 _____2,000_____ = __20__ hundreds

19. **1**6,331 _____10,000_____ = __10__ thousands

20. Look at the number shown below. Under each digit, write the letter of the matching description.

6	6	8	,	8	8	4
d	e	f		c	b	a

a. The number of ones

b. Has a value of 80

c. Represents 10 times the value of the tens

d. The number of hundred thousands

e. Has a place value 10 times the value of the thousands place

f. Represents 10 times the value of the hundreds

21. $80 \times 10 =$ _____800_____

22. $600 \times 10 =$ _____6,000_____

23. $5,000 \div 500 =$ _____10_____

24. $7,500 \div 750 =$ _____10_____

Unit 2 ■ Focus on Number and Operations in Base Ten **61**

Common Errors

Item 20

For parts c, e, and f, students may write the letter below the place value given in the description rather than in the place that is 10 times the value. Remind students that the place that is 10 times the value is one place to the left of the given value.

Teaching Tips

Items 17-19

Some students may struggle with regrouping. Provide place-value models or place-value charts for students to use to regroup the values.

Items 23-24

If students have difficulty working with division, suggest they rewrite the equations as multiplication by using a symbol for the missing factor.

Digital Connection

Internet Resources Use a search engine to locate games and activities that focus on place value at the fourth-grade level. Select a game or activity to complete with students. Have students record their work as they play the game.

Independent Practice

Common Errors

Item 26

If students struggle to interpret the values of the models, it may be helpful to review place-value models before completing the exercises.

Teaching Tips

Item 25

Remind students to compare the place of like digits in both numbers when writing their explanations.

Independent Practice

MP6 **25.** John makes a mistake when he inputs the number 1,205. He inputs the number 2,105 instead. Use place value to explain John's mistake. Explanations will vary. Possible explanation: John inputs the digits 1 and 2 in the wrong places. 1,205 has 1 thousand and 2 hundreds. 2,105 has 2 thousands and 1 hundred.

MP1 **26.** What number is represented by the model? Explain the value of each digit in the number.

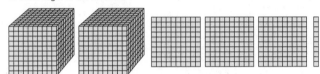

The model shows 2,310. The 2 in the thousands place represents 2,000. The 3 in the hundreds place represents 300. The 1 in the tens place is for the 10 ones in the model. The ones digit is 0 to show there are no extra ones.

Solve the problems.

MP7 **27.** A cashier counts 25 ten-dollar bills and writes the total amount of money as a number. What is this number, and what is the place of the digit 2?

　　Show your work.
Work will vary. Possible work:
$25 \times 10 = (10 + 10 + 5) \times 10$
$ = (10 \times 10) + (10 \times 10) + (5 \times 10)$
$ = 100 + 100 + 50 = 250$

Answer The total amount of money as a number is $250; the 2 will be in the hundreds place.

MP2 **28.** Tanya says that 36,000 is the same as 360 hundreds. Is Tanya correct?

　　Show your work.
Work will vary. Possible work:
$36,000 = 36 \times 1,000$
$ = 36 \times (10 \times 100)$
$ = (36 \times 10) \times 100$
$ = 360 \times 100$

Answer Yes, Tanya is correct.

Mathematical Practices	
MP1	**Make sense of problems and persevere in solving them.**
Item 26: Students use pictures to explain the value of a number.	
MP2	**Reason abstractly and quantitatively.**
Item 28: Students represent a problem using symbols.	
MP6	**Attend to precision.**
Item 25: Students calculate accurately and formulate a full explanation.	
MP7	**Look for and make use of structure.**
Item 27: Students apply number patterns to place-value relationships.	

MP6 **29.** Samantha is taking $2,000 out of her savings. She asks to have the money in 20-dollar bills. How many 20-dollar bills should Samantha receive?

▸ **Show your work.**
Work will vary. Possible work:
$$2,000 = 2 \times 1,000$$
$$= 2 \times 10 \times 100$$
$$= 20 \times 100$$

Answer Samantha should receive 100 20-dollar bills.

MP7 **30.** Alejandro and Erin estimate the number of people at a football game. Alejandro thinks there are about 60,000 people in the stadium. Erin says there are about 6,000 people. How many times as much is Alejandro's estimate as Erin's estimate?

▸ **Show your work.**
Work may not include calculations if students understand that moving the digit 6 one place is the same as multiplying by 10. Possible work:
$$60,000 \div 6,000 = 10$$

Answer Alejandro's estimate is 10 times as much as Erin's estimate.

MP8 **31.** Briana says that $1,200 \div 12 = 10$. Is Briana's answer correct?

Answer Briana's answer is not correct.

▸ **Justify your answer using words, drawings, or numbers.**
Possible justification: Briana's answer would be correct if she was dividing 1,200 by 120, but the 1 and 2 in 12 are each moved more than one place to the right from the 1 and 2 and 1,200.
$1,200 = 12 \times 100$ so $1,200 \div 12 = 100$, not 10.

MP6 **32.** Nicole and Micah are talking about the number 12,459. Micah says that the value of the thousands digit is 10 times the value of the hundreds digit. Nicole says this is not true, since the two digits are not the same. Who is correct?

Answer Nicole is correct.

▸ **Justify your answer using words, drawings, or numbers.**
Possible justification: The values of the digits 2 and 4 are 2,000 and 400, and 2,000 is not 10 times 400. $10 \times 400 = 4,000$. But the value of the thousands place is 10 times the value of the hundreds place: $1,000 = 10 \times 100$.

Common Errors

Item 32
Some students may disregard the given number when answering the question. The value of each place is 10 times as much as the place to the right. The value of a digit, however, is 10 times as much if and only if the digit to the right is identical. Remind students that they must pay attention to the digits in a given number when comparing the value of digits.

Mathematical Practices
MP6 **Attend to precision.**
Item 29: Students accurately calculate values and communicate with precision.
Item 32: Students carefully formulate a full explanation.
MP7 **Look for and make use of structure.**
Item 30: Students use a pattern to solve a problem.
MP8 **Look for and express regularity in repeated reasoning.**
Item 31: Students use patterns to evaluate the reasonableness of a given solution.

Common Core Focus:

4.NBT.2 Read and write multi-digit whole numbers using base-ten numerals, number names, and expanded form. Compare two multi-digit numbers based on meanings of the digits in each place, using >, =, and < symbols to record the results of comparisons.

OBJECTIVE
Use place value to read, write, and compare whole numbers.

ESSENTIAL QUESTION
Explain that understanding place value is very important when reading, writing, and comparing whole numbers. This, in turn, will help students in later lessons to round whole numbers as well as add, subtract, multiply, and divide whole numbers.

FLUENCY PRACTICE
Fluency practice is available at **sadlierconnect.com**.

Concept Development

Understand: Names for whole numbers

■ The Common Core State Standards for Mathematics expect that students are able to read, write, and compare base-ten numerals. To accomplish this, students will need to apply their understanding of place-value relationships.

■ When reading a number of thousands or greater, students need to break the number into periods. Each period groups hundreds, tens, and ones. Understanding that commas are placed to separate the periods will help students to more accurately read the numbers.

✏️ Most students will find it helpful to write numbers in a place-value chart.

Lesson 7

Read, Write, and Compare Whole Numbers

Essential Question: How do you use place value to name and compare numbers?
4.NBT.2

Words to Know:
period
expanded form

In this lesson you will learn how to read, write, and compare whole numbers.

Understand: Names for whole numbers

> Kendra is reading her report about Mount Everest aloud. The height of Mount Everest is 29,035 feet. How should Kendra read this number?

To find how Kendra should read the number, write the number 29,035 in a place-value chart.

To read a number of thousands or greater, read each group of digits. A period is a group of 3 places. For example in the chart below, the periods are the thousands period, and the ones period. A comma usually separates periods.

Thousands			Ones		
hundreds	tens	ones	hundreds	tens	ones
	2	9	0	3	5

Read the total number of thousands written before the comma or in the thousands period:

numeral   number name
29,035   twenty-nine thousand

The ones period groups the values less than 1,000. Read the total value of the ones group of digits.
29,035   thirty five

➡️ Kendra can read 29,035 as *twenty-nine thousand, thirty five*.

✏️ Write the numeral for *six hundred fifteen thousand, two hundred one* and the numeral for *fifty-two thousand, forty-nine*.
615,201 and 52,049

Remember!
You don't need to say or write "ones" for a number less than 1,000.

Words to Know

period: a group of 3 places

This place-value chart shows the Thousands period and the Ones period

Example:

Thousands			Ones		
hundreds	tens	ones	hundreds	tens	ones
	2	9	0	3	5

expanded form: a number expressed in a way that shows the value of each digit

Glossary can be found on pp. 347-350.

MORE ONLINE sadlierconnect.com

Lesson 7

Guided Instruction

Understand: Numbers in expanded form

> You can think about the height of Mount Everest in another way. Use the expanded form to see the value of each digit in 29,035.

You can also write a number in expanded form. The expanded form of a number shows the value of each digit. Find the value of each digit in 29,035.

2	9	,	0	3	5
↓	↓		↓	↓	↓
20,000	9,000		0	30	5

Remember!
Multiply a digit by its place value to find its value.

$29,035 = 20,000 + 9,000 + 30 + 5$

➡ The expanded form of 29,035 is $20,000 + 9,000 + 30 + 5$.

Understand: Comparisons of whole numbers

> The height of Mount McKinley is 20,320 feet. Which mountain is taller, Mount McKinley or Mount Everest?

To compare numbers, first line up the digits by place value. You can use a place-value chart to help.

	Thousands			Ones		
	hundreds	tens	ones	hundreds	tens	ones
Mt. Everest		2	9	0	3	5
Mt. McKinley		2	0	3	2	0

Compare the digits in each place, starting with the greatest place. Stop in the first place where the digits are different.

Ten thousands: $2 = 2$
Thousands: $9 > 0$

Remember!
= means *is equal to.*
< means *is less than.*
> means *is greater than.*

29,035 has the greater number of thousands, so $29,035 > 20,320$.

➡ Mount Everest is taller than Mount McKinley.

Understand: Numbers in expanded form

■ In this presentation, students examine how multiplying a digit by its place value can help them find its value. To use this strategy, students should start by writing the number in a place-value chart.

■ Help students realize that the position of a digit in a number gives them a clue to that digit's value. They can multiply the place and the digit to find the digit's value.

■ For assistance, students can follow these steps when writing the number in expanded form: list the values in the same order as the digits, do not include any values of 0, and write an addition sign between each of the values.

Understand: Comparisons of whole numbers

■ In this presentation, students compare magnitudes of numbers. To compare, students can start by writing the numbers in a place-value chart.

■ Remind students to compare the numbers by starting with the greatest place. They can stop as soon as they reach the place where the digits are different.

Support English Language Learners

Relate the term *period* to the punctuation at the end of a sentence. In reading, a period indicates the end of a group of words. In math, the term *period* indicates a group of three place values. Write a six-digit number on the board and circle the periods.

Students will also need to understand the *expanded form* of a number. Model how stretching out a rubber band causes it to expand, or get longer. Writing a number in expanded form makes it longer. Model writing the previous number in expanded form. Write several other numbers up to six digits long on the board. Ask students to take turns circling the digits in each period starting at the far right. Then have them write each number in expanded form. Use a place-value chart to help students read each number aloud.

Connect: Represent and compare whole numbers Use this page to help students strengthen their understanding of comparing whole numbers.

■ Remind students that *standard form* means writing a number using just the digits 0–9.

■ In Step 3, point out to students that 0 < 7 is the same as 7 > 0.

■ Be sure students make the connection that when comparing numbers, it is important that the numbers are written in the same form.

✏️ Remind students that the number name is how the number is written in words, or *word form*. Explain the importance of the comma in both standard form and word form. Point out that this comma separates the periods and allows students to read the number more easily.

Guided Instruction

Connect: Represent and compare whole numbers

> A radio announcer says that two hundred fifteen thousand, four hundred seven people lost power in a storm. A news article reported that 215,470 people lost power. How do these numbers compare?

Write the numbers in the same form and then compare them.

Step 1

Write this number name in standard form:
two hundred fifteen thousand, four hundred seven.

Write the total number of thousands: 215.
Write the total number of ones given after the comma: 407.
Now write the full number with a comma: 215,407.
215,407 is not the same as 215,470, the number from the news article.

Step 2

To see why the numbers are different, write them in expanded form. Find and list the values of the digits in each number.

215,407   200,000 + 10,000 + 5,000 + 400 + 0 + 7
215,470   200,000 + 10,000 + 5,000 + 400 + 70 + 0

There are different numbers of tens and ones.

Step 3

Compare the numbers. Line up the digits by place value and stop in the first place where the digits are different.

215,407   0 tens is less than 7 tens: 0 < 7.
215,470

215,407 has fewer tens than 215,470.

➡️ 215,407 < 215,470.

✏️ Read aloud 215,470, the number from the news article. Write the number name.
The number name is: two hundred fifteen thousand, four hundred seventy.

Math-to-Current Events Connection

Newspapers A strong understanding of how to read, write, and compare whole numbers is used in everyday life. Numbers are used to describe many things such as measurements, temperatures, money, and sports statistics. Provide small groups of students with a newspaper. Have each group find ten examples of numbers in the newspaper and write each number in a place-value chart. Groups should share some of their numbers with the rest of the class and explain how the numbers were used.

Guided Practice

Fill in the blanks to write the number in a different form.

1. 21,109

number name: ___twenty___ -one ___thousand___ , one ___hundred___ nine

2. 492,013

number name: ___four___ hundred ___ninety___ - ___two___

thousand, ___thirteen___

3. sixty-three thousand, eight hundred fifty two

numeral: _6_ _3_ , _8_ _5_ _2_

4. five hundred fourteen thousand, three hundred three

numeral: _514,303_

5. 89,780

expanded form: ___80,000___ + 9,000 + ___700___ + ___80___

6. 307,326

expanded form: ___300,000___ + ___7,000___ + ___300___ + _20_ + _6_

Write <, =, or > to compare the numbers.

7. 6,**5**89 _<_ 6,**9**28

8. 2**1**,807 _>_ 2**0**,931

9. 37,146 _=_ 37,146

10. 458,923 _<_ 459,823

☼ Think • Pair • Share

MP1 **11.** Extend the place-value chart on page 64 to show 21,385,604. Be sure to label the millions period. Explain the value of each digit.
Possible explanation: I extend the place-value chart to show the millions period. The digits represent 20 million, 1 million, 3 hundred thousand, 80 thousand, 5 thousand, 6 hundred, 0 tens, 4 ones.

Observational Assessment

Use page 67 to assess whether students are able to write numbers using different forms, and compare numbers using >, <, or =.

☼ Think•Pair•Share

Peer Collaboration Ask each student to extend the place-value chart on page 64 to include the millions period. Then, have each student write the number from problem 11 in their newly extended place-value chart. Have pairs of students compare how they each wrote the number in the place-value chart. If some pairs are still struggling, ask:

• *What is the value of each digit in the place-value chart?*

• *How would you read this number?*

Return to the Essential Question

Reread the Lesson 7 Essential Question on page 64: *How do you use place value to name and compare numbers?*

Ask volunteers to use what they learned in this lesson to answer this question. (Possible responses: I can use place value to help me read numbers. Place value helps me find the values of each individual digit in a number. These values help me compare numbers.)

Invite as many volunteers as possible to express ideas about using place value to name and compare numbers in their own words.

Mathematical Practices

Mathematical Practice Standards underline the teaching and understanding of all concepts and skills presented. The emphasis of specific practices is noted throughout the guided and independent practice of this lesson.

MP1   **Make sense of problems and persevere in solving them.**

Item 11: Students relate to a similar problem by extending a place-value chart to include the millions period.

Independent Practice

Concept Application

Students may work independently on these pages in the classroom or at home. They may refer to the first four pages of the lesson to revisit the instruction or to see a worked-out example.

Common Errors and **Teaching Tips** may help you support student learning either in the classroom or as a follow-up for work done at home.

Teaching Tips

Items 1–6

Students need to recognize the three different forms of writing numbers—standard form, expanded form, and number name form (word form). Let students use a place-value chart, if needed.

Independent Practice

Fill in the blanks to write each number in three forms. Look at all three forms to find the information you need.

1. 68,223

   sixty-___eight___ thousand, two ___hundred___ twenty three

   ___60,000___ + 8,000 + 200 + _20_ + 3

2. 104, _8_ _1_ _6_

   one hundred ___four___ ___thousand___ , eight hundred ___sixteen___

   ___100,000___ + 4,000 + ___800___ + 10 + 6

3. 98 _5_ , _0_ 31

   ___nine___ ___hundred___ eighty-five ___thousand___ , thirty one

   ___900,000___ + ___80,000___ + 5,000 + _30_ + 1

Circle the correct answer.

4. Which is the number name for 712,358?

   a. seven hundred thousand twelve, three fifty eight

   b. seventy one thousand, twenty-three hundred fifty-eight

   c. seven hundred twelve thousand, three hundred fifty eight

   d. seven hundred twelve thousand, thirty-five hundred eight

5. Which of these is a different number from the others?

   a. 42,211

   b. 40,000 + 2,000 + 200 + 1

   c. 4 ten thousands + 2 thousands + 2 hundreds + 1 one

   d. forty-two thousand, two hundred one

6. Which of these shows one million?

   a. 10,000

   b. 100,000

   c. 1,000,000

   d. 100,000,000

Writing About Math

✏ ▸ **Write an Explanatory Text** Ask students to write a paragraph that examines how to read, write, and compare whole numbers. Have students develop the topic with concrete facts and definitions. Make sure students provide a concluding statement relating to the information they provided in the paragraph.

Ask volunteers to read their paragraphs aloud. Remind students that these are explanatory paragraphs, so the information is presented in a manner that makes sense to the writer. These paragraphs may help other students digest and more clearly understand the information presented in the lesson.

Independent Practice

Write the given number in two other forms.

7. 33,410

expanded form: __30,000__ + __3,000__ + __400__ + __10__

number name: __thirty-three thousand, four hundred ten__

8. 200,000 + 80,000 + 4,000 + 90 + 9

numeral: __284,099__

number name: __two hundred eighty-four thousand, ninety nine__

Name the first place where the digits in both numbers are different. Then write < , =, or > to compare the numbers.

9. **4**9,603
57,213

__ten thousands__

49,603 __<__ 57,213

10. 64,**8**19
64,**5**47

__hundreds__

64,819 __>__ 64,547

11. 12,213
9,547

__ten thousands__

12,213 __>__ 9,547

12. 197,687
861,070

__hundred thousands__

861,070 __>__ 197,687

Write < , =, or > to compare the numbers. Circle the first digit that is different in the number pairs.

13. 3,526 __=__ 3,526

14. ⑨9,287 __>__ ⑧9,999

15. 28,8④3 __<__ 28,8⑦1

16. 7④0,489 __>__ 7③9,501

Common Errors

Items 9–16

Some students may struggle with using the correct symbol when comparing the magnitudes of numbers. Students may benefit by knowing that the wider part of the symbols points to the number with the greater value, and the smaller part of the symbol points to the number with the least value.

Teaching Tips

Items 9–12

Make sure to point out to students that they are writing the first place where the digits are different in both numbers rather than the greatest place value of each number.

Digital Connection

Random Number Generator Use a search engine to find a random number generator Web site. Assign parameters for the random number generator to select two numbers between 100,000 and 999,999. Have students read the two randomly selected numbers. Next, have students write each of the numbers in standard form, expanded form, and number name form. Finally, have students compare the numbers with and without the use of a place-value chart. In some instances, the random number generator may select the same number twice. This can provide a great topic of discussion about how to compare two numbers that are the same.

Independent Practice

Common Errors

Item 17

Students may not be able to recognize the mistake immediately. Remind students that even though the number 0 represents none, it is still important to include it in the number, as it is needed to hold a place value.

Item 18

Some students might fail to look at the value of each digit in a number before they compare the number. If students do not recognize a number's value, they might compare digits with different place values. Encourage students who are struggling with this common error to compare the numbers using a place-value chart.

Independent Practice

Use place values in your explanation.

MP3 **17.** Colin is taking notes in class. The teacher says the number *eighty-five thousand, sixty two*. Colin writes *85,602* in his notebook. Explain the mistake Colin made.
Answers will vary. Possible explanation: The number the teacher said was 85,062. Colin should have used a zero to hold the hundreds place, since there are no hundreds in the number. Instead, he wrote "60" and "2" separately, so the 6 ended up in the hundreds place with a value of 600 instead of 60.

MP6 **18.** Mara says that 28,597 is greater than 101,200 because 2 is greater than 1. Is Mara correct? Explain your answer.
No, Mara is wrong. Possible explanation: She is not comparing digits with the same place value. The 2 in 28,597 represents 2 ten thousands, or 20,000. The first 1 in 101,200 is in the hundred thousands place and represents 100,000. 20,000 < 100,000, so 101,200 is the greater number.

Solve the problems.

MP8 **19.** James counts the number of times his heart beats in one minute. He figures out that his heart beats about 125,280 times in one day. What is 125,280 in expanded form?

▱▶ **Show your work.**
Work may vary. Possible work:
$$100,000$$
$$20,000$$
$$5,000$$
$$200$$
$$80$$

Answer The expanded form of 125,280 is 100,000 + 20,000 + 5,000 + 200 + 80

MP7 **20.** Lucia says that sixteen thousand, two hundred seventeen has fewer tens than sixteen thousand, one hundred forty eight. What is the difference in the number of tens for these numbers?

▱▶ **Show your work.**
Work may vary, to include the expanded form of each number. Possible work:
16,217 has 1 ten.
16,148 has 4 tens.
$4 - 1 = 3$

Answer The difference in the number of tens is 3.

70   Unit 2 ■ Focus on Number and Operations in Base Ten

Mathematical Practices

MP3	Construct viable arguments and critique the reasoning of others.
Item 17: Students analyze a problem and determine the mistake made.	
MP6	Attend to precision.
Item 18: Students explain their conclusion using precise language.	
MP7	Look for and make use of structure.
Item 20: Students explain the logic used to compare two numbers.	
MP8	Look for and express regularity in repeated reasoning.
Item 19: Students gain fluency in writing numbers in expanded form.	

Lesson 7

Independent Practice

For exercises 21–24, use the table at the right.

Land Areas of Four States	
State	Land Area (square miles)
Arizona	113,634
California	155,959
Colorado	103,717
Kansas	81,815

MP2 **21.** Humberto writes the area of each state shown in the table in expanded form. Which two states have the same number of thousands in their expanded forms?

▪ Show your work.
Work may vary. Possible work:
Colorado: 103,717 = 100,000 + 3,000 + 700 + 10 + 7
Arizona: 113,634 = 100,000 + 10,000 + 3,000 + 600 + 30 + 4

Answer Arizona and Colorado both have 3 thousands in their expanded forms.

MP6 **22.** Laurel reads the area of Arizona as *one hundred three thousand, six hundred thirty four* square miles. Which area has a greater number of ten thousands, Laurel's or the area in the table?

▪ Show your work.
Work may vary. Possible work:
Laurel's number: 103,634 has 0 ten thousands.
Area from table: 113,634 has 1 ten thousand.

Answer The area in the table has a greater number of ten thousands.

MP7 **23.** Max knows that one state definitely has the least area, just by looking at the table. Which state is Max thinking of?

Answer Max is thinking of Kansas.

▪ Justify your answer using words, drawings, or numbers.
Possible justification: Kansas is the only state that has an area with five digits, and is in the ten thousands. All the other areas have six digits, so they are in the hundred thousands and greater than the area of Kansas.

MP2 **24.** After Max identifies the state with the least area, he compares the areas of the three other states shown. Which place in the numbers will tell Max which state has the greatest area?

Answer place ten thousands

state California

▪ Justify your answer using words, drawings, or numbers.
Possible justification: The areas of Arizona, California, and Colorado all have the same digit in the hundred thousands place. The digits in the ten thousands place are the first ones that are different: 0 < 1 < 5, so California has the greatest area with a digit 5 in the ten thousands.

Unit 2 ▪ Focus on Number and Operations in Base Ten   71

Teaching Tips

Item 21
Emphasize to students that they are looking for thousands only, not ten thousands or hundred thousands.

Items 21-24
If any students are struggling to compare these numbers, be sure to suggest that they use a place-value chart.

Mathematical Practices

MP2   Reason abstractly and quantitatively.

Item 21: Students analyze four different numbers to determine which two have the same number in the thousands place.

Item 24: Students compare three numbers to justify which state has the greatest area.

MP6   Attend to precision.

Item 22: Students explain which digit has the greater value.

MP7   Look for and make use of structure.

Item 23: Students evaluate the difference between a number with 5-digits as opposed to a number with 6-digits.

Common Core Focus:

4.NBT.3 Use place value understanding to round multi-digit whole numbers to any place.

OBJECTIVE

Understand how to round whole numbers to any place using place value.

ESSENTIAL QUESTION

Students learned about rounding numbers in previous grades. In this lesson, students will use place value to round the same number to more than one place.

PREREQUISITE SKILLS

Use Item C on page 338 of the Foundational Skills Handbook, to review the relationship between 10 tens and 1 hundred before students round numbers to the nearest hundred.

FLUENCY PRACTICE

Fluency practice is available at **sadlierconnect.com**.

Concept Development

Understand: The numbers you use to round

■ In order for students to understand how to use place value to round whole numbers to any place, they need a strong understanding of place value and number sense.

■ Rounding is one way to estimate. Students will learn two methods for rounding—using the number line and comparing digits. Make sure students understand how to use both methods.

✏ After students have answered this question, ask a few volunteers to read their answers aloud. As an extension, ask students to find the least number that can be rounded to the ten thousands place of 60,000. Let volunteers explain their reasoning.

Apply Place Value to Round Whole Numbers

Essential Question: How can place value help you round to different places in a whole number? · 4.NBT.3

Guided Instruction

In this lesson you will learn how to round to any place in a whole number.

Understand: The numbers you use to round

> In one day, 56,147 people watch a video of the baby panda at the zoo. Lily says that 56,147 is about 60,000 people. Is this a reasonable estimate?

To find an estimate for 56,147, you can round the number.

The greatest place in 56,147 is ten thousands. Between which two ten thousands is 56,147 the closest? You can make a number line to help.

$50,000 < 56,147 < 60,000$

To find which ten thousand 56,147 is nearer to, you can use the number line or compare the digits.

Use the number line:
Mark the number that is exactly halfway between 50,000 and 60,000: 55,000. On the number line, 56,147 is to the right of 55,000, the halfway mark. Since 56,147 is nearer to 60,000 than to 50,000, round 56,147 up to 60,000.

Compare the digits: 56,147   6 > 5
                                       55,000
Look at the digit to the right of the place to which you are rounding, in this case the thousands place. If it is 5 or greater, then round up.

Since 6 thousands is greater than 5 thousands, 56,147 is greater than 55,000. Then 56,147 is nearer to 60,000 than to 50,000.

➡ Yes. 60,000 is a reasonable estimate for 56,147 people.

✏ What place can you round 56,147 to for a closer estimate?
Possible explanation: You can round to the thousands place instead of the ten thousands place. 56,000 is a closer estimate than 60,000.

Support English Language Learners

The terms *estimate* and *round* are used throughout this lesson. Explain that rounding is one way to estimate. Discuss the characteristics of things that are round. Students should understand that round things roll. Explain that rounding a number is like rolling its value up or down. Draw a hill on the board. Write the digits 0, 1, 2, 3, and 4 going up the left-hand side of the hill and the digits 5, 6, 7, 8, and 9 going down the right-hand side. Below the hill, draw the number line 10–20. Label the points for 10 and 20 at the ends below the hill and 15 just to the right of the peak. Write 13 on the board and draw a ball at the 3 on the side of the hill. Ask students which way the ball will roll. Students should realize the ball rolls downhill. Explain that 13 rounds down to 10. Draw a ball at the 5 and repeat the activity. Students will see that 15 rounds up to 20. Continue the activity using greater numbers on the number line.

Lesson 8

Guided Instruction

Connect: What you know about rounding and closer estimates

The zoo gives a free panda poster to visitors each Saturday. Last Saturday, 4,532 people visited the zoo. If approximately the same number of people visit each Saturday, estimate the number of posters the zoo should have ready to give out this Saturday.

You can use place value to round a number to different places.

Step 1

For a first estimate, look at the digit in the greatest place in the number.

The 4 in 4,532 is in the thousands place. Round to the nearest thousand.

$4,000 < 4,532 < 5,000$

To find which thousand 4,532 is nearer to, compare it to the halfway mark. The number that is halfway between 4,000 and 5,000 is 4,500.

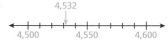

Step 2

To round to the nearest thousand, compare the hundreds digit in 4,532 to the hundreds digits in 4,500; $5 = 5$

4,532 has the same number of hundreds as 4,500, the number halfway between 4,000 and 5,000.

So 4,532 rounds up to 5,000.

Remember!

If the digit to the right of the place to which you are rounding is 5 or greater, round up.

Step 3

To find a closer estimate, you can round 4,532 to the hundreds place.

The next closest hundred to 4,500 is 4,600. 4,550 is the number halfway between 4,500 and 4,600.

To round to the nearest hundred, compare the tens digit in 4,532 to the tens digit in 4,550: $3 < 5$

So rounding to the nearest hundred, 4,532 rounds down to 4,500.

➡ Depending on which place value you estimated to, the zoo should have about 5,000 or 4,500 posters ready to give out on Saturday.

Guided Instruction

Connect: What you know about rounding and closer estimates Use this page to help students strengthen their understanding of rounding numbers to an indicated place-value position.

■ Students learn that a multi-digit number can be rounded in more than one way to provide greater accuracy. Depending on which place the estimated answer is rounded to, the estimate may be closer to or further from the actual answer. Students must pay attention to the context of the problem to make the best estimate.

■ After working through this page with students, discuss when it may be necessary to use a closer estimate. Ask students to give specific examples.

Math-to-Language Arts Connection

Number Riddles Have students work in pairs to write a riddle describing a given number. All riddles must include a rounding clue. For example, a riddle might include clues that the number is a four-digit number, with a thousands digit that is 2 more than 5, and a hundreds digit that is 1 less than 7. Clues would continue to describe the number, but it is essential that at least one clue focuses on the place to round to. For example, the final clue might ask what the tens digit could be if the number rounded to the nearest hundred is 7,700. Have pairs exchange riddles with another pair and solve.

Observational Assessment

Use pages 74–75 to assess whether students understand rounding rules. As the amount of scaffolding in the problems decreases, note those students who do not round to the correct place. To help these students, implement the strategy to circle the digit to the right of the place they are rounding to.

Explain to students that for exercises 4 and 5, there are many possible answers. You might challenge students to find the least number that can be rounded up to 200,000 and the greatest number that can be rounded down to 190,000.

Round each number to the underlined place. You can use the number line to help.

1. 2**3**,485

3 is in the __thousands__ place.

The closest thousands are __23,000__ and 24,000.

Compare the hundreds digit in 23,485 to the 5 hundreds in __23,500__.

4 $\leq$ 5

23,485 rounds __down__ to __23,000__.

2. 23,**4**85

4 is in the __hundreds__ place.

__23,400__ < 23,485 < __23,500__

Compare the __tens__ digit in 23,485 to the __5__ tens in __23,450__.

8 $>$ 5

23,485 rounds __up__ to __23,500__.

For exercises 3–5, use the number line at the right.

3. What number is exactly halfway between 190,000 and 200,000?

__195,000__

4. Write four numbers that can be rounded up to 200,000.

Answers will vary. Possible answers: 196,000; 197,000; 198,000; 199,000

5. Write four numbers that can be rounded down to 190,000.

Answers will vary. Possible answers: 194,000; 193,000; 192,000; 191,000

Math-to-Social Studies Connection

Population Have students research the population of six different cities in the United States. Ask students to make a chart with columns showing the actual population, the population rounded to the nearest thousand, the population rounded to the nearest ten thousand, and the population rounded to the nearest hundred thousand.

Guided Practice

Round each number to the underlined place. Write the numbers you can round to. Then circle the correct rounded number.

6. ___6,000___ < **6**,742 < (7,000)

7. (10,000) < **1**2,099 < 20,000

8. (38,000) < 3**8**,250 < 39,000

9. ___540,000___ < 5**4**5,123 < (550,000)

For exercises 10 and 11, you can use a number line.

10. Ross is going to Australia to visit his grandparents. The airline says the distance between Boston and Brisbane is 9,773 miles. What is a reasonable estimate for this distance? Explain your answer.
10,000 miles is a reasonable distance, because 9,500 is about halfway between 9,000 and 10,000.

11. Audrey read that the area of a new shopping mall is 57,600 square feet. What are the greatest and least possible actual areas of the mall if 58,000 square feet is an estimate to the nearest thousand?
The actual area of the mall can be between 57,500 and 58,499 square feet.

Think • Pair • Share

MP4 **12.** Toni draws a number line and uses it to round 83,768 to the nearest ten thousand. Then she decides to round 83,768 to the nearest thousand. Show how Toni can use the same number line to do this?
Possible answer: To round 83,768 to the nearest thousand, Toni can identify 83,000 and 84,000 on the same number line. She can mark 83,500 as the halfway mark between 83,000 and 84,000. Then Toni can show that the nearest thousand to 83,768 is 84,000.

83,500 83,768

80,000   83,000 84,000 85,000   90,000

Think•Pair•Share

Peer Collaboration Help student pairs as needed to draw a number line that will help them round 83,768 to the nearest ten thousand as well as the nearest thousand. Lead student pairs to draw a number line from 80,000 to 90,000 with increments of 10,000. After student pairs round to the nearest ten thousand, help them refine the number line to round to the nearest thousand. Ask:

- *Can you use this number line to show how to round to the nearest hundred?*

- *Can you use this number line to show how to round to the nearest ten?*

Students can mark the segment from 83,000 to 84,000 in half and label the point 83,500. Then students should mark 83,785 about halfway between 83,500 and 84,000. Students should see that 83,785 is closer to 84,000 than 83,000.

Return to the Essential Question

Reread the Lesson 8 Essential Question on page 72: *How can place value help you round to different places in a whole number?*

Ask volunteers to use what they learned in this lesson to answer this question. (Possible response: Using place value allows you to focus on the place you want to round a number to and the digit to the right of that place. Place value can be used to round a multi-digit whole number to different places and the place you round to determines how close your estimate is to the actual number.)

Mathematical Practices

Mathematical Practice Standards underline the teaching and understanding of all concepts and skills presented. The emphasis of specific practices is noted throughout the guided and independent practice of this lesson.

MP4	**Model with mathematics.**

Item 12: Students use a number line to justify estimations of two multi-digit numbers.

Concept Application

Students may work independently on these pages in the classroom or at home. They may refer to the first four pages of the lesson to revisit the instruction or to see a worked-out example.

Common Errors and **Teaching Tips** may help you support student learning either in the classroom or as a follow-up for work done at home.

Teaching Tips

Item 5

This is the only six-digit number in the section, and some students may struggle with labeling the number line. Provide students will extra guidance by prompting them to think about what place they are rounding to and to identify which numbers should appear at both ends of the number line.

Independent Practice

Round the number to the underlined place. You can use the number line to help.

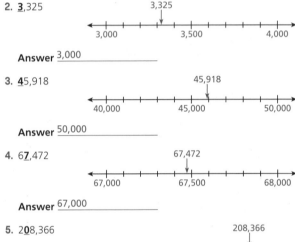

1. 5**2**,143

   2 is in the ___thousands___ place.

   The closest thousands are ___52,000___ and ___53,000___.

   Compare the ___hundreds___ digit in 52,143 to the ___5 hundreds___ in ___52,500___.

   1 ___<___ 5

   52,143 rounds ___down___ to ___52,000___.

Round each number to the underlined place. Label the number line to show the numbers you are using.

2. **3**,325

   3,325

   |—+—+—+—+—+—+—+—|
   3,000   3,500   4,000

   Answer ___3,000___

3. **4**5,918

   45,918

   |—+—+—+—+—+—+—+—|
   40,000   45,000   50,000

   Answer ___50,000___

4. 6**7**,472

   67,472

   |—+—+—+—+—+—+—+—|
   67,000   67,500   68,000

   Answer ___67,000___

5. 2**0**8,366

   208,366

   |—+—+—+—+—+—+—+—|
   200,000   205,000   210,000

   Answer ___210,000___

Writing About Math

 • **Write an Explanatory Text** Ask students to write instructions to a third-grade student on how to round a multi-digit number to an indicated place. Remind students to be mindful of their audience and use clear, concise language.

If possible, have students partner with a third-grade student. The third-grade student should use the directions to round a given number to an indicated place.

Lesson 8

Independent Practice

Match the number with the estimate rounded to the underlined place. Write the letter of the correct estimate.

Estimates

6. **7**16,549 c
7. 7**1**6,549 b
8. 71**6**,549 a
9. 716,**5**49 d

a. 717,000
b. 720,000
c. 700,000
d. 716,500

Round each number to the given place.

10. 10,401 to the thousands place
10,000

11. 26,792 to the ten thousands place
30,000

12. 48,638 to the thousands place
49,000

13. 84,151 to the hundreds place
84,200

14. 447,950 to the hundred thousands place
400,000

15. 625,099 to the ten thousands place
630,000

16. 773,646 to the thousands place
774,000

17. 998,979 to the hundreds place
999,000

Solve the problems.

18. A restaurant owner is ordering supplies for the week. Last week, she ordered 1,458 pounds of potatoes. Which is the best estimate for this number?

a. 1,000 pounds
b. 1,400 pounds
c. 1,500 pounds
d. 2,000 pounds

19. Chung's family is hiking all 2,184 miles of the Appalachian Trail. He estimates the trail length as 2,000 miles. Which estimate will better help the family make sure that they bring enough supplies?

a. 1,000 miles
b. 2,100 miles
c. 2,200 miles
d. 3,000 miles

Common Errors
Items 10–17
Be sure students pay attention to the place they are rounding to in each of these exercises. Some students may tend to round every number to the same place or round each number to the greatest place. It might help students to underline the digit of the place value they are rounding.

Digital Connection

Internet Resources Use a search engine to locate videos that focus on rounding at the fourth-grade level. Ensure that videos explain the different ways to round based on place value. Struggling students may benefit from the interactive approach used in some of these videos. Make a list of videos for students to use after you have reviewed them.

Independent Practice

Common Errors

Item 20

Students may think that all the numbers in this problem are rounded because they end in 0. Have students identify the place value of the least non-zero digit.

Teaching Tips

Item 21

Ask students to include an example in their explanation. This will help them visualize the problem and determine if their answer makes sense.

Independent Practice

MP5 20. The local news says that ticket sales for a new movie were $256,500 on Friday night, $421,000 on Saturday, and $301,850 on Sunday. Do you think these numbers are estimates or exact amounts? Explain.

Answers will vary. Possible explanation: The only number that looks like an estimate is $421,000, because it ends with more zeros than the others. If $256,500 is an estimate, it should be changed to $257,000 so it is rounded to the same place as $421,000.

MP6 21. Does it make sense to round a six-digit number to the tens place? Explain your answer with an example.

Answers will vary. Possible explanation: It does not make sense. An example is rounding 123,456 to 123,460. If you are only going to drop the ones digit, you might as well use the exact number.

Solve the problems.

MP2 22. At a carnival, Jenn correctly guesses the exact number of pennies in a jar as 124,983. The closest guess the day before was 124,983 rounded to the hundreds place. What was this guess?

▶ **Show your work.**

Work may vary. Possible work:
124,983: 8 > 5, so 9 hundreds should round up to 10 hundreds, or 1,000.
124,000 + 1,000 = 125,000.

Answer The closest guess the day before was 125,000.

MP8 23. A store owner is adding $5,641 and $5,238 to find his total sales for the past two days. He rounds each amount to the nearest hundred dollars and then adds the rounded numbers. What is the store owner's estimated total sales amount?

▶ **Show your work.**

Work may vary. Possible work:
$5,641 rounds to $5,600. $5,238 rounds to $5,200.
$5,600 + $5,200 = $10,800.

Answer The store owner's estimated total sales amount is $10,800.

Mathematical Practices

MP2	**Reason abstractly and quantitatively.**
Item 22: Students use rounding to analyze an estimation problem.	
MP5	**Use appropriate tools strategically.**
Item 20: Students deepen their understanding of rounding by assessing information concerning possible estimated numbers.	
MP6	**Attend to precision.**
Item 21: Students use rounding to formulate a full explanation.	
MP8	**Look for and express regularity in repeated reasoning.**
Item 23: Students accurately round numbers to solve a problem.	

Lesson 8

Independent Practice

MP1 **24.** Victor estimates the sum of 289 and 532 in two ways. First he rounds both numbers and then adds them. Then he adds the exact numbers and rounds the sum. Both methods give him the same final number, but he gets a different answer when he rounds to a different place. What two estimated sums does Victor find?

Show your work. Work may vary. Possible work: Rounding first: 290 + 530 = 820, or 300 + 500 = 800. Adding first: 289 + 532 = 821, which is 820 rounded to the nearest ten and 800 rounded to the nearest hundred.

Answer The estimated sums that Victor finds are 820 and 800.

MP7 **25.** Ben and Lisa round the same number to different places. Ben rounds to the nearest ten thousand and gets 70,000. Lisa rounds to the nearest thousand and gets 68,000. If they both rounded correctly, what are the greatest and least possible numbers they could have rounded?

Show your work. Work may vary. Possible work: 65,000 and greater rounds up to 70,000, but the number has to be at least 67,500 to also round up to 68,000. 74,999 and less rounds down to 70,000, but the greatest number that rounds down to 68,000 is 68,499.

Answer least number 67,500, greatest number 68,499

MP3 **26.** An Arctic tern can fly more than 43,496 miles as it migrates each year. Round this number to the nearest ten thousand miles. Then round 43,496 miles to the place of your choice for a better estimate.

Answer nearest ten thousand 40,000 miles, second estimate 43,500 miles

Justify your answer using words, drawings, or numbers.
Possible justification: 43,496 rounded to the ten thousands place is 40,000. Rounding to the thousands place gives an estimate that is closer to the exact number: 43,000. But since 496 is so close to 500, it seems better to round to the hundreds place: 43,500.

MP8 **27.** Owen incorrectly rounds 384,478 to the thousands place by rounding in three steps. He rounds to the nearest ten first, and then rounds two more times until he reaches 385,000. Is it possible that Owen rounded correctly at each step, even though his final estimate is wrong?

Answer Yes, it is possible that Owen rounded correctly at each step.

Justify your answer using words, drawings, or numbers.
Possible justification: 384,478 rounded to the tens place is 384,480. 384,480 rounded to the hundreds place is 384,500. And 384,500 rounded to the thousands place is 385,000. If Owen rounded 384,478 directly to the thousands place, he would have the correct answer: 384,000.

Unit 2 ■ Focus on Number and Operations in Base Ten **79**

Common Errors

Item 25

Some students may name 69,000 as the halfway point between the two given numbers. Be sure students read the problem carefully to identify the place to which each number is being rounded. Students should make a list of numbers that meet the descriptions for each rounded number.

Teaching Tips

Item 24

If students are struggling, tell them to execute both methods described in the problem.

Item 26

Ask students what an "Arctic tern" is. Remind students that when they come across a word that they do not know, they can use context clues to give meaning to the word. Explain that students can still solve the problem without having knowledge about this particular bird.

Mathematical Practices	
MP1	**Make sense of problems and persevere in solving them.**
Item 24: Students analyze different ways of estimating sums.	
MP3	**Construct viable arguments and critique the reasoning of others.**
Item 26: Students justify why their estimate is more reasonable.	
MP7	**Look for and make use of structure.**
Item 25: Students recognize the structure of rounding rules.	
MP8	**Look for and express regularity in repeated reasoning.**
Item 27: Students identify a pattern used in rounding.	

Common Core Focus:

4.NBT.4 Fluently add and subtract multi-digit whole numbers using the standard algorithm.

OBJECTIVE
Use the standard algorithms for adding and subtracting multi-digit whole numbers using place value.

ESSENTIAL QUESTION
Skills students have learned related to place value are vitally important as they now use place value to add and subtract. Students will move from estimating to mentally calculating with precision. Explain that the mastery of the addition and subtraction algorithms will enable students to add and subtract whole numbers of any magnitude.

FLUENCY PRACTICE
Fluency practice is available at **sadlierconnect.com**.

Concept Development

Understand: Place value and addition

■ The Common Core State Standards for Mathematics expect students to fluently add and subtract multi-digit whole numbers using the standard algorithm. Be sure to focus on place value when presenting the addition algorithm so students understand the relative size when adding the digits in each place.

■ Students will need to understand when to regroup. Explain that adding 1 hundred + 6 hundreds + 2 hundreds is an example of when regrouping is not needed.

■ Use base-ten blocks to model adding ones, tens, hundreds, and thousands to help.

Add and Subtract Fluently with Whole Numbers

Essential Question: How can you add and subtract whole numbers efficiently?
4.NBT.4

Guided Instruction

In this lesson you will learn the standard algorithms for adding and subtracting using place value.

Understand: Place value and addition

> One report states that scientists have discovered 307,674 different kinds of plants and 64,283 kinds of vertebrates, or animals with a backbone. How many different kinds of plants and vertebrates are there altogether?

To find the sum of 307,674 and 64,283, you can add. Align the digits by place value.

Add the ones: $4 + 3 = 7$.
Add the tens: $7 + 8 = 15$.
15 tens is the same as 1 hundred 5 tens.
Regroup 15 tens as 1 hundred 5 tens.
Write the 1 hundred above the hundreds place, and write the 5 tens in the sum.

Remember!
You can only write one digit for each place of the sum.

$$\begin{array}{r} \overset{1}{3\,0\,7,6\,7\,4} \\ +\ \ 6\,4,2\,8\,3 \\ \hline 5\,7 \end{array}$$

Keep adding the digits in each place, regrouping whenever the sum for that place is 10 or greater.

Add the hundreds: $1 + 6 + 2 = 9$
Add the thousands: $7 + 4 = 11$.
11 thousands is the same as 1 ten thousands 1 thousand.
Regroup 11 thousands as 1 ten thousand 1 thousand.

$$\begin{array}{r} \overset{1}{3}\,0\,\overset{1}{7},6\,7\,4 \\ +\ \ 6\,4,2\,8\,3 \\ \hline 1,9\,5\,7 \end{array}$$

Add the ten thousands: $1 + 0 + 6 = 7$
There is nothing to add to the 3 hundred thousands, so write 3 in the sum.

$$\begin{array}{r} \overset{1}{3}\,0\,\overset{1}{7},6\,7\,4 \\ +\downarrow 6\,4,2\,8\,3 \\ \hline 3\,7\,1,9\,5\,7 \end{array}$$

▶ There are 371,957 different kinds of plants and vertebrates altogether.

Support English Language Learners

The term *regroup* is used in this lesson and may be unfamiliar to some students. However, they should be familiar with the term *group* and have some exposure to the prefix *re-*. Make connections to this knowledge by asking students to identify when these terms are used.

Tell students that the prefix *re-* means "again." Ask students what the word *regroup* means. Help them see that it means to make a group again.

Have students practice regrouping using base-ten blocks. Invite a student to show the number 85 one way. Then invite another student to regroup the blocks to show the same number a different way. For example, the student may trade one of the tens rods for 10 ones cubes. Explain that the student has made the same group "again," or *regrouped*.

Lesson 9

Guided Instruction

Understand: Subtraction and regrouping

Spiders, scorpions, and other animals with eight legs are called *arachnids*. The report also states that there are 102,248 kinds of arachnids. How many more kinds of arachnids are there than the 64,283 kinds of vertebrates?

To find how many more kinds of arachnids there are, start by estimating the difference. This estimate will allow you to judge the reasonableness of your exact answer.

$$102{,}248 - 64{,}283$$
$$100{,}000 - 64{,}000 = 36{,}000$$

Next align the digits by place value. Subtract in each place.

Start with the ones: $8 - 3 = 5$.
To subtract 4 tens − 8 tens, more tens are needed. Regroup.

```
  102,248
−  64,283
       ? 5
```

Regroup 2 hundreds 4 tens as 1 hundred 14 tens.
Then subtract: $14 - 8 = 6$.

```
        1 14
  102,2 4 8
−  64,2 8 3
         6 5
```

Since you must subtract 1 hundred − 2 hundreds,
regroup the thousands:
2 thousands 1 hundred as 1 thousand 11 hundreds.
Then subtract the hundreds. $11 - 2 = 9$

```
      1 11 14
  102,2 4 8
−  64,2 8 3
       9 6 5
```

To subtract 1 thousand − 4 thousands, regroup ten thousands:
10 ten thousands 1 thousand as 9 ten thousand 11 thousands.
Subtract the thousands. $11 - 4 = 7$

```
   9  11 11 14
  10 2,2 4 8
−  6 4,2 8 3
   7,9 6 5
```

Now subtract the ten thousands. $9 - 6 = 3$

```
   9 11 11 14
  10 2,2 4 8
−  6 4,2 8 3
   3 7,9 6 5
```

37,965 is close to the estimate of 36,000 so the exact answer is reasonable.

➤ There are exactly 37,965 more kinds of arachnids than vertebrates.

Understand: Subtraction and regrouping

■ Students will use what they know about place value to align subtraction algorithms correctly. Invite students to name the place values in each number to be sure the same values are aligned vertically in the subtraction algorithm.

■ Some students may benefit from writing the subtractions on grid paper. The grid can be helpful in keeping place values aligned in columns.

■ Be sure students can support their reasoning for regrouping. They must be able to express the need to regroup because it is not possible to subtract a greater digit from a lesser digit.

Math-to-Science Connection

Arachnids Arachnids are a class of joint-legged animals. All arachnids have eight legs and two distinct body features. Some of the most common arachnids are spiders, scorpions, and mites. According to some reports, there are an estimated 40,462 species of spiders on Earth.

Millipedes and centipedes, on the other hand, are part of a subphylum of arthropods called Myriapoda. These animals have various numbers of legs ranging between 10 legs to over 750 legs. There are an estimated 11,460 species of myriapods in the world. Have students estimate the difference between the number of species of spiders and the number of Myriapoda. Then have them find the actual difference. Ask students how to use an estimate to determine whether an actual answer is reasonable.

Guided Instruction

Connect: Subtraction and addition

Use this page to help students strengthen their understanding of the inverse relationship between addition and subtraction.

- Remind students that related additions and subtractions have the same numbers.

- Ask students to compare using an inverse operation to check their answers to the estimation strategy used previously on page 81. Point out that using addition to check subtraction requires students to be precise in their computations.

✏️ Invite a volunteer to use place-value language to describe each regrouping, such as, "I regrouped 1 ten thousand as 10 thousands."

Ask another student to model using addition to check the answer. Again, encourage the use of place-value language, such as, "I regrouped 10 ones as 1 ten."

Guided Instruction

Connect: Subtraction and addition

> Sometimes scientists disagree over their findings. One report says that there are 310,129 kinds of plants instead of 307,674. What is the difference between the number of plants?

Subtract to find the difference between the number of plants. Then add to check.

Step 1

To subtract, align the digits by place value.
Subtract the ones: $9 - 4 = 5$.
Regroup hundreds and tens.
Subtract the tens.

$$\begin{array}{r} \scriptstyle 0\,12 \\ 310,\cancel{1}\cancel{2}9 \\ -307,674 \\ \hline 55 \end{array}$$

Regroup thousands and hundreds as needed.
Subtract the hundreds.

$$\begin{array}{r} \scriptstyle 0\ 9\ 10\,12 \\ 3\cancel{1}\cancel{0},\cancel{1}\cancel{2}9 \\ -307,674 \\ \hline 455 \end{array}$$

Subtract the thousands.
Subtract the ten thousands.
Subtract the hundred thousands.
$310,129 - 307,674 = 2,455$

$$\begin{array}{r} \scriptstyle 0\ 9\ 10\,12 \\ 3\cancel{1}\cancel{0},\cancel{1}\cancel{2}9 \\ -307,674 \\ \hline 2,455 \end{array}$$

> **Remember!**
> The expanded form of a number shows the values of all its digits.
> $310,129 = 300,000 + 10,000 + 100 + 20 + 9$

Step 2

You can add to check your answer.
If the sum is the number you started with, then you subtracted correctly.

$$\begin{array}{r} \scriptstyle 1\ 1\ 1 \\ 307,674 \\ +\ \ 2,455 \\ \hline 310,129 \end{array}$$

> **Remember!**
> Addition and subtraction are inverse operations.

➡️ The difference between the number of plants is 2,455.

✏️ You know that $10,000 - 1 = 9,999$. Show the regrouping that is needed to find the answer.
Possible answer:

$$\begin{array}{r} \scriptstyle 9\ 9\ 9\ 10 \\ \cancel{1}\cancel{0},\cancel{0}\cancel{0}\cancel{0} \\ -\qquad 1 \\ \hline 9,999 \end{array}$$

Math-to-Statistics Connection

Census Census takers collect data about individuals and families. The data are compiled into tables of various categories and groups. Have students find census data for their community or state. Ask students to use the data to determine the difference between population totals for two different years. Have students determine whether the population increased or decreased during the time period.

Guided Practice

For each step in exercises 1–4, write the missing digits to add or subtract.

1.

$$
\begin{array}{r}
\boxed{1} \\
3,584 \\
+2,456 \\
\hline
\boxed{0}
\end{array}
\qquad
\begin{array}{r}
\boxed{1}\ 1 \\
3,584 \\
+2,456 \\
\hline
\boxed{4}\,0
\end{array}
\qquad
\begin{array}{r}
\boxed{1}\ 1\ 1 \\
3,584 \\
+2,456 \\
\hline
6,\boxed{0}\,40
\end{array}
$$

2.

$$
\begin{array}{r}
\boxed{1} \\
46,179 \\
+38,644 \\
\hline
\boxed{3}
\end{array}
\qquad
\begin{array}{r}
\boxed{1}\ 1 \\
46,179 \\
+38,644 \\
\hline
\boxed{2}\,3
\end{array}
\qquad
\begin{array}{r}
\boxed{1}\ 1\ 1 \\
46,179 \\
+38,644 \\
\hline
\boxed{8}\,4,\boxed{8}\,23
\end{array}
$$

3.

$$
\begin{array}{r}
\boxed{6\ 15} \\
53,7\cancel{8}5 \\
-14,381 \\
\hline
\boxed{4}
\end{array}
\qquad
\begin{array}{r}
6\ 15 \\
53,7\cancel{8}5 \\
-14,381 \\
\hline
\boxed{3}\,74
\end{array}
\qquad
\begin{array}{r}
\boxed{4\ 13}\ 6\ 15 \\
\cancel{5}3,7\cancel{8}5 \\
-14,381 \\
\hline
\boxed{3}\,9,374
\end{array}
$$

4.

$$
\begin{array}{r}
80,092 \\
-66,571 \\
\hline
\boxed{2}\boxed{1}
\end{array}
$$

Regroup to make hundreds.

$80,000 = 70,000 + \underline{\ 10,000\ }$

$10,000 = 9,000 + \underline{\ 1,000\ }$

$1,000 = \underline{\ 10\ }$ hundreds

$$
\begin{array}{r}
\boxed{7}\ \boxed{9}\ \boxed{10} \\
\cancel{8}\,\cancel{0},\cancel{0}92 \\
-66,571 \\
\hline
\boxed{1}\,3,\boxed{5}\,21
\end{array}
$$

� Think · Pair · Share

MP4 **5.** To understand the problem at the right, Hunter writes the numbers in expanded form. How can Hunter regroup to keep subtracting and finish the problem?
Possible answer: Hunter can regroup 1,000 from 7,000 as 900 and 100, which is 10 tens. Then, 10 tens + 3 tens = 13 tens, or 130, so he can subtract.

$$
\begin{array}{r}
7,034 \\
-5,653 \\
\hline
1
\end{array}
\qquad
\begin{array}{r}
7,000 + \boxed{\ \ } + 30 + 4 \\
-5,000 + 600 + 50 + 3 \\
\hline
1
\end{array}
$$

$$
\begin{array}{r}
6 \quad 130 \\
\cancel{7},000 + 900 + \cancel{3}\cancel{0} + 4 \\
-5,000 + 600 + \ 50 + 3 \\
\hline
1,000 + 300 + \ 80 + 1
\end{array}
\qquad
\begin{array}{r}
7,034 \\
-5,653 \\
\hline
1,381
\end{array}
$$

Observational Assessment

Use page 83 to assess whether students use the standard addition and subtraction algorithms accurately. As students fill in missing digits, check that they are recording each regrouping correctly.

� Think•Pair•Share

Peer Collaboration Ask pairs to model how to regroup using the expanded form to find the difference. Have other pairs use base-ten models to show regrouping. Ask:

- *What were the place values of the digits you needed to regroup?*

- *How does your model show regrouping?*

Return to the Essential Question

Reread the Lesson 9 Essential Question on page 80: *How can you add and subtract whole numbers efficiently?*

Ask volunteers to use what they learned in this lesson to answer this question. (Possible responses: I can add and subtract the digits in each place of the whole numbers, being careful to record any regrouping to ensure that I use the correct digits. I can use estimation to check the reasonableness of my solutions. I can use the inverse operation to check the correctness of my solutions.)

Ask students to list the steps needed to add two six-digit numbers and to subtract two six-digit numbers. Have students consider how the steps are the same and different.

Mathematical Practices

Mathematical Practice Standards underline the teaching and understanding of all concepts and skills presented. The emphasis of specific practices is noted throughout the guided and independent practice of this lesson.

MP4	Model with mathematics.

Item 5: Students explain the relationships of quantities as they regroup to solve the problem.

Independent Practice

Concept Application

Students may work independently on these pages in the classroom or at home. They may refer to the first four pages of the lesson to revisit the instruction or to see a worked-out example.

Common Errors and **Teaching Tips** may help you support student learning either in the classroom or as a follow-up for work done at home.

Common Errors

Items 10–13

Students often make addition errors when they work too quickly or when they fail to focus. Remind students to compare their estimates to the actual sums to determine whether their actual sums are reasonable.

Teaching Tips

Items 1–9

Remind students to complete each algorithm from right to left, even though some of the work is already completed for them.

Items 7–9

Ask students to describe how they will use the inverse operation to check their work.

Independent Practice

Write the missing digits to complete each exercise.

1.
```
      1
  7,3 6 0
+ 1,4 5 9
  8,8 1 9
```

2.
```
    1   1
  8,5 4 8
+ 8,9 3 4
1 7,4 8 2
```

3.
```
    1   1 1
 5 2,7 2 6
+4 4,9 7 6
 9 7,7 0 2
```

4.
```
      6 13
  6,7 3 9
- 2,6 8 3
  4,0 5 6
```

5.
```
        8 17
  9,2 9 7
- 2,1 4 8
  7,1 4 9
```

6.
```
   3 11  4 11 10
 4 5,8 2 0
-1 5,4 6 1
 2 6,0 5 9
```

Add or subtract to check your answers.

7.
```
      1
  7,1 4 9
+ 2,1 4 8
  9,2 9 7
```

8.
```
   16 14 7 12
 5 7,4 8 2
-   8,9 3 4
   8,5 4 8
```

9.
```
   6 16 9 12
 9 7,7 0 2
-4 4,9 7 6
 5 2,7 2 6
```

Estimate each sum. Then find the actual sum. Show how you regroup.   Estimates may vary.

10. Estimate:

    $38{,}000 + 3{,}000 = 41{,}000$

```
  1 1 1
  38,434
+  2,575
  41,009
```

11. Estimate:

    $60{,}000 + 50{,}000 = 110{,}000$

```
   1    1
   59,149
 +52,612
 1 11,761
```

12. Estimate:

    $225{,}000 + 200{,}000 = 425{,}000$

```
  1 1 1  1
  223,458
+198,837
  422,295
```

13. Estimate:

    $460{,}000 + 260{,}000 = 720{,}000$

```
  1 1 1 1
  464,772
+257,432
  722,204
```

Writing About Math

▪ **Write a Narrative Text** Ask students to write a narrative that includes addition or subtraction of whole numbers as part of the story. Suggest that students include an activity or hobby with which they are familiar as the topic of the narrative. Remind students to organize the narrative in a way that allows events to unfold in a natural order and provides a conclusion based on the narrative.

Ask volunteers to read their narratives aloud and allow listeners to model a solution on the board. Discuss whether students included the solution to their problems within the narratives and how those solutions were worked into the story.

MORE ONLINE sadlierconnect.com   Lesson 9

Independent Practice

Estimate each difference. Then find the actual difference. Show how you regroup. Estimates may vary.

14. Estimate:

$9,000 - 4,000 = 5,000$

```
  8 11
  9,1 8 5
− 3,9 6 4
  5,2 2 1
```

15. Estimate:

$17,000 - 13,000 = 4,000$

```
   6 11 16
  1 7,2 6 8
− 1 2,9 7 0
     4,2 9 8
```

16. Estimate:

$640,000 - 300,000 = 340,000$

```
  5 13 10   8 13
  6 4 0,5 9 3
− 2 8 6,4 0 6
  3 5 4,1 8 7
```

17. Estimate:

$500,000 - 400,000 = 100,000$

```
  4 9 10 5 14
  5 0 0,6 4 2
− 3 7 1,3 5 1
  1 2 9,2 9 1
```

For problems 18–19, use the table at the right.

Greatest Known Ocean Depths	
Ocean	Depth in feet
Pacific	36,198
Atlantic	30,246
Southern	23,736
Arctic	18,456

MP1 **18.** Naomi says the combined depth of the Southern Ocean and Artic Ocean is less than the depth of the Pacific Ocean. Estimate and then find the combined depth. Is Naomi correct? Work may vary. Possible work:

Estimate: $18,000 + 24,000 = 42,000$

$42,192 > 36,198$

```
   1 1  1
  2 3,7 3 6
+ 1 8,4 5 6
  4 2,1 9 2
```

Answer The combined depth is 42,192 feet, so Naomi is not correct.

MP2 **19.** Vince wants to know how much deeper the Atlantic Ocean is than the Southern Ocean. What is the difference between the greatest depths of the two oceans? Work may vary. Possible work:

```
    2 9 12
  3 0,2 4 6
− 2 3,7 3 6
    6,5 1 0
```

Answer The Atlantic Ocean is 6,510 feet deeper.

MP7 **20.** Naomi rounds the greatest depth of the Pacific Ocean to 36,200 feet. The deepest a scuba diver has gone underwater is 1,044 feet. What is the difference between the two depths? Work may vary. Possible work:

```
    1 9 10
  3 6,2 0 0
−    1,0 4 4
  3 5,1 5 6
```

Answer The difference between the two depths is 35,156 feet

Unit 2 ■ Focus on Number and Operations in Base Ten   **85**

Common Errors

Item 20

Some students may use the actual depth of the Pacific Ocean listed in the table. Reread the problem with students, pointing out that they need to use Naomi's rounded value of the depth.

Teaching Tips

Items 14–17

Guide students to compare their estimates to the actual differences to determine whether their actual differences are reasonable.

Item 18

Point out that this is a multistep problem. Discuss the steps before students solve the problem. First, students will find the sum of the depths of the Southern and Artic Oceans. Then they will compare that sum to the depth of the Pacific Ocean.

Item 20

Ask students to explain which would be greater, the actual difference or the estimated difference between the two depths. Help students reason that since the estimated depth is greater than the actual depth, the estimated difference will be greater than the actual difference.

Mathematical Practices

MP1	**Make sense of problems and persevere in solving them.**

Item 18: Students check and analyze a solution to a problem.

MP2	**Reason abstractly and quantitatively.**

Item 19: Students pay attention to mathematical language and use symbols to represent and solve a problem.

MP7	**Look for and make use of structure.**

Item 20: Students evaluate the structure of a problem and use place value to determine the difference.

Teaching Tips

Item 21

If students are having difficulty finding the mistake, suggest they use addition to check.

Item 24

Point out that this problem requires addition of three numbers. Checking the solution is also different because it must account for all three addends.

Independent Practice

MP7   21. Michael made a mistake while subtracting. What mistake did Michael make?

$$
\begin{array}{r}
5,543 \\
-4,895 \\
\hline
1,352
\end{array}
$$

Answers will vary. Possible answer: Michael did not regroup to subtract. Instead, he just subtracted the lesser number from the greater number.

MP6   22. Rosie says that when you regroup while adding, the amount that you add to the next place to the left will always be 1. Is Rosie correct? Explain.
Answers will vary. Possible explanation: Rosie is only correct when you add no more than two numbers. Then the greatest digits you will add in any place are 9 + 9, so you will regroup the 1 from 18. But depending on the place in the numbers, the digit 1 could represent 1 ten, 1 hundred, and so on.

For problems 23–26, use the table at the right. Use addition or subtraction to check your answer.

Aquarium Visitors	
Month	Number of Visitors
May	85,628
June	97,134
July	101,942
August	123,291
September	64,417

MP1   23. How many people visited the aquarium in May and June?

➤ **Show your work.**
Work may vary. Possible work:

$$
\begin{array}{r}
\overset{1}{9}\,\overset{1}{7},134 \\
+85,628 \\
\hline
182,762
\end{array}
\qquad
\text{Check:}
\begin{array}{r}
\overset{17}{1}\overset{12}{8}\overset{5}{2},\overset{12}{7}6\,2 \\
-85,628 \\
\hline
97,134
\end{array}
$$

Answer 182,762 people visited the aquarium in May and June.

MP1   24. How many visitors went to the aquarium in June, July, and August?

➤ **Show your work.**
Work may vary. Possible work:

$$
\begin{array}{r}
\overset{1}{9}\overset{1}{7},\overset{1}{1}\overset{1}{3}4 \\
+101,942 \\
123,291 \\
\hline
322,367
\end{array}
\qquad
\text{Check:}
\begin{array}{r}
\overset{2}{3}\overset{11}{2}\overset{12}{2},\overset{2}{3}\overset{16}{6}7 \\
-123,291 \\
\hline
199,076
\end{array}
\qquad
\begin{array}{r}
\overset{8}{1}9\overset{10}{9},076 \\
-101,942 \\
\hline
97,134
\end{array}
$$

Answer 322,367 visitors went to the aquarium in June, July, and August.

86   Unit 2 ■ Focus on Number and Operations in Base Ten

Mathematical Practices

MP1	**Make sense of problems and persevere in solving them.**

Item 23: Students analyze information in a table to determine a solution.

Item 24: Students relate to a similar problem to solve a different problem.

MP6	**Attend to precision.**

Item 22: Students communicate with precision and carefully formulate a full explanation.

MP7	**Look for and make use of structure.**

Item 21: Students evaluate the structure of a subtraction to explain an error.

MP1 **25.** How many more visitors went to the aquarium in August than in June?

> ▭ **Show your work.**
> Work may vary. Possible work:

$$
\begin{array}{r}
\overset{11\,13}{\cancel{1}}\,\overset{8\,11}{2\,\cancel{3},\cancel{2}\,9\,\cancel{1}} \\
-\;\;\;97,134 \\
\hline
26,157
\end{array}
\qquad
\text{Check:}
\begin{array}{r}
\overset{1}{2}\,\overset{}{6}\,\overset{1}{1}\,57 \\
+\;97,134 \\
\hline
123,291
\end{array}
$$

> **Answer** 26,157 more visitors went to the aquarium in August than in June.

MP2 **26.** What is the difference between the greatest and least numbers of visitors to the aquarium in one month?   Work may vary. Possible work: The greatest number is 123,291 in August and the least number is 64,417 in September.

> ▭ **Show your work.**

$$
\begin{array}{r}
\overset{11\,1212}{\cancel{1}}\,\overset{8\,11}{2\,\cancel{3},\cancel{2}\,9\,\cancel{1}} \\
-\;\;\;64,417 \\
\hline
58,874
\end{array}
\qquad
\text{Check:}
\begin{array}{r}
\overset{1}{5}\,\overset{1}{8},874 \\
+\;64,417 \\
\hline
123,291
\end{array}
$$

> **Answer** The difference between the greatest and least numbers of visitors in one month is 58,874.

MP6 **27.** Trey is teaching his brother how to add. Here is how his brother added. Is Trey's brother's work correct? If not, what mistake did Trey's brother make?

$$
\begin{array}{r}
\overset{1\;1\;1\;1\;1\;1}{1\,2\,3,4\,5\,6} \\
+\,1\,2\,3,4\,5\,6 \\
\hline
3\,5\,7,9\,1\,3
\end{array}
$$

> **Answer** No, Trey's brother's work is not correct. He added 1 to each place whether or not he needed to regroup.
> ▭ **Justify your answer using words, drawings, or numbers.**
> Possible justification:

$$
\begin{array}{r}
\overset{1\;1}{1\,2\,3,4\,5\,6} \\
+\,1\,2\,3,4\,5\,6 \\
\hline
2\,4\,6,9\,1\,2
\end{array}
$$
The correct sum is 246,912, not 357,913. Trey's brother does not need to add 1 to the ones, thousands, ten thousands, or hundred thousands columns.

MP3 **28.** Trey says that before you subtract, you can regroup all of the values that you need to at once. Does this method give you the same difference as when you regroup one place at a time, while you subtract?

> **Answer** Yes.
> ▭ **Justify your answer using words, drawings, or numbers.**
> Possible justification:

$$
\begin{array}{r}
\overset{3\;1212}{\cancel{4}\,\cancel{3}\,\cancel{2}} \\
-\;\;1\,5\,6 \\
\hline
2\,7\,6
\end{array}
\qquad
\begin{array}{r}
\overset{1\;1}{2\,7\,6} \\
+\,1\,5\,6 \\
\hline
4\,3\,2
\end{array}
$$
I tried it Trey's way, and my answer is correct. The only difference is that you need to compare the digits in the top and bottom numbers before you start subtracting. But after you finish all the regrouping, subtracting is easy.

Unit 2 ▪ Focus on Number and Operations in Base Ten   87

Common Errors
Item 26
Some students may assume that the values in the table on page 86 are listed from least to greatest. Remind students to look carefully at the value of each number in the table before solving the problem.

Teaching Tips
Items 25–26
Remind students to use the data from the table on page 86.

Items 27–28
Students may be more comfortable justifying their answers in one particular way. If students have extra time, encourage them to use a separate sheet of paper to describe their answers in different ways.

Mathematical Practices	
MP1	**Make sense of problems and persevere in solving them.**
Item 25: Students decipher necessary information to solve the problem.	
MP2	**Reason abstractly and quantitatively.**
Item 26: Students compare quantities to solve a problem.	
MP3	**Construct viable arguments and critique the reasoning of others.**
Item 28: Students analyze and validate a student's solution process.	
MP6	**Attend to precision.**
Item 27: Students articulate a solution process after identifying the error.	

Common Core Focus:

4.NBT.5 Multiply a whole number of up to four digits by a one-digit whole number, and multiply two two-digit numbers, using strategies based on place value and the properties of operations. Illustrate and explain the calculation by using equations, rectangular arrays, and/or area models.

OBJECTIVE

Use place value and patterns to multiply whole numbers.

ESSENTIAL QUESTION

Students will use place value patterns in relationships among products to multiply mentally. Students will continue using place value patterns in later lessons when they divide whole numbers.

PREREQUISITE SKILLS

Use Item D on page 338 of the Foundational Skills Handbook to review two strategies for multiplying.

FLUENCY PRACTICE

Fluency practice is available at **sadlierconnect.com**.

Concept Development

Understand: Products of tens, hundreds, and thousands

■ The Common Core State Standards for Mathematics expect that students will be able to apply place-value understanding to multiply whole numbers. Students must recognize place-value patterns and understand that a digit in one place represents ten times the value of the same digit in the place to its right.

■ Help students realize that when one or both factors end in zeros, they multiply the nonzero digits, count the number of zeros in the factors, and then write the same number of zero(s) at the end of the product.

Lesson 10 — Multiply Whole Numbers: Use Place Value

Guided Instruction

Essential Question: How can you use place value and patterns to multiply?
4.NBT.5

Words to Know: partial products

In this lesson you will learn how to use place value to multiply greater factors.

Understand: Products of tens, hundreds, and thousands

> At a swimming pool guests are charged $5 to swim for the day. How much money does the pool receive if 20, 200, or 2,000 people swim?

To find each product, use the fact 5×2 and place-value patterns.

Remember!
Each place in a number is 10 times the value of the place to its right.

5×20
$= 5 \times 2$ tens
$= 10$ tens
$= 100$

5×200
$= 5 \times 2$ hundreds
$= 10$ hundreds
$= 1,000$

$5 \times 2,000$
$= 5 \times 2$ thousands
$= 10$ thousands
$= 10,000$

➡ The pool receives $100 for 20 people, $1,000 for 200 people, and $10,000 for 2,000 people.

You can also multiply the nonzero digits, $5 \times 2 = 10$ and then compare the number of zeros in the factors with the number of zeros after the 10 in each product. You can use this pattern with zeros to multiply.

$5 \times 20 = 100$
$5 \times 200 = 1,000$
$5 \times 2,000 = 10,000$

Note that it works in other problems. Look at the problem 10×20. There are two zeros in the factors.
Multiply the nonzero digits: $1 \times 2 = 2$.
Then write the number of zeros in the factors to the end of that product, to show the correct place value.

$10 \times 20 = 1$ ten $\times 2$ tens
$= 2$ hundreds
$= 200$

This pattern helps you when you multiply tens, hundreds, and thousands.

Words to Know

partial products: numbers that are formed by multiplying the value of each digit by a factor

Glossary can be found on pp. 347-350.

Lesson 10

Guided Instruction

Understand: Place value and partial products

> Rob is using a garden hose to fill a swimming pool. In one hour there will be 924 gallons of water. How many gallons of water will the pool have in it after 6 hours?

To find the total number of gallons, you can multiply 6 times the value of each digit in 924. Partial products are formed by multiplying the value of each digit by a factor.

Find the partial products.

Multiply the ones first. Multiply 6 times the value of the digit 4. Write the product below.	Next, multiply 6 times the value of the digit 2.	Then multiply 6 times the value of the digit 9.
924 × 6 24 ← 6 × 4 ones	924 × 6 24 ← 6 × 4 ones 120 ← 6 × 2 tens	924 × 6 24 ← 6 × 4 ones 120 ← 6 × 2 tens 5400 ← 6 × 9 hundreds

Now add all the partial products.
$924 \times 6 = 24 + 120 + 5{,}400 = 5{,}544$

```
  924
×   6
   24
  120
+5400
5,544
```

You can use an area model to show the partial products in the final product. Use the value of the digits in each factor as the side lengths of the area model.

	900	+ 20	+ 4	= 924
6	6 × 900 = 5,400	6 × 20 = 120	6 × 4 = 24	

➡ The pool will have 5,544 gallons of water in it after 6 hours.

Understand: Place value and partial products

■ In this presentation, students will use place value and partial products to find the product of a multi-digit whole number and a one-digit whole number. Emphasize that the *value* of each digit in a multi-digit factor is multiplied. Students who are proficient at writing numbers in expanded form will already have a strong understanding of place value.

■ The area model will help students think about place value as they calculate partial products.

Support English Language Learners

The term *partial products* is used throughout this lesson. Have students draw an area model and work through the multiplication equation that the model represents. Have them identify the partial products in both the area model and the multiplication. It is important that students comprehend the meaning and use of mathematical words, beyond just a definition.

Connect: What you know about multiplication and partial products Use this page to help students strengthen their understanding of how multiplication and partial products are related.

■ Students will need an understanding of rounding rules in order to estimate products of two two-digit factors.

■ In this presentation, students will connect the visual representation of the area model to written numerical work. By reasoning about the connection between the area model and the algorithm, students will begin to understand the multiplication algorithm as an abbreviation of their reasoning.

■ By estimating the product first, students will be able to identify and correct place-value errors as they multiply.

Guided Instruction

Connect: What you know about multiplication and partial products

> A lifeguard works at a pool for 28 hours each week. How many hours will the lifeguard work in 12 weeks?

To multiply two 2-digit numbers, use the expanded form of each factor to find partial products. Begin by estimating to judge the reasonableness of your exact answer.

Step 1

Estimate the product. You can round down 12 and round up 28.
$12 \times 28 \rightarrow 10 \times 30 = 300$.

> Find the products of the nonzero factors. Count the zeros in the factors. Write the total number of zeros at the end of the product.

Step 2

Make an area model to show the partial products you need to find. In the area model the sides represent the 12 weeks, $12 = 10 + 2$, and the 28 hours, $28 = 20 + 8$, worked each week.

The sum of the areas of each part is the total product. Side lengths of the rectangle:
$12 = 10 + 2 \qquad 28 = 20 + 8$

	20	+ 8
10	10×20 = 200	10×8 = 80
+ 2	2×20 = 40	2×8 = 16

Step 3

Now multiply to find each partial product.

```
  28              28              28              28
× 12            × 12            × 12            × 12
  16 ← 2 × 8      16 ← 2 × 8      16 ← 2 × 8      16 ← 2 × 8
                  40 ← 2 × 20     40 ← 2 × 20     40 ← 2 × 20
                                  80 ← 10 × 8     80 ← 10 × 8
                                                 200 ← 10 × 20
```

Step 4

Add the partial products to find the total product. How does this compare to your estimate?

The exact answer, 336, is reasonably close to the estimate of 300.

➡ The lifeguard will work 336 hours in 12 weeks.

```
    28
  × 12
    16
    40
    80
 + 200
   336
```

Math-to-Shopping Connection

Finding the Total Cost A strong understanding of the relationship between multiplication and partial products will be helpful when students need to find the total cost of a quantity of the same item.

Using a sales flyer, ask students to choose items to "purchase" that costs more than $10. Have students round each price to a whole dollar amount. First, have students estimate the cost of buying a quantity between 3 and 8 of the same item. Ask students to use an area model to find the actual cost. Then have students use the multiplication partial-products algorithm. Remind students to check for reasonableness by comparing their actual products to their estimates. Repeat the activity, asking students to calculate the cost of buying a quantity between 12 and 15 of the same item.

Use place value to find each product.

1. 4 × 700
   = 4 × __7__ hundreds
   = __28__ hundreds
   = 2,800

2. 9 × 5,000
   = 9 × __5__ thousands
   = __45__ thousands
   = __45,000__

Complete the multiplication pattern.

3. 8 × 3 = __24__
   8 × 30 = 240
   8 × 300 = __2,400__
   8 × 3,000 = __24,000__

4. 5 × 6 = __30__
   5 × 60 = __300__
   5 × __600__ = 3,000
   5 × 6,000 = __30,000__

Use the area model to multiply. Label the model with the partial products. Then complete the multiplication.

5.
	300	+ 10	+ 8	= 318
4	4 × 300 = 1,200	4 × 10 = 40	4 × 8 = 32	

```
  3 1 8
×     4
─────────
    3 2  ← 4 × 8 ones
    4 0  ← 4 × 1 ten
+1,2 0 0  ← 4 × 3 hundreds
─────────
1,2 7 2
```

6.
	4,000	+ 200	+ 50	+ 6	= 4,256
8	32,000	1,600	400	48	

```
  4,2 5 6
×       8
─────────
      4 8
    4 0 0
  1,6 0 0
+3 2,0 0 0
─────────
3 4,0 4 8
```

Think • Pair • Share

MP2 **7.** Mia says the product of 21 and 53 is about the same as 2 × 500. Is Mia correct? Explain her method for estimating, and why it does or does not work.
Possible answer: Yes, Mia is correct. 2 × 500 = 1,000 and 20 × 50 = 1,000 too. She estimated the factors to be 20 × 50, then, she broke apart the factors to be 2 × 5 × 10 × 10 which equals 2 × 500.

Unit 2 ■ Focus on Number and Operations in Base Ten   91

Observational Assessment

Use page 91 to assess whether students are able to use place value, multiplication patterns, area models, and the multiplication algorithm to find products.

Think•Pair•Share

Peer Collaboration Ask each student to determine how Mia solved the problem. Then, have students work in small groups to discuss how she may have arrived at her estimation. Students should record the different possible strategies. Have students consider these questions during their group discussions:

- *What is the estimate of each factor?*
- *What is the expanded form of each factor?*
- *How can you break apart each factor to get 2 × 500?*

Return to the Essential Question

Reread the Lesson 10 Essential Question on page 88: *How can you use place value and patterns to multiply?*

Ask volunteers to use what they learned in this lesson to answer this question. (Possible response: I can use place value to write numbers in expanded form. These numbers allow me to recognize multiplication patterns and relationships, which help me multiply more efficiently.)

Invite as many volunteers as possible to express ideas about using place value and patterns to multiply.

Mathematical Practices

Mathematical Practice Standards underline the teaching and understanding of all concepts and skills presented. The emphasis of specific practices is noted throughout the guided and independent practice of this lesson.

MP2 Reason abstractly and quantitatively.

Item 7: Students use mathematical language and symbols to explain their reasoning.

Independent Practice

Concept Application

Students may work independently on these pages in the classroom or at home. They may refer to the first four pages of the lesson to revisit the instruction or to see a worked-out example.

Common Errors and **Teaching Tips** may help you support student learning either in the classroom or as a follow-up for work done at home.

Common Errors

Item 6

A common misconception is that the number of zeros in the product is always the same as the total number of zeros at the end of the factors. Point out that the product of 5 and an even tens, hundreds, or thousands number has one more 0 than the number of zeros in the factors. This is because the product of the fact already includes a zero.

Teaching Tips

Items 1-6

Remind students to find the products of the nonzero factors first.

Items 8-9

After students complete both the area model and the multiplication algorithm, have them add the numbers within the model to check their multiplication. Both answers should be the same.

Independent Practice

Use multiplication patterns to multiply.

1. $200 \times 4 =$
___8___ ___0___ ___0___

2. $3,000 \times 4 =$
___1___ ___2,___ ___0___ ___0___ ___0___

3. $20 \times 30 =$
___6___ ___0___ ___0___

4. $9 \times 500 =$
___4,500___

5. $8 \times 7,000 =$
___56,000___

6. $50 \times 40 =$
___2,000___

Use the area model to multiply. Label the model with the partial products. Then complete the multiplication.

7.

	200	+	30	+	9	= 239
6	6×200 = 1,200		6×30 = 180		6×9 = 54	

The order of addends may vary.

$6 \times 239 =$ ___1,200___ $+$ ___180___ $+$ ___54___

$=$ ___1,434___

8.
```
    5,804
  ×     7
       28
        0
    5,600
 + 35,000
   40,628
```

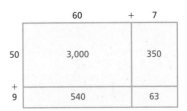

	5,000	800	+ 4	= 5,804
7	35,000	5,600	28	

9.
```
       67
  ×    59
       63
      540
      350
   +3,000
    3,953
```

	60	+ 7
50	3,000	350
+ 9	540	63

92   Unit 2 ▪ Focus on Number and Operations in Base Ten

Writing About Math

🖊 · **Write an Explanatory Text** Ask each student to write a short essay about using an area model to multiply. Remind students that explanatory essays help teach something about a topic. Have students begin by explaining what an area model is and how to create one. Remind students to include concrete facts, definitions, and examples in their essays. The essays should include concluding statements about ways area models are helpful when multiplying.

Ask volunteers to read their short essays aloud. Have one or two students tell the writer something done well in the essay. You may also choose to have one or two students tell something they would like the writer to clarify.

MORE ONLINE sadlierconnect.com   Lesson 10

Independent Practice

Multiply. Use the area model to help you.

10. A store at the beach sells 9,586 bottles of sunscreen in one summer. Each bottle costs $8. How much does the store receive for sunscreen?

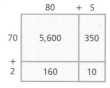

	9,000	+ 500	+ 80	+ 6
8	72,000	4,000	640	48

9,586 × $8 = _The store receives $76,688 for sunscreen._

11. Crystal is training for a swimming competition. She swims 72 feet in 1 minute. If Crystal could keep up this pace, how far would she swim in 85 minutes?

	80	+ 5
70	5,600	350
+ 2	160	10

72 × 85 = _Crystal would swim 6,120 feet in 85 minutes._

Solve the problem.

12. Oscar uses the expanded form of the factors to find and record partial products without a model. Use Oscar's method to multiply 8,954 by 9.

```
8,000 + 900 + 50 + 4 →    8,954
×                9      ×      9
              ┌────────┐  ┌────────┐
              │ 72,000 │  │ 80,586 │
              └────────┘  └────────┘
              │  8,100 │
              └────────┘
              │    450 │
              └────────┘
           +  │     36 │
              └────────┘
              │ 80,586 │
              └────────┘
```

Estimate each product. Then multiply. Estimates and work will vary.

13. 3,362 × 5 Estimate: 3,400 × 5 =
15,000 + 2,000 = 17,000

```
      3,362
   ×      5
         10
        300
      1,500
   + 15,000
     16,810
```
Product: 16,810

14. 77 × 43 Estimate: 80 × 40 = 3,200

```
        77
   ×    43
        21
       210
       280
   + 2,800
     3,311
```
Product: 3,311

Unit 2 ■ Focus on Number and Operations in Base Ten   93

Common Errors

Items 12-14

Students may find each correct partial product, but make addition errors. Remind students of the importance of place value for each partial product.

Teaching Tips

Items 10-11

Students may have difficulty solving the problems because they do not use the area model. Remind students to break apart each factor to show the place value of each digit. Students can refer to items 7–9 on page 92 if they need assistance.

Have students use a complete sentence to answer the question.

Item 12

Point out that to find the partial products when one of the factors is written in expanded form, the greatest addend of the expanded form of the factor 8,954 is multiplied first. Usually, multiplication is completed from the least place value to the greatest, but the order of multiplication when recording partial products will not affect the final product.

Digital Connection

Online Games Use a search engine to find an online multiplication game that allows students to multiply two-digit, three-digit, and four-digit numbers by one-digit numbers or to multiply two-digit numbers by two-digit numbers. Encourage students to use the strategies they learned in the lesson to help them multiply. Allow them to use pencil and paper to find products they are unable to find mentally. Discuss strategies students found to be most useful.

Independent Practice

Common Errors

Item 15

Students may be unable to identify George's mistake. Suggest that they use an area model to multiply, and then compare the partial products with those that George wrote.

Teaching Tips

Item 16

Explain that because the product of 0 and any number is 0, and the sum of 0 and any number is that number, there is no need to multiply 42 by the 0 in 80. The 0 can simply be written at the end of the product of 42 and 8.

Items 17-18

Encourage students to solve each problem using a method they feel will work best for them. Remind students to show all of their work so you can follow their thought process. Tell students to use a complete sentence to record the answer to the question.

Independent Practice

MP2 **15.** George multiplies 3 times 3,519. His work is shown to the right. What mistake does George make?
Answers will vary. Possible answer: The value of the 5 in 3,519 is 500, and $3 \times 500 = 1,500$. George has a partial product of 150 instead, so he multiplied wrong and then added the wrong amount.

$$
\begin{array}{r}
3,519 \\
\times \quad 3 \\
\hline
27 \\
30 \\
150 \\
+9,000 \\
\hline
9,207
\end{array}
$$

MP7 **16.** Robin is multiplying 80 times 42. How many partial products will Robin have to add? Explain your answer.
Answers will vary. Possible answer: Robin will only have two partial products, from multiplying the 8 in 80 by the value of each digit in 42: 80×2 and 80×40.

Solve the problems.

MP1 **17.** An airline has planes in two sizes. The small planes have 135 seats, and the larger planes have 172 seats. What is the total number of seats on 5 small planes and 4 large planes?

Show your work.
Work may vary. Possible work:
$135 \times 5 = 500 + 150 + 25 = 675$ seats
$172 \times 4 = 400 + 280 + 8 = 688$ seats

$$
\begin{array}{r}
1\ 1 \\
675 \\
+688 \\
\hline
1,363
\end{array}
$$

Answer The total number of seats is 1,363.

MP2 **18.** A large, older airplane uses 1,193 gallons of fuel each hour that it is flying. How many gallons of fuel will the plane use for a 6-hour flight?

Show your work.
Work may vary. Possible work:

$$
\begin{array}{r}
1,193 \\
\times \quad 6 \\
\hline
18 \\
540 \\
600 \\
+6,000 \\
\hline
7,158
\end{array}
$$

Answer The plane will use 7,158 gallons for a 6-hour flight.

94   Unit 2 ■ Focus on Number and Operations in Base Ten

Mathematical Practices

MP1	**Make sense of problems and persevere in solving them.**

Item 17: Students analyze a problem and find the solution using the strategy that makes the most sense to them.

MP2	**Reason abstractly and quantitatively.**

Item 15: Students identify a computational error using place value.
Item 18: Students represent problems using symbols.

MP7	**Look for and make use of structure.**

Item 16: Students use patterns and structure to evaluate the problem.

Lesson 10

Independent Practice

MP2 **19.** Chicago is about 4,254 miles from Honolulu. If an airplane could make this trip 3 times in one day, how many miles would the airplane fly altogether?

> **Show your work.** Work may vary. Possible work:

$$
\begin{array}{r}
4{,}254 \\
\times \qquad 3 \\
\hline
12 \\
150 \\
600 \\
+\,12{,}000 \\
\hline
12{,}762
\end{array}
$$

Answer The airplane would fly 12,762 miles altogether.

MP1 **20.** A group of 55 tourists order a special meal at a restaurant. The cost of each person's meal is $38. Each person will pay a $7 tip. What is the total restaurant bill for the group?

> **Show your work.** Work may vary. Possible work:
> 38 + 7 = 45

$$
\begin{array}{r}
55 \\
\times 45 \\
\hline
25 \\
250 \\
200 \\
+2{,}000 \\
\hline
2{,}475
\end{array}
$$

Answer The total bill for the group is $2,475

MP4 **21.** Jessica uses a number line to find the product 4 × 15. She skip-counts by 15 four times, and reaches a product of 60.

Miles says this is not the best method for multiplying greater numbers. Do you agree with Miles? Give one example.

Answer Yes, I agree with Miles.

> **Justify your answer using words, drawings, or numbers.**
> Possible justification: It is more work to use a number line for greater numbers, because skip counting is the same as repeated addition instead of multiplication. This is not a practical way to multiply 95 by 25, for example, because the number line would have to go to about 2,500 in order to count 25 groups of 95 or 95 groups of 25.

Unit 2 ■ Focus on Number and Operations in Base Ten **95**

Common Errors

Item 21

Some students may think that using a number line is always best since this number line displays the correct answer. Present 4 × 312. Ask students to predict how long it will take to skip-count by 4s on the number line to find the product. Have students summarize why using partial products might be a better method than using a number line to find the product of 4 × 312.

Mathematical Practices	
MP1	**Make sense of problems and persevere in solving them.**
Item 20: Students analyze a problem and find a multistep solution.	
MP2	**Reason abstractly and quantitatively.**
Item 19: Students represent problems using symbols and find a solution.	
MP4	**Model with mathematics.**
Item 21: Students use tools to explain operations.	

Common Core Focus:

4.NBT.5 Multiply a whole number of up to four digits by a one-digit whole number, and multiply two two-digit numbers, using strategies based on place value and the properties of operations. Illustrate and explain the calculation by using equations, rectangular arrays, and/or area models.

OBJECTIVE

Use the Distributive Property and other properties of operations to multiply whole numbers.

ESSENTIAL QUESTION

In Grade 3, students learned how to use the Distributive Property to break apart a factor so that they could add two simpler multiplications to find a product. In this lesson, students will use the same strategy to find products by decomposing multi-digit factors.

PREREQUISITE SKILLS

Use Item D on page 338 of the Foundational Skills Handbook to review two strategies for multiplying.

FLUENCY PRACTICE

Fluency practice is available at **sadlierconnect.com**.

Concept Development

Understand: The Distributive Property and expanded form

■ After students use the Distributive Property to multiply 5 × 384, be sure they can connect the area model to the numerical multiplication presentation. Have students explain how the side lengths of the parts of the area model represent the Distributive Property.

✏ A multi-digit number can be decomposed into base-ten units in more than one way. Help students to break apart 384 in ways other than 300 + 80 + 4.

Lesson 11 — Multiply Whole Numbers: Use Properties of Operations

Essential Question: How can you break apart greater factors to multiply? 4.NBT.5

Guided Instruction

In this lesson you will learn how to multiply greater whole numbers using the Distributive and other properties.

Understand: The Distributive Property and expanded form

> To raise money, a school will have a concert and it will charge $5 for each ticket to the concert. How much will the school receive if the school sells 384 tickets?

To find how much the school will receive you can use the Distributive Property to multiply 5 × 384.

First, decompose 384, the greater factor. Write 384 in expanded form, to break it into a sum of hundreds, tens, and ones.

$$5 \times 384 = 5 \times (300 + 80 + 4)$$

Multiply each addend by 5, the lesser factor. Then add the partial products.

$$5 \times (300 + 80 + 4) = (5 \times 300) + (5 \times 80) + (5 \times 4)$$
$$= 1{,}500 + 400 + 20$$
$$= 1{,}920$$

> You use the Distributive Property when you multiply the addends in the expanded form of one factor by the other factor.

➡ The school will receive $1,920 from the sale of 384 tickets.

Use an area model to represent the partial products.

	300	+ 80	+ 4	= 384
5	5 × 300 = 1,500	5 × 80 = 400	5 × 4 = 20	

The area model can be helpful when using the Distributive Property. It shows how multiplying 5 times the hundreds, tens, and ones in 384 is the same as multiplying 5 × 384.

✏ What are some other ways you can break apart 384? Possible answer(s): 384 = 300 + 40 + 40 + 4, 384 = 200 + 100 + 80 + 4

Support English Language Learners

There are several terms in this lesson that students may need to review, for example, *decompose, factor, addend*. As a class, conduct an online search for a dictionary that provides audio pronunciation as well as multiple definitions. Have students listen to the audio. Have small groups of students discuss their findings and agree upon a definition appropriate to the lesson. Ask volunteers to share their group's conclusions with the class.

Write at least two of the definitions on the board. Suggest that students provide examples for each of the definitions.

Lesson 11

Guided Instruction

Understand: The Distributive Property and two-digit factors

> There are 64 fourth graders at the school. If each fourth grader sells 15 concert tickets, how many tickets will the fourth graders sell altogether?

To find how many tickets will be sold, multiply 64×15.

Write the multiplication using the expanded form of both factors.
Use the Commutative Property to change the order of the factors.
$15 \times 64 = (10 + 5) \times (60 + 4)$

You can use an area model to help you. Use the value of the digits in each factor as the side lengths of the area model.

You can use the Distributive Property more than once.
To distribute, multiply *each addend* for 64 by *each addend* for 15.

First, multiply by 5, the ones digit in 15.

$5 \times (60 + 4) = (5 \times 60) + (5 \times 4)$

Next, multiply by 10, the tens digit in 15.

$10 \times (60 + 4) = (10 \times 60) + (10 \times 4)$

Then, write an equation showing the sum of the four partial products and solve.

$$(10 + 5) \times (60 + 4) = (10 \times 60) + (10 \times 4) + (5 \times 60) + (5 \times 4)$$
$$= 600 + 40 + 300 + 20$$
$$= (600 + 300) + (40 + 20)$$
$$= 900 + 60$$
$$= 960$$

Remember!
You can use the Commutative and Associative properties to help you add.

➡ The fourth graders will sell 960 concert tickets altogether.

✏ Look at the highlighted digits to the right. How are they related to the partial products that you found above?
$$\begin{array}{c} 64 \\ \times 15 \end{array} \qquad \begin{array}{c} 64 \\ \times 15 \end{array}$$
Possible answer: Multiplying the digits gives you two partial products instead of four. 64×5 is the bottom two areas in the model, and 64×10 is the top two areas.

Understand: The Distributive Property and two-digit factors

■ In this presentation, students learn how to use the Distributive Property to find the product of two two-digit factors.

■ Discuss with students how using the Commutative Property can help to simplify the multiplication. As students work through the multiplication, they should notice that multiplying by 10 is usually easier than multiplying by 60.

■ Point out that when two two-digit factors are decomposed into base-ten units, the Distributive Property will be used more than once to find the product.

■ Make sure students can explain how the area model connects to the numerical multiplication method and using the Distributive Property.

✏ Remind students that they multiplied two two-digit factors using the vertical algorithm and partial products in the previous lesson. Some students may need to revisit Lesson 10 before they answer the question.

Math-to-Math Connection

Arithmetic and Algebra Understanding and using the Distributive Property is essential for later work in algebra. At this level, the Distributive Property and the Associative and Commutative Properties are used to rewrite and simplify numeric equations. As students begin to work formally with algebra, they will utilize these same properties to simplify algebraic expressions and solve multi-step equations.

Connect: What you know about the Distributive Property and other multiplication strategies Use this page to help students strengthen their understanding of how to use various properties and strategies to multiply.

■ Learning multiple methods for finding a product provides students with more problem-solving options and lays some of the groundwork for multiplying decimals in Grade 5.

■ Most students should be comfortable with Ruby's expanded form and Distributive Property Method shown in Step 1.

■ For Omar's Method shown in Step 2, be sure students understand the compensation that Omar used. Ask why Omar had to subtract 4 × 3 from the product, instead of just subtracting 4.

■ As an extension to Omar's Method, you can use the Distributive Property with subtraction. Since $1,300 - 1,296 = 4$, the equation can be written as $1,296 × 3 = (1,300 × 3) - (4 × 3) = 3,900 - 12 = 3,888$

Connect: What you know about the Distributive Property and other multiplication strategies

> Ruby and Omar both multiply $1,296 × 3$. Ruby uses the expanded form of 1,296 and the Distributive Property. Omar multiplies a number close to 1,296 and uses other properties. Can both Ruby and Omar find the correct product using their different methods?

Try each method to compare Ruby and Omar's work.

Step 1

Ruby's Method

Write the problem using the expanded form of 1,296.	$1,296 × 3$
	$= (1,000 + 200 + 90 + 6) × 3$
Multiply each addend for 1,296 by 3.	$= (1,000 × 3) + (200 × 3) + (90 × 3) + (6 × 3)$
Multiply inside the parentheses.	$= 3,000 + 600 + 270 + 18$
Add the partial products.	$= 3,888$

Step 2

Omar's Method

Omar uses an estimate. 1,296 is almost 1,300, or 13 hundreds. He uses the Commutative Property to reorder the factors.	$1,300 × 3 = 13 × 100 × 3$
	$= 13 × 3 × 100$
Omar uses the Associative Property to group 13 and 3. Then he uses multiplication patterns with zero to multiply.	$= (13 × 3) × 100$
	$= 39 × 100$
	$= 3,900$
Since $1,300 - 1,296 = 4$, he compensates for the difference. There are 3 groups of 1,300 in 3,900, so he subtracts 4 three times.	$1,296 × 3 = 3,900 - (4 × 3)$
	$= 3,900 - 12$
	$= 3,888$

➡ Yes, Ruby and Omar can both find the correct product using their different methods.

Math-to-Art Connection

Make a Poster Ask students do an online search for definitions and examples of the Distributive, Commutative, and Associative Properties. Have small groups work together to create posters, using definitions written in their own words and illustrating the three properties using both numbers and pictures. When completed, groups can present and explain their work to the class.

Lesson 11

Guided Practice

Use the Distributive Property to multiply. You can use the area model to help.

1. 6 × 573

$= 6 \times (\underline{500} + 70 + \underline{3})$

$= (\underline{6} \times \underline{500}) + (6 \times 70) + (\underline{6} \times \underline{3})$

$= \underline{3,000} + 420 + \underline{18}$

$= \underline{3,438}$

	500	+ 70	+ 3
6	6 × 500	6 × 70	6 × 3

2. 32 × 29

$= (\underline{30} + 2) \times (\underline{20} + 9)$

$= (30 \times \underline{20}) + (30 \times \underline{9}) + (2 \times \underline{20}) + (2 \times \underline{9})$

$= \underline{600} + 270 + 40 + \underline{18}$

$= \underline{928}$

	20	+ 9
30	30 × 20	30 × 9
+ 2	2 × 20	2 × 9

Use the Distributive Property and expanded form to multiply.

3. $4 \times 6,725 = \underline{4} \times (6,000 + \underline{700} + \underline{20} + 5)$

$= (4 \times 6,000) + (\underline{4 \times 700}) + (\underline{4 \times 20}) + (4 \times 5)$

$= \underline{24,000} + 2,800 + \underline{80} + \underline{20}$

$= \underline{26,900}$

✔ Think • Pair • Share

MP6 **4.** Leo multiplies 4 × 285 as shown below.

$4 \times (250 + 30 + 5) = 1,000 + 120 + 20 = 1,140$

Does Leo use the Distributive Property? Does he find the correct product? Explain why or why not.
Possible explanation: Yes, Leo uses the Distributive Property and his product is correct. He breaks apart 285 into addends that are easy to multiply, but he does not use the expanded form of 285. He multiplies each addend by 4, the other factor, and adds the partial products. I used the expanded form to check his answer: 4 × (200 + 80 + 5) = 800 + 320 + 20 = 1,140.

Mathematical Practices

Mathematical Practice Standards underline the teaching and understanding of all concepts and skills presented. The emphasis of specific practices is noted throughout the guided and independent practice of this lesson.

MP6 **Attend to precision.**

Item 4: Students carefully formulate a full explanation for a given solution.

Observational Assessment

Use page 99 to assess whether students are able to use the Distributive Property to multiply. As the amount of scaffolding in the problems drops off, note those students who need extra support with the Distributive Property, expanded form, and area models.

✔ Think•Pair•Share

Peer Collaboration Have students work in pairs. Ask one student to evaluate Leo's method and determine whether Leo used the Distributive Property correctly. Ask the other student to show the expanded form of 285 another way, and then use the Distributive Property to multiply. As students work, ask questions such as:

- *How did you break apart the factors differently from Leo?*

- *Do you think expanded form is the most efficient way to break apart factors? Explain.*

Create a class list showing the different ways students decomposed 285. To summarize, remind students that there are different ways to break apart factors, but the sum of the partial products is always the same.

Return to the Essential Question

Reread the Lesson 11 Essential Question on page 96: *How can you break apart greater factors to multiply?*

Ask volunteers to use what they learned in this lesson to answer this question. (Possible responses: I can write one factor in expanded form as a sum then multiply each addend by the other factor. Then I can add the partial products.)

Independent Practice

Concept Application

Students may work independently on these pages in the classroom or at home. They may refer to the first four pages of the lesson to revisit the instruction or to see a worked-out example.

Common Errors and **Teaching Tips** may help you support student learning either in the classroom or as a follow-up for work done at home.

Teaching Tips

Item 4

Students' work should match the area model. If a student breaks apart either 72 or 84, or both, differently, have them make an area model to illustrate the partial products.

Independent Practice

Use the Distributive Property and expanded form to multiply.

1. $5 \times 468 = 5 \times (\underline{400} + \underline{60} + 8)$

   $= (5 \times 400) + (\underline{5 \times 60}) + (\underline{5 \times 8})$

   $= \underline{2{,}000} + 300 + \underline{40}$

   $= \underline{2{,}340}$

2. $7 \times 5{,}619 = 7 \times (\underline{5{,}000} + \underline{600} + 10 + \underline{9})$

   $= (\underline{7 \times 5{,}000}) + (\underline{7 \times 600}) + (7 \times 10) + (7 \times 9)$

   $= \underline{35{,}000} + \underline{4{,}200} + \underline{70} + \underline{63}$

   $= \underline{39{,}333}$

Use the Distributive Property and area model to multiply. Label the model with the partial products to help you.

3. 28×53

	50	+	3
20	20×50 $= 1{,}000$		20×3 $= 60$
+			
8	8×50 $= 400$		8×3 $= 24$

$28 \times 53 = (\underline{20} + 8) \times (\underline{50} + 3)$

$= (20 \times \underline{50}) + (\underline{20} \times 3) + (8 \times \underline{50}) + (\underline{8} \times 3)$

$= \underline{1{,}000} + 60 + \underline{400} + 24$

$= \underline{1{,}484}$

4. 72×84 Order of addends and factors may vary.

	80	+	4
70	70×80 $= 5{,}600$		70×4 $= 280$
+			
2	2×80 $= 160$		2×4 $= 8$

$72 \times 84 = (\underline{70 + 2}) \times (\underline{80 + 4})$

$= (\underline{70 \times 80}) + (\underline{70 \times 4}) + (\underline{2 \times 80}) + (\underline{2 \times 4})$

$= \underline{5{,}600} + \underline{280} + \underline{160} + \underline{8}$

$= \underline{6{,}048}$

Writing About Math

▸ **Interpret Information** Present students with two area models: one representing the multiplication of a 3-digit number by a 1-digit number and the other representing the multiplication of two 2-digit numbers. Have students write a paragraph for each model, explaining how the model represents multiplication. Each paragraph should include how to use the model to write a corresponding multiplication equation. This activity will help students organize and express their thinking.

Circle the correct answer.

5. Each equation below shows a different method for multiplying 40×48. Which equation is incorrect?

a. $40 \times 48 = 40 \times (40 + 8)$

b. $40 \times 48 = (20 + 20) \times (40 + 8)$

c. $40 \times 48 = 10 \times 4 \times (40 + 8)$

(d.) $40 \times 48 = (2 \times 20) + (40 + 8)$

▶ **Justify your answer using words, drawings, or numbers.**

Possible justification: The equation for answer d uses a plus sign instead of a multiplication sign before $(40 + 8)$. $(2 \times 20) + (40 + 8) = 40 + 48$, not 40×48.

Match each equation with the correct product.

	Products
6. $8 \times 198 = 8 \times (100 + 90 + 8)$ __e__	a. 972
7. $3 \times 325 = 3 \times (300 + 20 + 5)$ __b__	b. 975
8. $5 \times 264 = 5 \times (200 + 60 + 4)$ __d__	c. 1,200
9. $16 \times 75 = (10 + 6) \times (70 + 5)$ __c__	d. 1,320
10. $27 \times 36 = (20 + 7) \times (30 + 6)$ __a__	e. 1,584

Estimate the product. Then multiply using the properties of operations. Show your work. Estimates and work will vary.

11. $4,462 \times 9$

Estimate: __$4,500 \times 10 - 4,500 = 40,500$__

$$4,462 \times 9 = (4,000 + 400 + 60 + 2) \times 9$$
$$= 36,000 + 3,600 + 540 + 18$$
$$= 39,000 + 600 + 400 + 140 + 18$$
$$= 40,000 + 158$$
$$= 40,158$$

Answer 40,158

12. 34×56

Estimate: __$30 \times 60 = 1,800$__

$$34 \times 56 = (30 + 4) \times (50 + 6)$$
$$= (30 \times 6) + (4 \times 6) + (30 \times 50) + (4 \times 50)$$
$$= 180 + 24 + 1,500 + 200$$
$$= 1,500 + 200 + 180 + 24$$
$$= 1,880 + 24$$
$$= 1,904$$

Answer 1,904

Unit 2 ■ Focus on Number and Operations in Base Ten **101**

Teaching Tips

Item 5
Struggling students may be overwhelmed by the answer options. Suggest that students first compute within the parentheses, and then compare both sides of the equation.

Items 6–10
Remind students to use the Distributive Property to find each product.

Item 11
Students may round 4,462 to the nearest thousand. Point out that since 4,462 is about half way between 4,000 and 5,000, a more reasonable approximation is made by rounding it to the nearest hundred.

Digital Connection

Interactive Whiteboard Provide more practice of multiplication using a whiteboard. Have students draw area models to represent the multiplication, and then have the class use the models to write the equations and find the products. Encourage students to use different colors as they draw each part of the model and have the class use the same colors as they write and solve the corresponding partial products.

Independent Practice

Common Errors

Item 16

Students may automatically think that a month is only 4 weeks, and may be confused by the store using 5 times the number of bags. Explain that the problem is not saying there are 5 weeks in one month, but rather that more bags were used some weeks than other weeks. The total number of bags used happened to be 5 times greater than the amount of bags used in the one week cited.

Teaching Tips

Item 14

Students may need help interpreting the vertical representation of the Distributive Property. Suggest they write the multiplication as an equation, showing 6 multiplied by the expanded form of 9,059. Students can match each of their partial products to the partial products shown.

Independent Practice

MP6 **13.** Compare your work for exercises 11 and 12. How is multiplying by a factor with one digit different from multiplying two factors with two digits? Answers will vary. Possible answer: When a factor has just one digit, you only have to multiply the value of each digit in the other factor once. When both factors have two digits, you have to multiply the value of each digit in one factor twice—by the ones and by the tens in the other factor.

MP2 **14.** Jenny multiplies $9,059 \times 6$ as shown below.

$$
\begin{array}{r}
9,059 \\
\times \quad 6 \\
\hline
\end{array}
$$

$6 \times 9,000$	$54,000$
6×0	0
6×50	300
6×9	$+ \quad 54$
	$54,354$

How is Jenny using the Distributive Property with this method? Explain. Answers will vary. Possible explanation: Jenny breaks apart 9,059 into the values of its digits, multiplies each value by 6, and then adds the partial products back together. It looks like she is not using the Distributive Property, because she does not write equations for the partial products and sum.

Solve the problems using the method of your choice.

MP4 **15.** The students are helping to set up chairs for their school's concert. They make 24 rows with 32 chairs in each row. How many chairs do the students set up altogether?

▸ **Show your work.**
Work may vary. Possible work:
$$24 \times 32 = (20 + 4) \times (30 + 2)$$
$$= (20 \times 30) + (4 \times 30) + (20 \times 2) + (4 \times 2)$$
$$= 600 + 120 + 40 + 8$$
$$= 768$$

Answer The students set up 768 chairs altogether.

MP2 **16.** A grocery store uses 3,452 plastic bags in one week. If the store uses 5 times as many bags for the whole month, how many bags does the store use that month?

▸ **Show your work.**
Work may vary. Possible work: $3,452 \times 5 = (3,000 + 400 + 50 + 2) \times 5$
$$= 15,000 + 2,000 + 250 + 10$$
$$= 17,260$$

Answer The store uses 17,260 bags that month.

Mathematical Practices

MP2	**Reason abstractly and quantitatively.**

Item 14: Students use properties of operations to justify a solution.

Item 16: Students analyze a problem and plan a solution.

MP4	**Model with mathematics.**

Item 15: Students relate mathematics to everyday problems.

MP6	**Attend to precision.**

Item 13: Students communicate with precision and carefully formulate a full explanation.

Independent Practice

Common Errors

Item 18

Students may make an error by multiplying the length and width of the soccer field, and then attempting to multiply that product by 36. Emphasize that the problem asks for both the width and the length in inches. To help students visualize the problem, suggest that first they draw a rectangle to represent the soccer field. Have them label the length and width. Then students can use the diagram to help them decide how to find each dimension in inches.

Teaching Tips

Item 19

Caution students about making quick conclusions. Suggest that students provide multiple examples to support their conclusion before writing an answer and justification. Students should realize that just one counterexample makes the entire statement false.

MP1 **17.** An athlete training for the Olympics eats 9,655 calories of food each day for 7 days in a row. What is the total number of calories the athlete eats that week?

> **Show your work.**
> Work may vary. Possible work:

$$
\begin{array}{r}
9{,}655 \\
\times\ \ \ \ 7 \\
\hline
35 \\
350 \\
4{,}200 \\
+6\,3{,}000 \\
\hline
6\,7{,}585
\end{array}
$$

Answer The athlete eats 67,585 calories that week.

MP4 **18.** The soccer field at the park is 48 yards wide and 75 yards long. There are 36 inches in 1 yard. What are the width and length of the field in inches?

> **Show your work.**
> Work may vary. Possible work:
> $36 \times 48 = 1{,}200 + 240 + 240 + 48$
> $\qquad\quad = 1{,}728$ inches wide
> $36 \times 75 = 2{,}100 + 150 + 420 + 30$
> $\qquad\quad = 2{,}700$ inches long

40	+	8		70	+	5
30	30 × 40	30 × 8	30	30 × 70	30 × 5
+ 6	6 × 40	6 × 8	+ 6	6 × 70	6 × 5

Answer The width of the field is 1,728 inches and the length is 2,700 inches.

MP8 **19.** Brian says that the product of two whole numbers with 2 digits each will always have 4 digits. Do you agree? Give at least one example to support your answer.

Answer No, I do not agree with Brian.

> **Justify your answer using words, drawings, or numbers.**

$$
\begin{array}{r}
99 \\
\times 99 \\
\hline
81 \\
810 \\
810 \\
+8{,}100 \\
\hline
9{,}801
\end{array}
$$

Possible justification: The smallest two-digit whole number is 10, and $10 \times 10 = 100$, which only has three digits. But the product will never have more than four digits, since the greatest two-digit whole number is 99, and $99 \times 99 = 9{,}801$.

Mathematical Practices

MP1	**Make sense of problems and persevere in solving them.**
Item 17: Students analyze and plan a solution to a problem.	
MP4	**Model with mathematics.**
Item 18: Students apply the relationship of measurement quantities.	
MP8	**Look for and express regularity in repeated reasoning.**
Item 19: Students evaluate the reasonableness of a given solution.	

Common Core Focus:

4.NBT.6 Find whole-number quotients and remainders with up to four-digit dividends and one-digit divisors, using strategies based on place value, the properties of operations, and/or the relationship between multiplication and division. Illustrate and explain the calculation by using equations, rectangular arrays, and/or area models.

OBJECTIVE

Find whole-number quotients and remainders using place value and estimation to divide.

ESSENTIAL QUESTION

Students will use basic division facts and place-value relationships to estimate quotients and to find the quotient of up to four-digit dividends and one-digit divisors.

PREREQUISITE SKILLS

Use Item E on page 339 of the Foundational Skills Handbook to review using strategies to find a quotient.

FLUENCY PRACTICE

Fluency practice is available at **sadlierconnect.com**.

Concept Development

Understand: Quotients of tens, hundreds, and thousands

■ When dividing multiples of 10, 100, or 1,000 and one-digit numbers, students can use their understanding of place value and patterns to reason that 200 ÷ 5 means partitioning 20 tens into 5 equal groups.

■ Help students realize that the number line division model also shows a relationship to multiplication.

🖉 Let volunteers draw their number lines on the board. Have them explain how they used the number line to model 2,000 ÷ 5.

Lesson 12

Divide Whole Numbers: Use Place Value

Essential Question:
How can place value and estimation help you divide?
4.NBT.6

Words to Know:
dividend
divisor
quotient
compatible numbers

In this lesson you will learn how to use place value to estimate quotients and divide greater whole numbers.

Understand: Quotients of tens, hundreds, and thousands

> An article in a magazine states that scientists estimate that lightning strikes about 200 times around the world every 5 seconds. Following this pattern, find the number of times lightning strikes each second.

To find the number of lightning strikes in 1 second, divide 200 by 5.

In this division 200 represents the dividend, the number you divide; 5 represents the divisor, the number you divide by in the division to find a quotient, the unknown number that is the answer to the problem.

$$200 \div 5 = n$$
dividend divisor quotient

Use the fact 20 ÷ 5 = 4 and the pattern of zeros to find the quotient, n.
20 ÷ 5 = 4   200 ÷ 5 = n
20 tens ÷ 5 = 4 tens ⟶ 200 ÷ 5 = 40, so n = 40

➡ Lightning strikes about 40 times each second.

You can use a number line to show a model of 200 ÷ 5 = 40.

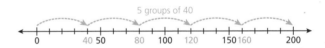

5 groups of 40

0   40 50   80   100   120   150 160   200

🖉 Continue the pattern of zeros to find 2,000 ÷ 5. How can you change the number line to model 2,000 ÷ 5?
Possible answer: You can change the number line labels to 500, 1,000, 1,500, and 2,000.

Words to Know

dividend: the number being divided

divisor: the number by which the dividend is divided

quotient: the result when two numbers are divided

Example: 200   ÷   5   =   40
                   ↑   ↑   ↑
              dividend divisor quotient

compatible numbers: numbers that are easy to compute mentally

Glossary can be found on pp. 347–350.

Understand: Place value and regrouping

Julia will drive 324 miles to go camping. If Julia drives the same number of miles each hour, how many miles should Julia drive each hour to reach the camp in 6 hours?

To find the number of miles that Julia has to drive each hour, divide 324 by 6. Use place value models to represent the miles. Divide 3 hundreds, 2 tens, 4 ones into 6 equal groups.

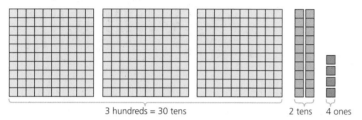

3 hundreds = 30 tens   2 tens   4 ones

To find 324 ÷ 6, find the partial quotients. Then add them.
Look at the model. Regroup 3 hundreds as 30 tens.
30 tens + 2 tens = 32 tens total to share equally in groups.

Divide 32 tens into 6 equal groups.
32 tens ÷ 6 = 5 tens in each group
and 2 tens left over.

2 tens left over is not enough
to make 6 groups of ten.

Regroup the 2 left over tens as 20 ones.
20 ones + 4 ones = 24 ones to share

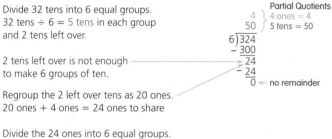

Divide the 24 ones into 6 equal groups.
24 ones ÷ 6 = 4 ones in each group.

Add the partial quotients.
324 ÷ 6 = 50 + 4 = 54

➡ Julia should drive 54 miles each hour to reach the camp in 6 hours.

Understand: Place value and regrouping

■ In this presentation, students learn to decompose the dividend into its base-ten units. Then starting with the largest unit, they find the quotient unit by unit, recording each partial quotient.

■ Some students may struggle with regrouping as they complete the division algorithm. Guide students as they apply their understanding of place value to regroup.

Support English Language Learners

Review the mathematical terms associated with division: *dividend, divisor,* and *quotient.* Have students write 12 ÷ 3 = 4 on one side of an index card. Provide support as they label each part of the equation with the correct term. On the other side of the card, have students write and label $3\overline{)12}$. Encourage students to refer to this card as needed.

Point out that the root word of the term *partial quotient* is "part." Encourage students to recall how partial products were used in Lesson 10. Relate their understanding of partial products to the partial quotients. Have students use the word *part* to describe how partial quotients are used in division.

Connect: **What you know about regrouping to divide whole numbers into equal groups** Use this page to help students strengthen their understanding of regrouping and dividing into equal groups.

■ When dividing a multi-digit number, students will start by finding the greatest multiple of the divisor that is less than the dividend. When dividing 1,217 by 4, the greatest multiple of 4 less than 1,217 is 4 × 300 = 1,200. Students can think in terms of putting objects in groups. For example, when 1,200 batteries are put into groups of 4, the largest hundreds number of groups that can be made is 300.

■ For Steps 1 and 2, be sure students understand how to regroup.

■ Dividing a multi-digit number often results in a remainder. Have students explain the meaning of the remainder in this situation.

■ There will be students who always want to use rounding to estimate. When estimating quotients, rounding is not always the best method.

Lesson 12   Divide Whole Numbers: Use Place Value

Guided Instruction

Connect: **What you know about regrouping to divide whole numbers into equal groups**

A television manufacturer puts 4 batteries in each remote controller. The manufacturer has 1,217 batteries. How many remote controllers can the manufacturer fill with batteries?

To find the number of remote controllers, divide 1 thousand, 2 hundreds, 1 ten, 7 ones by 4.   1,217 ÷ 4

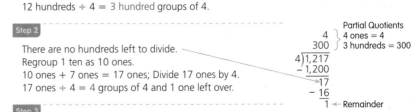

1 thousand   2 hundreds   1 ten 7 ones

Step 1

Regroup 1 thousand as 10 hundreds.
10 hundreds + 2 hundreds
= 12 hundreds
Divide 12 hundreds by 4.
12 hundreds ÷ 4 = 3 hundred groups of 4.

Step 2

There are no hundreds left to divide.
Regroup 1 ten as 10 ones.
10 ones + 7 ones = 17 ones; Divide 17 ones by 4.
17 ones ÷ 4 = 4 groups of 4 and 1 one left over.

Partial Quotients
4 ⎱ 4 ones = 4
300 ⎰ 3 hundreds = 300

$$4\overline{)1{,}217}$$
$$-\ 1{,}200$$
$$\quad\quad 17$$
$$-\ \ \ 16$$
$$\quad\quad\ 1 \leftarrow \text{Remainder}$$

Step 3

Add the partial quotients.
1,217 ÷ 4 = 304 groups of 4 batteries and 1 battery left over.

The 1 battery left over does not make another group of 4.

1217 ÷ 4 = 304 R1

Remember!
A remainder (R) is the amount left over after dividing.

Step 4

You can estimate to make sure that the answer is reasonable. Use a number that is close to 1,217 and easy to divide by 4.

Estimate   1,200 ÷ 4 = 300; about 300 groups
Answer   1,217 ÷ 4 = 304 R1

The estimate 300 is close to 304 R1, so 304 R1 is a reasonable answer.

1,200 and 4 are compatible numbers. Compatible numbers are those that are easy to compute mentally.

➡ The manufacturer can fill 304 remote controllers with 1,216 batteries.

106 Unit 2 ■ Focus on Number and Operations in Base Ten

Math-to-Math Connection

Unit Rates Students will learn to determine unit rates in later grades. A *rate* compares two different quantities such as reading 20 pages in 2 hours. A *unit rate* tells how many pages are read in 1 hour. There are many unit rates that are used in real life such as miles per hour, miles per gallon, cost per foot, and cost per pound.

Present a situation such as a car trip of 450 miles that takes 9 hours. Ask students to determine the average distance traveled in 1 hour. Discuss how division can be used to solve this problem. Have students use place value and/or models to explain how they found the answer.

Lesson 12

Guided Practice

Complete exercises 1 and 2 to solve the problem. Show your work.

Arly's Movie Triplex has a total of 825 seats in 3 theaters that are the same size. How many seats are in each theater?

1. Estimate the number of seats in each theater. Use compatible numbers.

   Estimate 825 ÷ 3. _750 ÷ 3 = 250_ Estimates may vary.

2. Divide 825 to find the actual quotient.
   825 = 8 hundreds + 2 tens + 5 ones

   a. Divide the hundreds. 8 hundreds ÷ 3

   There are 3 groups of __2__ hundreds in 825.

   __6__ hundreds represent seats shared equally among

   the 3 theaters. __2__ hundreds are left over.

   b. Regroup the hundreds that are left over.

   2 hundreds = __20__ tens

   __20__ tens + 2 tens = __22__ tens

   c. Divide the tens.

   There are 3 groups of __7__ tens in 22 tens.

   __21__ tens are shared equally among the 3 theaters.

   __1__ ten is left over.

   d. Regroup the 1 ten left over with the 5 ones.

   1 ten = __10__ ones

   __10__ ones + __5__ ones = __15__ ones to share equally among the 3 theaters.

   e. 15 ones = 3 groups of __5__ ones.
   There are 275 seats in each theater.

$$
\begin{array}{r}
5 \\
70 \\
200
\end{array}\Big\} 275
$$

$$
\begin{array}{r}
3\overline{)825} \\
-\ 600 \\
\hline
225 \\
-\ 210 \\
\hline
15 \\
-\ 15 \\
\hline
0
\end{array}
$$

Think • Pair • Share

MP7   3. Is the actual quotient close to the estimated quotient? Explain why it is helpful to estimate before solving the problem. Yes, the actual quotient 275 is close to the estimate 250. It is helpful to estimate first so that you have a number to compare the actual quotient with to determine if the actual quotient is reasonable.

Unit 2 ■ Focus on Number and Operations in Base Ten   **107**

Mathematical Practices

Mathematical Practice Standards underline the teaching and understanding of all concepts and skills presented. The emphasis of specific practices is noted throughout the guided and independent practice of this lesson.

MP7	**Look for and make use of structure.**

Item 3: Students share reasoning with others.

Observational Assessment

Use page 107 to assess whether students understand how to divide multi-digit numbers using place value relationships and regrouping. Note those students who need additional instruction and practice with regrouping or finding partial quotients.

Think•Pair•Share

Peer Collaboration As a class, discuss the importance of estimating before finding the actual answer. To further the discussion, ask questions such as:

- *Could there be more than one pair of compatible numbers that could be used to estimate an answer?*

- *What are some ways to determine if an answer is reasonable or unreasonable?*

To summarize, remind students there is more than one way to estimate a quotient. In order to get a good estimate, however, it is important to use numbers that are close to the actual numbers in the division.

Return to the Essential Question

Reread the Lesson 12 Essential Question on page 104: *How can place value and estimation help you divide?*

Ask volunteers to use what they learned in this lesson to answer this question. (Possible responses: I can use place value to find partial quotients and then add the partial quotients to find the quotient. I can use estimation to make sure that my answer is reasonable.)

Independent Practice

Concept Application

Students may work independently on these pages in the classroom or at home. They may refer to the first four pages of the lesson to revisit the instruction or to see a worked-out example.

Common Errors and **Teaching Tips** may help you support student learning either in the classroom or as a follow-up for work done at home.

Teaching Tips

Items 1–6

It may be helpful for some students to write the basic division fact first and then use patterns to find the quotient.

Items 7–16

Students should rewrite the problems using the division algorithm. Some students may benefit by using grid paper to help align the digits as they divide.

Independent Practice

Use division patterns with zeros to find each quotient.

1. 500 ÷ 5 =
   __1__ __0__ __0__

2. 6,000 ÷ 3 =
   __2__ __0__ __0__ __0__

3. 200 ÷ 4 =
   __5__ __0__

4. 2,400 ÷ 8 =
   __300__

5. 1,800 ÷ 9 =
   __200__

6. 4,000 ÷ 5 =
   __800__

Find each quotient. You can use a model to help.

7. 620 ÷ 5 =
   __124__

8. 337 ÷ 9 =
   __37__ R __4__

9. 2,908 ÷ 4 =
   __727__

10. 2,909 ÷ 4 =
    __727__ R __1__

11. 197 ÷ 8 =
    __24__ R __5__

12. 508 ÷ 5 =
    __101__ R __3__

13. 1,344 ÷ 6 =
    __224__

14. 7,249 ÷ 8 =
    __906__ R __1__

15. 5,320 ÷ 7 =
    __760__

16. 4,545 ÷ 3 =
    __1515__

Writing About Math

◗ · **Write an Informative Text** Ask students to write a paragraph about how to interpret a remainder. Students should provide examples of when a remainder must be considered in the solution and when it can be ignored. Other examples might include when the remainder is the solution. Remind students to consider whether quantities must be whole numbers such as people or objects, and whether quantities do not have to be whole numbers such as measurements.

Independent Practice

Estimate each quotient. Use compatible numbers. Estimates may vary.

17. $71 \div 3$

Estimate: ___$75 \div 3 = 25$___

18. $409 \div 8$

Estimate: ___$400 \div 8 = 50$___

19. $3,514 \div 9$

Estimate: ___$3,600 \div 9 = 400$___

20. $5,247 \div 5$

Estimate: ___$5,000 \div 5 = 1,000$___

Divide. Then estimate to find if your quotient is reasonable. Show your work. Estimates and work will vary.

21. $421 \div 3 =$ ___140 R1___

Estimate: ___$330 \div 3 = 110$;___

___$90 \div 3 = 30$; $110 + 30 = 140$___

Is your quotient reasonable?

_____

22. $4,298 \div 7$ ___614___

Estimate: ___$4,200 \div 7 = 600$___

_____

Is your quotient reasonable?

_____

Circle the correct answer.

23. Which quotient below has a remainder?

(**a.**) $248 \div 9$

b. $700 \div 4$

c. $2,905 \div 5$

d. $6,332 \div 4$

Common Errors

Item 17

Some students may not understand the difference between using rounding and using compatible numbers to estimate. Remind students that compatible numbers are numbers that are close to the actual numbers but result in a whole-number quotient. Watch for students who have difficulty determining appropriate compatible numbers and offer help as needed.

Teaching Tips

Item 23

Remind students to look for answer choices that can be eliminated. For example, answer choice **c.** can be eliminated because any number that is divisible by 5 ends in a 0 or 5.

Digital Connection

Interactive Whiteboard Have students work in pairs to complete divisions on a whiteboard. One student can model the division using place value models while the partner uses the division algorithm, writing partial quotients for each step. Encourage students to work collaboratively as they work through the solutions. If possible, have the colors of the models match the color of the pens when writing out the partial quotients.

Teaching Tips

Item 24
This problem requires students to interpret the remainder. Students can use multiplication to check their answers and to help them understand why Jordan will have $2 left over.

Item 25
Students should be better able to identify the errors if they work through the division themselves.

Item 26
Remind students to interpret the remainder before writing their final answer.

Lesson 12 **Divide Whole Numbers: Use Place Value**

Independent Practice

MP6 **24.** A music store is selling all of its CDs for $9 each. Jordan has a gift card worth $110. He divides $110 by 9 correctly, and says that he can buy 12 R2 CDs with the gift card. Why is Jordan's statement incorrect?
Possible answer: Jordan should not include the remainder. He can only buy 12 CDs, and then he will have $2 left over.

MP5 **25.** Lucy divides 7,062 by 8 as shown at the right. $7,062 \div 8 = 95$ R2
The correct quotient is 882 R6. What mistakes might Lucy have made? Explain at least two mistakes.
Answers will vary. Possible explanation: Lucy did not estimate the quotient first, otherwise she would have known that the answer is in the hundreds. She also left out the 0 hundreds in 7,062, and divided 76 tens by 8 instead of dividing 70 hundreds by 8.

Solve the problems.

MP2 **26.** A garden has 4 rain barrels. When the 4 barrels are full, they hold 255 gallons of rain water altogether. If all 4 barrels are the same size, how many gallons of rain water does each barrel hold?

▮▮▮▸ **Show your work.**
Work may vary. Possible work:
$255 \div 4 = 63$ R3

Answer Each barrel holds a little less than 64 gallons of water.

MP1 **27.** A farm offers horseback trail rides on weekends. The riding trail is 3 miles long. If the horses covered 1,221 miles altogether in one month, how many trail rides were taken at the farm?

▮▮▮▸ **Show your work.**
Work may vary.

Answer 407 trail rides were taken in one month.

Mathematical Practices

MP1	**Make sense of problems and persevere in solving them.**
Item 27: Students analyze a word problem and plan a solution.	
MP2	**Reason abstractly and quantitatively.**
Item 26: Students write and solve an equation that represents a problem.	
MP5	**Use appropriate tools strategically.**
Item 25: Students use paper and pencil to detect errors in computation.	
MP6	**Attend to precision.**
Item 24: Students carefully formulate a full explanation.	

MORE ONLINE sadlierconnect.com

Lesson 12

Independent Practice

MP2 **28.** A statue at an art museum is 8 times as old as a famous painting. If the statue is 2,376 years old, how old is the painting?

▪ **Show your work.**
Work may vary.

Answer The painting is 297 years old.

MP1 **29.** The Water Warehouse store sells 6,093 bottles of water on Friday. The bottles come in packs of 9 bottles each. On Monday, the store sells 215 fewer packs of water than it sells on Friday. How many packs of water does the store sell on Monday?

▪ **Show your work.**
Work may vary. Possible work:
$6,093 \div 9 = 677$

$$\begin{array}{r} 677 \\ -215 \\ \hline 462 \end{array}$$

Answer The store sells 462 packs of water on Monday.

MP2 **30.** Carmen knows that when you use an area model, you multiply the side lengths to find the area. She says that if the area of the rectangle is 1,800 square feet, then its length must be 200 feet. Is Carmen correct?

9 feet | area = 1,800 square feet | ?

Answer Yes, Carmen is correct.

▪ **Justify your answer using words, drawings, or numbers.**
Possible justification: You can divide the area of any rectangle by its width to find its length. $1,800 \div 9 = 200$, so the length of the rectangle is 200 feet.

MP6 **31.** The bowling league allows no more than 5 people on a team. Is it possible to have 28 teams if there are 142 people?

Answer No, it is not possible.

▪ **Justify your answer using words, drawings, or numbers.**
Possible justification: The maximum number of people with 28 teams is $5 \times 28 = 140$; 140 people. Since no more than 5 people can be on each team, there should be 1 more team for the 2 extra people. So the total number of teams should be 29, not 28.

Unit 2 ▪ Focus on Number and Operations in Base Ten **111**

Teaching Tips

Item 29
Students who struggle with reading comprehension may struggle with this problem. Help students organize the information before solving the problem.

Item 30
Remind students of methods they can use to efficiently and accurately solve problems. Point out that there is more than one way to find the length of the longer side.

Mathematical Practices

MP1	**Make sense of problems and persevere in solving them.**

Item 29: Students analyze and solve a multistep problem.

MP2	**Reason abstractly and quantitatively.**

Item 28: Students decontextualize and solve a word problem.

Item 30: Students attend to the meaning of quantities to justify a solution.

MP6	**Attend to precision.**

Item 31: Students communicate their own reasoning with precision.

Common Core Focus:

4.NBT.6 Find whole-number quotients and remainders with up to four-digit dividends and one-digit divisors, using strategies based on place value, the properties of operations, and/or the relationship between multiplication and division. Illustrate and explain the calculation by using equations, rectangular arrays, and/or area models.

OBJECTIVE

Use properties and the relationship between multiplication and division to divide numbers.

ESSENTIAL QUESTION

In Lesson 11, students used properties of operations to multiply. Now, they will apply the properties to division of multi-digit numbers.

PREREQUISITE SKILLS

Use Item E on page 339 of the Foundational Skills Handbook to review using arrays and related multiplication facts to find a quotient.

FLUENCY PRACTICE

Fluency practice is available at **sadlierconnect.com**.

Concept Development

Understand: Division and multiples of the divisor

■ Be sure students understand that a *multiple* is the product of a given number and another whole number. When dividing a multi-digit number, start by finding the greatest multiple of the divisor that is less than the dividend.

■ Discuss similarities and differences between multiplication and division area models.

✏️ Before students answer this question, encourage them to break apart 765 into smaller multiples of 9.

Lesson 13 — Divide Whole Numbers: Use Properties of Operations

Essential Question: How can breaking apart whole numbers make them easier to divide? 4.NBT.6

Guided Instruction

In this lesson you will learn how to divide using properties and the relationship between multiplication and division.

Understand: Division and multiples of the divisor

> There are 9 innings in a baseball game. Last season Tom pitched all complete games. If he pitched 765 innings, how many games did Tom pitch last season?

To find how many games Tom pitched, divide the number of games he pitched by the number of innings in a game. You can use an area model to represent 765 divided by 9. In the area model at the right, the quotient $765 \div 9$ is the unknown side length.

Remember! Use basic facts and patterns with 0 to find the products.

Find a multiple of 9 that is close to but not greater than 765.

$9 \times 100 = 900 \qquad 9 \times 90 = 810 \qquad 9 \times 80 = 720$

720 is easy to divide: $720 \div 9 = 80$.

80 is part of the unknown side length of the area model. Show 720 as the area of the 9×80 region. Subtract this area from 765:
$765 - 720 = 45$.
Draw another region to show 45 as the remaining area. Divide by 9 to find the other part of the unknown side length.

45 is a multiple of 9. Divide to find the side length of the new region: $45 \div 9 = 5$.
Subtract: $45 - 45 = 0$. There is nothing left over.
Look at the completed model of $765 \div 9$ below.

	80	+	5
9	720		45

To find the quotient, add the side lengths you found.
$80 + 5 = 85$

➡️ Tom pitched 85 games last season.

✏️ What happens if you break 765 into smaller multiples of 9?
Possible answer: If you use smaller multiples, you have more partial quotients and then it is not as easy to divide.

Support English Language Learners

Some students may confuse the terms *dividend* and *divisor* as they work through the lesson. Review these terms with students.

Write *dividend* and *divisor* on the board. First say each term aloud and have students repeat. Next, have students look up the meaning and use of the suffix *–or*. This suffix refers to one that "does" something. Ask students to relate this meaning to *divisor* as the number that divides, or "does the dividing". At this point, say *The dividend gets divided by the divisor.* Have students repeat the sentence.

Finally, write various division expressions on the board and add labels for each part of the division expression. Ask for volunteers to complete the label for each part of the expression.

Lesson 13

Guided Instruction

Understand: Division and the Distributive Property

A new high-speed train in Japan will travel 2,280 feet in 5 seconds. How many feet will the high-speed train travel in 1 second?

You can break apart a dividend to divide. The Distributive Property states that to divide a sum by a number, you can divide each addend of the sum by that number and add the partial quotients.

Remember!
The dividend is the number you divide.

To find how many feet the train will travel in 1 second, divide 2,280 by 5. Break apart 2,280.

Choose a hundreds number that when multiplied by 5 would be close to 2,280.
$5 \times 400 = 2,000$

Subtract.

Next choose a tens number that when multiplied by 5 would be close to 280.

$5 \times 50 = 250$. Subtract.

Now choose a ones number that when multiplied by 5 would be close to 30.

$5 \times 6 = 30$. Subtract.

$$
\begin{array}{r}
2,280 \\
-2,000 \leftarrow 5 \times 400 \\
\hline
280 \\
-250 \leftarrow 5 \times 50 \\
\hline
30 \\
-30 \leftarrow 5 \times 6 \\
\hline
0
\end{array}
$$

Remember!
The divisor is the number you divide by in a division problem.

Write 2,280 as a sum of $2,000 + 250 + 30$.

You can distribute the divisor, 5, the same way you distributed a factor when using the Distributive Property of multiplication.

When dividing 2,280, each addend is divided by 5. Add these partial quotients to find the answer.

$$
\begin{aligned}
2,280 \div 5 &= (2,000 \div 5) + (250 \div 5) + (30 \div 5) \\
&= 400 + 50 + 6 \leftarrow \text{partial quotients} \\
&= 456
\end{aligned}
$$

➡ The high-speed train will travel 456 feet in 1 second.

Unit 2 ■ Focus on Number and Operations in Base Ten **113**

Understand: Division and the Distributive Property

■ Make sure students understand that using the Distributive Property enables them to break apart a number by place value and then divide the parts.

■ In this presentation, each step of the calculation results in a partial answer. These partial answers are added to find the quotient.

■ Remind students that the Distributive Property is used to multiply each place value by the same factor. Since division is the inverse operation, they divide each place value by the same divisor to find the partial quotients.

■ After working through this page with students, have students compare the partial quotients in the equation to the factors that were used to find multiples of 5. Students should notice they are the same.

Math-to-Math Connection

Distance Formula In later grades, students will learn the distance formula: *rate* × *time* = *distance*. Since multiplication and division are inverse operations, the formula can be restated as *distance* ÷ *time* = *rate* or *distance* ÷ *rate* = *time*.

Present this problem: If a person rides a bicycle at a constant rate of 7 miles per hour, how many hours would it take to ride 959 miles? (137 hours) If the person rides for 7 hours a day, about how many days would it take to ride 959 miles? Point out that the solution will be an estimate, using the compatible number 140 hours. Dividing the compatible number 140 by 7 results in about 20 days to ride 959 miles.

Connect: Multiples and partial quotients Use this page to help students strengthen their understanding of how to find quotients using multiples, partial quotients, and the Distributive Property.

■ This presentation also includes an area model. Make sure students understand how the area model relates to the division 2,207 ÷ 3.

■ Remind students that when a division problem has a remainder, it important to interpret the remainder in the context of the situation.

■ Have students explain how to check a quotient that includes a remainder. Students should recognize that they need to add the remainder to the product of the quotient and divisor.

▧▧▧▶ Students should realize that the rectangle represents complete parts of the whole. Because the remaining 2 steps cannot be evenly divided into 3 parts, they cannot be shown in the model.

Guided Instruction

Connect: Multiples and partial quotients

> Marco uses a pedometer to count the steps he takes. He takes 2,207 steps in 3 hours. If he takes the same number of steps each hour, how many steps does Marco take in one hour?

To find how many steps Marco takes in one hour, divide 2,207 by 3. Use the Distributive Property to find 2,207 ÷ 3.

Break apart 2,207. Divide each addend by 3 and add the partial products. Use basic facts and patterns with 0.

$3 \times 800 = 2,400 \qquad 3 \times 700 = 2,100 \qquad 3 \times 6 = 1,800$

You can use 2,100 as the first addend.
Find the first partial quotient:
$2,100 \div 3 = 700$

Subtract. Find the other partial products.
You can record your work either way shown.

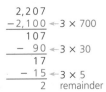

```
   2,207
 − 2,100  ← 3 × 700
     107
   −  90  ← 3 × 30
      17
   −  15  ← 3 × 5
       2   remainder
```

Look at the area model.
Add the partial quotients to find 2,205 ÷ 3.

$2205 \div 3 = (2,100 \div 3) + (90 \div 3) + (15 \div 3)$ ← Distributive Property of Division
$\qquad\quad = (700 + 30 + 5)$
$\qquad\quad = 735$

Note that the quotient for the full quantity has a remainder of 2.
$2,207 \div 3 = 735 \text{ R2}$
$735 \text{ R2} \longrightarrow (2,100 \div 3) + (90 \div 3) + (15 \div 3) + 2$

Since Marco takes 1 extra step for 2 of the 3 hours, increase the quotient by 1 to include the remainder 2 as part of your answer.

▶ Marco takes about 736 steps in one hour.

▧▧▧▶ Look at the area model again. Why is the remainder not shown as part of the rectangle? The remainder 2, is not a side length of the rectangle.

Math-to-Money Connection

Budgets Discuss the meaning of the word *budget*. Tell students that some parts of a budget may include monthly expenses, while other parts include weekly expenses. Have the class brainstorm a list of weekly expenses with estimated values, such as $20 for lunch, $25 for transportation, $5 for pet food, and $30 for entertainment.

In small groups, have students roll a number cube three times to find the total amount of money their group has each month. The first roll is the hundreds place, the second roll is the tens place, and the third roll is the ones place. Then have each group divide their number by 4 weeks to calculate and explain whether they will have enough money each week to meet their budget.

Guided Practice

Complete each area model. Write the unknown side lengths to find the partial quotients. Then add to find the quotient.

1.

	60	+	5
5	300		25

$325 \div 5 = \underline{60} + \underline{5}$

$ = \underline{65}$

2.

	100	+	30	+	8
4	400		120		32

$552 \div 4 = \underline{100} + \underline{30} + \underline{8}$

$ = \underline{138}$

Complete each area model. Then write the quotient below.

3.

	100	+	9
8	800		72

$872 \div 8 = \underline{109}$

4.

	200	+	80	+	2
6	1,200		480		12

$1,692 \div 6 = \underline{282}$

Complete each division.

5. $496 \div 2 = (\underline{400} \div 2) + (80 \div 2) + (\underline{16} \div 2)$

$ = 200 + 40 + 8$

$ = \underline{248}$

6. $2,189 \div 7 = \underline{312\ R5}$

```
  2,189
 −2,100  ← 7 × 300
     89
   − 70  ← 7 × 10
     19
   − 14  ← 7 × 2
      5
```

🙌 Think•Pair•Share

MP2

7. A snack company has 1,102 granola bars to give out as samples. A sample pack has 4 bars. Use the Distributive Property to find out how many sample packs the company can make. Then explain your answer.

$1,102 \div 4 = (1,000 \div 4) + (100 \div 4) + 2$

$ = (250) + (25) + 2$

$ = 275 + 2; 1,102 \div 4 = 275\ R2.$

Possible explanation: The company can make 275 full packs and there will be 2 granola bars left over.

Observational Assessment

Use page 115 to assess whether students are able to find the quotients using area models and partial quotients. Take note of those students who struggle to use the Distributive Property when dividing.

🙌 Think•Pair•Share

Peer Collaboration After pairs of students solve the problem, explain that the snack company has decided it does not want any granola bars left over. Have partners work together to find how many granola bars would be in each new sample pack and how many sample packs the company could make. If needed, ask:

- *What is the greatest common factor of 4 and 2?*

- *How can you find the total number of 2-bar sample packs without dividing again?*

Return to the Essential Question

Reread the Lesson 13 Essential Question on page 112: *How can breaking apart whole numbers make them easier to divide?*

Ask volunteers to use what they learned in this lesson to answer this question. (Possible response: By breaking apart numbers, you make the numbers easier to work with so that you can use place value, properties, and multiplication to more easily find the quotient.)

Invite volunteers to express their ideas about the Distributive Property and division in their own words.

Mathematical Practices

Mathematical Practice Standards underline the teaching and understanding of all concepts and skills presented. The emphasis of specific practices is noted throughout the guided and independent practice of this lesson.

MP2 **Reason abstractly and quantitatively.**

Item 7: Students use properties of operations to represent problems using symbols.

Concept Application

Students may work independently on these pages in the classroom or at home. They may refer to the first four pages of the lesson to revisit the instruction or to see a worked-out example.

Common Errors and **Teaching Tips** may help you support student learning either in the classroom or as a follow-up for work done at home.

Teaching Tips

Items 1–2

It may be helpful for some students to complete the area model first, and then complete the equation. Students can then use the area model to divide using the Distributive Property.

Items 3–5

Some students may benefit by subtracting the given multiple from the dividend first, and then apply basic division facts to separate the remaining number into place values.

Independent Practice

Use the area model and the Distributive Property to divide. Complete the model and equations.

1. $434 \div 7$

	60	+	2
7	420		14

$434 \div 7 = (\underline{420} \div 7) + (\underline{14} \div 7)$

$\qquad = \underline{60} + \underline{2}$

$\qquad = \underline{62}$

2. $3,605 \div 5$

	700	+ 20	+ 1
5	3,500	100	5

$3,605 \div 5 = (\underline{3,500 \div 5}) + (\underline{100 \div 5}) + (\underline{5 \div 5})$

$\qquad = \underline{700} + \underline{20} + \underline{1}$

$\qquad = \underline{721}$

Use the Distributive Property to divide. Complete the equation to represent the problem. Then solve.

3. $476 \div 2 = (\underline{400 \div 2}) + (60 \div 2) + (\underline{16 \div 2})$

$\qquad = \underline{200} + \underline{30} + 8$

$\qquad = \underline{238}$

4. $728 \div 4 = (\underline{400 \div 4}) + (\underline{320 \div 4}) + (8 \div 4)$

$\qquad = \underline{100} + 80 + \underline{2}$

$\qquad = \underline{182}$

5. $1,932 \div 6 = (\underline{1,800 \div 6}) + (120 \div 6) + (\underline{12 \div 6})$

$\qquad = 300 + \underline{20} + \underline{2}$

$\qquad = \underline{322}$

Writing About Math

▪ **Write an Opinion Text** Ask students to write a paragraph giving their opinion about which multi-digit division strategy is most helpful to them when solving problems. Have students provide reasons that support their opinion and use linking words such as *for instance, in order,* and *in addition* when writing their paragraph.

Ask volunteers to read their paragraphs aloud. Remind students that these are opinion paragraphs, so there is no right or wrong answer.

Lesson 13

Independent Practice

Divide. Show the partial quotients. Use a strategy that works for you. Partial quotients and work may vary.

6. $830 \div 2 = \underline{415}$

$$830 \div 2 = (800 \div 2) + (20 \div 2) + (10 \div 2)$$
$$= 400 + 10 + 5$$
$$= 415$$

7. $675 \div 3 = \underline{225}$

$$
\begin{array}{r}
675 \\
-600 \leftarrow 3 \times 200 \\
\hline
75 \\
-60 \leftarrow 3 \times 20 \\
\hline
15 \\
-15 \leftarrow 3 \times 5 \\
\hline
0
\end{array}
$$

8. $2{,}072 \div 4 = \underline{518}$

$$
\begin{array}{r}
2{,}072 \\
-2{,}000 \leftarrow 4 \times 500 \\
\hline
72 \\
-40 \leftarrow 4 \times 10 \\
\hline
32 \\
-32 \leftarrow 4 \times 8 \\
\hline
0
\end{array}
$$

9. $1{,}968 \div 6 = \underline{328}$

	300	+ 20	+ 8
6	1,800	120	48

Match each of the following.

10. $(800 \div 4) + (28 \div 4)$ __d__   **a.** $855 \div 5$

11. $(5 \times 100) + (5 \times 30) + (5 \times 2) + 1$ __b__   **b.** $661 \div 5$

12. $(500 \div 5) + (300 \div 5) + (55 \div 5)$ __a__   **c.** $774 \div 4$

13. $(4 \times 100) + (4 \times 90) + (4 \times 3) + 2$ __c__   **d.** $828 \div 4$

Unit 2 ■ Focus on Number and Operations in Base Ten **117**

Teaching Tips

Items 6-9
Monitor students closely as they work through these exercises. If students are struggling with their current strategy, encourage them to try a different strategy.

Items 10-13
It might help students to differentiate between the exercises that show the Distributive Property (exercises 10 and 12) and those that show partial products (exercises 11 and 13).

Digital Connection

Internet Resources Use a search engine to find videos about the partial quotients method. Select a few videos that you feel are good examples to show to students. Then have students work in small groups to act out a video showing how to divide by using the partial quotients method.

Independent Practice

Common Errors

Item 17

Students may disregard the remainder and say that Ben can save just 128 songs on each CD. Remind students to interpret the remainder in the context of the problem. Ben wants to save all of his songs, so 769 songs must be accounted for in the answer.

Independent Practice

MP7 14. Look at exercises 10–13. Which of the quotients have a remainder? Explain how you know. Use the words *dividend*, *divisor*, and *addend* in your answer.
Answers will vary. Possible answer: Exercises 11 and 13 have a remainder. Both problems are represented with the dividend, and the divisor is shown as a factor multiplying each addend except for the remainder. This is because the remainder is not a multiple of the divisor.

MP8 15. To divide 144 by 3, Pranav subtracts 3 from 144 until he has a difference of 0. Then he counts the number of times he subtracted 3. How can Pranav divide more efficiently? Use your method to find the quotient.
Answers will vary. Possible answer: Pranav can subtract multiples of 3 instead of subtracting single 3s over and over. For example, $40 \times 3 = 120$ so there are 40 groups of 3 in 120. That leaves 24, and since $8 \times 3 = 24$ there are 8 groups of 3 in 24. $40 + 8 = 48$ groups of 3 altogether, so $144 \div 3 = 48$.

Solve the problems. You may use any method to divide.

MP4 16. Laura joins a walkathon to help raise money for a charity. The walkathon distance is 80 blocks. If you assume that 80 blocks is the same as 5 miles, how many blocks are in 1 mile?

▸ **Show your work.** Work may vary. Possible work:

	10	+	6	$10 + 6 = 16$
5	50		30	

Answer If 80 blocks is the same as 5 miles, then there are 16 blocks in 1 mile.

MP2 17. Ben has 769 songs on his computer that he wants to save on CDs. He has 6 blank CDs and wants to save the same number of songs on each CD. How many songs can Ben save on each CD?

▸ **Show your work.** Work may vary. Possible work:
$100 + 20 + 8 = 128$, with 1 left over

```
   7 6 9
 - 6 0 0  ← 6 × 100
   1 6 9
 - 1 2 0  ← 6 × 20
     4 9
 -   4 8  ← 6 × 8
       1
```

Answer Ben can save 128 songs on each of 5 CDs and 129 songs on 1 CD.

Mathematical Practices

MP2	**Reason abstractly and quantitatively.**
Item 17: Students represent problems using symbols and properties.	
MP4	**Model with mathematics.**
Item 16: Students represent a word problem and interpret the solution.	
MP7	**Look for and make use of structure.**
Item 14: Students identify a pattern between the divisor and the dividend.	
MP8	**Look for and express regularity in repeated reasoning.**
Item 15: Students use patterns to relate operations.	

Lesson 13

Independent Practice

MP8 **18.** A 7-night vacation package costs $2,583 altogether. What is the cost for each night?

Show your work. Work may vary. Possible work:

$300 + 60 + 9 = 369$

Answer The cost for each night is $369.

```
  2,583
 -2,100  ←7 × 300
    483
  -  420  ←7 × 60
     63
  -   63  ←7 × 9
      0
```

MP2 **19.** Yuna says that 9 times as many people are at the football game as at the basketball game. The ticket office sold 7,052 tickets to the football game. If Yuna is correct, about how many people are at the basketball game?

Show your work. Work may vary. Possible work:

$7,052 \div 9 = 783 \text{ R5}$

Answer There are about 783 people at the basketball game.

```
       783
   9)7,052
    - 63↓
       75
     - 72
       32
     - 27
        5
```

MP4 **20.** Carrie divides 4,981 by 4 and finds the correct quotient, 1,245 R1. Then she represents the problem with the equation below.

$4,981 \div 4 = (4,400 \div 4) + (400 \div 4) + (160 \div 4) + (20 \div 4) + 1$

Is Carrie's equation correct?

Answer No, Carrie's equation is not correct.

Justify your answer using words, drawings, or numbers.
Possible justification: 1,246 is not exactly the same as 1,245 R1, because if you multiply it by 4 the product is greater than the dividend, 4,981.

```
 1,100    1,246
   100  ×     4
    40       24
     5      160
     1      800
 1,246   +4,000
          4,984
```

MP3 **21.** Sean uses place value to find $5,672 \div 8$ with the method shown at the right. He says that he also uses the Distributive Property with this method. Do you agree with Sean?

```
       709
   8)5,672
   - 5 6↓↓
      072
    -  72
        0
```

$\begin{array}{r} 709 \\ 5 \\ + \quad 1 \\ \hline 1,246 \end{array}$

Answer Yes, Sean is correct.

Justify your answer using words, drawings, or numbers.
Possible justification: The Distributive Property lets you break apart a number and multiply or divide its parts instead of the number itself. Sean is breaking up the dividend into 5,600 and 72 and dividing each by 8 separately. This method does not show the partial quotients being added together.

Common Errors

Item 21

Some students may disagree with Sean because the Distributive Property is used within the algorithm. Replacing the green arrows with 0s may help students better visualize how the Distributive Property is being applied.

Teaching Tips

Items 18–19

If students struggle with finding the quotients, encourage them to draw area models.

Return to the

Remind students to return to the Progress Check self-assessment, page 53, to check off additional items they have mastered during the unit.

Mathematical Practices

MP2	**Reason abstractly and quantitatively.**

Item 19: Students use properties of operations to solve a problem.

MP3	**Construct viable arguments and critique the reasoning of others.**

Item 21: Students explain an approach to a problem.

MP4	**Model with mathematics.**

Item 20: Students interpret the solution in the context of a situation.

MP8	**Look for and express regularity in repeated reasoning.**

Item 18: Students obtain fluency using patterns.

The Common Core Review covers all the standards presented in the unit. Use it to assess your students' mastery of the unit's concepts and skills.

Depth of Knowledge

The depth of knowledge is a ranking of the content complexity of assessment items based on Webb's Depth of Knowledge (DOK) levels. The levels increase in complexity as shown below.

Level 1: Recall and Reproduction
Level 2: Basic Skills and Concepts
Level 3: Strategic Reasoning and Thinking
Level 4: Extended Thinking

Item	Standard	DOK
1	4.NBT.1	1
2	4.NBT.3	1
3	4.NBT.4	2
4	4.NBT.4	2
5	4.NBT.4	2
6	4.NBT.4	2
7	4.NBT.4	2
8	4.NBT.4	2
9	4.NBT.2	1
10	4.NBT.2	2
11	4.NBT.5	2
12	4.NBT.5	2
13	4.NBT.6	2
14	4.NBT.6	2
15	4.NBT.6	2
16	4.NBT.2	2
17	4.NBT.6	3
18	4.NBT.5	3
19	4.NBT.4	4
20	4.NBT.3	4

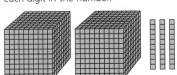 **UNIT 2 Common Core Review**

1. What number is represented by the model below? Explain the value of each digit in the number.

Possible explanation: The model shows 2,037. The 2 in the thousands place represents 2,000. The 0 in the hundreds place show there are no hundreds in the model. The 3 in the tens place is for 30. The 7 in the ones place shows there are 7 ones.

2. Draw a point on the number line to show 7,352. Then round 7,352 to the nearest hundred.

7,000   7,352   8,000

Answer To the nearest hundred, 7,352 rounds to ___7,400___.

Estimate. Then add or subtract. Estimates will vary.

3.
```
  4,389
 +7,915
─────────
 12,304
```

4.
```
 112,075
 + 38,472
─────────
 150,547
```

5.
```
 581,227
+378,978
─────────
 960,205
```

6.
```
  9,302
 −1,842
─────────
  7,460
```

7.
```
 53,891
−48,089
─────────
  5,802
```

8.
```
 827,354
−609,378
─────────
 217,976
```

Circle the correct answer.

9. Which is the number name for 805,392?

   a. eight hundred thousand five, three nine two

   b. eight hundred fifty thousand, three hundred ninety-two

   (c.) eight hundred five thousand, three hundred ninety-two

   d. eight hundred five thousand, thirty-nine two

10. Which of these is a different number from the others?

   a. 30,000 + 7,000 + 40 + 5

   b. 3 ten thousands + 7 thousands + 4 tens + 5 ones

   c. 37,045

   (d.) thirty-seven thousand, four hundred five

11. Complete the area model at the right. Then multiply.

$43 \times 48 =$ ___2,064___

Students can use either partial products or the Distributive Property to multiply.

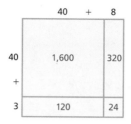

	40 +	8
40	1,600	320
+ 3	120	24

12. Use the Distributive Property and expanded form to multiply.

$4 \times 3,725 = 4 \times ($ ___3,000___ $+$ ___700___ $+$ ___20___ $+$ ___5___ $)$

$= ($ ___$4 \times 3,000$___ $) + ($ ___4×700___ $) + ($ ___4×20___ $) + ($ ___4×5___ $)$

$=$ ___12,000___ $+$ ___2,800___ $+$ ___80___ $+$ ___20___

$=$ ___14,900___

Use division patterns with zeros to find each quotient.

13. $600 \div 6 =$ ___100___   **14.** $9,000 \div 3 =$ ___3,000___   **15.** $2,400 \div 8 =$ ___300___

16. For a report on the world's longest rivers, Justine finds that the Lena River in Russia is 2,734 miles long and the Amur River in northeast Asia is 2,744 miles long. Which river is longer? ___The Amur River is longer.___

Solve the problems.

MP4 **17.** The Obricki family is buying a computer for $765. To pay for it, they will make 9 monthly payments of the same amount. How much will one month's payment be?

Show your work.
Work may vary. Possible work:

	80 +	5
9	720	45

$80 + 5 = 85$

Answer ___One month's payment will be $85.___

Unit 2 ■ Focus on Number and Operations in Base Ten **121**

This chart correlates the Common Core Review items with the lessons in which the concepts and skills are presented.

Item	Lesson
1	6
2	8
3	9
4	9
5	9
6	9
7	9
8	9
9	7
10	7
11	10
12	11
13	12
14	12
15	12
16	7
17	13
18	11
19	9
20	8

Mathematical Practices

MP4	**Model with mathematics.**

Item 17: Students relate mathematics to everyday problems.

Writing About Math

 Direct students to respond to the Unit 2 Essential Question. (This can also be found on student page 55.)

> **Essential Question:**
> How does understanding place value help you with number relationships and computing efficiently?

Possible responses:

- Place value helps when comparing numbers.
- Using place value to round numbers can provide an estimate for a problem. The estimate can then be used to justify the reasonableness of a solution.
- Numbers can be manipulated using place value. Rewriting numbers according to place value can make them easier to work with when computing.

Unit Assessment

- Unit 2 Common Core Review, *pp. 120–122*
- Unit 2 Performance Task (ONLINE)

Additional Assessment Options

Optional Purchase:

- iProgress Monitor (ONLINE)
- Progress Monitor Student Benchmark Assessment Booklet

UNIT 2 Common Core Review

MP1 **18.** The ruby-throated hummingbird beats its wings 52 times per second. How many times does the hummingbird beat its wings per minute?

▸ **Show your work.** Work may vary. Possible work:
$$52 \times 60 = (50 + 2) \times 60$$
$$= (50 \times 60) + (2 \times 60)$$
$$= 3,000 + 120$$
$$= 3,120$$

Answer The hummingbird beats its wings 3,120 times per minute.

MP3 **19.** Lennon found the sum of the following two numbers.

```
  1
 57,024
+38,983
 95,907
```

What is Lennon's mistake? What is the correct sum?

▸ **Justify your answer using words, drawings, or numbers.**

Possible justification:
```
  1 1 1
 57,024
+38,983
 96,007
```
The correct sum is 96,007, not 95,907.

Lennon correctly regrouped 2 tens + 8 tens as 10 tens, but did not add the 1 hundred to the other hundreds. So, his answer is 100 less than the correct answer.

Answer The correct sum is 96,007.

MP2 **20.** Charlotte and Finn round the same number to different places. Charlotte rounds to the nearest thousand and gets 0. Finn rounds to the nearest hundred and gets 400. If they both rounded correctly, what are the greatest and least possible numbers they could have rounded?

▸ **Justify your answer using words, drawings, or numbers.**

Possible drawing:

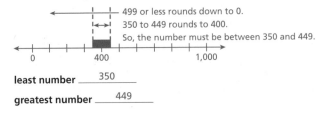

499 or less rounds down to 0.
350 to 449 rounds to 400.
So, the number must be between 350 and 449.

least number ___350___

greatest number ___449___

Mathematical Practices

MP1	**Make sense of problems and persevere in solving them.**
Item 18: Students analyze a problem and plan a solution.	
MP2	**Reason abstractly and quantitatively.**
Item 20: Students make sense of quantities and their relationships in problem situations.	
MP3	**Construct viable arguments and critique the reasoning of others.**
Item 19: Students explain an approach to a problem and share their reasoning with others.	

Student Page 123

Progress Check · UNIT 3

Look at how the Common Core standards you have learned and will learn connect.
It is very important for you to understand the standards from the prior grade level so that you will be able to develop an understanding of fractions in this unit and be prepared for next year. To practice your skills, go to sadlierconnect.com.

GRADE 3 — I Can...	Before Unit 3	GRADE 4 — Can I?	After Unit 3	GRADE 5 — I Will...
3.NF.3 Find equivalent fractions	☐	**4.NF.1** Explain why fractions are equivalent	☐	
3.NF.3 Compare fractions with the same numerator or denominator	☐	**4.NF.2** Compare fractions with different numerators and denominators	☐	
3.NF.1 Understand the meaning of the numerator of a fraction	☐	**4.NF.3** Add and subtract fractions and mixed numbers with like denominators	☐	**5.NF.1** Add and subtract fractions and mixed numbers
Understand the meaning of the denominator of a fraction	☐	Solve word problems involving addition and subtraction of fractions with like denominators	☐	**5.NF.2** Solve word problems involving addition and subtraction of fractions
3.NF.2 Represent unit fractions on a number line	☐	**4.NF.4** Multiply a unit fraction by a whole number	☐	**5.NF.4** Multiply a fraction or whole number by a fraction
Represent fractions on a number line	☐	Multiply a fraction by a whole number	☐	**5.NF.6** Solve word problems involving multiplication of fractions and mixed numbers
		Solve word problems involving multiplication of fractions by whole numbers	☐	**5.NF.7** Divide with unit fractions
3.NF.3 Find equivalent fractions	☐	**4.NF.5** Add two fractions with denominators of 10 and 100	☐	**5.NBT.7** Add and subtract decimals to hundredths
		4.NF.6 Express as decimals, fractions with denominators of 10 or 100	☐	**5.NBT.3** Read and write decimals to thousandths
		4.NF.7 Compare two decimals to hundredths using >, =, or <	☐	**5.NBT.3** Compare two decimals to thousandths

Unit 3 ■ Focus on Number and Operations—Fractions

Progress Check

Progress Check is a self-assessment tool that students can use to gauge their own progress. Research shows that when students take accountability for their learning, motivation increases.

Before students begin work in Unit 3, have them check any items they know they can do well. Explain that it is fine if they don't check any of the boxes; they will have the opportunity to learn and practice all the standards through the course of the unit.

Let them know that at the end of the unit they will review their checklists to check their progress. After students have completed the last lesson of the unit, before they begin Common Core Review, you will be prompted to have students revisit this page.

HOME ✦ CONNECT...

The Home Connect feature is a way to keep parents or other adult family members apprised of what their children are learning. The key learning objectives are listed, and some ideas for related activities and discussions are included.

Explain to students that they can share the Home Connect page at home with their families. Let students know there is an activity connected to their classroom learning that they can do with their families.

Encourage students and their parents to share their experiences using the suggestions on the Home Connect. You may wish to invite students to share this work with the class.

Student Page 124

HOME ✦ CONNECT...

Models can help your child to visualize and solve problems. Visuals model are effective tools that can help your child to better understand fraction concepts. A visual model of a fraction should show the number of equal parts as indicated by the denominator of the fraction.

numerator number of equal parts you are talking about
denominator total number of equal parts in the whole

Support your child by using visual models such as the following when solving problems involving fractions.

Sarah has a watercolor paint set with 8 colors. She uses $\frac{1}{8}$ of the colors first. Then she uses another $\frac{5}{8}$ of the colors. How much of the paint set is left?

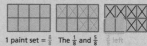

1 paint set = $\frac{8}{8}$ The $\frac{1}{8}$ and $\frac{5}{8}$ Sarah uses $\frac{2}{8}$ left

Activity: Coins values are fractional parts of a dollar. A dime is $\frac{1}{10}$ of a dollar and a penny is $\frac{1}{100}$ of a dollar. While you are shopping with your child, find prices that are less than one dollar. Ask your child to tell you how many dimes and/or pennies each price represents. Then ask your child to name each price as a fraction with either 10 or 100 as the denominator.

124 Unit 3 ■ Focus on Number and Operations—Fractions

In this unit your child will:

- Understand and write equivalent fractions.
- Compare fractions.
- Add and subtract fractions with like denominators.
- Add and subtract mixed numbers with like denominators.
- Multiply fractions by whole numbers.
- Write and compare decimal fractions.

NOTE: All of these learning goals for your child are based on the Grade 4 Common Core State Standards for Mathematics.

Ways to Help Your Child

Manipulatives are objects that students can use to see relationships and solve problems. Virtual manipulatives exist digitally. They can also be a great tool to help your child visualize concepts. Libraries of virtual manipulatives are available online.

ONLINE
For more Home Connect activities, continue online at sadlierconnect.com

UNIT PLANNER

	Lesson	Standard(s)	Objective
14	Understand Equivalent Fractions	4.NF.1	Understand how to model and recognize equivalent fractions.
15	Write Equivalent Fractions	4.NF.1	Understand how to write equivalent fractions by using multiplication, division, and fraction models.
16	Compare Two Fractions	4.NF.2	Compare two fractions that have different numerators and different denominators.
17	Add and Subtract Fractions with Like Denominators	4.NF.3a	Add and subtract fractions of the same whole.
18	Decompose a Fraction as a Sum of Fractions	4.NF.3b	Decompose a fraction or mixed number into a sum of fractions with like denominators.
19	Add and Subtract Mixed Numbers with Like Denominators	4.NF.3c	Learn different methods for adding and subtracting mixed numbers with like denominators.
20	Problem Solving: Add and Subtract Fractions	4.NF.3d	Solve word problems that involve addition and subtraction of fractions and mixed numbers with like denominators using models and equations.
21	Multiply Unit Fractions by Whole Numbers	4.NF.4a	Use multiplication to write a fraction as the product of a whole number and a unit fraction.
22	Multiply Fractions by Whole Numbers	4.NF.4b	Multiply fractions by whole numbers.
23	Problem Solving: Multiply Fractions by Whole Numbers	4.NF.4c	Understand how to multiply fractions and mixed numbers by whole numbers to help solve real-world problems.
24	Add Fractions: Denominators of 10 and 100	4.NF.5	Write equivalent fractions to add fractions with denominators of 10 and 100.
25	Write and Compare Decimal Fractions	4.NF.6; 4.NF.7	Write decimal numbers for tenths and hundredths and compare their magnitude.

Essential Question: How can writing fractions more than one way help you to compare and compute fractions?

UNIT 3

Essential Question	Words to Know
Why can different fractions name the same amount?	unit fraction, fraction, equivalent fractions
How can you multiply to write equivalent fractions?	
How can you use equivalent fractions to compare fractions?	benchmark
What happens when you find a sum or difference of fractions?	like denominators
How can you decompose a fraction or mixed number into a sum of fractions with the same denominator?	decompose, mixed number
What methods can you use for adding and subtracting mixed numbers?	
How can modeling a fraction word problem help you understand it?	
How is multiplying a unit fraction by a whole number like multiplying a whole number by a whole number?	
How can you multiply a fraction that is not a unit fraction by a whole number?	
How can multiplying fractions by whole numbers help you to solve real-world problems?	
How can you use the relationship between 10 and 100 to add tenths and hundredths?	tenth, hundredth
How can you use place value to write and compare tenths and hundredths?	decimal, decimal point

Unit Assessment

- Unit 3 Common Core Review, *pp. 222–224*
- Unit 3 Performance Task ONLINE

Additional Assessment Options

- Performance Task 1, *pp. 225–230*
  ALSO ONLINE

Optional Purchase:
- iProgress Monitor ONLINE
- Progress Monitor Student Benchmark Assessment Booklet

ONLINE Digital Resources

- Home Connect Activities
- Unit Performance Tasks
- Additional Practice
- Fluency Practice
- Teacher Resources
- iProgress Monitor (optional purchase)

Go to SadlierConnect.com to access your Digital Resources.

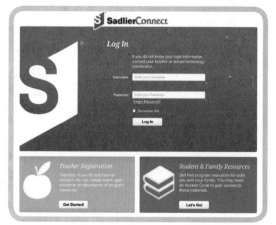

For more detailed instructions see page T3.

LEARNING PROGRESSIONS

This page provides more in-depth detail on the development of the standards across the grade levels. See also the unit Progress Check page in the Student Edition for a roadmap of the Learning Progressions.

Grade 3

- Students understand that the numerator signals the number of constituent unit fractions, while the denominator signals the number of parts that make up the whole. (3.NF.1)
- Students represent unit fractions on a number line and progress to representing fractions of form *a/b* on a number line. (3.NF.2)
- Students develop an understanding of the equivalence of simple fractions by working with fractions on the number line, fraction strips, and other representations. Students understand how whole numbers may be represented by equivalent fractions. They compare fractions with the same numerator or denominator using =, <, and >. (3.NF.3)

Grade 4

- It is crucial for students to understand that fractions must refer to the same whole in situations involving determining equivalent fractions, comparing fractions, and in solving real world problems involving fractions. (4.NF)
- The concept of equivalent fractions is extended to general cases. Students recognize, generate, and explain equivalent fractions. (4.NF.1)
- Students compare two fractions that have different numerators and denominators. (4.NF.2)
- Students add and subtract fractions and mixed numbers with like denominators and solve related word problems. (4.NF.3)
- Students multiply fractions by whole numbers and solve related word problems. (4.NF.4)
- The final three lessons connect fractions to decimals. Students begin by expressing a fraction with a denominator of 10 as a fraction with a denominator of 100 and apply this to adding two fractions with denominators of 10 and 100. They use decimal notation for tenths and hundredths and compare two decimals. (4.NF.5, 4.NF.6, 4.NF.7)

Grade 5

- Students apply use of equivalent fractions to add and subtract fractions with unlike denominators and solve related story problems. (5.NF.1, 5.NF.2)
- Multiplication with fractions extends to multiplying fractions and whole numbers by fractions and solving related story problems (5.NF.4, 5.NF.6)
- Students perform and interpret division of whole numbers by unit fractions and division of unit fractions by non-zero whole numbers, and solve related real world problems. (5.NF.7)
- Students write, interpret, and compare decimals to thousandths. They add, subtract, multiply, and divide decimals. (5.NBT.3, 5.NBT.7)

Focus on Number and Operations—Fractions

UNIT 3

Essential Question:
How can writing fractions more than one way help you to compare and compute fractions?

Essential Question:
How can writing fractions more than one way help you to compare and compute fractions?

As students become involved with the Essential Question, they will extend their knowledge of equivalence to manipulate fractions to have common denominators. They will then use this knowledge to compare fractions and solve problems involving fractions.

Conversation Starters

Have students discuss the photograph. Ask questions such as: *Who might use a map with this viewpoint? What can you tell about the individual houses from this point of view?*

Ask students to look at the block shown above the Essential Question. Point out that one of the houses has a red roof. *How many houses can we see on that street?* (3) *What fraction can we write to show this?* ($\frac{1}{3}$)

Have students write other fractions for things they see in the picture, such as the number of houses with tan roofs on a block, the number of black cars on a street, or the number of houses with swimming pools. *Suppose two houses on a block have a swimming pool and there are 10 houses on the block. What fraction can we write to show this?* ($\frac{2}{10}$)

Let students work in pairs to write fractions about things they see in the picture. Lead them to see that their understanding of fractions is helpful in describing the picture.

Activity

Materials: grid paper, pencil
Explain that the arrangement of the blocks in a housing development is often standardized, so a part of a housing development can be used to determine totals for an entire development. Tell students that all the blocks in the development must have the same fraction of houses with pools. There are 8 blocks in the development. Let students work in pairs to determine the total number of houses with pools.

Have a class discussion to compare strategies used to solve this problem. Many students may have drawn a picture to solve. Encourage students to create a mathematical problem that represents the total number of houses in the development, and then multiply that by the fraction of houses with pools.

Common Core Focus:

4.NF.1 Explain why a fraction *a/b* is equivalent to a fraction (*n* × *a*)/(*n* × *b*) by using visual fraction models, with attention to how the number and size of the parts differ even though the two fractions themselves are the same size. Use this principle to recognize and generate equivalent fractions.

OBJECTIVE

Understand how to model and recognize equivalent fractions.

ESSENTIAL QUESTION

Discuss whether it is possible for one person to eat two pieces of pizza and another to eat one piece of pizza, yet both eat the same amount of pizza. Students need to understand that even though the number and size of the parts differ, equivalent fractions represent exactly the same amount.

PREREQUISITE SKILLS

Use Item F on page 339 of the Foundational Skills Handbook to review finding equivalent fractions on a number line.

FLUENCY PRACTICE

Fluency practice is available at **sadlierconnect.com**.

Concept Development

Understand: Model equivalent fractions

■ Have students fold two equal-size papers into two equal parts and color one part of each sheet. Then have them fold one of the papers into fourths. They have created more parts, but the size of the colored part remains the same.

■ Emphasize that multiplying any number by 1 does not change the value of a number, so multiplying any fraction by $\frac{a}{a}$, or 1, does not change the value of the fraction.

Lesson 14 Understand Equivalent Fractions

Essential Question: Why can different fractions name the same amount? 4.NF.1

Words to Know:
unit fraction
fraction
equivalent fractions

Guided Instruction

In this lesson you will learn how to model and recognize equivalent fractions.

Understand: Model equivalent fractions

> Dina's mother says that one of her plants is $\frac{1}{3}$-foot taller than last year. Dina agrees, since she measured the plant growth as $\frac{4}{12}$ foot. Are $\frac{1}{3}$ and $\frac{4}{12}$ equivalent fractions?

You can model $\frac{1}{3}$ and $\frac{4}{12}$ to decide whether they are equivalent fractions. To compare fractions, they must have the same whole.

When a whole is partitioned, or divided, into equal parts, one of those parts is a unit fraction.

A number formed by putting together unit fractions is a fraction. Fractions that describe the same amount are equivalent fractions.

Draw 2 same-size rectangles to represent the whole.

Divide one into 3 equal-size parts.   Divide the other into 12 equal-size parts.
Color 1 part to represent $\frac{1}{3}$.   Color 4 parts to represent $\frac{4}{12}$.

$\frac{1}{3}$ ←→ parts colored in ←→ $\frac{4}{12}$
      ←→ total parts ←→

Compare the areas that you colored in. Both cover the same area of the rectangle, so the fractions they represent are equivalent.

➡ The models show that $\frac{1}{3}$ and $\frac{4}{12}$ are equivalent fractions.

Look at the area models above.

You can see that the whole with 12 equal parts has 4 times as many total parts as the whole with 3 equal parts.

numerator ⟶ $\frac{1}{3} = \frac{4 \times 1}{4 \times 3} = \frac{4}{12}$
denominator ⟶

You can see that to cover the same area as $\frac{1}{3}$ with the smaller twelfths unit fractions, you colored in 4 times as many twelfths as thirds.

When you multiply both the numerator and the denominator by the same number you get an equivalent fraction.

126 Unit 3 ▪ Focus on Number and Operations—Fractions

Words to Know

unit fraction: represents the quantity, or amount, in one of the equal parts of a whole when the whole is partitioned, or divided

fraction: a number that names part of a whole, an area, or a group. It can be expressed in the form $\frac{a}{b}$

equivalent fraction: fractions that have different names, but are at the same point on the number line

Example: $\frac{1}{4} = \frac{2}{8}$

Glossary can be found on pp. 347–350.

Lesson 14

Guided Instruction

Connect: Recognize and identify equivalent fractions

Jay, Will, and Nasir have cherries for a snack. Jay has $\frac{2}{5}$ pound, Will has $\frac{1}{3}$ pound, and Nasir has $\frac{4}{10}$ pound. Which friends have the same amount of cherries?

To find which amounts are the same, you can use a number line to decide whether any of the fractions are equivalent.

Remember!
Equivalent fractions name the same point on a number line.

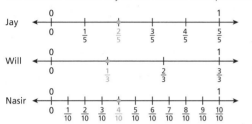

Look at the number line models. The distance from 0 to 1 is the whole.

Use the model to identify the equivalent fractions.

$\frac{2}{5}$ and $\frac{4}{10}$ are the same distance from 0. They name the same point on the number line, so they are equivalent fractions.

$\frac{1}{3}$ is a different point on the number line. It is closer to 0 than both $\frac{2}{5}$ and $\frac{4}{10}$, so it is not equivalent to the other two fractions.

equivalent fractions
$\frac{2}{5} = \frac{4}{10}$
not equivalent fractions
$\frac{1}{3} \neq \frac{2}{5}$, $\frac{1}{3} \neq \frac{4}{10}$

▸ Jay and Nasir have the same amount of cherries, because $\frac{2}{5}$ and $\frac{4}{10}$ are equivalent fractions.

Use the number line to look at the relationship between unit fractions of $\frac{1}{5}$ and unit fractions of $\frac{1}{10}$. The whole has 2 times as many $\frac{1}{10}$ unit fractions as $\frac{1}{5}$ unit fractions, so 1 unit fraction of $\frac{1}{5}$ is equal to 2 unit fractions of $\frac{1}{10}$. So, $\frac{1}{5} = \frac{2}{10}$.

The two fractions are equivalent if you can multiply both the numerator and the denominator of one fraction by the same number to get the other fraction.

Look at $\frac{4}{5}$ and $\frac{8}{10}$. Recall that $10 = 2 \times 5$. Multiplying the numerator and denominator of $\frac{4}{5}$ by 2 you get $\frac{8}{10}$, so $\frac{4}{5}$ and $\frac{8}{10}$ are equivalent fractions.

$$\frac{4}{5} = \frac{2 \times 4}{2 \times 5} = \frac{8}{10}$$

Unit 3 ▪ Focus on Number and Operations—Fractions **127**

Connect: Recognize and identify equivalent fractions

◼ This presentation reinforces students' previous learning from Grade 3 that two fractions are equivalent if they name the same point on a number line. Students extend their learning by using a number line to understand that a fraction $\frac{a}{b}$ is equivalent to a fraction $\frac{n \times a}{n \times b}$ even though the two fractions differ in the number and size of the individual parts.

◼ Emphasize to students that the distance from 0 to 1 is the same on each number line, but the size of the intervals differ. This is a good opportunity to point out that as the value of the denominator increases, the size of the unit fraction $\frac{1}{b}$, or interval, decreases.

◼ A common error that students make at this level is that they do not multiply both the numerator and the denominator by the same number. Remind students to show their work by writing the step that shows $\frac{n \times a}{n \times b}$ with the understanding that $\frac{n}{n} = 1$ and that the variable n can be any number, but must be the same number in a given equation.

Support English Language Learners

The term *equivalent* may present some difficulties for English language learners. Explain that *equivalent* means to be equal, the same, or identical. Relate that in math, we use *equal* to also mean *having the same value*. Explore how two fractions can be equivalent without being the same two fractions. Draw models of two equivalent fractions on the board and provide a sentence frame for students to repeat, such as: *These fractions have equal values. These fractions are _____ [equivalent].* Make sure students understand that while they are equivalent fractions, they are not the same fraction. Students can practice writing their own equivalent fractions and use the sentence frame to tell about the fractions.

Guided Practice

Observational Assessment

Use pages 128–129 to assess whether students are able to recognize equivalent fractions using models and number lines. Watch for students who have trouble determining what fractions to use to generate equivalent fractions.

Guided Practice

For exercises 1–4, use the model at the right.

1. Each model represents 1 whole.
   Color the models to show $\frac{2}{3}$ and $\frac{4}{6}$.

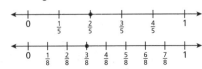

2. Write = or ≠ to tell if the fractions are equivalent.
   $$\frac{2}{3} \underline{\quad = \quad} \frac{4}{6}$$

3. Complete the sentences to explain the relationship.

   The fractions name the ___**same**___ area.

   One whole has __**2**__ times as many $\frac{1}{6}$ unit fractions as $\frac{1}{3}$ unit fractions.

   Each $\frac{1}{3}$-unit fraction is equal to __**2**__ $\frac{1}{6}$-unit fractions.

4. Write the number you can use to show that $\frac{2}{3}$ and $\frac{4}{6}$ are equivalent.
   $$\frac{2}{3} = \frac{2 \times 2}{2 \times 3} = \frac{4}{6}$$

For exercises 5–8, use the number lines at the right.

5. Place points on the number lines to show $\frac{2}{5}$ and $\frac{3}{8}$.

6. Write = or ≠ to tell whether the fractions are equivalent.
   $$\frac{2}{5} \underline{\quad \neq \quad} \frac{3}{8}$$

7. Complete the sentences.

   The fractions name ___**different**___ points on the number line.

   There is no whole number of ___**eighths**___ that equal $\frac{2}{5}$.

   There is no whole number of ___**fifths**___ that equal $\frac{3}{8}$.

8. Is there a whole number, n, that you can use to find an equivalent fraction?
   $$\frac{2}{5} = \frac{n \times 2}{n \times 5} = \frac{3}{8}$$

   Try some whole numbers.

   Answer No, there is no whole number that can be used to find an equivalent fraction.

Math-to-Cooking Connection

Recipes and Fractions Recipes often use fractional measurements for listing ingredients. Provide students with a variety of recipes that include fractional measurements. Have students work in pairs or small groups to rewrite the fractions in the ingredients lists.

Have groups trade their revised recipes with another group. Using the new recipes, groups will check that the fractions were rewritten correctly as equivalent fractions. Allow groups to share their strategies for identifying and writing equivalent fractions.

Lesson 14

Guided Practice

Model the fractions. Write = or ≠. If the fractions are equivalent, write the number you can use to show they are equivalent.

9. $\frac{2}{3}$ ____ = ____ $\frac{8}{12}$

$\frac{2}{3} = \frac{4 \times 2}{4 \times 3} = \frac{8}{12}$

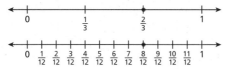

10. $\frac{3}{4}$ ≠ $\frac{2}{5}$

$\frac{2}{5} = \frac{\times 2}{\times 3} = \frac{3}{4}$

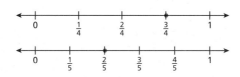

11. $\frac{1}{4}$ ≠ $\frac{2}{6}$

$\frac{1}{4} = \frac{\times 1}{\times 4} = \frac{2}{6}$

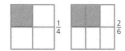

Write = or ≠. If the fractions are equivalent, write the number you can use to show they are equivalent. You can use models to help.

12. $\frac{1}{2}$ ____ = ____ $\frac{3}{6}$

$\frac{1}{2} = \frac{3 \times 1}{3 \times 2} = \frac{3}{6}$

13. $\frac{5}{4}$ ____ = ____ $\frac{10}{8}$

$\frac{5}{4} = \frac{2 \times 5}{2 \times 4} = \frac{10}{8}$

☺☺ Think · Pair · Share

MP3 14. Pick a pair of fractions from the previous exercises that are not equivalent. Explain why the fractions are not equivalent.
Possible explanation: $\frac{3}{4}$ and $\frac{2}{5}$ are not equivalent because they are different points on the number line, so they represent different distances from 0. Also, there is no whole number of fifths that will equal $\frac{3}{4}$ or of fourths that will equal $\frac{2}{5}$.

Unit 3 ■ Focus on Number and Operations—Fractions **129**

☺☺ Think·Pair·Share

Peer Collaboration Have students work with a partner and explain why their fractions are not equivalent. Listen for students' explanations to address these questions:

- *Where does each fraction fall on a number line?*
- *What part of the whole does each fraction show?*
- *How do these parts compare to each other?*

Return to the Essential Question

Reread the Lesson 14 Essential Question on page 126: *Why can different fractions name the same amount?*

Ask volunteers to use what they learned in this lesson to answer this question. (Possible response: The unit fractions can be different, but if the sum of each of the different unit fractions represents the same part of the whole, then the different fractions name the same amount.)

Invite as many volunteers as possible to express ideas about using area models and number lines to recognize and explain equivalent fractions.

Mathematical Practices

Mathematical Practice Standards underline the teaching and understanding of all concepts and skills presented. The emphasis of specific practices is noted throughout the guided and independent practice of this lesson.

MP3	**Construct viable arguments and critique the reasoning of others.**

Item 14: Students share their reasoning with others and provide constructive feedback to their classmates.

Independent Practice

Concept Application

Students may work independently on these pages in the classroom or at home. They may refer to the first four pages of the lesson to revisit the instruction or to see a worked-out example.

Common Errors and **Teaching Tips** may help you support student learning either in the classroom or as a follow-up for work done at home.

Common Errors

Items 1–8

Students may try to write 1 as a fraction using any value they choose, knowing that they need to multiply the numerator and the denominator by the same number to get an equivalent fraction. However, if the fractions are equivalent in items 1–8, then they need to complete the equation by writing the one fraction that makes the product true.

Teaching Tips

Items 1–5

Remind students to complete each model to show why the pairs of fractions are or are not equivalent.

Independent Practice

Use the models to show the fractions. Write = or ≠. If the fractions are equivalent, write the number you can use to show they are equivalent.

1. $\frac{1}{2} = \frac{4}{8}$

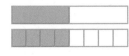

$\frac{1}{2} = \frac{4 \times 1}{4 \times 2} = \frac{4}{8}$

2. $\frac{2}{4} \neq \frac{4}{10}$

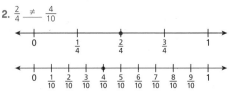

$\frac{2}{4} = \frac{\times 2}{\times 4} = \frac{4}{10}$

3. $\frac{1}{3} = \frac{2}{6}$

$\frac{1}{3} = \frac{2 \times 1}{2 \times 3} = \frac{2}{6}$

4. $\frac{4}{5} \neq \frac{9}{10}$

$\frac{4}{5} = \frac{\times 4}{\times 5} = \frac{9}{10}$

5. $\frac{8}{6} = \frac{16}{12}$

$\frac{8}{6} = \frac{2 \times 8}{2 \times 6} = \frac{16}{12}$

Write = or ≠. If the fractions are equivalent, write the number you can use to show they are equivalent. You can use models to help.

6. $\frac{2}{4} \neq \frac{2}{5}$

$\frac{2}{4} = \frac{\times 2}{\times 4} = \frac{2}{5}$

7. $\frac{2}{10} = \frac{1}{5}$

$\frac{1}{5} = \frac{2 \times 1}{2 \times 5} = \frac{2}{10}$

8. $\frac{1}{4} = \frac{3}{12}$

$\frac{1}{4} = \frac{3 \times 1}{3 \times 4} = \frac{3}{12}$

130 Unit 3 ■ Focus on Number and Operations—Fractions

Talking About Math

Collaborative Conversations Ask students to share with a partner what they have learned about equivalent fractions from this lesson. Students should discuss what an equivalent fraction is and how area models and number lines are used to show equivalent fractions. Ask students to tell which tool they prefer to use as a visual model of equivalent fractions and why. Remind students that they are expressing their opinions, so there are no right or wrong answers, but they should be able to support their opinions with reasons.

MORE ONLINE sadlierconnect.com   Lesson 14

Independent Practice

Write = or ≠. If the fractions are equivalent, write the number you can use to show they are equivalent. You can use models to help.

9. $\frac{2}{6}$ —≠— $\frac{4}{5}$ 10. $\frac{6}{5}$ —=— $\frac{12}{10}$ 11. $\frac{5}{10}$ —≠— $\frac{5}{12}$

$\frac{2}{6} = \frac{\times 2}{\times 6} = \frac{4}{5}$ $\frac{6}{5} = \frac{2 \times 6}{2 \times 5} = \frac{12}{10}$ $\frac{5}{10} = \frac{\times 5}{\times 10} = \frac{5}{12}$

For exercises 12–14, use the model. Each model represents 1 whole.

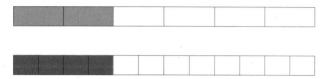

12. Which pair of equivalent fractions is shown in the model?

   a. $\frac{2}{4}$ and $\frac{1}{2}$ (b.) $\frac{2}{6}$ and $\frac{4}{12}$

   c. $\frac{2}{4}$ and $\frac{4}{8}$ d. $\frac{6}{2}$ and $\frac{12}{2}$

13. Which sentence does NOT help to explain why the two fractions shown are equivalent?

   a. The fractions represent the same area.

   b. The fractions would share the same point on the number line.

   c. There are two unit fractions of $\frac{1}{12}$ for each unit fraction of $\frac{1}{6}$.

   (d.) One whole has more equal parts than the other.

14. Which of the fractions below are equivalent to the fractions shown in the model?

   (a.) $\frac{1}{3}$ b. $\frac{2}{4}$

   (c.) $\frac{2}{6}$ d. $\frac{1}{2}$

Unit 3 ■ Focus on Number and Operations—Fractions   **131**

Teaching Tips

Items 9–11

Remind students that if the equations cannot be made true, then the fractions are not equivalent.

Item 14

Point out that more than one of the fractions is equivalent to the models, and students should circle each correct answer.

Digital Connection

Interactive Whiteboard Have students take turns using the interactive whiteboard to show a fraction using an area model or a number line. Have them choose a friend to create an equivalent fraction using the same type of model. Ask the class to name another equivalent fraction. Repeat the activity using different fractions and models.

Independent Practice

Common Errors

Item 15

Students may forget that smaller unit fractions have greater numbers in the denominator. Fraction strips may help students reason about which fraction of a cup would be useful.

Independent Practice

MP2 **15.** Zach needs $\frac{3}{4}$ cup of sugar for a recipe. He does not have a $\frac{1}{4}$-cup measuring cup, so he fills a different measuring cup more times. What must be true about the size of the measuring cup Zach uses, compared to a $\frac{1}{4}$-cup? Explain. Possible explanation: The cup Zach uses must hold less than $\frac{1}{4}$ cup, since he has to fill it more times. It could be a $\frac{1}{8}$-cup measuring cup, since there are two eighths for every fourth.

MP6 **16.** The number line shows two equivalent fractions, $\frac{1}{2}$ and $\frac{5}{10}$.

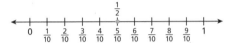

What is the relationship between the unit fractions, $\frac{1}{2}$ and $\frac{1}{10}$? Describe both the number and size of the parts. Answers will vary.
Possible answer: With halves, the whole has 2 equal parts. With tenths, the whole has 10 equal parts. There are 5 times as many tenths as halves in 1 whole. So $\frac{1}{10}$ is a much smaller unit fraction than $\frac{1}{2}$, and 5 tenths equals 1 half.

Solve the problems.

MP7 **17.** The students have $\frac{5}{6}$ hour for recess. Vinh says this is the same as $\frac{10}{12}$ hour. Is Vinh's thinking correct? Write = or ≠.

▸ **Show your work.** Work may vary. Possible work: $\frac{5}{6} = \frac{2 \times 5}{2 \times 6} = \frac{10}{12}$

$\frac{5}{6}$ ——— $\frac{10}{12}$

Answer Yes, Vinh's thinking is correct.

MP4 **18.** An egg carton holds 12 eggs. Lucy uses 5 of the eggs and says there is $\frac{2}{3}$ of a carton left. Is Lucy's thinking correct?

▸ **Show your work.** Work may vary. Possible work:

$12 - 5 = 7$

$\frac{7}{12}$ $\frac{2}{3}$ $\frac{7}{12} \neq \frac{2}{3}$

Answer No, Lucy's thinking is not correct.

132   Unit 3 ■ Focus on Number and Operations—Fractions

Mathematical Practices

MP2	**Reason abstractly and quantitatively.**
Item 15: Students make sense of quantities and their relationships.	
MP4	**Model with mathematics.**
Item 18: Students relate mathematics to everyday life.	
MP6	**Attend to precision.**
Item 16: Students carefully formulate and communicate full explanations.	
MP7	**Look for and make use of structure.**
Item 17: Students search for patterns in equivalent fractions.	

MORE ONLINE sadlierconnect.com   Lesson 14

Independent Practice

MP1 **19.** One lap around the track at Dennis's school is $\frac{1}{8}$ mile. When Dennis runs, he stops to rest only when he has completed one or more $\frac{1}{4}$-mile distances. Would Dennis stop to rest when he reaches $\frac{14}{8}$ miles?

Answer Yes, Dennis would stop to rest.

▸ **Justify your answer using words, drawings, or numbers.**
Possible justification:

One whole mile has 8 eighths, which is the same as 4 fourths. There are twice as many eighths as fourths, so 2 eighths equal 1 fourth. That means $\frac{14}{8}$ is equivalent to $\frac{7}{4}$, and Dennis has finished his seventh $\frac{1}{4}$ of a mile.

MP7 **20.** Tracy says that $\frac{30}{100}$ must be a greater amount than $\frac{3}{10}$, since 30 is greater than 3. Do you agree? You can use the model of 100 below to justify your answer.

Answer No, I do not agree. Tracy is wrong.

▸ **Justify your answer using words, drawings, or numbers.**
Possible justification:

If the whole square equals 1, then each square is $\frac{1}{100}$ and each row is $\frac{1}{10}$, since there are 10 rows in the square. The three shaded rows show both $\frac{30}{100}$ and $\frac{3}{10}$, so the fractions are equivalent. Also, $100 = 10 \times 10$, so there are 10 times as many $\frac{1}{100}$ units as $\frac{1}{10}$ units. You can multiply to show that $\frac{3}{10}$ equals $\frac{30}{100}$: $\frac{3}{10} = \frac{10 \times 3}{10 \times 10} = \frac{30}{100}$.

MP3 **21.** Holly says that you cannot write equivalent fractions that have 3 and 5 as denominators. Susan says that $\frac{6}{3}$ and $\frac{10}{5}$ are equivalent fractions because they both equal 2 wholes. Whose reasoning is correct?

▸ **Show your work.**

Work may vary. Possible work:

Answer Susan's reasoning is correct.

Common Errors

Item 19

This problem may be misinterpreted to mean Dennis rests any number of times after the first $\frac{1}{4}$ mile. Careful reading makes it clear that Dennis rests only at $\frac{1}{4}$-mile intervals. Have students find whether there are an exact number of $\frac{1}{4}$ parts written as equivalent eighths in the distance of $\frac{14}{8}$ miles.

Teaching Tips

Item 20

Encourage students to apply what they know about multiples as they reason about the solution. Thirty is a multiple of 3, and 100 is a multiple of 10. Ten is a common factor of both multiples.

Item 21

Holly's statement is only true when the fractions do not represent whole numbers. Ask students to write $\frac{6}{3}$ as a group of $\frac{1}{3}$ parts: $\frac{1}{3}, \frac{1}{3}, \frac{1}{3}, \frac{1}{3}, \frac{1}{3}, \frac{1}{3}$. Have students circle the number of thirds it takes to equal one whole. Students should realize there are 2 wholes in $\frac{6}{3}$. Repeat the strategy for $\frac{10}{5}$ and compare the results.

Mathematical Practices	
MP1	**Make sense of problems and persevere in solving them.**
Item 19: Students use concrete objects or pictures to conceptualize and solve a problem.	
MP3	**Construct viable arguments and critique the reasoning of others.**
Item 21: Students analyze a problem situation and construct arguments by using drawings.	
MP7	**Look for and make use of structure.**
Item 20: Students search for patterns to justify a solution.	

Common Core Focus:

4.NF.1 Explain why a fraction *a/b* is equivalent to a fraction (*n* × *a*)/(*n* × *b*) by using visual fraction models, with attention to how the number and size of the parts differ even though the two fractions themselves are the same size. Use this principle to recognize and generate equivalent fractions.

OBJECTIVE

Understand how to write equivalent fractions by using multiplication, division, and fraction models.

ESSENTIAL QUESTION

Students will multiply to generate equivalent fractions with greater denominators and divide to generate equivalent fractions with smaller denominators.

PREREQUISITE SKILLS

Use Item F on page 339 of the Foundational Skills Handbook to review finding equivalent fractions.

FLUENCY PRACTICE

Fluency practice is available at **sadlierconnect.com**.

Concept Development

Understand: Multiply to write equivalent fractions

■ Even though the total number of parts and the size of the parts differ, both models represent the same whole because both whole figures are the same size. Both models represent the same part of a whole because both shaded areas are the same size.

✏ ▸ Ask students to share how they could show 8 equal parts in a different way. Students may reason that drawing two horizontal lines would show eighths. Drawing diagonal lines from corner to corner would also show eighths.

Lesson 15 — Write Equivalent Fractions

Essential Question: How can you multiply to write equivalent fractions? 4.NF.1

Guided Instruction

In this lesson you will learn how to write equivalent fractions.

Understand: Multiply to write equivalent fractions

> An apple bread recipe calls for $\frac{3}{4}$ cup of apple sauce. Cheng only has an $\frac{1}{8}$-cup measuring cup. How many times does Cheng need to fill the $\frac{1}{8}$ cup to measure $\frac{3}{4}$ cup?

To answer this question, find an equivalent fraction with a denominator of 8.

Draw an area model.
$\frac{3}{4}$ is 3 of 4 equal parts, or fourths.
To have a denominator of 8, you need to partition, or divide, the whole into 8 equal parts, or eighths.

Draw lines in the model to make 8 equal parts.
There are 2 eighths for each of the 1 fourths.
The 3 blue fourths equal 6 eighths.

Since $\frac{3}{4}$ and $\frac{6}{8}$ cover the same area, they are equivalent.

➡ Cheng needs to fill the $\frac{1}{8}$ cup 6 times to measure $\frac{3}{4}$ cup.

Another way to write an equivalent fraction is to use multiplication.

Since 8 = 2 × 4, the equivalent fraction has 2 times the total number of equal parts in $\frac{3}{4}$. $\;\;\longrightarrow\;\; \frac{3}{4} = \frac{}{2 \times 4} = \frac{}{8}$

There are 2 eighths for each fourth.
Multiply 3, the number of fourths, by 2 to find the number of eighths in the equivalent fraction. $\;\;\longrightarrow\;\; \frac{3}{4} = \frac{2 \times 3}{2 \times 4} = \frac{6}{8}$

✏ ▸ In the area model above, suppose you made 8 equal parts in a different way. Explain why the model will still show that $\frac{3}{4} = \frac{6}{8}$.
Possible answer: No matter how you make the 8 equal parts, each fourth will have 2 eighths in it.

Support English Language Learners

Some students may confuse the terms *numerator* and *denominator*. One difference between the terms is their position in a fraction. Another difference is how they are read. Remind students that a fraction such as $\frac{3}{8}$ is read as *three eighths*. The numerator is read the same way as a whole number is read, "three." The denominator is read using a suffix, usually –*th*, to represent that it is a part of a whole, "eighths."

Have students make a list of numbers 2, 3, 4, 5, 6, 8, 10, 12, and 100 and write the fractional words that correspond with each number, such as halves, thirds, fourths, and so on. Students can work in pairs writing and reading fractions with these denominators. Provide support for students who have difficulty reading the denominators correctly.

Lesson 15

Guided Instruction

Understand: Divide to write fractions

> Grace wants to see 4 of the 10 movies at the theater. She tells Zena she wants to see $\frac{4}{10}$ of the movies. Zena wants to see the same movies, but she wants to use a fraction with a smaller denominator to describe the number of movies. How can Zena do this?

You can model $\frac{4}{10}$ to see whether you can find a smaller denominator.

Draw a number line with tenths. Place a point to show $\frac{4}{10}$.

Think: $10 \div 2 = 5$. Using the same whole unit, draw another number line with fifths.

You can see that $\frac{4}{10}$ and $\frac{2}{5}$ are at the same point on the number line. It is possible to write an equivalent fraction for $\frac{4}{10}$ that has a smaller denominator.

➡ Zena can use the number lines to write $\frac{2}{5}$ to show the number of movies she wants to see.

Another way to write an equivalent fraction is to use division.

Since $5 = 10 \div 2$, the number of equal parts in the fraction equivalent to $\frac{4}{10}$ is 5. You start by dividing the denominator 10 by 2.

$$\frac{4}{10} = \frac{4}{10 \div 2} = \frac{}{5}$$

There is 1 fifth for every 2 tenths. You find the numerator of the equivalent fraction, which represents the number of fifths, by dividing the numerator 4 by 2. By dividing the numerator and the denominator by the same number, you see that $\frac{4}{10} = \frac{2}{5}$.

$$\frac{4}{10} = \frac{4 \div 2}{10 \div 2} = \frac{2}{5}$$

✏ Compare writing equivalent fractions by multiplying and by dividing. Possible answer: If you multiply, the denominator is greater and so is the numerator. If you divide, the denominator is smaller and so is the numerator.

Unit 3 ■ Focus on Number and Operations—Fractions 135

Understand: Divide to write fractions

■ In this presentation, students are using division to write an equivalent fraction.

■ If students struggle relating equivalent fractions on a number line, suggest they model the fractions by folding and/or drawing on equivalent sheets of paper.

■ In the previous lesson, students multiplied a fraction by a fraction equivalent to 1 ($\frac{a}{a}$) to write an equivalent fraction with a greater denominator. Explain that since division is the inverse operation of multiplication, they can divide a fraction by a fraction equivalent to 1 ($\frac{a}{a}$) to find an equivalent fraction with a lesser denominator.

✏ Ask students whether all fractions can be rewritten as equivalent fractions by multiplying and dividing. Students should understand that any fraction can be rewritten as an equivalent fraction by multiplying, but it is only possible to use division to write an equivalent fraction if the numerator and denominator have a common factor other than 1. Use $\frac{2}{10}$ and $\frac{3}{10}$ as examples to illustrate this point.

Math-to-Art Connection

Facial Fractions When learning to draw portraits, art students are often instructed on how to use fractions to maintain balance among the various features of the human face. Research a kid-friendly version of these dimensions on the Internet. Summarize them and provide a copy for students to reference. Have students find examples of portraits on the Internet and evaluate whether the artist has applied the fractional guidelines in his/her work. Allow time for students to share their findings with the class.

Connect: What you know about equivalent fractions Use this page to help students strengthen their understanding of how to find equivalent fractions.

■ Students should understand that each part of the whole is greater when using division to write an equivalent fraction, and each part of the whole is smaller when using multiplication to write an equivalent fraction. The fractional part of the whole, however, remains the same.

■ Point out that although the number and size of the parts of the whole in the three models are different, the shaded part of each model represents an equivalent part of the same whole.

■ Ask students to name other fractions that are equivalent to $\frac{4}{6}$ and identify ways they can check that their fractions are equivalent.

✏️ Make sure students understand that any fraction with the same number in the numerator and denominator is equal to 1. So, multiplying or dividing by $\frac{2}{2}$ is the same as multiplying or dividing by 1. Have students explore what happens to the value of a fraction when it is multiplied or divided by a fraction with different numbers in the numerator and denominator.

Lesson 15   Write Equivalent Fractions

Guided Instruction

Connect: What you know about equivalent fractions

Cheng wants to give away $\frac{4}{6}$ of his apple bread. He can give bigger pieces to fewer people or smaller pieces to more people. What equivalent fractions can represent these two ways for Cheng to share the bread?

To find the answer, use models or multiply or divide both the numerator and the denominator by the same number.

If Cheng gives away $\frac{4}{6}$ of the bread which he cut into 6 pieces, he will give pieces of bread to 4 people.

Suppose he decides to give bread to fewer people. He can divide 6 by 2 and cut the bread into only 3 pieces. To find the equivalent fraction, divide the numerator and the denominator of $\frac{4}{6}$ by 2.

$$\frac{4}{6} = \frac{4 \div 2}{6 \div 2} = \frac{2}{3}$$

If Cheng gives away the same amount of bread but cuts it into 3 pieces, he will give pieces of bread to 2 people.

Suppose he decides to give bread to more people. He can multiply 6 by 2 and cut the bread into 12 pieces. To find the equivalent fraction, multiply the numerator and the denominator of $\frac{4}{6}$ by 2.

$$\frac{4}{6} = \frac{4 \times 2}{6 \times 2} = \frac{8}{12}$$

If Cheng gives away the same amount of bread but cuts it into 12 pieces, he will give pieces of bread to 8 people.

➡️ Equivalent fractions representing two other ways for Cheng to share the apple bread are $\frac{2}{3}$ and $\frac{8}{12}$.

Remember!
You must multiply or divide both the numerator and the denominator by the same number.

✏️ Why is it important to use the same operation with the same number on both the numerator and the denominator when you want to find an equivalent fraction? Possible answer: If you do not multiply or divide both the numerator and the denominator by the same number, you change the fraction and you do not get an equivalent fraction.

Math-to-Measurement Connection

Rulers Standard customary rulers are divided into sixteenths of an inch; however, we usually read measurements using the simplest form of a fraction. Have students refer to the ruler as they list all equivalent fractions for each tick mark between 0 and 1. Remind them to multiply or divide using fractions equivalent to 1 to find and record all the equivalent fractions.

When students have finished, ask them to compare the lengths of the tick marks and identify which tick marks represent sixteenths, eighths, fourths, and halves. Point out that the tick marks on a ruler help them identify the simplest form of the fractional measurement.

Guided Practice

Draw on the area model to make an equivalent fraction with the given denominator. Then show what number to use to write the equivalent fraction.

1. 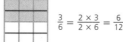 $\frac{1}{3} = \frac{2 \times 1}{2 \times 3} = \frac{2}{6}$

2. $\frac{3}{6} = \frac{2 \times 3}{2 \times 6} = \frac{6}{12}$

3. $\frac{2}{4} = \frac{2 \div 2}{4 \div 2} = \frac{1}{2}$

4. $\frac{2}{8} = \frac{2 \div 2}{8 \div 2} = \frac{1}{4}$

For exercises 5–8, use the number line.

5. Write an equivalent fraction for $\frac{3}{5}$.

$\frac{3}{5} = \frac{6}{10}$

6. Label the number line to show the fraction you wrote for exercise 5.

7. Write an equivalent fraction for $\frac{4}{10}$.

$\frac{4}{10} = \frac{2}{5}$

8. Circle any equivalent fractions.

$\boxed{\frac{1}{5}}$ $\frac{1}{10}$ $\frac{2}{5}$ $\boxed{\frac{2}{10}}$

Think • Pair • Share

MP6 9. You used a number line to write an equivalent fraction for exercise 7. Explain how to use two other methods to write the equivalent fraction. Possible explanation: One way is to draw an area model with 4 of 10 equal parts shaded, put $\frac{2}{10}$ together to make $\frac{1}{5}$, and then show that $\frac{4}{10}$ equals $\frac{2}{5}$. Another way is to divide both the numerator and denominator of $\frac{4}{10}$ by 2 to get $\frac{2}{5}$.

Unit 3 ■ Focus on Number and Operations—Fractions **137**

Mathematical Practices

Mathematical Practice Standards underline the teaching and understanding of all concepts and skills presented. The emphasis of specific practices is noted throughout the guided and independent practice of this lesson.

MP6	**Attend to precision.**

Item 9: Students carefully formulate a full explanation.

Observational Assessment

Use page 137 to assess whether students can find equivalent fractions by using area models, number lines, and multiplication or division.

✦✦ Think•Pair•Share

Peer Collaboration Ask each student to find an equivalent fraction using another method. In pairs, have students compare their methods. If the methods are the same, students should work together to find another method. If pairs struggle, ask:

- *How do area models and number lines show the same equivalent fractions?*

- *How do multiplication or division and number lines show the same equivalent fractions?*

To summarize, have students share their methods and talk about the relationship between the three different ways to show equivalent fractions.

Return to the Essential Question

Reread the Lesson 15 Essential Question on page 134: *How can you multiply to write equivalent fractions?*

Ask volunteers to use what they learned in this lesson to answer this question. (Possible response: Since any fraction with the same number in the numerator and denominator is equal to 1, I can multiply a fraction by any fraction equal to 1 to find an equivalent fraction.)

Concept Application

Students may work independently on these pages in the classroom or at home. They may refer to the first four pages of the lesson to revisit the instruction or to see a worked-out example.

Common Errors and **Teaching Tips** may help you support student learning either in the classroom or as a follow-up for work done at home.

Teaching Tips

Items 1–4

Remind students to use the provided denominator of the equivalent fraction to determine how to complete the model.

Items 5–6

Be aware that there are an infinite number of equivalent fractions that students can write. Some students may choose to use multiplication to find an equivalent fraction, while others may choose to use division.

Item 9

Using denominators of 12 or less, students may choose to list three equivalent fractions for exercise 5 ($\frac{6}{12}, \frac{3}{6}, \frac{2}{4}, \frac{1}{2}$), exercise 6 ($\frac{8}{12}, \frac{4}{6}, \frac{2}{3}$), or exercise 8 ($\frac{2}{6}, \frac{1}{3}, \frac{4}{12}$) There are only two equivalent fractions with denominators of 12 or less for exercise 7.

Draw on the model to make an equivalent fraction with the given denominator. For 1 and 2, show what number to use to write the equivalent fraction. For 3 and 4, complete the equation.

1.
$\frac{1}{3} = \frac{4 \times 1}{4 \times 3} = \frac{4}{12}$

2.
$\frac{2}{5} = \frac{3 \times 2}{3 \times 5} = \frac{6}{15}$

3.
$\frac{3}{6} = \frac{1}{2}$

4.
$\frac{8}{12} = \frac{2}{3}$

Write an equivalent fraction. You can use the number line to help.

5. $\frac{6}{12} = \frac{1}{2}$ or $\frac{3}{6}$

6. $\frac{8}{12} = \frac{4}{6}$

7. $\frac{5}{6} = \frac{10}{12}$

8. $\frac{2}{6} = \frac{4}{12}$

9. One point on the number line shows that three fractions are equivalent. What are the three equivalent fractions?

The three equivalent fractions are $\frac{1}{2}$, $\frac{3}{6}$, and $\frac{6}{12}$.

Writing About Math

▪ **Write an Opinion Text** Ask students to write a paragraph giving their opinions on which equivalent-fraction strategy is most helpful to them. Students should have a clear topic sentence, support their opinion with facts and details, and provide a concluding statement. When students have finished their paragraphs, have them trade papers with another student to review. Students should review their partner's paragraph to make sure the paragraph is written in the correct format, includes all parts of the assignment, and does not contain spelling or grammar errors.

Ask volunteers to read their paragraphs aloud. Remind students that these are opinion paragraphs, so there are no right or wrong answers.

MORE ONLINE sadlierconnect.com

Independent Practice

Model the fraction. Then write an equivalent fraction. Models may vary.

10. $\frac{4}{8} = \frac{1}{2}$

11. $\frac{6}{8} = \frac{3}{4}$

12.  $\frac{2}{12} = \frac{1}{6}$

13. 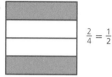 $\frac{2}{4} = \frac{1}{2}$

14. $\frac{4}{6} = \frac{2}{3}$

15. $\frac{70}{100} = \frac{7}{10}$

Show how to write an equivalent fraction. You can draw models to help. Fractions may vary. Possible answers are shown.

16. $\frac{1}{5} = \frac{2 \times 1}{2 \times 5} = \frac{2}{10}$

17. $\frac{6}{10} = \frac{6 \div 2}{10 \div 2} = \frac{3}{5}$

18. $\frac{5}{4} = \frac{2 \times 5}{2 \times 4} = \frac{10}{8}$

Write an equivalent fraction.

19. $\frac{10}{12} = \frac{5}{6}$

20. $\frac{3}{12} = \frac{1}{4}$

21. $\frac{8}{10} = \frac{4}{5}$

22. $\frac{2}{5} = \frac{4}{10}$

23. $\frac{9}{12} = \frac{3}{4}$

24. $\frac{4}{10} = \frac{2}{5}$

25. $\frac{2}{6} = \frac{1}{3}$ or $\frac{4}{12}$

26. $\frac{2}{3} = \frac{4}{6}, \frac{6}{9},$ or $\frac{8}{12}$

27. $\frac{5}{6} = \frac{10}{12}$

Unit 3 ■ Focus on Number and Operations—Fractions **139**

Common Errors
Items 19–27
Students may forget to multiply or divide both the numerator and the denominator when finding an equivalent fraction. Remind students that the value of any number multiplied or divided by 1 does not change. Students must multiply or divide by a fraction equivalent to 1 in order to find an equivalent fraction.

Teaching Tips
Items 10–27
Remind students that they can use multiplication or division to find equivalent fractions. However, dividing produces an equivalent fraction only when the numerator and denominator have a common factor that can be used as the divisor when dividing by a fraction equivalent to 1.

Digital Connection

Interactive Whiteboard Students can use the fraction models from the tools section of the interactive whiteboard to create equivalent fractions. Divide students into teams to play a game. Have one player from each team come to the whiteboard. Provide students with a fraction. Each student needs to model an equivalent fraction using the fraction models. The first student to correctly model the equivalent fraction wins a point. Play until one team reaches 10 points.

Independent Practice

Teaching Tips

Item 30

Remind students that the numerator is the number of goals Kim scored, and the denominator represents the total number of goals scored by all the players.

Item 31

Suggest that students write each player's goals in terms of the total number of goals scored. Then have students compare the corresponding fractions to see how they are similar and different.

Independent Practice

MP7 **28.** Stan says that when you multiply to get an equivalent fraction, the equivalent fraction is greater than the other fraction. Explain the error in Stan's thinking.
Answers will vary. Possible explanation: With equivalent fractions, when you multiply, you get a greater numerator and denominator but this does not mean that the fraction is greater. The size of the whole does not change, and neither does the size of the fraction. Stan's error is that the two fractions name the same amount, even though the numerator and denominator of one are greater than the numerator and denominator of the other.

MP3 **29.** Dylan says that when you rename $\frac{5}{10}$ as $\frac{1}{2}$, you change the situation you are working with. Do you agree? Explain your thinking.
Answers will vary. Possible explanation: I agree with Dylan. I think that working with 10 equal parts of the same whole is different from working with 2 equal parts of it. $\frac{1}{2}$ means one of two bigger parts and $\frac{5}{10}$ means 5 of 10 smaller parts. So, 5 of 10 equal parts is different from 1 of 2 equal parts.

For exercises 30 and 31, use the table.

MP6 **30.** What fraction of the total number of goals did Kim make?

▶ **Show your work.** Work may vary. Possible work:
Kim: 4; Total: 1 + 4 + 2 + 3 + 2 = 12
$\frac{4}{12} = \frac{4 \div 4}{12 \div 4} = \frac{1}{3}$

Kim made $\frac{1}{3}$ of the goals. ($\frac{2}{6}$ or $\frac{4}{12}$ are also acceptable answers.)

Answer _____

Soccer Goals Scored	
Player	Number of Goals
Angie	1
Kim	4
Mateo	2
Pete	3
Ricky	0
Sabrina	2

MP3 **31.** Sabrina made $\frac{1}{6}$ of the total goals. Pete made $\frac{1}{4}$ of the total goals. Explain why these two fractions do not have the same denominator even though they describe fractions of the same whole.

▶ **Show your work.** Work may vary. Possible work:
Sabrina: $\frac{2}{12}$

Pete: $\frac{3}{12}$ The fractions for the goals scored by Sabrina and Pete are equivalent fractions. The fractions for their goals using the total number of goals as the denominator are $\frac{2}{12}$ and $\frac{3}{12}$. These fractions show what the original whole is.

Answer _____

140 Unit 3 ▪ Focus on Number and Operations—Fractions

Mathematical Practices

MP3	**Construct viable arguments and critique the reasoning of others.**

Item 29: Students share their reasoning with others.

Item 31: Students analyze a problem situation.

MP6	**Attend to precision.**

Item 30: Students calculate accurately.

MP7	**Look for and make use of structure.**

Item 28: Students evaluate the structure of equivalent fractions.

Lesson 15

Independent Practice

Common Errors

Item 34

Students may assume that the garden sections are equal, but we only know that Jack's garden is equal in size to Louise's garden. Remind students to read the question carefully and make sure they have enough information to solve the problem.

Solve the problems.

MP4 **32.** Curtis draws a model of the fraction $\frac{5}{6}$. Then he divides each equal part into 2 smaller equal parts to help him write an equivalent fraction for $\frac{5}{6}$. What is the equivalent fraction?

 Show your work. Work may vary.
Possible work:

$$\frac{5}{6} = \frac{2 \times 5}{2 \times 6} = \frac{10}{12}$$

Answer The equivalent fraction is $\frac{10}{12}$.

MP2 **33.** Karl says that when you write an equivalent fraction, the size of each equal part in the equivalent fraction will always be greater than in the original fraction. Meg says this is not true, since you can multiply the numerator and denominator in a fraction to write an equivalent fraction. Whose reasoning is correct?

Answer Meg's reasoning is correct.

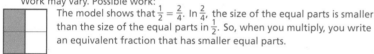 **Justify your answer using words, drawings, or numbers.**
Work may vary. Possible work:
The model shows that $\frac{1}{2} = \frac{2}{4}$. In $\frac{2}{4}$, the size of the equal parts is smaller than the size of the equal parts in $\frac{1}{2}$. So, when you multiply, you write an equivalent fraction that has smaller equal parts.

MP6 **34.** Jack and Louise have equal-size gardens. Jack lays out his garden in 6 spaces and plants melons in 2 spaces. Louise lays out her garden in 12 spaces and plants melons in 4 spaces. Is the fraction of the garden planted with melons the same for both gardens?

Answer There is not enough information to answer this question.

Justify your answer using words, drawings, or numbers.
Work may vary. Possible work:
The problem says that Jack and Louise lay out their gardens in 6 and 12 spaces, but it does not say whether the spaces are equal parts of their gardens. So you cannot tell whether the same fraction of both gardens is planted with melons.

Unit 3 ■ Focus on Number and Operations—Fractions **141**

Mathematical Practices

MP2	**Reason abstractly and quantitatively.**

Item 33: Students make sense of quantities and their relationships in problem situations.

MP4	**Model with mathematics.**

Item 32: Students use tools such as diagrams to draw conclusions.

MP6	**Attend to precision.**

Item 34: Students carefully formulate full explanations.

Common Core Focus:

4.NF.2 Compare two fractions with different numerators and different denominators. Recognize that comparisons are valid only when the two fractions refer to the same whole. Record the results of comparisons with symbols >, =, or <, and justify the conclusions.

OBJECTIVE

Compare two fractions that have different numerators and different denominators.

ESSENTIAL QUESTION

Students will use equivalent fractions and benchmarks to compare fractions that have different numerators and different denominators.

PREREQUISITE SKILLS

Use Item G on page 340 of the Foundational Skills Handbook to review comparing fractions on a number line.

FLUENCY PRACTICE

Fluency practice is available at **sadlierconnect.com**.

Concept Development

Understand: Using benchmarks to make comparisons

■ Common benchmarks for fractions are 0, $\frac{1}{2}$, and 1. Students must be able to write the benchmarks as equivalent fractions with denominators 8 and 10. Remind students that to write a fraction equal to one, the numerator and denominator are the same.

■ Be sure students understand that comparisons are only valid when the two fractions refer to the same whole.

■ Have volunteers who used benchmark fractions, who drew a number line, or who used a different method, explain their reasoning for the method they chose.

Lesson 16 — Compare Two Fractions

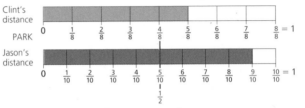

Guided Instruction

Essential Question: How can you use equivalent fractions to compare fractions? 4.NF.2

Words to Know: benchmark

In this lesson you will learn how to compare fractions that have different numerators and different denominators.

Understand: Using benchmarks to make comparisons

> Clint and Jason are meeting at the park. Clint is $\frac{5}{8}$ mile away, and Jason is $\frac{9}{10}$ mile away. If the boys ride their bicycles at the same speed, who will reach the park first?

A benchmark is an amount that you know and can use to compare or estimate other amounts.
To compare $\frac{5}{8}$ and $\frac{9}{10}$, you can use $\frac{1}{2}$ and 1 as benchmarks.

Look at the models. Compare the fractions to $\frac{1}{2}$ and 1.

Clint's distance
PARK
$0 \quad \frac{1}{8} \quad \frac{2}{8} \quad \frac{3}{8} \quad \frac{4}{8} \quad \frac{5}{8} \quad \frac{6}{8} \quad \frac{7}{8} \quad \frac{8}{8} = 1$

Jason's distance
$0 \quad \frac{1}{10} \quad \frac{2}{10} \quad \frac{3}{10} \quad \frac{4}{10} \quad \frac{5}{10} \quad \frac{6}{10} \quad \frac{7}{10} \quad \frac{8}{10} \quad \frac{9}{10} \quad \frac{10}{10} = 1$
$\frac{1}{2}$

Notice that $\frac{4}{8} = \frac{1}{2}$, and $\frac{5}{8}$ is greater than $\frac{4}{8}$ by 1 eighth.

Clint's distance: $\frac{5}{8} = \frac{1}{2} + \frac{1}{8}$. So $\frac{5}{8}$ is much closer to $\frac{1}{2}$ than $\frac{8}{8}$, or 1.

Notice that $\frac{10}{10} = 1$, and $\frac{9}{10}$ is less than 1 by 1 tenth.

Jason's distance: $\frac{9}{10} = \frac{10}{10} - \frac{1}{10}$. So $\frac{9}{10}$ is much closer to 1 than to $\frac{1}{2}$.

$\frac{9}{10}$ is closer to 1 on the number line than $\frac{5}{8}$ is, so $\frac{9}{10} > \frac{5}{8}$.

➡ Jason is farther from the park, so Clint will reach the park first.

You can compare the fractions in this problem because both distances are fractions of a mile. They refer to the same whole amount, 1 mile.

✏➤ Suppose that Clint is $\frac{7}{8}$ mile away and Jason is $\frac{9}{10}$ mile away and both travel at the same speed. Who will reach the park first? **Clint will, as $\frac{7}{8} < \frac{9}{10}$.**

> **Remember!**
> When fractions have the same denominator, compare the numerators to see which is greater.

142   Unit 3 ▪ Focus on Number and Operations—Fractions

Words to Know

benchmark: a known amount that can be used to compare or estimate other amounts

Glossary can be found on pp. 347–350.

Lesson 16

Guided Instruction

Understand: Using equivalent fractions to make comparisons

> Allison has to buy clay for her art class. She is choosing between two pieces of clay. One piece is $\frac{2}{3}$ pound, and the other piece is $\frac{3}{4}$ pound. The pieces feel about the same weight. Which piece is heavier?

To decide which piece is heavier, use equivalent fractions to find the greater fraction. You can compare $\frac{2}{3}$ and $\frac{3}{4}$ because they are parts of the same whole, 1 pound.

One way to compare the fractions is to write equivalent fractions with the same denominator. Use the product of the two denominators as the denominator of the equivalent fractions: $\frac{2}{3}$ and $\frac{3}{4}$; $3 \times 4 = 12$

Write equivalent fractions for $\frac{2}{3}$ and $\frac{3}{4}$ with 12 as the denominator.

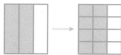
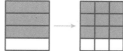

$$\frac{2}{3} = \frac{2 \times 4}{3 \times 4} = \frac{8}{12} \qquad \frac{3}{4} = \frac{3 \times 3}{4 \times 3} = \frac{9}{12}$$

Compare the numerators to compare the fractions.

$\frac{8}{12} < \frac{9}{12}$, so $\frac{2}{3} < \frac{3}{4}$ and $\frac{3}{4} > \frac{2}{3}$

➡ The $\frac{3}{4}$ pound piece of clay is heavier.

Another way to compare the fractions is to write equivalent fractions with the same numerator. Use the product of the numerators as the numerator of the equivalent fractions: $\frac{2}{3}$ and $\frac{3}{4}$; $2 \times 3 = 6$.

Write equivalent fractions for $\frac{2}{3}$ and $\frac{3}{4}$ with 6 as the numerator.

$$\frac{2}{3} = \frac{2 \times 3}{3 \times 3} = \frac{6}{9} \qquad \frac{3}{4} = \frac{3 \times 2}{4 \times 2} = \frac{6}{8}$$

To compare the fractions, compare the denominators. Recall that unit fractions of $\frac{1}{9}$ are smaller than unit fractions of $\frac{1}{8}$.

$\frac{1}{9} < \frac{1}{8}$, so $\frac{6}{9} < \frac{6}{8}$. This means $\frac{2}{3} < \frac{3}{4}$ and $\frac{3}{4} > \frac{2}{3}$.

Unit 3 ▪ Focus on Number and Operations—Fractions **143**

Support English Language Learners

The term *benchmark* is used in a variety of ways and contexts. Write the word *benchmark* on the board and draw a web around it. As a class, think of descriptions of the word, such as something used as a reference point or something used to measure other things against, and write them in the outer circles of the web. Ask volunteers to suggest things that are used as benchmarks and to use the term in a sentence. Finally, ask students to explain which meaning is closest to the context of the lesson.

Understand: Using equivalent fractions to make comparisons

■ In this presentation, students compare two fractions with different denominators and numerators by writing equivalent fractions with the same denominator (or numerator). To use this strategy, students must determine a denominator (or numerator) for the equivalent fractions.

■ When two fractions have the same denominator, the fraction with the greater numerator is greater. Explain that the fractions represent a multiple of the same unit fraction. So, students can compare the numerators, just as they would compare whole numbers.

■ When two fractions have the same numerator, the fraction with the smaller denominator is greater. This may seem counterintuitive to some students that $\frac{6}{9} < \frac{6}{8}$, because students know that $9 > 8$. Students must reason about the size of the fractions. Have students recall that a greater number in the denominator means that the size of the unit fractions is smaller, so $\frac{1}{9} < \frac{1}{8}$. Use visual fraction models to support this conclusion.

■ After working through the page with students, check students' understanding by asking: *Why can you use equivalent fractions with either the same denominator or the same numerator to compare two fractions?* Students should explain that it does not matter how you rewrite a fraction because equivalent fractions still represent the same amount.

Guided Instruction

Connect: Benchmarks and equivalent fractions Use this page to help students strengthen their understanding of how to compare fractions using visual fraction models and equivalent fractions with the same denominator.

■ Some students may suggest multiplying the denominators to find a common denominator of 48. Tell students this method will yield a common multiple of 4 and 12, but they should look for a smaller common denominator to make calculations easier.

■ Have students rewrite the answer using a less than symbol (<) instead of the greater than symbol (>).

✏ Suggest that students reread the word problem and focus on the measurement unit used with the fractions. They should notice that both fractions describe part of an hour.

■ Extend students' understanding of comparing the same whole by presenting these situations: *Can you compare $\frac{1}{4}$ pound of apples to $\frac{3}{4}$ pound of oranges? Can you compare a large container of water that is $\frac{1}{4}$ of the way full to a small container of water that is $\frac{3}{4}$ of the way full?* Be sure students can correctly identify the whole in each situation.

Students should explain that in the first situation, a pound is the whole, so you can compare pounds of apples to pounds of oranges. Even though the items are different, the fractions refer to the same whole, a pound. In the second situation, the whole is a container. Since the containers are two different sizes, the fractions do not refer to the same whole, so you cannot compare the fractions.

Guided Instruction

Connect: Benchmarks and equivalent fractions

> Kevin needs to buy poster board before the stores close. The drugstore closes in $\frac{3}{4}$ hour. The office supply store closes in $\frac{8}{12}$ hour. Which store is open longer?

You can use models or the same denominator to compare the fractions $\frac{3}{4}$ and $\frac{8}{12}$.

Notice that $12 = 3 \times 4$. You can use 12 as the denominator for the fractions. This means you only need to find one equivalent fraction.

Method 1 Compare with Models
Draw models of the fractions.

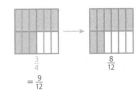

$$\frac{3}{4}$$ $$\frac{8}{12}$$

$$= \frac{9}{12}$$

$\frac{9}{12}$ covers more area than $\frac{8}{12}$.
This means $\frac{9}{12} > \frac{8}{12}$, so $\frac{3}{4} > \frac{8}{12}$.

Method 2 Compare with the Same Denominator
Use 12 as the denominator to compare $\frac{3}{4}$ and $\frac{8}{12}$.
Write an equivalent fraction for $\frac{3}{4}$.

$$\frac{3}{4} = \frac{3 \times 3}{3 \times 4} = \frac{9}{12}$$

$\frac{9}{12} > \frac{8}{12}$, so $\frac{3}{4} > \frac{8}{12}$.

➡ The drugstore is open a little longer than the office supply store.

✏ Why can you compare the two fractions to compare the amounts of time?
Both fractions are parts of the same whole, 1 hour.

Math-to-Measurement Connection

Tools A socket wrench is a tool used to tighten or remove a bolt. Since bolts come in different sizes, a socket wrench has different sockets to fit around a variety of bolts. The size of the sockets in one set are $\frac{1}{4}$-, $\frac{5}{16}$-, $\frac{3}{8}$-, $\frac{7}{16}$-, $\frac{1}{2}$-, $\frac{9}{16}$-, $\frac{5}{8}$-, $\frac{11}{16}$-, $\frac{3}{4}$-, $\frac{13}{16}$-, and $\frac{7}{8}$-inch. It helps to know how to compare fractions with different denominators when using a socket wrench. For example, if you are using a $\frac{5}{8}$-inch socket and it is too small, you need to try the next bigger size socket.

If possible, have a socket wrench set available for the class. Each socket has a fraction imprinted on it to indicate the size. Have students compare some of the fractions listed above. Students can check their answers by comparing the actual size of the sockets. This activity allows students to see how fractions are used in the real world.

MORE ONLINE sadlierconnect.com

Lesson 16

Guided Practice

For exercises 1–3, use the models.

1. Label the model to show:

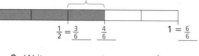

- $\frac{6}{10}$ and $\frac{4}{6}$
- equivalent fractions for $\frac{1}{2}$
- equivalent fractions for 1
- the unit from $\frac{1}{2}$ to $\frac{6}{10}$
- the unit from $\frac{1}{2}$ to $\frac{4}{6}$

$0 \qquad \frac{1}{2}=\frac{5}{10} \quad \frac{6}{10} \qquad 1=\frac{10}{10}$

$0 \qquad \frac{1}{2}=\frac{3}{6} \quad \frac{4}{6} \qquad 1=\frac{6}{6}$

2. Circle the fraction that is farther from $\frac{1}{2}$.

$\frac{6}{10}$ $\boxed{\frac{4}{6}}$

3. Write <, =, or > to compare the fractions.

$\frac{6}{10} \; \underline{<} \; \frac{4}{6}$

Use the models to compare the fractions. Label the models to show any benchmarks you use. Then write >, =, or <.

4. $\frac{2}{6} \; \underline{>} \; \frac{3}{12}$

5. $\frac{4}{10} \; \underline{<} \; \frac{5}{8}$

Use equivalent fractions to compare.

6. Use the same numerator to compare $\frac{1}{4}$ and $\frac{2}{10}$.

$\frac{1}{4} = \frac{2 \times 1}{2 \times 4} = \frac{2}{8} \qquad \frac{2}{10} = \frac{1 \times 2}{1 \times 10} = \frac{2}{10}$

$\frac{2}{8} \; \underline{>} \; \frac{2}{10}$, so $\frac{1}{4} \; \underline{>} \; \frac{2}{10}$

7. Use the same denominator to compare $\frac{9}{12}$ and $\frac{4}{5}$.

$\frac{9}{12} = \frac{5 \times 9}{5 \times 12} = \frac{45}{60} \qquad \frac{4}{5} = \frac{12 \times 4}{12 \times 5} = \frac{48}{60}$

$\frac{45}{60} \; \underline{<} \; \frac{48}{60}$, so $\frac{9}{12} \; \underline{<} \; \frac{4}{5}$

Think • Pair • Share

MP8 8. Which pair of fractions from exercises 1–7 could you easily compare using a different method? Discuss your choice with a partner and explain your reasoning below. Possible explanation: In exercise 5, instead of a model I could use $\frac{1}{2}$ as a benchmark to compare $\frac{4}{10}$ and $\frac{5}{8}$. I know $\frac{4}{8} = \frac{1}{2}$, so $\frac{5}{8} > \frac{1}{2}$. Since $\frac{5}{10} = \frac{1}{2}$, and $\frac{4}{10} < \frac{5}{10}$, $\frac{4}{10} < \frac{1}{2}$. So $\frac{4}{10} < \frac{5}{8}$.

Unit 3 ■ Focus on Number and Operations—Fractions **145**

Observational Assessment

Use page 145 to assess whether students are able to use visual fraction models to compare two fractions. Watch for students who are unable to transfer the visual comparison to a written conclusion.

Think•Pair•Share

Peer Collaboration Ask students to answer the question then choose a partner. Partners should discuss their choices and explain their reasoning. When students have finished discussing, ask the class questions such as:

- *Did you use benchmarks for any of the exercises? Which benchmarks did you use?*

- *Did you use equivalent fractions for any of the exercises? Which equivalent fractions did you use?*

To summarize, tell students that when comparing fractions, the fractions can be rewritten as equivalent fractions with the same denominator or the same numerator or the fractions can be compared to benchmark fractions.

Return to the Essential Question

Reread the Lesson 16 Essential Question on page 142: *How can you use equivalent fractions to compare fractions?*

Ask volunteers to use what they learned in this lesson to answer this question. (Possible responses: I can write the fractions as equivalent fractions with the same denominator and compare the numerators. I can write the fractions as equivalent fractions with the same numerator and compare the denominators.)

Invite as many volunteers as possible to express ideas in their own words about comparing fractions.

Mathematical Practices

Mathematical Practice Standards underline the teaching and understanding of all concepts and skills presented. The emphasis of specific practices is noted throughout the guided and independent practice of this lesson.

MP8	**Look for and express regularity in repeated reasoning.**

Item 8: Students must determine and explain which pair of fractions could be compared using a different method.

Independent Practice

Concept Application

Students may work independently on these pages in the classroom or at home. They may refer to the first four pages of the lesson to revisit the instruction on comparing fractions or to see a worked-out example.

Common Errors and **Teaching Tips** may help you support student learning either in the classroom or as a follow-up for work done at home.

Teaching Tips

Items 1–4

If students have difficulty writing the fraction pairs as equivalent fractions with the same denominator or numerator, remind them that they can also use fraction strips to compare the two fractions.

Independent Practice

Write >, =, or < to compare each fraction to $\frac{1}{2}$.

1. $\frac{8}{10}$ __>__ $\frac{1}{2}$
2. $\frac{6}{12}$ __=__ $\frac{1}{2}$
3. $\frac{45}{100}$ __<__ $\frac{1}{2}$
4. $\frac{1}{1}$ __>__ $\frac{1}{2}$

Color or label the models to show the fractions and any benchmarks you use. Then write >, =, or < to compare. Coloring and benchmarks may vary.

5. $\frac{6}{8}$ __=__ $\frac{3}{4}$

6. $\frac{1}{4}$ __<__ $\frac{2}{6}$ 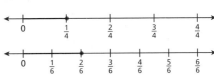

7. $\frac{9}{12}$ __>__ $\frac{7}{10}$ 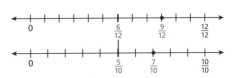

Draw a model to show the fractions. Then write >, =, or < to compare. Models will vary.

8. $\frac{1}{6}$ __<__ $\frac{2}{5}$

9. $\frac{2}{8}$ __<__ $\frac{3}{4}$

Writing About Math

✏ • **Write an Explanatory Text** Ask students to choose one of the methods from the lesson that they used to compare fractions with different denominators. Have them write a paragraph explaining how to use the method they chose. Tell students that they can include details and examples from the lesson, as well as any illustrations that help them explain the method. When students are finished, have volunteers present their work to the class.

Lesson 16

Independent Practice

Write equivalent fractions with the same denominator or numerator to compare the fractions. Show your work.

10. Compare $\frac{5}{6}$ and $\frac{7}{12}$.

$$\frac{5}{6} = \frac{2 \times 5}{2 \times 6} = \frac{10}{12}$$

$$\frac{10}{12} > \frac{7}{12} \qquad \frac{5}{6} \; > \; \frac{7}{12}$$

11. Compare $\frac{3}{8}$ and $\frac{1}{3}$.

$$\frac{1}{3} = \frac{3 \times 1}{3 \times 3} = \frac{3}{9}$$

$$\frac{3}{8} > \frac{3}{9}$$

$$\frac{3}{8} \; > \; \frac{1}{3}$$

12. Compare $\frac{11}{12}$ and $\frac{3}{4}$.

$$\frac{3}{4} = \frac{3 \times 3}{3 \times 4} = \frac{9}{12}$$

$$\frac{11}{12} > \frac{9}{12}$$

$$\frac{11}{12} \; > \; \frac{3}{4}$$

13. Compare $\frac{5}{4}$ and $\frac{7}{5}$.

$$\frac{5}{4} = \frac{5 \times 5}{5 \times 4} = \frac{25}{20} \qquad \frac{7}{5} = \frac{4 \times 7}{4 \times 5} = \frac{28}{20}$$

$$\frac{25}{20} < \frac{28}{20}$$

$$\frac{5}{4} \; < \; \frac{7}{5}$$

Write >, =, or < to compare the fractions. You can use models to help.

14. $\frac{2}{4} \; = \; \frac{5}{10}$

15. $\frac{3}{5} \; < \; \frac{8}{10}$

16. $\frac{6}{8} \; > \; \frac{4}{6}$

17. $\frac{4}{12} \; < \; \frac{2}{5}$

18. $\frac{2}{2} \; > \; \frac{1}{3}$

19. $\frac{9}{12} \; < \; \frac{9}{8}$

For exercises 20 and 21, circle the correct answer.

20. Tricia has $\frac{5}{6}$ hour before she has to go to bed. How much time can she spend reading before she goes to bed?

a. $\frac{3}{4}$ hour

b. $\frac{7}{8}$ hour

c. $\frac{9}{10}$ hour

d. $\frac{11}{12}$ hour

21. Adam needs red balloons for a party. In a package of long balloons, $\frac{1}{3}$ of the balloons are red. In a package of jumbo balloons, $\frac{2}{5}$ of the balloons are red and $\frac{3}{5}$ are white. Which of these statements is true?

a. The package of jumbo balloons has more red balloons.

b. The package of long balloons has more red balloons.

c. The fractions cannot be compared without knowing the number of balloons in each package.

d. The total number of red balloons is less than the number of white jumbo balloons.

Common Errors

Items 10-19

If students reverse the meaning of the > and < symbols, have them write each symbol and its meaning at the top of their paper.

Teaching Tips

Items 10-12

Students may compare each pair using like denominators. Encourage them to compare at least one pair using like numerators.

Item 20

Point out that students are looking for the answer choice that is less than $\frac{5}{6}$ hour. It might help some students to represent the parts of an hour on a clock.

Digital Connection

Online Activities Use a search engine to find activities and games about equivalent fractions or comparing fractions. Make sure to use a program that allows for parameters on the numerators and denominators, so that you do not reach out of students' realm of understanding fractions. Also, be sure to use a program that includes the use of fraction strips, number lines, or another modeling technique.

Independent Practice

Teaching Tips

Item 22

Encourage students to compare the two fractions by first using 30 as the denominator and then using 3 as the numerator. Then have them compare the work for each method.

Items 24–25

Point out that the fractions in these problems can be compared because they refer to the same whole.

Independent Practice

MP6 **22.** Kelly uses 30 as a denominator for equivalent fractions to compare $\frac{3}{10}$ and $\frac{1}{3}$. Is this easier than using 3 as a numerator for equivalent fractions to compare $\frac{3}{10}$ and $\frac{1}{3}$? Explain.

Possible explanation: No, it is easier to use 3 as a numerator. Then you only have to find an equivalent fraction for $\frac{1}{3}$ instead of both fractions, since $\frac{3}{10}$ already has 3 as a numerator.

MP1 **23.** When can writing equivalent fractions be more helpful for comparing fractions than visual models? Give one example.

Answers will vary. Possible answer: To compare fractions with many parts, like $\frac{27}{100}$ and $\frac{3}{5}$, I would rather multiply to write equivalent fractions than draw a number line or area model. It would be hard to make sure the models and each equal part are the same size for both fractions.

Solve the problems.

MP2 **24.** In art class, Amber uses $\frac{7}{12}$ pound of modeling clay and Cole uses $\frac{5}{8}$ pound. Who uses more clay, Amber or Cole?

▸ **Show your work.** Work may vary. Possible work:
Use $\frac{1}{2}$ to compare. $\frac{1}{2} = \frac{6}{12} = \frac{4}{8}$
$\frac{7}{12} = \frac{1}{2} + \frac{1}{12}$
$\frac{5}{8} = \frac{1}{2} + \frac{1}{8}$
$\frac{1}{8} > \frac{1}{12}$, there are fewer equal parts in the whole, so each equal part is bigger.
So $\frac{5}{8} > \frac{7}{12}$.
Answer Cole uses more clay.

MP7 **25.** Two cereal boxes are the same size. The box of corn flakes is $\frac{11}{12}$ full. The box of wheat puffs is $\frac{9}{10}$ full. Which cereal box has more cereal?

▸ **Show your work.** Work may vary. Possible work: The corn flakes box has more cereal. Both boxes are missing just 1 equal part of the whole box. $\frac{1}{12} < \frac{1}{10}$, because the whole is divided into a greater number of parts, so each part is smaller. This means the corn flakes box is missing less cereal than the wheat puffs box.

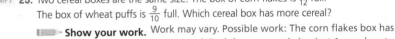

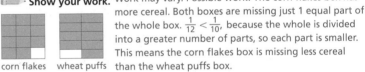

corn flakes   wheat puffs

Answer The corn flakes box has more cereal.

Mathematical Practices

MP1	**Make sense of problems and persevere in solving them.**
Item 23: Students draw a conclusion and explain their reasoning.	
MP2	**Reason abstractly and quantitatively.**
Item 24: Students select a solution method and show their work.	
MP6	**Attend to precision.**
Item 22: Students analyze and explain ways to compare fractions.	
MP7	**Look for and make use of structure.**
Item 25: Students see that the missing parts can be used to compare.	

MP6 **26.** Jeff has $\frac{200}{100}$ dollars in pennies, and Michelle has $\frac{25}{10}$ dollars in dimes. Who has more money, Jeff or Michelle?

> **Show your work.** Work may vary. Possible work:

$$\frac{200}{100} = \frac{200 \div 10}{100 \div 10} = \frac{20}{10}$$

$$\frac{20}{10} < \frac{25}{10} \text{ because } 20 < 25$$

$$\frac{200}{100} < \frac{25}{10}$$

Answer Michelle has more money.

MP3 **27.** Sam says that you cannot use $\frac{1}{2}$ as a benchmark when you are comparing fractions with odd denominators, like $\frac{2}{5}$. Do you agree? Use this example to support your answer.

Answer No, I do not agree.

> **Justify your answer using words, drawings, or numbers.**

Possible justification: With any number of parts, $\frac{1}{2}$ will always be exactly in between 0 and 1. $\frac{1}{3}$ has an odd denominator, but you can still find $\frac{1}{2}$ between $\frac{1}{3}$ and $\frac{2}{3}$ on a number line.

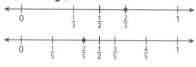

To compare $\frac{2}{3}$ and $\frac{2}{5}$, I know $\frac{2}{3}$ is to the right of $\frac{1}{2}$ and $\frac{2}{5}$ is to the left of $\frac{1}{2}$, because $\frac{1}{2}$ is in between $\frac{2}{5}$ and $\frac{3}{5}$. So $\frac{2}{3}$ has to be greater than $\frac{2}{5}$.

MP1 **28.** Donna and her brother are raking leaves. Donna rakes $\frac{1}{4}$ of her yard and her brother rakes $\frac{1}{2}$ of her neighbor's yard. Donna's brother says he has raked more than Donna, because $\frac{1}{2} > \frac{1}{4}$. Is this always true?

Answer No, it is not always true.

> **Justify your answer using words, drawings, or numbers.**

Possible justification:

Neighbor's yard   Donna's yard

The problem does not say that the whole yards are the same size. The neighbor's yard could be much smaller than Donna's yard, like in my model. Even if her brother rakes $\frac{1}{2}$ of this yard, Donna might rake twice as much as he does.

Teaching Tips

Items 27-28

Caution students about drawing quick conclusions. Suggest that students draw models to illustrate the problem situation and then consider whether the problem could be interpreted another way.

Mathematical Practices

MP1	**Make sense of problems and persevere in solving them.**
Item 28: Students analyze a problem and draw a conclusion.	
MP3	**Construct viable arguments and critique the reasoning of others.**
Item 27: Students draw a conclusion and present an argument to support it.	
MP6	**Attend to precision.**
Item 26: Students write equivalent fractions with the same numerator or denominator and compare them.	

Common Core Focus:

4.NF.3a Understand addition and subtraction of fractions as joining and separating parts referring to the same whole.

OBJECTIVE

Add and subtract fractions of the same whole.

ESSENTIAL QUESTION

Remind students that fractions represent parts of a whole. Tell students that the situations for adding and subtracting fractions are very similar to the situations for adding and subtracting whole numbers. Students use parts of a whole in many different ways, such as sharing a sandwich or figuring out how much pizza is left over.

PREREQUISITE SKILLS

Use Item H on page 340 of the Foundational Skills Handbook to review the meaning of unit fractions.

FLUENCY PRACTICE

Fluency practice is available at **sadlierconnect.com**.

Concept Development

Understand: Addition of fractions with like denominators

■ Students must understand that a combination of unit fractions, fractions with 1 in the numerator, join together to make a fraction with a number greater than 1 in the numerator. This provides an understanding of fractions as a sum of their parts, which helps students add and subtract greater fractional amounts.

✏➤ Encourage students to draw a picture similar to the one in the middle of the page to represent the equation they write. Point out that as the numerator of the sum increases, more of the total area is shaded, and that the denominator stays the same.

Lesson 17

Add and Subtract Fractions with Like Denominators

Essential Question:
What happens when you find a sum or difference of fractions?
4.NF.3a

Words to Know:
like denominators

Guided Instruction

In this lesson you will learn why you can add and subtract fractions of the same whole.

Understand: Addition of fractions with like denominators

> Tanya cuts a pan of brownies into 12 equal pieces. She puts 1 piece on a plate for her mother. Then she adds 1 piece for herself, and 1 piece for her sister. What fraction of the brownies does Tanya put on the plate?

To find the fraction of the brownies Tanya put on the pan, think of each brownie as one twelfth, or $\frac{1}{12}$, of the whole pan.

Write the number of twelfths and a fraction for each number of twelfths. Then add the numerators to find the total number of twelfths.

Remember!
The numerator is the number of equal parts in a fraction.

Mother		Tanya		Sister		Total on Plate
1 twelfth	+	1 twelfth	+	1 twelfth	=	3 twelfths
$\frac{1}{12}$	+	$\frac{1}{12}$	+	$\frac{1}{12}$	=	$\frac{3}{12}$

➤ Tanya puts $\frac{3}{12}$ of the brownies on the plate.

In this problem, the addends and the sum have like denominators. This means that the denominators are alike or the same. Fractions with like denominators are made up by putting together the same unit fractions.

✏➤ Write an equation to show Tanya putting 1 more brownie on the plate.

$$\frac{3}{12} + \frac{1}{12} = \frac{4}{12}$$

Words to Know

like denominators: the denominators of two or more fractions that are the same

Example: In $\frac{3}{8} + \frac{1}{8} = \frac{4}{8}$ the fractions have like denominators.

Glossary can be found on pp. 347–350.

MORE ONLINE ⊕ sadlierconnect.com Lesson 17

Guided Instruction

Understand: Adding unit fractions to add fractions

Tanya and her sister drink milk with their brownies. Tanya drinks $\frac{3}{4}$ pint of milk. Her sister drinks $\frac{2}{4}$ pint of milk. How much milk do Tania and her sister drink in all?

To find the amount of milk Tania and her sister drink, add the fractions $\frac{3}{4}$ and $\frac{2}{4}$.

$$\frac{3}{4} + \frac{2}{4} = \overbrace{\frac{1}{4} + \frac{1}{4} + \frac{1}{4}}^{\frac{3}{4}} + \overbrace{\frac{1}{4} + \frac{1}{4}}^{\frac{2}{4}}$$ Decompose the fractions into unit fractions.

$$= \frac{1 + 1 + 1 + 1 + 1}{4}$$ Add the numerators.

$$= \frac{5}{4}$$ Notice that 5 is the sum of 3 + 2.

➡ Tania and her sister drink $\frac{5}{4}$ pints of milk in all.

Understand: Subtraction of fractions with like denominators

Tanya has put a total of $\frac{4}{12}$ of the pan of brownies on a plate. What fraction of the brownies does Tanya leave in the pan?

A whole pan of brownies is $\frac{12}{12}$. Subtract $\frac{4}{12}$ from $\frac{12}{12}$ to find the number of twelfths left in the pan.

When fractions have like denominators, you can subtract the numerators to find the difference.

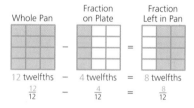

Whole Pan		Fraction on Plate		Fraction Left in Pan
12 twelfths	−	4 twelfths	=	8 twelfths
$\frac{12}{12}$	−	$\frac{4}{12}$	=	$\frac{8}{12}$

➡ Tanya leaves $\frac{8}{12}$ of the brownies in the pan.

Support English Language Learners

Help students understand the meaning of *like denominators*. Ask students what *like* means. Students will probably say that it means to think something or someone is good or cool. Explain that *like* can also be used to describe objects that are similar or the same. Tell students that fractions with *like* denominators have the *same* denominator.

As students proceed through the lesson, use fraction strips to demonstrate the meaning of *like denominators*. Show examples of unit fractions with like and unlike denominators and compare them. Allow students to see and feel the differences between like and unlike denominators.

Understand: Adding unit fractions to add fractions

■ Help students see the similarity between the area model on the previous page and the symbolic model used to show addition.

■ If students have difficulty breaking fractions into their unit fractional equivalents, ask them to add ones to equal 3 and add ones to equal 2. Then show that *fourths* are just a unit name added to each of the ones: 1 + 1 + 1 = 3 becomes 1 fourth + 1 fourth + 1 fourth = 3 fourths.

■ A common error when adding fractions is adding the numerators and adding the denominators. Use models to show that this reasoning is incorrect.

■ Have students read the addition equation aloud to help them connect the meaning of the denominator as the size of the unit fraction. Relate fraction addition to whole number addition by comparing the strategy of adding 3 tens + 2 tens = 5 tens to adding 3 fourths + 2 fourths = 5 fourths.

Understand: Subtraction of fractions with like denominators

■ Make connections between what students already know about whole number subtraction and what occurs in the numerator when they subtract fractions with like denominators. Help students see that they can use the basic subtraction fact 12 − 4 = 8 to solve this question.

■ Use this example to strengthen the understanding that when adding or subtracting like fractions, only the numerators are added or subtracted; the denominator is unchanged. Demonstrate that subtracting the denominators in this example would give a denominator of 0.

Connect: Add and subtract fractions with the same denominator Use this page to help students connect models of fraction addition and subtraction with symbolic representations.

■ Explain the differences and similarities between a number line and a fraction bar. Allow students to explain the benefits of each type of model. Point out that fraction representations are similar to whole number representations in that they increase in value when moving to the right and decrease in value when moving to the left.

■ Encourage kinesthetic learning by asking students to use their fingers to "jump" along the number line as they add and subtract unit fractions. Show students that the answer is the final point where they land.

■ Fraction strips are an effective tool for modeling addition and subtraction of fractions with the same denominator. Provide students with their own strip of paper to draw and shade a fraction bar model.

Connect: Add and subtract fractions with the same denominator

> Gavin has a wood board that is $\frac{7}{8}$ yard long. If he uses only $\frac{5}{8}$ yard for his project, how much wood does Gavin have left over?

To find the length of wood left over, subtract $\frac{5}{8}$ from $\frac{7}{8}$. You can use number lines and fraction bars as models.

Identify the whole: 1 yard. Show the board length on the models.

The blue point locates $\frac{7}{8}$. | The blue bar shows $\frac{7}{8}$.

Find the number of unit fractions in the amount to subtract:
$\frac{5}{8} = \frac{1}{8} + \frac{1}{8} + \frac{1}{8} + \frac{1}{8} + \frac{1}{8}$

Use the number line to subtract. Count back 5 unit fractions of $\frac{1}{8}$. | Use the fraction bar to subtract. Cross out 5 unit fractions of $\frac{1}{8}$.

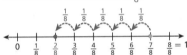 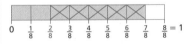

The red point locates $\frac{2}{8}$, the amount left over. The difference is $\frac{2}{8}$. $\frac{7}{8} - \frac{5}{8} = \frac{2}{8}$ | The red fraction $\frac{2}{8}$ shows the amount left over.

Add to check the difference, just like with whole numbers. Start at $\frac{5}{8}$.

From $\frac{5}{8}$, count up 2 unit fractions of $\frac{1}{8}$. | From $\frac{5}{8}$, add on 2 unit fractions of $\frac{1}{8}$.

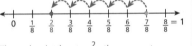 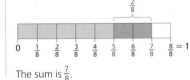

The sum is $\frac{7}{8}$. | The sum is $\frac{7}{8}$.

➡ Gavin has $\frac{2}{8}$ yard of wood left over.

Math-to-Cooking Connection

Fractions in Recipes Fraction addition and subtraction has practical applications in cooking and baking, which often uses fractional parts of measures in recipes. Students may have doubled a recipe and may understand the idea of adding an additional amount of each ingredient to keep the recipe balanced. Practicing this skill provides an introduction to later fraction multiplication. Suggest that students find a recipe at home that they or their parents make regularly and rewrite the recipe so that it will make twice as much. Point out that this will be the equivalent of making the recipe twice. Ask students to write out both the original recipe and its double, showing the fraction addition necessary to create the second recipe.

Guided Practice

Complete the equation to represent the problem. Add or subtract to solve.

1.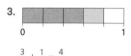

$\frac{1}{4} + \frac{1}{4} = \frac{2}{4}$

1 fourth + 1 fourth = __2__ fourths

2.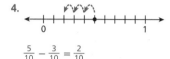

$\frac{6}{6} - \frac{2}{6} = \frac{4}{6}$

6 sixths − 2 sixths = __4__ sixths

3.

$\frac{3}{5} + \frac{1}{5} = \frac{4}{5}$

4.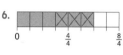

$\frac{5}{10} - \frac{3}{10} = \frac{2}{10}$

Color or draw on the model to represent the problem. Then add or subtract to solve.

5.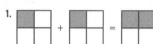

$\frac{1}{2} + \frac{1}{2} = \frac{2}{2} = 1$

6.

$\frac{6}{4} - \frac{3}{4} = \frac{3}{4}$

Find the sum or difference.

7. $\frac{5}{3} - \frac{1}{3} = \frac{4}{3}$

8. $\frac{5}{12} + \frac{9}{12} = \frac{14}{12}$

☺ Think • Pair • Share

MP4   9. Lisa drew the model at the right to add $\frac{1}{3} + \frac{1}{3}$. What sum did she find?

Explain Lisa's mistake. Possible explanation:
Lisa's sum is $\frac{2}{6}$, which is equal to $\frac{1}{3}$. She added the numerators, but she added the denominators too. This gave her a different whole with 6 equal parts. The correct sum is 2 thirds, or $\frac{2}{3}$, since she is adding 1 third and 1 third.

Unit 3 ■ Focus on Number and Operations—Fractions   **153**

Mathematical Practices

Mathematical Practice Standards underline the teaching and understanding of all concepts and skills presented. The emphasis of specific practices is noted throughout the guided and independent practice of this lesson.

MP4   Model with mathematics.

Item 9: Students analyze a model to determine whether the solution is accurate.

Observational Assessment

Use page 153 to assess whether students add and subtract fractions with like denominators accurately. Ensure that they focus on addition and subtraction using the numerators of the fractions.

Before students complete exercise 6, discuss that they should use Xs to represent subtraction in the model. Suggest that they can first shade the fractional part of the whole, and then place an X over the parts that are being subtracted.

☺ Think•Pair•Share

Peer Collaboration Encourage students to draw their own models and compare their models with Lisa's model. Ask students to share their models in small groups and use them to explain Lisa's error. If groups still have difficulty determining the error, ask:

- *How would you describe each fractional part in Lisa's model?*

- *How would you read the fact that Lisa modeled aloud?*

- *How did the size of Lisa's models change?*

Lisa's mistake is a common mistake that students make when they first learn to add and subtract fractions. Remind students that fractions can be added or subtracted only if they refer to the same whole, so the size of the model should not change.

Return to the Essential Question

Reread the Lesson 17 Essential Question on page 150: *What happens when you find a sum or difference of fractions?*

Ask volunteers to use what they learned in this lesson to answer this question. (Possible responses: I can add or subtract fractions with 1 in the numerator and the same denominator to equal the total number of parts of the same whole. When the denominators are the same, I can add or subtract the numerators.)

Independent Practice

Concept Application

Students may work independently on these pages in the classroom or at home. They may refer to the first four pages of the lesson to revisit the instruction or to see a worked-out example.

Common Errors and **Teaching Tips** may help you support student learning either in the classroom or as a follow-up for work done at home.

Teaching Tips

Items 1–2

Remind students to shade the models to match the problems and use Xs to show parts that are subtracted.

Item 4

Explain to students that they can use Xs to represent the subtrahend (the number being subtracted) in the subtraction problem. Point out that they need to subtract twice to find the difference.

Item 5

If students have difficulty identifying this problem, ask them whether it represents addition or subtraction. Explain that two fractional amounts are combined, which suggests addition.

Independent Practice

Color or draw on the model to represent the problem. Then add or subtract to solve.

1. $\frac{1}{3} + \frac{1}{3} = \frac{2}{3}$

2. $\frac{5}{6} - \frac{2}{6} = \frac{3}{6}$

Color or draw on the model to find the sum or difference. Then write an equation to represent the problem.

3.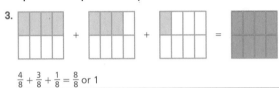

$\frac{4}{8} + \frac{3}{8} + \frac{1}{8} = \frac{8}{8}$ or 1

4.

$\frac{7}{5} - \frac{4}{5} - \frac{1}{5} = \frac{2}{5}$

5.

0                                    $\frac{10}{10} = 1$

$\frac{2}{10} + \frac{7}{10} = \frac{9}{10}$

6. Which difference is modeled below?

0                              $\frac{12}{12}$

   a. $\frac{7}{12} - \frac{3}{12} = \frac{4}{12}$ b. $\frac{10}{12} - \frac{3}{12} = \frac{7}{12}$

   c. $\frac{12}{12} - \frac{2}{12} = \frac{10}{12}$ d. $\frac{10}{12} - \frac{7}{12} = \frac{3}{12}$

Talking About Math

Collaborative Conversations Have students work in pairs. Have one partner explain how to add fractions with like denominators. Have the other partner explain how to subtract fractions with like denominators. Encourage students to use models to aid them in their explanations. Partners should then discuss the similarities and differences in their explanations and their models. This is a good exercise for students to communicate with precision and share reasoning with others.

Lesson 17

Independent Practice

Add or subtract. Draw a model to support your answer.   Models may vary.

7. $\frac{3}{4} - \frac{2}{4} = \frac{1}{4}$

8. $\frac{2}{2} + \frac{1}{2} = \frac{3}{2}$

9. $\frac{4}{5} + \frac{3}{5} = \frac{7}{5}$

$\frac{4}{5}$ $\frac{3}{5}$

10. $\frac{12}{10} - \frac{5}{10} = \frac{7}{10}$

Write a fraction to complete the equation. You can use models to help.

11. $\frac{5}{6} + \frac{1}{6} = \frac{6}{6}$

12. $\frac{6}{8} - \frac{3}{8} = \frac{3}{8}$

13. $\frac{8}{12} + \frac{5}{12} = \frac{13}{12}$

14. $\frac{7}{3} - \frac{5}{3} = \frac{2}{3}$

Unit 3 ■ Focus on Number and Operations—Fractions   **155**

Common Errors

Items 11–14

Students may be confused because they are now finding missing numbers in the problems, not just the sum or difference. Explain that students can use what they know about related facts and inverse operations to find the missing numbers. Remind students that when they use like denominators, the denominator for the missing number will be the same.

Teaching Tips

Items 7–10

Invite students to share different types of models for the same problem. Students who are having difficulty with one type of model may find another student's model easier to understand.

Digital Connection

Virtual Manipulatives Use a search engine to find online virtual manipulatives for fractions. Look for different types of manipulatives, such as fraction strip models and circle models. Invite students to use some of the online models to represent problems from this lesson or other problems that they create themselves. Ask students to represent the problem with a model and invite other students to write the symbols that match the problem. Be sure students include both addition and subtraction problems.

Independent Practice

Teaching Tips

Item 15

As a class, write a list of some possible situations that involve fractions. Leave this list on the board or wall so that students can use it as a springboard for ideas to write their own problems.

Independent Practice

MP6 **15.** Write an addition word problem that involves fractions. Then solve your problem.

Answers will vary. Possible answer: A pizza is cut into 6 equal slices. If I eat $\frac{2}{6}$ of the pizza, and my friend eats $\frac{2}{6}$ of the pizza, what fraction of the pizza did we eat altogether? The answer is $\frac{4}{6}$, because $\frac{2}{6} + \frac{2}{6} = \frac{4}{6}$. This is the same as $\frac{2}{3}$ of the pizza.

MP2 **16.** Jack buys a package of gum that has 4 packs. He gives 1 pack of gum to his friend and 1 pack to his father. Explain why the equation below represents this problem.

$$\frac{4}{4} - \frac{2}{4} = \frac{2}{4}$$

Possible explanation: The whole package is $\frac{4}{4}$, because it has 4 equal packs of gum. Each pack is $\frac{1}{4}$ of the package, so two packs is $\frac{2}{4}$. The two packs that Jack gives away are subtracted at the same time. The fraction of the whole package that is left is $\frac{2}{4}$.

Solve the problems.

MP4 **17.** There are 8 books in Audrey's favorite book series. Audrey reads 5 of the books over the winter vacation. What fraction of the series does Audrey have left to read?

▸ **Show your work.**
Work may vary.
Possible work:

$$\frac{8}{8} - \frac{5}{8} = \frac{3}{8}$$

Answer Audrey has $\frac{3}{8}$ of the series left to read.

MP6 **18.** Kenneth walks $\frac{1}{5}$ mile to his friend's house. Then they walk $\frac{3}{5}$ mile to the ice cream store, and $\frac{2}{5}$ mile back to Kenneth's house. How far does Kenneth walk altogether?

▸ **Show your work.** Work may vary. Possible work:

$$\frac{1}{5} + \frac{3}{5} + \frac{2}{5} = \frac{1 + 3 + 2}{5} = \frac{6}{5}$$

Answer Kenneth walks $\frac{6}{5}$ miles altogether.

Mathematical Practices

MP2	**Reason abstractly and quantitatively.**

Item 16: Students analyze a symbolic representation and determine whether it appropriately represents the problem.

MP4	**Model with mathematics.**

Item 17: Students use models to represent the fractional part of a whole.

MP6	**Attend to precision.**

Item 15: Students accurately use fraction addition or subtraction in a story.

Item 18: Students use computation and measurement units to solve.

Independent Practice

MP1 **19.** Mikayla makes smoothies with $\frac{3}{4}$ pound of blueberries and $\frac{2}{4}$ pound of strawberries. Carly makes smoothies with $\frac{1}{6}$ pound of banana and $\frac{4}{6}$ pound of strawberries. Whose smoothies have more than 1 whole pound of fruit?

▶ **Show your work.** Work may vary. Possible work:

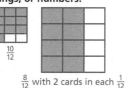

Mikayla's Smoothies
blueberries   strawberries

Carly's Smoothies
banana

strawberries

Answer _Mikayla's smoothies have more than 1 whole pound of fruit._

MP2 **20.** Jordan answers $\frac{8}{10}$ of the questions on a quiz correctly. On her second quiz, Jordan answers $\frac{9}{10}$ of the questions correctly. If both quizzes have the same number of questions, on which quiz did Jordan have more answers wrong?

Answer _Jordan had more wrong answers on the first quiz._

▶ **Justify your answer using words, drawings, or numbers.**
Possible justification: The whole quiz is $\frac{10}{10}$.
First quiz: $\frac{10}{10} - \frac{8}{10} = \frac{2}{10}$ wrong
Second quiz: $\frac{10}{10} - \frac{9}{10} = \frac{1}{10}$ wrong
$\frac{2}{10} > \frac{1}{10}$

MP7 **21.** Oliver is choosing between two packs of baseball cards. In one pack, $\frac{8}{12}$ of the cards are for his favorite teams. In the other pack, $\frac{10}{12}$ of the cards are for his favorite teams. Oliver says he will get more cards that he likes with the second pack. Is Oliver correct?

Answer _Oliver may not be correct._

▶ **Justify your answer using words, drawings, or numbers.**
Possible justification: $\frac{10}{12} - \frac{8}{12} = \frac{2}{12}$, but Oliver can only subtract the fractions if both packs are the same size, or have the same total number of cards. For example, $\frac{1}{12}$ could represent 1 of 12 cards in a pack or 2 of 24 cards in a pack.

$\frac{10}{12}$

$\frac{8}{12}$ with 2 cards in each $\frac{1}{12}$

Common Errors

Item 21

Students may simply complete the subtraction and think that they have solved the problem. Students must realize that the packs might contain different numbers of cards in order to determine the potential that Oliver is incorrect. Before answering this question, ask students to make a list of *what we know*, such as the fraction of cards for Oliver's favorite teams in each pack, and a list of what *we do not know*, such as the number of cards in each pack.

Teaching Tips

Item 19

When a lot of numbers are given in a word problem, students may have trouble organizing the data in a meaningful way. Suggest that they write the amount of each fruit in each smoothie by using a list or table before solving the problem. This will help them attribute values to the appropriate girl in the problem.

Mathematical Practices		
MP1	**Make sense of problems and persevere in solving them.**	
Item 19: Students determine the important information for each part of the problem and plan the solution process.		
MP2	**Reason abstractly and quantitatively.**	
Item 20: Students understand the meaning of fractions in determining the relative size of quantities.		
MP7	**Look for and make use of structure.**	
Item 21: Students step back for an overview of the different values the fractions potentially represent to solve the problem situation.		

Common Core Focus:

4.NF.3b Decompose a fraction into a sum of fractions with the same denominator in more than one way, recording each decomposition by an equation. Justify decompositions.

OBJECTIVE

Decompose a fraction or mixed number into a sum of fractions with like denominators.

ESSENTIAL QUESTION

Remind students that when they add or subtract whole numbers, they sometimes need to regroup 10 ones as a ten or break apart a ten into 10 ones. In this lesson, they will learn how to break apart, or decompose, fractions and mixed numbers.

FLUENCY PRACTICE

Fluency practice is available at **sadlierconnect.com**.

Concept Development

Understand: Ways to break apart a whole

■ Students need to understand that there is more than one way to decompose a fraction into a sum of fractions with like denominators.

■ Review unit fractions before beginning this lesson. In Grade 3, students learned that a fraction is composed of unit fractions: $\frac{3}{4} = \frac{1}{4} + \frac{1}{4} + \frac{1}{4}$. This presentation shows students that there is more than one way to decompose a fraction other than just using unit fractions.

▰▰▰▰ ▸ Some students may benefit from using real quarters to model Sydney's equations. Tell students that an easy way to write a different equation is to switch the order of the fractions. Challenge students to write 4 additional equations.

---

18 Decompose a Fraction as a Sum of Fractions

Essential Question: How can you decompose a fraction or mixed number into a sum of fractions with the same denominator?

4.NF.3b

Words to Know: decompose mixed number

Guided Instruction

In this lesson you will learn how to decompose fractions and mixed numbers and write them as sums of other fractions.

Understand: Ways to break apart a whole

> Sydney collects quarters. She arranges them in rows of 4 quarters. She arranges the quarters in each row in a different way. Then she writes an equation to describe the arrangement. What are some equations she writes?

To find the equations she writes, recall that 1 quarter is $\frac{1}{4}$ of 1 dollar. This means that 4 quarters are $\frac{4}{4}$ of 1 dollar.

She makes a row with 4 groups of 1 quarter each.

Remember!
$\frac{4}{4} = 1$, because 4 unit fractions of $\frac{1}{4}$ equal 1 whole.

She writes $\frac{4}{4} = \frac{1}{4} + \frac{1}{4} + \frac{1}{4} + \frac{1}{4}$.

She makes a row with 2 groups of 1 quarter and 1 group of 2 quarters.

She writes $\frac{4}{4} = \frac{1}{4} + \frac{1}{4} + \frac{2}{4}$.

She makes a row with 1 group of 1 quarter and 1 group of 3 quarters.

She writes $\frac{4}{4} = \frac{1}{4} + \frac{3}{4}$.

▸ Some equations Sydney writes are $\frac{4}{4} = \frac{1}{4} + \frac{1}{4} + \frac{1}{4} + \frac{1}{4}$, $\frac{4}{4} = \frac{1}{4} + \frac{1}{4} + \frac{2}{4}$, and $\frac{4}{4} = \frac{1}{4} + \frac{3}{4}$.

▰▰▰ ▸ Compare the equations that Sydney wrote. Possible answer: They all have a sum of $\frac{4}{4}$ but the fractions in each sum are different.

Words to Know

decompose: breaking apart a fraction by writing it as a sum of other fractions with the same denominator

mixed number: a number that shows the sum of a whole number and a fraction but does not have a plus sign

Example: $4\frac{1}{2}$

Glossary can be found on pp. 347–350.

Lesson 18

Guided Instruction

Understand: Ways to decompose a fraction

> For Fred's math and art project, he draws identical rectangles with 8 equal sections. He uses 6 sections in each rectangle to represent $\frac{6}{8}$ and paints them to show ways to decompose $\frac{6}{8}$. Then he writes equations to describe his work. What kinds of sums do Fred's equations describe?

You can decompose, or break apart, a fraction by writing it as the sum of other fractions with the same denominator.

One way to decompose $\frac{6}{8}$ is to write it as the sum of unit fractions.

$$\frac{6}{8} = \frac{1}{8} + \frac{1}{8} + \frac{1}{8} + \frac{1}{8} + \frac{1}{8} + \frac{1}{8}$$

Another way to decompose $\frac{6}{8}$ is to write it as the sum of unit fractions and other fractions.

$$\frac{6}{8} = \frac{1}{8} + \frac{2}{8} + \frac{3}{8}$$

A third way to decompose $\frac{6}{8}$ is to write it as the sum of fractions that are not unit fractions.

$$\frac{6}{8} = \frac{2}{8} + \frac{2}{8} + \frac{2}{8}$$

➤ Fred's equations describe sums of unit fractions, of unit fractions and other fractions, and of fractions that are not unit fractions.

▪️ Color the rectangle to show another way to decompose $\frac{6}{8}$. Then write an equation to describe your work. **Answers will vary. Possible answer shown.**

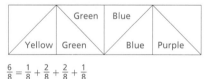

	Green	Blue	
Yellow	Green	Blue	Purple

$$\frac{6}{8} = \frac{1}{8} + \frac{2}{8} + \frac{2}{8} + \frac{1}{8}$$

Support English Language Learners

Discuss with students what it means to *decompose* a fraction. To compare the meaning of *compose* and *decompose*, explain that "de-" is a prefix that means "to do the opposite of." Comparing the definitions of compose and decompose will help strengthen students' understanding of prefixes and how they can be used to determine the meaning of an unfamiliar word.

Write both words on the board and have students read them aloud with you. Write the appropriate definition under each term. Include a few equations showing both composition and decomposition, and have students identify which method is being used by reciting the definitions on the board.

Understand: Ways to decompose a fraction

▪️ In this presentation, students examine how to decompose a fraction by writing it as the sum of other fractions with the same denominator. To use this strategy, students should start by determining the unit fraction that is used to build the fraction they want to decompose.

▪️ Explain that each color represents one of the fractions written below each model. Guide students to realize that the three models are not all of the possible ways to decompose the fraction, but that the models show a general approach: sums of unit fractions, sums of unit fractions and other fractions, and sums of fractions that are not unit fractions.

▪️ It may help students to decompose the numerator first. There are many different ways to decompose 6, such as 1 + 5, 2 + 4, 3 + 3, and so on. Each number that is greater than one can be decomposed further.

▪️ Challenge students to identify the greatest fraction they can use when decomposing $\frac{6}{8}$. They should identify $\frac{5}{8}$ as the greatest fraction.

▪️ Have students explain why they cannot use $\frac{7}{8}$ in their equations.

✏️ After students have answered this question, ask a few volunteers to read their answers aloud. Keep a list of the different equations students find. Point out that there are many possible combinations.

Guided Instruction

Connect: Fractions and mixed numbers

Use this page to help students strengthen their understanding of how to decompose a fraction or a mixed number into a sum of fractions with like denominators.

■ Explain to students that a fraction with a numerator greater than its denominator can be rewritten as a mixed number.

■ Use a number line to show that the location of $\frac{9}{4}$ is the same as the location of $2\frac{1}{4}$.

■ Have the class determine a general approach they can use to write a fraction as a mixed number. Students should look for ways to decompose a fraction into fractions that will result in a 1.

✏ Have students share their comparisons. Be sure to discuss the possible answer given on the page. Ask students which way was easier for them to use.

■ After working through the page, students should be able to explain that the whole number part of the mixed number can be written as a fraction and then added to the fraction part to get another fraction. A mixed number is a fraction in a different form.

Guided Instruction

Connect: Fractions and mixed numbers

> Jason has $\frac{9}{4}$ quarts of milk. Is that more or less than 2 quarts of milk?

To decide, write $\frac{9}{4}$ as a mixed number. Then compare the mixed number to 2. A mixed number shows the sum of a whole number and a fraction but does not have a + sign.

$$\frac{9}{4} = \frac{4}{4} + \frac{4}{4} + \frac{1}{4} \qquad \text{Write } \frac{9}{4} \text{ as a sum of fractions.}$$
$$= 1 + 1 + \frac{1}{4} \qquad \text{Write } \frac{4}{4} \text{ as 1.}$$
$$= \quad 2 \quad + \frac{1}{4} \qquad \text{Add the whole numbers.}$$
$$= 2\frac{1}{4} \qquad \text{Write the sum as a mixed number.}$$

Remember!
$\frac{4}{4} = 1$

Compare. $2\frac{1}{4} > 2$, because $2 + \frac{1}{4}$ is more than 2.

➡ Jason has more than 2 quarts of milk.

✏ Try a different way to compare $\frac{9}{4}$ and 2. Write 2 as a fraction and compare it with $\frac{9}{4}$. Why is the answer the same?
Possible answer: $2 = \frac{8}{4}$, $\frac{9}{4} > \frac{8}{4}$. If $\frac{9}{4}$ is greater than $\frac{8}{4}$ then $\frac{9}{4}$ is greater than 2 since you are using equivalent fractions which represent the same amount.

> Ms. Gordon has $4\frac{1}{2}$ dozen eggs to make scrambled eggs for breakfast at camp. She uses $\frac{1}{2}$ dozen for each batch. How many batches can she make?

To find out, write $4\frac{1}{2}$ as a fraction with a denominator of 2. The numerator will be the number of half-dozens of eggs.

$$4\frac{1}{2} = 4 + \frac{1}{2} \qquad \text{Write } 4\frac{1}{2} \text{ as a sum of 4 plus } \frac{1}{2}.$$
$$= 1 + 1 + 1 + 1 + \frac{1}{2} \qquad \text{Write 4 as a sum of 1s.}$$
$$= \frac{2}{2} + \frac{2}{2} + \frac{2}{2} + \frac{2}{2} + \frac{1}{2} \qquad \text{Write 1 as a fraction with the denominator 2.}$$
$$= \frac{2 + 2 + 2 + 2 + 1}{2} \qquad \text{Add the numerators.}$$
$$= \frac{9}{2}; \text{ The numerator is 9. There are 9 half-dozens of eggs.}$$

➡ Ms. Gordon can make 9 batches of scrambled eggs.

Math-to-Geometry Connection

Composite Figures Students have already worked with composing and decomposing two- and three-dimensional figures in previous grades. In later grades, students will learn to find perimeters, areas, and volumes of composite figures.

Have students work with manipulatives to compose and decompose various shapes. Use the models on page 159 to show how triangles can be used to form squares, trapezoids, and rectangles. Have students write fraction equations for their models.

Guided Practice

Complete each equation to write the fraction as a sum of other fractions. Use the model to help you.

1. $\frac{3}{5} = \frac{1}{5} + \frac{1}{5} + \frac{1}{5}$

$\frac{3}{5} = \frac{2}{5} + \frac{1}{5}$ Addends may vary.

2. $\frac{9}{8} = \frac{2}{8} + \frac{2}{8} + \frac{2}{8} + \frac{2}{8} + \frac{1}{8}$

| $\frac{1}{8}$ | $\frac{1}{8}$ | $\frac{1}{8}$ | $\frac{1}{8}$ | $\frac{1}{8}$ | $\frac{1}{8}$ | $\frac{1}{8}$ | $\frac{1}{8}$ |

$\frac{9}{8} = \frac{1}{8} + \frac{2}{8} + \frac{3}{8} + \frac{3}{8}$ Addends may vary.

| $\frac{1}{8}$ | | | | | | | |

$\frac{9}{8} = \frac{3}{8} + \frac{2}{8} + \frac{4}{8}$

Write each mixed number as a fraction. Show your work.

3. $2\frac{2}{3} = \frac{8}{3}$

4. $1\frac{5}{8} = \frac{13}{8}$

5. $4\frac{3}{5} = \frac{23}{5}$

Write each fraction as a mixed number.

6. $\frac{9}{4} = \underline{2\frac{1}{4}}$

7. $\frac{7}{2} = \underline{3\frac{1}{2}}$

8. $\frac{10}{3} = \underline{3\frac{1}{3}}$

⚘ Think · Pair · Share

MP6 **9.** Michael writes $\frac{10}{12}$ as $\frac{10}{10} + \frac{2}{12}$. Draw a model to show Michael's sum.
Is his sum correct? If not, what mistakes did he make?
Possible answer: Michael's sum is not correct. First, $\frac{10}{12}$ is
less than 1, but his sum is the mixed number $1\frac{2}{12}$. Second,
the denominator shows the total number of equal parts
in the whole, not the numerator. He should also use the
same unit fraction for both parts of a mixed number.

$\frac{10}{10} = 1$ $\frac{2}{12}$

Mathematical Practices

Mathematical Practice Standards underline the teaching and understanding of all concepts and skills presented. The emphasis of specific practices is noted throughout the guided and independent practice of this lesson.

| MP6 | **Attend to precision.** |

Item 9: Students use fractions appropriately to find the mistakes made in the item.

Observational Assessment

Use page 161 to assess whether students are able to decompose fractions and mixed numbers into the sum of other fractions.

⚘ Think·Pair·Share

Peer Collaboration Ask each student to draw a model of Michael's solution and then use it to solve the problem. Have students work with a partner to discuss their answers. As students work, ask questions such as:

- *What is the unit fraction for this problem?*

- *How can you rewrite $\frac{10}{10}$?*

- *How does your model help you identify Michael's mistake?*

To summarize, tell students that to decompose a fraction or mixed number, they can use unit fractions or fractions that are not unit fractions, but their fractions must have the same denominator.

Return to the Essential Question

Reread the Lesson 18 Essential Question on page 158: *How can you decompose a fraction or mixed number into a sum of fractions with the same denominator?*

Ask volunteers to use what they learned in this lesson to answer this question. (Possible response: I can break apart a fraction or a mixed number and write it as a sum of other fractions with like denominators.)

Independent Practice

Concept Application

Students may work independently on these pages in the classroom or at home. They may refer to the first four pages of the lesson to revisit the instruction or to see a worked-out example.

Common Errors and **Teaching Tips** may help you support student learning either in the classroom or as a follow-up for work done at home.

Teaching Tips

Items 3–5

Remind students that each fraction can be composed of a sum of unit fractions, a sum of unit fractions and other fractions, and a sum of fractions that are not unit fractions.

Independent Practice

Complete each equation to write the number as a sum of other fractions in different ways. Use the model to help you. Addends may vary.

1. $\frac{3}{4} = \frac{1}{4} + \frac{1}{4} + \frac{1}{4}$

   $\frac{3}{4} = \frac{1}{4} + \frac{2}{4}$

2. $1\frac{4}{5} = \frac{1}{} + \frac{4}{5}$

   $1\frac{4}{5} = \frac{5}{5} + \frac{4}{5}$

   $1\frac{4}{5} = \frac{2}{5} + \frac{3}{5} + \frac{4}{5}$

Write the fraction as a sum of other fractions in four different ways. Draw a model if it helps. Addends may vary.

3. $\frac{9}{12}$

   $\frac{9}{12} = \frac{1}{12} + \frac{1}{12} + \frac{1}{12} + \frac{1}{12} + \frac{1}{12} + \frac{1}{12} + \frac{1}{12} + \frac{1}{12} + \frac{1}{12}$

   $\frac{9}{12} = \frac{1}{12} + \frac{3}{12} + \frac{5}{12}$

   $\frac{9}{12} = \frac{3}{12} + \frac{3}{12} + \frac{3}{12}$

   $\frac{9}{12} = \frac{2}{12} + \frac{3}{12} + \frac{4}{12}$

4. $\frac{10}{10}$

   $\frac{10}{10} = \frac{2}{10} + \frac{2}{10} + \frac{2}{10} + \frac{2}{10} + \frac{2}{10}$

   $\frac{10}{10} = \frac{1}{10} + \frac{2}{10} + \frac{3}{10} + \frac{4}{10}$

   $\frac{10}{10} = \frac{5}{10} + \frac{5}{10}$

   $\frac{10}{10} = \frac{1}{10} + \frac{2}{10} + \frac{1}{10} + \frac{2}{10} + \frac{1}{10} + \frac{2}{10} + \frac{1}{10}$

5. $\frac{12}{5}$

   $\frac{12}{5} = \frac{5}{5} + \frac{5}{5} + \frac{2}{5}$

   $\frac{12}{5} = \frac{1}{5} + \frac{1}{5} + \frac{1}{5} + \frac{2}{5} + \frac{2}{5} + \frac{5}{5}$

   $\frac{12}{5} = \frac{4}{5} + \frac{4}{5} + \frac{4}{5}$

   $\frac{12}{5} = \frac{1}{5} + \frac{2}{5} + \frac{3}{5} + \frac{1}{5} + \frac{2}{5} + \frac{3}{5}$

Writing About Math

■──── › **Write an Explanatory Text** Have students write an explanation about how to decompose a fraction. Tell students their paper should have three parts: words, numbers, and a model. Students often have a choice to explain their reasoning using words, numbers, or models, but they should be proficient in all three areas.

When students are done, ask for volunteers to share their work. Ask students which method was easiest for them to use in their explanations and which method was most difficult. For a method that was difficult for a student, ask another student to share their thought process for that method.

MORE ONLINE sadlierconnect.com   Lesson 18

Independent Practice

Circle the correct answer.

6. Which sum is not equivalent to $\frac{5}{6}$?

    a. $\frac{1}{6} + \frac{2}{6} + \frac{2}{6}$ **b.** $\frac{3}{6} + \frac{2}{6}$

    (c.) $\frac{1}{6} + \frac{1}{6} + \frac{1}{6}$ **d.** $\frac{4}{6} + \frac{1}{6}$

7. Which sum is equivalent to $\frac{10}{3}$?

    (a.) $3 + \frac{1}{3}$ **b.** $\frac{3}{3} + \frac{6}{3}$

    c. $2 + \frac{3}{3}$ **d.** $10 + \frac{1}{3}$

8. Look at the red point on the number line. It represents a fraction. Jessica wants to write the fraction as a sum of three addends.

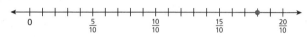

So far, she has two addends, $\frac{4}{10}$ and $\frac{6}{10}$. Which of the following can Jessica use as the third addend?

    a. $\frac{10}{10}$ **b.** $\frac{18}{10}$

    c. $1\frac{8}{10}$ **(d.)** $\frac{8}{10}$

Write each number as a sum in three different ways. You can use a model to help. Then answer the question below. Answers may vary.

9. $2\frac{2}{12}$

    $= \underline{\quad 2 + \frac{2}{12} \quad}$

    $= \underline{\quad 1 + 1 + \frac{2}{12} \quad}$

    $= \underline{\quad \frac{12}{12} + \frac{8}{12} + \frac{6}{12} \quad}$

10. $\frac{22}{12}$

    $= \underline{\quad \frac{12}{12} + \frac{10}{12} \quad}$

    $= \underline{\quad 1 + \frac{10}{12} \quad}$

    $= \underline{\quad \frac{10}{12} + \frac{10}{12} + \frac{2}{12} \quad}$

11. Compare $2\frac{2}{12}$ and $\frac{22}{12}$. Write $<$, $=$, or $>$.

    $2\frac{2}{12} \underline{\quad > \quad} \frac{22}{12}$

Common Errors

Item 6

Some students may read the item incorrectly and miss the word *not* in the question. This may lead to further confusion choosing the correct answer since three of the sums are equivalent to $\frac{5}{6}$. Remind students to look for *not* in multiple-choice items.

Teaching Tips

Item 11

Point out that the numbers being compared were used in items 9 and 10. Tell students they can rewrite the mixed number as a fraction or rewrite the fraction as a mixed number. Both numbers should be either in the form of mixed numbers or in the form of fractions before they make a comparison.

Digital Connection

Interactive Whiteboard Use the interactive whiteboard to create a fraction or mixed number. You can show it in number form or with models. Then invite students to come up and show a way to decompose the fraction or mixed number. Have another student show a different way to decompose the same fraction or mixed number. Repeat this process with another fraction or mixed number. You can vary between equations and models. Invite a student to give the class a fraction or mixed number to decompose. Make sure students are paying attention to like denominators and are able to name the unit fraction for each example.

Common Errors

Item 14

Be sure that students understand that Juan could buy more than one scoop of ice cream per visit. Students need to determine how to break up the fraction into 4 addends since there were 4 visits.

Teaching Tips

Item 15

Guide students to see that there is more than one correct solution for this problem. After you have given students a chance to solve, invite volunteers to share their answers. Record all the different solutions they find.

Independent Practice

MP3 **12.** To write $\frac{35}{10}$ as a sum, Matt says you can find addends by subtracting fractions from $\frac{35}{10}$ until there is nothing left. Does Matt's method work? Explain.

Yes, Matt's method works. Possible explanation: This is like using subtraction to check an addition problem. If you subtract correctly, the fractions subtracted will add back up to $\frac{35}{10}$, the amount you started with. For example, $\frac{35}{10} - \frac{10}{10} = \frac{25}{10}$, $\frac{25}{10} - \frac{10}{10} = \frac{15}{10}$, and $\frac{15}{10} - \frac{15}{10} = 0$. So $\frac{35}{10} = \frac{10}{10} + \frac{10}{10} + \frac{15}{10}$.

MP2 **13.** Brianna is making a patchwork quilt with different size patches. She has a strip of fabric that is $1\frac{4}{8}$ yards long. How can writing $1\frac{4}{8}$ as a sum help Brianna to cut up the strip of fabric?

Answers will vary. Possible answer: Brianna can write $1\frac{4}{8}$ as a sum with different addends to decide how many pieces to cut and what size the pieces should be. This can help her to use all of the fabric and cut it correctly.

Solve the problems.

MP4 **14.** For each scoop of ice cream that you buy, the ice-cream shop crosses out 1 of the 8 boxes on a card. After 4 visits, $\frac{7}{8}$ of Juan's card is crossed out. Write an addition equation to show how Juan's card could have been crossed out in 4 visits.

▬▬► **Show your work.**
Work and answers may vary.
Possible work:

$\frac{8}{8} - \frac{1}{8} = \frac{7}{8}$
4 visits mean 4 addends.
$\frac{7}{8} = \frac{1}{8} + \frac{2}{8} + \frac{1}{8} + \frac{3}{8}$

Answer $\frac{7}{8} = \frac{1}{8} + \frac{2}{8} + \frac{1}{8} + \frac{3}{8}$ _____

MP7 **15.** Bella serves pizza at her birthday party. Each pizza is cut into 6 equal slices. There are $\frac{13}{6}$ pizzas left after the party is over. The slices are in 3 different pizza boxes, and none of the boxes are full. What fraction of a whole pizza can be in each box?

▬▬► **Show your work.**

Work and answers may vary. Possible work:

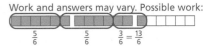

$\frac{5}{6}$ $\frac{5}{6}$ $\frac{3}{6} = \frac{13}{6}$

Answer The boxes can have $\frac{5}{6}$, $\frac{5}{6}$, and $\frac{3}{6}$ of a pizza. _____

Mathematical Practices

MP2	**Reason abstractly and quantitatively.**
Item 13: Students decompose mixed numbers to solve.	
MP3	**Construct viable arguments and critique the reasoning of others.**
Item 12: Students explain how to relate addition and subtraction to decompose fractions.	
MP4	**Model with mathematics.**
Item 14: Students interpret the solution to arrive at one possible answer.	
MP7	**Look for and make use of structure.**
Item 15: Students evaluate the context of a real-world problem.	

Independent Practice

MP2 **16.** Travis's family uses an automatic cat feeder when they are not home. The feeder has 8 sections that can each hold 1 cup of food. Travis has $\frac{26}{4}$ cups of cat food. Does he have enough to fill each section in the feeder with a full cup?

▮▬ **Show your work.** Work may vary.
Possible work:

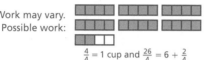

$\frac{4}{4} = 1$ cup and $\frac{26}{4} = 6 + \frac{2}{4}$

Answer <u>No, Travis can fill 6 sections with a full cup of food, and 1 more section with $\frac{2}{4}$ cup.</u>

MP1 **17.** A piece of wood is $4\frac{2}{6}$ yards long. If $\frac{3}{6}$ yard is needed to make 1 shelf, how many shelves can you make from the piece of wood?

Answer <u>I can make 8 shelves from the piece of wood.</u>

▮▬ **Justify your answer using words, drawings, or numbers.**

Possible justification: $4\frac{2}{6} = 1 + 1 + 1 + 1 + \frac{2}{6}$
$= \frac{6}{6} + \frac{6}{6} + \frac{6}{6} + \frac{6}{6} + \frac{2}{6}$
$= \frac{3}{6} + \frac{3}{6} + \frac{3}{6} + \frac{3}{6} + \frac{3}{6} + \frac{3}{6} + \frac{3}{6} + \frac{3}{6} + \frac{2}{6}$

There are 8 addends of $\frac{3}{6}$ yard, so there are 8 pieces that are each $\frac{3}{6}$-yard long.

MP8 **18.** To find the whole amounts in $\frac{27}{5}$, Molly divides the numerator by the denominator. Then she writes the remainder as the fraction part of a mixed number. Does Molly's method work? Draw a model and write $\frac{27}{5}$ as a sum to help support your answer.

Answer <u>Yes, Molly's method works.</u>

▮▬ **Justify your answer using words, drawings, or numbers.**
Possible justification:

$$5\overline{)27} \\ \underline{-25} \\ 2 \leftarrow \text{remainder}$$

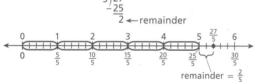

remainder $= \frac{2}{5}$

$\frac{27}{5} = 1 + 1 + 1 + 1 + 1 + \frac{2}{5} = 5\frac{2}{5}$

Unit 3 ▪ Focus on Number and Operations—Fractions   **165**

Teaching Tips

Item 18

This is an introduction to the method of using division to write fractions as mixed numbers. Students may not know how to form the fraction from the remainder and the divisor after completing the division. Be sure to review this with students and then encourage them to solve the problem by decomposing the fraction.

Mathematical Practices

MP1	**Make sense of problems and persevere in solving them.**

Item 17: Students use pencil and paper and/or models to solve the problem.

MP2	**Reason abstractly and quantitatively.**

Item 16: Students consider units in order to solve this item.

MP8	**Look for and express regularity in repeated reasoning.**

Item 18: Students explain the relationship between division and decomposition of fractions to justify their solution.

Common Core Focus:

4.NF.3c Add and subtract mixed numbers with like denominators.

OBJECTIVE

Learn different methods for adding and subtracting mixed numbers with like denominators.

ESSENTIAL QUESTION

In this lesson, students extend their understanding of adding and subtracting fractions with like denominators to adding and subtracting mixed numbers with like denominators.

FLUENCY PRACTICE

Fluency practice is available at **sadlierconnect.com**.

Concept Development

Understand: Adding mixed numbers

■ In this presentation, students will add mixed numbers with like denominators by replacing each mixed number with an equivalent fraction, and by using properties of operations.

■ The first method uses models of equivalent fractions. Explain that the first step when adding mixed numbers is to write the mixed numbers as equivalent fractions. Students should see that they can then add the numerators and write the sum over the like denominator.

■ Be sure students understand how to write the sum as a mixed number. Review decomposing fractions by showing $\frac{13}{4}$ as $\frac{4}{4} + \frac{4}{4} + \frac{4}{4} + \frac{1}{4} = 1 + 1 + 1 + \frac{1}{4}$.

■ The second method uses properties of addition. Remind students that a mixed number can be decomposed into the sum of a whole number and a fraction. This allows students to apply the properties of addition to add the whole numbers and then the fractions.

Lesson 19 — Add and Subtract Mixed Numbers with Like Denominators

Essential Question: What methods can you use for adding and subtracting mixed numbers? 4.NF.3c

Guided Instruction

In this lesson you will learn different methods for adding and subtracting mixed numbers with like denominators.

Understand: Adding mixed numbers

> Max is training his puppy to walk with a leash. He spends $1\frac{3}{4}$ hours at dog school. He also practices with his dog at the park for $1\frac{2}{4}$ hours. How much time does Max spend training his puppy altogether?

You can use models of equivalent fractions or properties of addition to find the sum of $1\frac{3}{4} + 1\frac{2}{4}$.

One way is to use models of equivalent fractions.

Model each mixed number.

$1\frac{3}{4}$

$1\frac{2}{4}$

Rename each mixed number as an equivalent fraction.

$1\frac{3}{4} = \frac{7}{4}$

$1\frac{2}{4} = \frac{6}{4}$

Add. Write the sum as a mixed number.

$\frac{7}{4} + \frac{6}{4} = \frac{13}{4} = \frac{12}{4} + \frac{1}{4}$

$= 3 + \frac{1}{4} = 3\frac{1}{4}$

Another way is to use properties of addition. Using the properties of addition, you can add mixed numbers by first breaking them apart and then adding the whole numbers and the fractions separately.

$1\frac{3}{4} + 1\frac{2}{4}$	Write the sum you want to find.
$(1 + \frac{3}{4}) + (1 + \frac{2}{4})$	Write the mixed numbers as sums.
$1 + (\frac{3}{4} + 1) + \frac{2}{4}$	Use the Associative Property.
$1 + (1 + \frac{3}{4}) + \frac{2}{4}$	Use the Commutative Property.
$(1 + 1) + (\frac{3}{4} + \frac{2}{4})$	Use the Associative Property.
$2 \quad + \quad \frac{5}{4}$	Add the whole numbers. Add the fractions.
$2 \quad + 1 + \frac{1}{4}$	Rename $\frac{5}{4}$.
$3 \quad + \frac{1}{4}$	Add the whole numbers.
$3\frac{1}{4}$	Write the mixed number.

➡ Max spends $3\frac{1}{4}$ hours training his puppy.

Support English Language Learners

The term *mixed numbers* may cause confusion for some students. The term *mixed numbers* is used only in mathematics, but *mixed* is used in other contexts. Ask students if they know the word *mix* or *mixed*. Some students may be familiar with these words as they relate to food, such as pancake mix, a salad of mixed greens, or a can of mixed nuts.

Help students see that each of these terms are a combination of different things. Students can think of a mixed number as a combination of a whole number and a fraction.

Lesson 19

Guided Instruction

Understand: Subtracting mixed numbers

Sofia is hanging a poster in her bedroom on the wall space between her windows. That space is $2\frac{1}{6}$ feet wide. Her poster is $1\frac{4}{6}$ feet wide. How much space is left after Sofia hangs her poster?

One way to subtract mixed numbers is to use equivalent fractions.

The models show that you need to regroup sixths to subtract $1\frac{4}{6}$ from $2\frac{1}{6}$.

Rename each mixed number as an equivalent fraction greater than 1, with 6 as the denominator.

$$2\frac{1}{6} = 1 + 1 + \frac{1}{6} \qquad 1\frac{4}{6} = 1 + \frac{4}{6}$$
$$= \frac{6}{6} + \frac{6}{6} + \frac{1}{6} \qquad = \frac{6}{6} + \frac{4}{6}$$
$$= \frac{13}{6} \qquad = \frac{10}{6}$$

Now subtract the fractions to find the difference.

$$2\frac{1}{6} - 1\frac{4}{6} = \frac{13}{6} - \frac{10}{6}$$
$$= \frac{13 - 10}{6}$$
$$= \frac{3}{6}$$

Remember!
To add or subtract fractions with like denominators, add or subtract the numerators.

➤ Sofia has $\frac{3}{6}$ foot of space left after she hangs the poster.

Another way to subtract is to use the relationship between addition and subtraction.

Change the subtraction problem to an addition problem with an unknown addend.

$$2\frac{1}{6} - 1\frac{4}{6} = ? \qquad 1\frac{4}{6} + ? = 2\frac{1}{6}$$

Use a number line to find the unknown addend. Locate $1\frac{4}{6}$, or $\frac{10}{6}$, and $2\frac{1}{6}$, or $\frac{13}{6}$.

The distance between them is the unknown addend: $\frac{3}{6}$.

Understand: Subtracting mixed numbers

■ In this presentation, students will subtract mixed numbers with like denominators by replacing each mixed number with an equivalent fraction, and also by using the relationship between addition and subtraction.

■ Instead of using equivalent fractions as shown in the first method, some students may subtract the whole number parts, $2 - 1 = 1$, and then subtract the lesser fraction from the greater fraction $\frac{4}{6} - \frac{1}{6} = \frac{3}{6}$ to get an incorrect difference of $1\frac{3}{6}$. Remind students that neither the Commutative Property nor the Associative Property applies to subtraction.

■ Students should understand that renaming mixed numbers with equivalent fractions can be used for both adding and subtracting mixed numbers.

■ The second method shows how to use the relationship between addition and subtraction to rewrite a subtraction as an addition. Student should then locate the known addend and the sum on the number line and find the difference.

Math-to-Real World Connection

Mixed Numbers Mixed numbers are commonly used with time and measurement. Ask students to think of real-life examples of mixed numbers. For example, when talking about time, the term $2\frac{1}{2}$ hours is commonly used rather than $\frac{5}{2}$ hours. Most notebook paper that students use is $8\frac{1}{2}$ inches by 11 inches. Many types of food are sold by weight, so you can buy $1\frac{1}{2}$ pounds of meat or $2\frac{3}{4}$ pounds of apples.

Have students find a real-life example of mixed numbers and write an addition or subtraction problem. Have students exchange their problems with another student and solve their partner's problems.

Connect: Using methods for adding and subtracting mixed numbers Use this page to help students strengthen their understanding of the methods used to add and subtract mixed numbers with like denominators.

■ Students may benefit from writing a word equation for this problem to see how the quantities are related.
Mitch's time + Ruby's time + Tony's time = 9 minutes

■ Encourage students to verbalize a plan to solve the problem in their own words. They should discuss what they know, what they need to find out, and what operations they will use to solve the problem.

■ In Step 1, ask students to explain how to represent each whole-number part of a mixed number as an equivalent fraction with the same denominator as the fraction part of the mixed number.

■ In Step 3, students should explain that if the fraction has a greater numerator than denominator then it can be decomposed into a whole number and a fraction.

Connect: Using methods for adding and subtracting mixed numbers

> Mitch, Ruby, and Tony are in a relay race. Mitch finishes the first part of the race in $3\frac{5}{10}$ minutes. Ruby does the second part in $2\frac{7}{10}$ minutes. If the team's total race time is 9 minutes, how long does Tony take to finish the last part?

To solve, add Mitch and Ruby's times, then subtract the sum from the team's total finishing time.

Step 1

Add $3\frac{5}{10}$ and $2\frac{7}{10}$ to find Mitch and Ruby's total time.

First, rename each mixed number as an equivalent fraction.

Since $1 = \frac{10}{10}$, you can find the total number of tenths in the whole number parts of the mixed numbers.

$$3\frac{5}{10} = \frac{10 \times 3}{10 \times 1} + \frac{5}{10} \qquad 2\frac{7}{10} = \frac{10 \times 2}{10 \times 1} + \frac{7}{10}$$
$$= \frac{30}{10} + \frac{5}{10} \qquad\qquad = \frac{20}{10} + \frac{7}{10}$$
$$= \frac{35}{10} \qquad\qquad\qquad = \frac{27}{10}$$

Remember!
You can write any whole number as a fraction with a denominator of 1.

Add the fractions. $\frac{35}{10} + \frac{27}{10} = \frac{35 + 27}{10} = \frac{62}{10}$

Step 2

Subtract $\frac{62}{10}$ from 9, the team's total time, to find Tony's time.

First, rename 9 as a fraction. $9 = \frac{10 \times 9}{10 \times 1} = \frac{90}{10}$

Subtract $\frac{62}{10}$ from $\frac{90}{10}$. $\frac{90}{10} - \frac{62}{10} = \frac{90 - 62}{10} = \frac{28}{10}$

Step 3

Rename the difference $\frac{28}{10}$ as a mixed number.

$$\frac{28}{10} = \frac{10}{10} + \frac{10}{10} + \frac{8}{10}$$
$$= 1 + 1 + \frac{8}{10}$$
$$= 2\frac{8}{10}$$

Remember!
Make sure the fraction in the mixed number is less than 1.

➡ Tony takes $2\frac{8}{10}$ minutes to finish the last part of the race.

Math-to-Art Connection

Framing Art Many artists build custom frames for their paintings. Frames come in varying widths based on the design. Artists can use a thin frame that may be $1\frac{1}{2}$ inches wide or a wide frame that is $5\frac{5}{8}$ inches wide. Search the Internet for a Web site that sells custom frames. Tell students that they need to frame a picture that is 24 inches by 18 inches. Have students choose a frame design and record the width of the frame. Students should draw a model for the picture and the frame and then determine how long and wide the final framed picture will be by adding the width of the frame to the dimensions of the picture. Remind students to add both sides of the frame to the length and width of the picture.

Guided Practice

Rename each mixed number as an equivalent fraction greater than 1. Then add or subtract.

1. Add $2\frac{1}{5}$ and $1\frac{3}{5}$.

   a. Rename $2\frac{1}{5}$ as a fraction. $2\frac{1}{5} = \frac{5}{5} + \frac{5}{5} + \frac{1}{5} = \frac{11}{5}$

   2 wholes

   b. Rename $1\frac{3}{5}$ as a fraction. $1\frac{3}{5} = \frac{5}{5} + \frac{3}{5} = \frac{8}{5}$

   c. Add the renamed fractions. $\frac{11}{5} + \frac{8}{5} = \frac{19}{5}$

   d. Write the sum as a mixed number. $\frac{19}{5} = \frac{5}{5} + \frac{5}{5} + \frac{5}{5} + \frac{4}{5} = 3\frac{4}{5}$

   e. Complete the addition equation. $2\frac{1}{5} + 1\frac{3}{5} = \underline{3}\ \underline{\frac{4}{5}}$

2. Subtract $1\frac{4}{8}$ from $3\frac{1}{8}$.

   a. To subtract $1\frac{4}{8}$ do you need to regroup $3\frac{1}{8}$? $\underline{Yes}$

   Why? Because $\frac{1}{8} \underline{<} \frac{4}{8}$

   b. Rename $1\frac{4}{8}$ as a fraction. $1\frac{4}{8} = \frac{8}{8} + \frac{4}{8} = \frac{12}{8}$

   c. Rename $3\frac{1}{8}$ as a fraction. $3\frac{1}{8} = \frac{8 \times 3}{8 \times 1} + \frac{1}{8} = \frac{24}{8} + \frac{1}{8} = \frac{25}{8}$

   d. Subtract the renamed fractions. $\frac{25}{8} - \frac{12}{8} = \frac{13}{8}$

   e. Write the difference as a mixed number. $\frac{13}{8} = \frac{8}{8} + \frac{5}{8} = \underline{1}\ \underline{\frac{5}{8}}$

   f. Complete the subtraction equation. $3\frac{1}{8} - 1\frac{4}{8} = \underline{1}\ \underline{\frac{5}{8}}$

3. Find the sum $5\frac{2}{12} + 2\frac{11}{12}$. Use the properties of addition to break apart the numbers to add. Show your work. Work may vary. Possible work:

   $5\frac{2}{12} + 2\frac{11}{12} = 5 + 2 + \frac{2}{12} + \frac{11}{12} = 7 + \frac{1}{12} + \frac{12}{12} = 7 + \frac{1}{12} + 1 = 8\frac{1}{12}$

👑 Think • Pair • Share

MP7 **4.** Compare the methods you used to add in exercises 1 and 3. Which method is easier for you? Why?

Possible answer: I think it is easier to use the properties of addition to add the whole numbers and fractions separately, and then add their sums. If the sum of the fractions is 1 or greater, then you have to rewrite the sum as a mixed number (as in step 1d), but you are not replacing the whole numbers with fractions.

Unit 3 ▪ Focus on Number and Operations—Fractions **169**

Observational Assessment

Use page 169 to assess whether students are able to use more than one method to add and subtract mixed numbers—using equivalent fractions or decomposing mixed numbers into whole numbers and fractions. Watch for students who struggle when renaming mixed numbers. Students may benefit from a generalized list of steps like those shown for addition in exercise 1 and for subtraction in exercise 2.

👑 Think•Pair•Share

Peer Collaboration After students have completed their work, ask them to discuss their comparisons. Ask questions such as:

- *What did you like or dislike about the method in exercise 1? Explain.*

- *What did you like or dislike about the method in exercise 3? Explain.*

- *How did using properties of operations help you find the sum in exercise 3?*

Return to the Essential Question

Reread the Lesson 19 Essential Question on page 166: *What methods can you use for adding and subtracting mixed numbers?*

Ask volunteers to use what they learned in this lesson to answer this question. (Possible response: I can rename mixed numbers as equivalent fractions and then add or subtract. I can use properties of addition to add the whole numbers and add the fractions separately. I can use the relationship between addition and subtraction to change a subtraction to an addition with an unknown addend.)

Mathematical Practices

Mathematical Practice Standards underline the teaching and understanding of all concepts and skills presented. The emphasis of specific practices is noted throughout the guided and independent practice of this lesson.

| MP7 | **Look for and make use of structure.** |

Item 4: Students compare two methods for adding mixed numbers.

Independent Practice

Concept Application

Students may work independently on these pages in the classroom or at home. They may refer to the first four pages of the lesson to revisit the instruction or to see a worked-out example.

Common Errors and **Teaching Tips** may help you support student learning either in the classroom or as a follow-up for work done at home.

Teaching Tips

Item 3

Point out to students that they should look at the fractional part of each mixed number to help them determine an effective method. In this exercise, students should notice that adding the fractions will result in a sum of 1.

Independent Practice

For exercises 1 and 2, use the model below.

$2\frac{1}{4}$ + $2\frac{3}{4}$

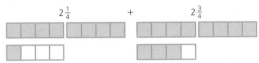

1. Break apart $2\frac{1}{4}$ and $2\frac{3}{4}$. Then use properties to add.

$$2\frac{1}{4} + 2\frac{3}{4} = \underline{2} + \frac{1}{4} + \underline{2} + \frac{3}{4}$$
$$= (\underline{2} + \underline{2}) + \frac{1}{4} + \frac{3}{4}$$
$$= \underline{4} + \frac{4}{4}$$
$$= \underline{4} + \underline{1}$$
$$= \underline{5}$$
$$2\frac{1}{4} + 2\frac{3}{4} = \underline{5}$$

2. Rename $2\frac{1}{4}$ and $2\frac{3}{4}$ as equivalent fractions greater than 1.

$$2\frac{1}{4} = \frac{4 \times 2}{4 \times 1} + \frac{1}{4} = \frac{8}{4} + \frac{1}{4} = \frac{9}{4}$$
$$2\frac{3}{4} = \frac{4 \times 2}{4 \times 1} + \frac{1}{4} + \frac{1}{4} + \frac{1}{4}$$
$$= \frac{8}{4} + \frac{1}{4} + \frac{1}{4} + \frac{1}{4} = \frac{11}{4}$$

Add the fractions.

$$\frac{9}{4} + \frac{11}{4} = \underline{\frac{20}{4} = 5}$$
$$2\frac{1}{4} + 2\frac{3}{4} = \underline{5}$$

Add with the method of your choice. Show your work. Methods may vary.

3. $6\frac{1}{2} + 3\frac{1}{2} = \underline{10}$

$$6\frac{1}{2} + 3\frac{1}{2} = 6 + 3 + \frac{1}{2} + \frac{1}{2}$$
$$= 9 + \frac{2}{2}$$
$$= 9 + 1$$
$$= 10$$

4. $4\frac{2}{6} + 2\frac{3}{6} = \underline{6\frac{5}{6}}$

$$4\frac{2}{6} + 2\frac{3}{6} = 4 + 2 + \frac{2}{6} + \frac{3}{6}$$
$$= 6 + \frac{5}{6}$$
$$= 6\frac{5}{6}$$

Find the difference. Use the model if it helps.

5. $3\frac{2}{3} - 2\frac{1}{3}$

Do you need to regroup? __No__

Subtract the whole numbers.

$$3 - 2 = 1$$

Subtract the fractions.

$$\frac{2}{3} - \frac{1}{3} = \frac{1}{3}$$

$$3\frac{2}{3} - 2\frac{1}{3} = \underline{1\frac{1}{3}}$$

Writing About Math

▪ **Write an Explanatory Text** Provide students with a pair of mixed numbers with like denominators. Have students write about the method they would use to add and to subtract the mixed numbers. Students may write a step-by-step process or a list of instructions. Tell students to use precise language and appropriate vocabulary to explain their method. Encourage them to include illustrations to reinforce their explanations.

Common Errors

Item 8

Students may try to subtract the fractions by subtracting the lesser fraction from the greater fraction. Remind students that they need to subtract the second number, $1\frac{4}{5}$, from the first number, $3\frac{2}{5}$, and that the Commutative Property does not apply to subtraction. To find the difference, they should rename the mixed numbers as equivalent fractions before subtracting.

Teaching Tips

Item 6

Suggest that students focus on the fraction part of each mixed number to determine if they need to regroup. Explain that students can cross out any of the 18 shaded parts in the model to show the subtraction.

Item 9

Remind students to check all of the answer choices because there may be more than one correct answer.

6. $3\frac{3}{5} - 2\frac{4}{5}$ Do you need to regroup? ___Yes___

Rename each number as an equivalent fraction greater than 1.

$3\frac{3}{5} = \frac{5 \times 3}{5 \times 1} + \frac{3}{5} = \frac{15}{5} + \frac{3}{5} = \frac{18}{5}$ $2\frac{4}{5} = \frac{5 \times 2}{5 \times 1} + \frac{4}{5} = \frac{10}{5} + \frac{4}{5} = \frac{14}{5}$

Subtract the fractions: $\frac{18}{5} - \frac{14}{5} = \frac{4}{5}$.
Use the model to show your work.

$3\frac{3}{5} - 2\frac{4}{5} = \frac{4}{5}$

Subtract with the method of your choice. Show your work.   Methods may vary.

7. $8\frac{7}{10} - 5\frac{2}{10} = $ ___$3\frac{5}{10}$___

$8 - 5 = 3$

$\frac{7}{10} - \frac{2}{10} = \frac{5}{10}$

8. $3\frac{2}{5} - 1\frac{4}{5} = $ ___$1\frac{3}{5}$___

$3\frac{2}{5} = \frac{5 \times 3}{5 \times 1} + \frac{2}{5} = \frac{15}{5} + \frac{2}{5} = \frac{17}{5}$

$1\frac{4}{5} = \frac{5}{5} + \frac{4}{5} = \frac{9}{5}$

$\frac{17}{5} - \frac{9}{5} = \frac{8}{5} = \frac{3}{5} + \frac{5}{5}$

$= \frac{3}{5} + 1 = 1\frac{3}{5}$

Circle the correct answer or answers.

9. For which of the following subtraction problems do you need to regroup?

   (a.) $5 - 2\frac{1}{2}$ **b.** $4\frac{6}{8} - 3\frac{5}{8}$

   (c.) $10\frac{1}{5} - 8\frac{3}{5}$ **d.** $2\frac{50}{100} - 1\frac{9}{100}$

10. Penny is mailing two packages. To find their total weight, she is adding $8\frac{5}{12}$ pounds and $3\frac{7}{12}$ pounds. Which of the following is the best way to group the addends to add mentally?

   a. $8 + \frac{5}{12} + 3 + \frac{7}{12}$ **b.** $3 + \frac{7}{12} + 8 + \frac{5}{12}$

   (c.) $8 + 3 + (\frac{5}{12} + \frac{7}{12})$ **d.** $8 + 3 + (\frac{5}{12} + \frac{5}{12}) + \frac{2}{12}$

Unit 3 ■ Focus on Number and Operations—Fractions   **171**

Digital Connection

Interactive Whiteboard Using whiteboard technology, create your own fraction strips with the shape division tool. Create wholes and wholes that have been divided into unit fractions. Have students add and subtract mixed numbers with the interactive fraction strips. Use the fraction strips to demonstrate how to rename each mixed number as an equivalent fraction. Students can move the unit fractions to create wholes when adding or decompose the wholes to complete subtraction.

Teaching Tips

Item 12

If students have difficulty explaining a general statement, tell them to use actual numbers to test the statement.

Item 14

Students can also solve this problem by adding the three mixed numbers in one step, or they can find the sum of the first two mixed numbers, and then add the third mixed number to find the total distance of the race.

Lesson 19 Add and Subtract Mixed Numbers with Like Denominators

Independent Practice

MP2 **11.** How is adding and subtracting mixed numbers different from adding and subtracting fractions less than 1? Answers will vary. Possible answer: When you add mixed numbers, you have two sums to find: the sum of the whole numbers and the sum of the fractions. In both cases, if a sum or partial sum is a fraction equal to or greater than 1, then you should rewrite it as a mixed number. When you subtract mixed numbers, sometimes you need to regroup whole amounts in order to subtract the fraction parts.

MP7 **12.** When you break apart a mixed number to add, does it matter if you add the whole numbers first or the fractions first? Explain.
Possible explanation: No, it does not matter. I add the whole amounts first. If the sum of the fractions is a mixed number, there is only one whole number to add to that to get the final sum.

Solve the problems.

MP6 **13.** Greg is making homemade pizzas. For the crust, he uses $2\frac{2}{4}$ cups of whole wheat flour and $4\frac{2}{4}$ cups of regular flour. How much flour does Greg use altogether?

✏ **Show your work.** Work may vary. Possible work:

$$2\frac{2}{4} + 4\frac{2}{4} = 2 + 4 + \frac{2}{4} + \frac{2}{4}$$
$$= 6 + 1$$
$$= 7$$

Answer Greg uses 7 cups of flour.

MP1 **14.** A sports club is having a beginner's triathlon race. To finish the race, each athlete must swim $1\frac{5}{10}$ miles, run $3\frac{1}{10}$ miles, and ride a bicycle for $5\frac{8}{10}$ miles. What is the total length of the race in miles?

✏ **Show your work.** Work may vary. Possible work:

$1 + 3 + 5 = 9$ whole miles

$$\frac{5}{10} + \frac{1}{10} + \frac{8}{10} = \frac{5}{10} + \frac{1}{10} + \frac{4}{10} + \frac{4}{10}$$
$$= \frac{5}{10} + \frac{5}{10} + \frac{4}{10}$$
$$= 1 + \frac{4}{10}$$

total miles $= 9 + 1 + \frac{4}{10} = 10\frac{4}{10}$

Answer The total length of the race is $10\frac{4}{10}$ miles.

Mathematical Practices	
MP1	**Make sense of problems and persevere in solving them.**
Item 14: Students solve a multistep problem with mixed numbers.	
MP2	**Reason abstractly and quantitatively.**
Item 11: Students contrast operations with fractions.	
MP6	**Attend to precision.**
Item 13: Students add two mixed numbers and rename the sum.	
MP7	**Look for and make use of structure.**
Item 12: Students analyze two addition methods to make a generalization.	

Independent Practice

Teaching Tips

Item 17
Suggest that students can find the sum of the given fractions and find the sum of the equivalent fractions with a denominator of 10. Then they can compare the sums to see if they are equivalent. Remind students that performing the actual calculations can help them explain a process.

MP2 **15.** There are 12 eggs in 1 carton. In the delivery truck, $4\frac{5}{12}$ cartons of eggs break. In the store, a total of $2\frac{9}{12}$ cartons break. How many more cartons of eggs break in the truck than in the store?

▶ **Show your work.**

Work may vary. Possible work: 2 whole cartons $= \frac{12 \times 2}{12 \times 1} = \frac{24}{12}$

$$4\frac{5}{12} = 2 + 2 + \frac{5}{12} = \frac{24}{12} + \frac{24}{12} + \frac{5}{12} = \frac{53}{12}$$

$$2\frac{9}{12} = 2 + \frac{9}{12} = \frac{24}{12} + \frac{9}{12} = \frac{33}{12}$$

$$\frac{53}{12} - \frac{33}{12} = \frac{20}{12} = \frac{12}{12} + \frac{8}{12} = 1\frac{8}{12}$$

Answer $1\frac{8}{12}$ more cartons of eggs break in the truck than in the store.

MP6 **16.** Justin subtracts $5\frac{1}{3}$ from $10\frac{2}{3}$ using the method shown at the right. Is Justin's difference correct?

$$10\frac{2}{3}$$
$$-\ 5\frac{1}{3}$$
$$\overline{\ \ 5\frac{1}{3}}$$

Answer Yes, Justin's difference is correct. $10\frac{2}{3} - 5\frac{1}{3} = 5\frac{1}{3}$.

▶ **Justify your answer using words, drawings, or numbers.**

Possible justification: I changed the subtraction to an addition with an unknown addend and I found that Justin's answer is correct.

$$10\frac{2}{3} - 5\frac{1}{3} = ?$$
$$5\frac{1}{3} + ? = 10\frac{2}{3}$$

Students can show the difference on a number line.

MP8 **17.** Mariah needs to add $4\frac{10}{100}$ and $3\frac{20}{100}$. She starts by using a denominator of 10 to write equivalent fractions for $\frac{10}{100}$ and $\frac{20}{100}$. Then she adds the mixed numbers. Can Mariah find the correct sum with this method?

Answer Yes, Mariah can find the correct sum.

▶ **Justify your answer using words, drawings, or numbers.**

Possible justification: If Mariah's fractions are really equivalent to $\frac{10}{100}$ and $\frac{20}{100}$, then their sum should have the same value as the sum of the original fractions. The only difference is they will have 10 as a denominator.

$$4\frac{10}{100} + 3\frac{20}{100} = 7\frac{30}{100}$$

Mariah's solution: $\frac{10}{100} = \frac{1}{10}$ and $\frac{20}{100} = \frac{2}{10}$; $4\frac{1}{10} + 3\frac{2}{10} = 7\frac{3}{10}$

$\frac{3}{10}$ is equivalent to $\frac{30}{100}$, so $7\frac{3}{10} = 7\frac{30}{100}$.

Unit 3 ▪ Focus on Number and Operations—Fractions   173

Mathematical Practices

MP2	**Reason abstractly and quantitatively.**

Item 15: Students use context to translate quantities into an expression and compute to solve the problem.

MP6	**Attend to precision.**

Item 16: Students calculate accurately and use clear language to explain their calculations.

MP8	**Look for and express regularity in repeated reasoning.**

Item 17: Students look for a pattern in the relationship between equivalent fractions and mixed numbers.

4.NF.3d Solve word problems involving addition and subtraction of fractions referring to the same whole and having like denominators.

OBJECTIVE
Solve word problems that involve addition and subtraction of fractions and mixed numbers with like denominators using models and equations.

ESSENTIAL QUESTION
Have students compare and contrast two fractions with like denominators. Ask students to tell how the two fractions can refer to the same whole. Encourage students to discuss how many are in the whole and in each part.

FLUENCY PRACTICE
Fluency practice is available at **sadlierconnect.com**.

Concept Development

Understand: Using fraction models to represent and solve problems

■ This lesson extends students' knowledge of adding and subtracting fractions with like denominators. Be sure students understand that the fractions in this presentation refer to the same whole. Students use a model that represents the whole, or 1.

■ Have students explain how the model represents the problem. Each of the 8 parts of the rectangle represents one paint color. Each crossed out section represents a paint color that Sarah used up.

✏️ Students should be able to explain how 2 and $\frac{2}{8}$ are related in the context of the problem. Have students refer to the model to show how many colors are used and how many colors are left.

Lesson 20 — Problem Solving: Add and Subtract Fractions

Essential Question: How can modeling a fraction word problem help you understand it?
4.NF.3d

Guided Instruction

In this lesson you will learn how to solve addition and subtraction problems involving fractions and mixed numbers with like denominators.

Understand: Using fraction models to represent and solve problems

> Sarah has a watercolor paint set with 8 colors. First she uses up her favorite $\frac{1}{8}$ of the colors. When she uses up another $\frac{5}{8}$ of the colors, she buys a new paint set. How much of the paint set is left when Sarah buys a new one?

To solve the problem, you can make a model to represent the problem.

First read for information.

Sarah uses up $\frac{1}{8}$ and $\frac{5}{8}$ of the set. The denominator 8 in $\frac{1}{8}$ and $\frac{5}{8}$ shows the whole is divided into eighths.

Draw a model to represent the whole as $\frac{8}{8}$.

1 paint set $= \frac{8}{8}$

Use different color Xs to show the $\frac{1}{8}$ and $\frac{5}{8}$ that Sarah uses.

Then read again to find the question. The problem asks how much of the paint set is left, not how much Sarah uses altogether. So you need to subtract the sum of $\frac{1}{8} + \frac{5}{8}$ from the whole.

$$\frac{8}{8} - \left(\frac{1}{8} + \frac{5}{8}\right) = \frac{2}{8}$$

$\frac{2}{8}$ left

➡️ When Sarah buys a new one, $\frac{2}{8}$ of the paint set is left. Notice that the model shows the same answer.

✏️ What if the problem asks how many of the 8 colors are left? Explain how to use your model to find this number. Each of the eighths in the model represents 1 color. Since 2 eighths are left, $2 \times 1 = 2$, so there are 2 colors left.

Support English Language Learners

The term *model* has many different uses outside of mathematics. A model can refer to a person that is used in advertising to sell products. A model can also refer to a version of a product like a car model. Models are also miniature versions of an object like a model airplane. Have students look up synonyms for *model* to get a better understanding of its varied uses. Just a few examples are *replica, sculpt, type, ideal,* and *example*.

Be sure students understand that *model* can be used as a noun or a verb. Students may see directions such as "make a model" (noun) or "model the equation" (verb). Support students as they write at least three sentences that use the word *model* in a different way. At least one of those sentences should be math-related.

Lesson 20

Guided Instruction

Understand: Using equations to represent and solve problems

> The library is $2\frac{5}{6}$ miles from the school. David's father picks him up from school to go to the library. On the way, they stop at a store. Then they walk $1\frac{4}{6}$ miles to the library. How far is the store from the school?

You can use a model to help write an equation.

Identify what you know.
- The distance between the school and the library is $2\frac{5}{6}$ miles.
- The store is between the school and library.
- The distance between the store and library is $1\frac{4}{6}$ miles.

Identify what you need to find.
- the distance from the store to the school

Draw a model to represent the problem. The store is $1\frac{4}{6}$ miles away from the library. This location on the number line is the distance from the store to the school.

Write an equation for the problem. You can use d to represent the unknown distance.

$$d + 1\frac{4}{6} = 2\frac{5}{6}$$

$$d = 2\frac{5}{6} - 1\frac{4}{6}$$

Subtract $1\frac{4}{6}$ from $2\frac{5}{6}$ to find d.

Since $\frac{4}{6} < \frac{5}{6}$, you can subtract without regrouping the 2 wholes.

school to library − store to library = school to store

$$2\frac{5}{6} \quad - \quad 1\frac{4}{6} \quad = \quad 1\frac{1}{6}$$

$$d = 1\frac{1}{6}$$

➡ The store is $1\frac{1}{6}$ miles from the school.

Remember!
Check whether you can subtract the whole numbers and the fractions separately.

Understand: Using equations to represent and solve problems

■ In this presentation, students solve a problem that involves the subtraction of mixed numbers with like denominators. Point out that that both mixed numbers in the problem refer to the same unit amounts, mile.

■ Remind students that when representing an unknown they should use a symbol that will remind them of what they are solving for. In this presentation, d is used to represent the unknown distance.

■ Be sure students understand that they can subtract the whole-number parts and then the fraction parts of these mixed numbers because $\frac{4}{6}$, the fraction being subtracted, is less than $\frac{5}{6}$.

Math-to-Math Connection

Meaning of Fractions A common meaning of fractions is the part-to-whole relationship. Fraction strips, number lines, and other models are often used to show this relationship.

Another meaning of fractions is division. Some students may already know that a fraction bar is also a symbol for division. In later grades, students will divide the numerator by the denominator to convert a fraction to a decimal. Interpreting fractions as division can be particularly useful when completing mathematical computations and when expressing fractional amounts as a percent.

Connect: What you know about writing equivalent fractions and using models Use this page to help students strengthen their understanding of solving word problems that involve fractions and mixed numbers with like denominators.

■ Remind students that a unit fraction represents one part of the total number of equal parts in a whole.

■ Help students understand that any whole number can be decomposed into a sum with an equivalent number of 1s as the addends.

■ Ask students to justify why the whole number 1 can be represented as the fraction $\frac{5}{5}$. The denominator means there are 5 parts in one whole. The numerator means 5 of the parts are being considered. If you have 5 parts in all and use 5 parts, you have used the entire whole. So, $\frac{a}{a}$ always equals 1.

■ Some students may suggest that repeated subtraction can be used to solve the problem. Students may rewrite $2\frac{4}{10}$ as $\frac{24}{10}$. Repeated subtraction shows that $\frac{2}{10}$ can be subtracted from $\frac{24}{10}$ a total of 12 times.

Connect: What you know about writing equivalent fractions and using models.

> Ava has $2\frac{4}{10}$ pounds of frozen strawberries. She needs $\frac{2}{10}$ pound of strawberries to make 1 shake. How many strawberry shakes can Ava make with all $2\frac{4}{10}$ pounds?

To solve the problem, use what you know about equivalent fractions to write an equation.

Step 1

Identify and model what you know.
- The total amount is $2\frac{4}{10}$ pounds.
- The amount for 1 shake is $\frac{2}{10}$ pounds.

Identify what you need to find.
- how many shakes Ava can make

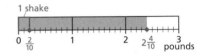

Step 2

Using a unit fraction makes it easier to find the number of shakes Ava can make. Find the unit fraction that is equivalent to $\frac{2}{10}$.

$\frac{2}{10} = \frac{2 \div 2}{10 \div 2} = \frac{1}{5}$

Ava needs $\frac{1}{5}$ pound of strawberries to make each shake.

Step 3

Plan how you will find the number of fifths in $2\frac{2}{5}$. You can count the unit fractions of $\frac{1}{5}$ on the model, or you can write $2\frac{2}{5}$ as a sum of unit fractions, or you can write $2\frac{2}{5}$ as a fraction to find the total number of fifths.

Remember!
The numerator in a fraction shows the number of equal parts in a fraction.

Step 4

$2\frac{2}{5} = 1 + 1 + \frac{2}{5} = \frac{5}{5} + \frac{5}{5} + \frac{2}{5} = \frac{12}{5}$

There are 12 fifths in $2\frac{2}{5}$.

➡ Ava can make 12 strawberry shakes with $2\frac{4}{10}$ pounds of strawberries.

Math-to-Art Connection

Tiling Patterns One of the most famous artists to use repeating patterns is Escher. Show students various examples of repeating patterns in art. Find a Web site with a geometric tessellation coloring page. Discuss the tessellation and have students color the page. Next, ask students to write the mixed number that is equal to the total number of times a design can be created from the shapes used in the geometric tessellations. For example, an equilateral triangle is $\frac{1}{6}$ the corresponding hexagon, so 14 equilateral triangles equal $2\frac{2}{6}$ hexagons. A right triangle is $\frac{1}{2}$ the corresponding square or rectangle, so 17 right triangles equal $8\frac{1}{2}$ squares (rectangles). A square is $\frac{1}{4}$ the corresponding larger square, so 15 squares equal $3\frac{3}{4}$ larger squares.

Ask volunteers to share their art and mixed numbers.

Use the model to answer the questions.

1. A town gets $2\frac{3}{4}$ inches of rain on Monday and $\frac{2}{4}$ inches of rain on Friday. How much rain does the town get on those two days?

Rain on Monday
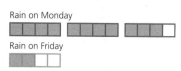
Rain on Friday

a. Color the model to show the given information.

b. Circle the equation you can use to solve the problem.

$2\frac{3}{4} - \frac{2}{4} = r$ $\boxed{2\frac{3}{4} + \frac{2}{4} = r}$ $2\frac{3}{4} + r = \frac{2}{4}$

c. Solve the problem. Show your work. Work may vary.

$2\frac{3}{4} + \frac{2}{4} = \underline{\quad 3\frac{1}{4} \quad}$

$2 + \frac{3}{4} + \frac{2}{4} = 2 + \frac{3}{4} + \frac{1}{4} + \frac{1}{4}$
$= 2 + 1 + \frac{1}{4}$
$= 3\frac{1}{4}$

Answer The town gets $3\frac{1}{4}$ inches of rain.

Write an addition or subtraction equation to represent the problem. You can use the model to help. Then solve.

2. Vincent has a bag of apples. Green apples fill $\frac{3}{5}$ of the bag. Yellow apples fill the rest of the bag. What fraction of the bag has yellow apples?

$\frac{3}{5}$ green $\frac{2}{5}$ yellow

a. Equation $\frac{5}{5} - \frac{3}{5} = y$

b. Solve the problem. Show your work. Work may vary. Possible work:

The whole bag is $\frac{5}{5}$. $\frac{5}{5} - \frac{3}{5} = \frac{2}{5}$

Answer The fraction of the bag with yellow apples is $\frac{2}{5}$.

Think • Pair • Share

MP1   3. What are the whole amounts in exercises 1 and 2? How do you know that the mixed numbers and the fractions in each exercise are for the same whole? Explain.
Possible explanation: In exercise 1, the whole is 1 inch. Since this is a unit of length, I know it is the same for both of the mixed numbers. In exercise 2, the whole is the same bag of apples for both of the fractions.

Unit 3 ▪ Focus on Number and Operations—Fractions   **177**

Mathematical Practices

Mathematical Practice Standards underline the teaching and understanding of all concepts and skills presented. The emphasis of specific practices is noted throughout the guided and independent practice of this lesson.

MP1   **Make sense of problems and persevere in solving them.**

Item 3: Students use models to analyze the relationship between two problems.

Observational Assessment

Use page 177 to assess whether students are able to use models and equations to solve word problems that involve addition and subtraction of mixed numbers with like denominators. As the amount of scaffolding decreases, note those students who need additional support.

Think•Pair•Share

Peer Collaboration Have students work in pairs to answer the question. Encourage them to consider these questions during the discussion:

- *What does each model represent?*
- *In what ways do the models in the two exercises represent the same thing?*
- *In what ways do the models in the two exercises represent different things?*
- *Why are the models in exercise 1 marked into 4 parts but the model in exercise 2 is marked into 5 parts?*

To summarize, make sure students realize that each model represents 1 whole. The number of parts in the whole depends on the context of the problem.

Return to the Essential Question

Reread the Lesson 20 Essential Question on page 174: *How can modeling a fraction word problem help you understand it?*

Ask volunteers to use what they learned in this lesson to answer this question. (Possible response: Modeling a fraction word problem can demonstrate the relationship between the two quantities and can show the steps needed to solve the problem.)

Invite as many volunteers as possible to express ideas about using models to solve word problems involving fractions with like denominators.

Independent Practice

Concept Application

Students may work independently on these pages in the classroom or at home. They may refer to the first four pages of the lesson to revisit the instruction or to see a worked-out example.

Common Errors and **Teaching Tips** may help you support student learning either in the classroom or as a follow-up for work done at home.

Common Errors

Items 1–2

Some students may subtract the denominators as well. Remind students that when subtracting fractions, they should subtract the numerators and keep the same denominator.

Teaching Tips

Item 4

Students may assume that Talia and Carl have the same mother. Explain that students should not assume facts that are not explicit in word problems.

Independent Practice

Use the model to represent the problem. Write and solve an equation to find the answer.

1. Brad has $1\frac{1}{3}$ boxes of birthday candles. He uses $\frac{2}{3}$ of the birthday candles on a birthday cake. What fraction of the candles is left?

   a. Equation ___ $1\frac{1}{3} - \frac{2}{3} = b$ ___  $1\frac{1}{3}$ boxes

   b. Solve the problem. Show your work. Work may vary.
   $$1\frac{1}{3} = \frac{3}{3} + \frac{1}{3} = \frac{3+1}{3} = \frac{4}{3}$$
   $$\frac{4}{3} - \frac{2}{3} = \frac{2}{3}$$
   Answer There is $\frac{2}{3}$ of a box of candles left.

2. Kate's favorite song is $3\frac{5}{8}$ minutes long. Ty's favorite song is $2\frac{7}{8}$ minutes long. How much longer is Kate's favorite song than Ty's?

   a. Equation
   $$3\frac{5}{8} - 2\frac{7}{8} = m$$

   $2\frac{7}{8} = \frac{23}{8}$ $3\frac{5}{8} = \frac{29}{8}$

   0   $\frac{4}{8}$ 1 $\frac{12}{8}$ 2 $\frac{20}{8}$ 3 $\frac{28}{8}$ 4

   b. Solve the problem. Show your work. Work may vary. Possible work:
   $$3\frac{5}{8} = \frac{8 \times 3}{8 \times 1} + \frac{5}{8} = \frac{24+5}{8} = \frac{29}{8} \qquad 2\frac{7}{8} = \frac{8 \times 2}{8 \times 1} + \frac{7}{8} = \frac{16+7}{8} = \frac{23}{8}$$
   $$\frac{29}{8} - \frac{23}{8} = \frac{6}{8}$$
   Answer Kate's song is $\frac{6}{8}$ of a minute longer than Ty's.

Circle the correct answer.

3. Ayden works on his homework for $1\frac{1}{6}$ hours before dinner. It takes him another $1\frac{3}{6}$ hours to finish his homework after dinner. How much time does Ayden spend on homework?

   a. $\frac{2}{6}$ hour

   b. $1\frac{2}{6}$ hours

   c. $1\frac{4}{6}$ hours

   d. $2\frac{4}{6}$ hours

4. Talia is $\frac{1}{4}$ of her mother's age. Carl is $\frac{1}{4}$ of his mother's age. Who is older, Talia or Carl? Which statement about the problem is true?

   a. Subtract $\frac{1}{4} - \frac{1}{4}$ to solve.

   b. Add $\frac{1}{4} + \frac{1}{4}$ to solve.

   c. Carl and Talia must be the same age, since they are the same fraction of their mothers' ages.

   d. The problem cannot be solved without the ages of Carl and Talia's mothers.

Writing About Math

· **Write Narrative Text** Have students write a story that includes a problem that needs to be solved by adding or subtracting mixed numbers. Students should have the characters in the story work together to solve the problem. Tell students that they may use real or imagined experiences or events to establish a situation, introduce characters, and organize an event sequence. Remind students to include dialogue in their narratives. Ask students to share their stories with the class.

For exercises 5–8, use the number line. For exercises 6–9, write and solve an equation.

A car gets on the highway at the starting point, 0 miles. The next five highway exits are shown on the number line below.

Distances Between Highway Exits

$$\begin{array}{ccccccccc} \text{Start} & A & & B & C & D & E & & \text{Exits} \\ 0 & \tfrac{2}{4} & 1 & 1\tfrac{3}{4} & 2 & 2\tfrac{2}{4} & 3 & 3\tfrac{1}{4} & 4 & \text{Miles} \end{array}$$

5. Label Exits A, B, C, and E with the fraction or mixed number for that location. See above.

6. What is the distance between Exits A and B?   Exit A: $\frac{2}{4}$ mile; Exit B: $1\frac{3}{4}$ miles

Equation _____ $1\frac{3}{4} - \frac{2}{4} = d$ _____

Work for exercises 6–9 may vary.

$1\frac{3}{4} = (1\frac{1}{4} + \frac{2}{4})$

$1\frac{1}{4} + \frac{2}{4} - \frac{2}{4} = 1\frac{1}{4}$

Answer _____ The distance between Exit A and Exit B is $1\frac{1}{4}$ miles. _____

7. A driver misses Exit B and has to get off at Exit C. How far is Exit C from Exit B?

Exit B: $1\frac{3}{4}$ miles; Exit C: $2\frac{2}{4}$ miles

Equation _____ $2\frac{2}{4} - 1\frac{3}{4} = d$ _____

$2\frac{2}{4} = 2 + \frac{2}{4} = \frac{8}{4} + \frac{2}{4} = \frac{10}{4}$

$1\frac{3}{4} = \frac{4}{4} + \frac{3}{4} = \frac{7}{4}$

$2\frac{2}{4} - 1\frac{3}{4} = \frac{10}{4} - \frac{7}{4} = \frac{3}{4}$

Answer _____ Exit C is $\frac{3}{4}$ mile from Exit B. _____

8. Mauricio and his mother get on the highway at Exit A and stay on it until Exit E. For how many miles do Mauricio and his mother stay on the highway?

Exit E: $3\frac{1}{4}$ miles; Exit A: $\frac{2}{4}$ mile

Equation _____ $3\frac{1}{4} - \frac{2}{4} = d$ _____

$3\frac{1}{4} = 2 + 1 + \frac{1}{4} = 2 + \frac{4}{4} + \frac{1}{4} = 2\frac{5}{4}$

$2\frac{5}{4} - \frac{2}{4} = 2\frac{3}{4}$

Answer _____ Mauricio and his mother stay on the highway for $2\frac{3}{4}$ miles. _____

9. Lauren's family is going to an amusement park. The drive usually takes $2\frac{2}{5}$ hours. Today it takes an extra $\frac{4}{5}$ hour. How long does it take Lauren's family today to drive to the amusement park?

Equation _____ $2\frac{2}{5} + \frac{4}{5} = h$ _____

$2\frac{2}{5} + \frac{4}{5} = 2 + \frac{1}{5} + \frac{1}{5} + \frac{4}{5}$

$= 2 + \frac{1}{5} + \frac{4}{5} + \frac{1}{5}$

$= 2 + \frac{5}{5} + \frac{1}{5}$

$= 2 + 1 + \frac{1}{5}$

$= 3\frac{1}{5}$

Answer _____ Today it takes Lauren's family $3\frac{1}{5}$ hours to drive to the amusement park. _____

Unit 3 ▪ Focus on Number and Operations—Fractions   **179**

Common Errors

Items 6–8

Students may use the value of the second exit to name the total distance. Remind students to subtract the value of the beginning exit from the value of the ending exit to find the total distance.

Item 9

Some students may not recognize $\frac{6}{5}$, the sum of the fractions, as representing an additional whole hour and part of an hour. Ask students how many fifths are in one whole hour and how many fifths are left over.

Digital Connection

Online Games Use a search engine to locate online games at the fourth-grade level that involve addition and subtraction of mixed numbers with like denominators. Make a list of the games for students to use after you have reviewed them. Some students might benefit from an interactive approach when practicing this skill.

Independent Practice

Common Errors

Item 10

Some students may assume that the denominator must represent the total number of pieces in the whole puzzle. Point out that $\frac{2}{100}$ and $\frac{4}{100}$ could be equivalent to fractions that represent the number of edge pieces and inside pieces in the puzzle. The total number of missing pieces depends on the total number of pieces in the whole puzzle, which may or may not be equal to 100.

Item 12

Students may argue that 3 players are missing from practice. The students are asked to state their answer as a fraction. Encourage students to write a fraction that names the number of missing players to the total number of players on the team.

Teaching Tips

Item 13

The problem asks for an estimate. Students may understand that $\frac{11}{12}$ is close to 1 and round the answer to 2 acres. Some students might recognize that $\frac{5}{12}$ is about $\frac{1}{2}$ of an acre and $\frac{6}{12}$ is $\frac{1}{2}$ of an acre, so $\frac{1}{2} + 1\frac{1}{2} = 1\frac{2}{2} = 2$.

Independent Practice

MP6 10. Dennis has a jigsaw puzzle that is missing $\frac{2}{100}$ of the edge pieces and $\frac{4}{100}$ of the inside pieces. Does this mean that the puzzle is only missing 6 pieces altogether?
Answers will vary. Possible answer: No, there is not enough information to answer the question. It is not clear how many edge pieces there are and how many inside pieces there are. This answer seems to involve 2 wholes and neither one is known.

MP3 11. Tracy says that the sum of the fractions modeled at the right could be either 1 or $\frac{2}{4}$. Do you agree? Explain.
Possible explanation: Yes. It depends on what the whole is for the problem. If each square is 1 whole, then the sum is $\frac{1}{2} + \frac{1}{2} = 1$. If you change the whole to be both squares, then 2 parts out of 4 equal parts are colored and the model shows $\frac{2}{4}$.

Solve the problems.

MP2 12. Two of the 10 players on Ryan's lacrosse team are sick. Another player has to miss practice to go to the dentist. What fraction of Ryan's team is missing from practice?

🖉 **Show your work.**
Work may vary. Possible work:

Answer $\frac{3}{10}$ of Ryan's team is missing from practice.

MP1 13. An acre is an area that is a little smaller than a football field. Jeremy says that the size of the school playground is about $\frac{5}{12}$ of an acre. Susan says that the playground is at least $1\frac{6}{12}$ acres bigger than Jeremy thinks it is. About what does Susan think the area of the playground is?

🖉 **Show your work.** Work may vary. Possible work:
$$\frac{5}{12} + 1\frac{6}{12} = \frac{5}{12} + 1 + \frac{6}{12}$$
$$= 1 + \frac{5}{12} + \frac{6}{12}$$
$$= 1 + \frac{11}{12}$$
$$= 1\frac{11}{12}$$

Answer Susan thinks the area of the playground is about $1\frac{11}{12}$ acres.

Mathematical Practices

MP1	**Make sense of problems and persevere in solving them.**
Item 13: Students use a verbal description to write and solve an equation.	
MP2	**Reason abstractly and quantitatively.**
Item 12: Students make sense of quantitative relationships to solve.	
MP3	**Construct viable arguments and critique the reasoning of others.**
Item 11: Students construct arguments using models.	
MP6	**Attend to precision.**
Item 10: Students give a carefully formulated explanation.	

Independent Practice

MP6 **14.** The southern elephant seal at the zoo weighs $3\frac{1}{8}$ tons. The biggest hippopotamus at the zoo weighs $1\frac{4}{8}$ tons. How much more does the elephant seal weigh than the hippopotamus?

$$3\frac{1}{8} = \frac{8 \times 3}{8 \times 1} + \frac{1}{8} = \frac{24}{8} + \frac{1}{8} = \frac{25}{8}$$

Show your work.

$$1\frac{4}{8} = \frac{8}{8} + \frac{4}{8} = \frac{12}{8}$$

Work may vary. Possible work: $\frac{25}{8} - \frac{12}{8} = \frac{13}{8} = \frac{8}{8} + \frac{5}{8} = 1\frac{5}{8}$

Answer The elephant seal weighs $1\frac{5}{8}$ tons more than the hippopotamus.

MP1 **15.** Jessica's bookcase is $4\frac{9}{12}$ feet tall. She wants to replace it with a taller bookcase that is $6\frac{1}{12}$ feet tall. Jessica says the new bookcase is about 1 foot taller. Is this a reasonable estimate? Work may vary. Possible work:

Show your work. Estimate: $4\frac{9}{12}$ rounds up to 5 and $6\frac{1}{12}$ rounds down to 6.

Exact answer: $6\frac{1}{12} = \frac{12 \times 6}{12 \times 1} + \frac{1}{12} = \frac{72}{12} + \frac{1}{12} = \frac{73}{12}$ $6 - 5 = 1$

$$4\frac{9}{12} = \frac{12 \times 4}{12 \times 1} + \frac{9}{12} = \frac{48}{12} + \frac{9}{12} = \frac{57}{12}$$

$$\frac{73}{12} - \frac{57}{12} = \frac{16}{12} = 1 + \frac{4}{12} = 1\frac{4}{12}$$

Answer Yes, $1\frac{4}{12}$ is close to 1, so 1 foot is a reasonable estimate.

MP2 **16.** Billy is estimating the combined amount of milk in two jugs. He says that $\frac{1}{2}$ gallon plus $\frac{4}{6}$ gallon must be greater than 1 whole gallon. Do you agree?

Answer Yes, I agree with Billy.

Justify your answer using words, drawings, or numbers.

Possible justification:
Since $\frac{1}{2} + \frac{1}{2} = 1$, the sum $\frac{1}{2} + \frac{4}{6}$ must be greater than 1 because $\frac{3}{6}$ is equal to $\frac{1}{2}$ and $\frac{4}{6} > \frac{3}{6}$ then $\frac{4}{6} > \frac{1}{2}$.

$\frac{1}{2} + \frac{4}{6} = 1\frac{1}{6}$

MP7 **17.** Damon says that to write $1\frac{63}{100}$ as a sum of unit fractions, you need 163 addends. Kenya says that you need 64 addends. Who is correct?

Answer Both may be correct.

Justify your answer using words, drawings, or numbers.

Possible justification: Damon may be thinking that there are 100 unit fractions of $\frac{1}{100}$ in 1 plus 63 unit fractions of $\frac{1}{100}$ in $\frac{63}{100}$ for 163 addends in all. Kenya may be thinking that 1 can be written as the unit fraction $\frac{1}{1}$, and adding that unit fraction to the 63 unit fractions of $\frac{1}{100}$ would make 64 addends.

Common Errors

Item 14

Students may subtract the lesser fraction from the greater fraction. Remind students that the Commutative Property does not apply to subtraction and that they must subtract the second number from the first number in a subtraction expression. Encourage students to rewrite the mixed numbers as fractions greater than 1 before subtracting.

Teaching Tips

Items 15–16

It may be helpful to review how to compare fractions to benchmark fractions in order to determine a reasonable estimate.

Item 17

Technically, $\frac{1}{1}$ cannot be added to any fraction with a denominator of 100, because fraction addition requires like denominators. The fraction $\frac{1}{1}$ must be rewritten as $\frac{100}{100}$, which is no longer a unit fraction. Although both are correct, Damon's reasoning can be supported mathematically, but Kenya's cannot.

Mathematical Practices	
MP1	**Make sense of problems and persevere in solving them.**
Item 15: Students check a solution.	
MP2	**Reason abstractly and quantitatively.**
Item 16: Students make sense of quantities and their relationships.	
MP6	**Attend to precision.**
Item 14: Students calculate accurately.	
MP7	**Look for and make use of structure.**
Item 17: Students see an entity as being composed of many entities.	

Common Core Focus:

4.NF.4a Understand a fraction a/b as a multiple of $1/b$.

OBJECTIVE
Use multiplication to write a fraction as the product of a whole number and a unit fraction.

ESSENTIAL QUESTION
The Essential Question invites students to make connections between what they already know about whole number multiplication and what they will learn about multiplying a fraction by a whole number. Invite students to define the meaning of multiplication using whole number examples and then use the same definition using unit fraction examples.

FLUENCY PRACTICE
Fluency practice is available at **sadlierconnect.com**.

Concept Development

Understand: Multiplying a unit fraction by a whole number

■ Students will understand that a fraction can be written as the product of a whole number and a unit fraction. The unit fraction is one part of the whole, and the whole number is the number of times the unit fraction is added to itself to equal the given fraction.

■ Students should recall multiplication as the sum of equal addends, or like groups. The argument also holds true when working with fractions, but the like groups are each one fractional part of the whole.

■ If time allows, you might guide kinesthetic learners in creating their own models.

✏ Review that the multiples of a number are the product of a given number and another number. In this case, the given number is $\frac{1}{8}$.

Lesson 21 — Multiply Unit Fractions by Whole Numbers

Essential Question:
How is multiplying a unit fraction by a whole number like multiplying a whole number by a whole number by a whole number?
4.NF.4a

Guided Instruction

In this lesson you will learn how to multiply a unit fraction by a whole number and how to write any fraction as a product of a whole number and a unit fraction.

Understand: Multiplying a unit fraction by a whole number

> There are 8 school photos on a whole sheet. So, each photo is $\frac{1}{8}$ of the sheet. Gary gives 6 of his school photos to friends. What fraction of a whole sheet does Gary give to his friends?

To find the fraction of a whole sheet made up of 6 photos that Gary gives to his friends you can use addition or multiplication.

The model shows that 6 photos are $\frac{6}{8}$ of a whole sheet.

Each photo is $\frac{1}{8}$ of a sheet. There are 6 photos.

$$\frac{1}{8} + \frac{1}{8} + \frac{1}{8} + \frac{1}{8} + \frac{1}{8} + \frac{1}{8} = \frac{1+1+1+1+1+1}{8} = \frac{6}{8}$$

Since all the addends are the same, you can think of them as equal groups.

$$\overbrace{\frac{1}{8} + \frac{1}{8} + \frac{1}{8} + \frac{1}{8} + \frac{1}{8} + \frac{1}{8}}^{\text{6 addends}} = 6 \times \frac{1}{8}$$

So, $6 \times \frac{1}{8} = \frac{6}{8}$

and $\frac{6}{8} = 6 \times \frac{1}{8}$.

➡ Gary gives $\frac{6}{8}$ of a whole sheet of photos to his friends.

Since $\frac{6}{8}$ is the product $6 \times \frac{1}{8}$, $\frac{6}{8}$ is a multiple of $\frac{1}{8}$.

✏ Count by eighths to write the first five multiples of $\frac{1}{8}$.
$\frac{1}{8}, \frac{2}{8}, \frac{3}{8}, \frac{4}{8},$ and $\frac{5}{8}$.

Remember!
To find the total of equal groups, multiply the number in each group by the number of groups.

Remember!
A multiple of a number is a product of that number and a whole number.

Support English Language Learners

Fraction concepts have a wide variety of applications, and English Language Learners need multiple representations to make connections between real-world examples and symbolic representations. This is especially true when solving word problems, which are presented in a narrative form, rather than symbolically.

Provide multiple models of unit fractions to help students visualize the meaning of a unit fraction as part of an area model or a linear model. Demonstrate and talk about unit fractions in the context of each model using manipulatives and drawings as necessary. Encourage students to use the models as they talk about the meaning of unit fractions. Listen and guide students to use correct vocabulary as they share their thinking.

Lesson 21

Guided Instruction

Connect: Writing a mixed number or a fraction greater than 1 as a product of a whole number and a unit fraction

Luz runs $1\frac{2}{5}$ miles around the park on Saturday. If one lap around the park is a distance of $\frac{1}{5}$ mile, how many laps around the park does Luz run in $1\frac{2}{5}$ miles?

To find the number of laps, write $1\frac{2}{5}$ as a product of a whole number and $\frac{1}{5}$.

number of laps

$1\frac{2}{5} = n \times \frac{1}{5}$

Step 1

Rewrite $1\frac{2}{5}$ as a fraction greater than 1.

$1\frac{2}{5} = 1 + \frac{2}{5} = \frac{5}{5} + \frac{2}{5} = \frac{7}{5}$

Step 2

Rewrite the equation $1\frac{2}{5} = n \times \frac{1}{5}$ as $\frac{7}{5} = n \times \frac{1}{5}$.

Step 3

Find n, the number of laps. You can use a number line as a model. The number line shows the first ten multiples of $\frac{1}{5}$. Label $\frac{7}{5}$ on the number line.

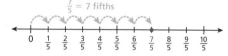

Number line: 0, $\frac{1}{5}$, $\frac{2}{5}$, $\frac{3}{5}$, $\frac{4}{5}$, $\frac{5}{5}$, $\frac{6}{5}$, $\frac{7}{5}$, $\frac{8}{5}$, $\frac{9}{5}$, $\frac{10}{5}$

Now, use the number line to find the number of fifths in $\frac{7}{5}$.

$\frac{7}{5} = 7$ fifths

Number line: 0, $\frac{1}{5}$, $\frac{2}{5}$, $\frac{3}{5}$, $\frac{4}{5}$, $\frac{5}{5}$, $\frac{6}{5}$, $\frac{7}{5}$, $\frac{8}{5}$, $\frac{9}{5}$, $\frac{10}{5}$

There are 7 fifths in $\frac{7}{5}$.
So, $\frac{7}{5} = 7 \times \frac{1}{5}$.
$n = 7$.

➤ Luz runs 7 laps around the park in $1\frac{2}{5}$ miles.

▸ Write $\frac{7}{5}$ as a sum of unit fractions. How many addends are there?
$\frac{1}{5} + \frac{1}{5} + \frac{1}{5} + \frac{1}{5} + \frac{1}{5} + \frac{1}{5} + \frac{1}{5} = \frac{7}{5}$. There are 7 addends.

Unit 3 ▪ Focus on Number and Operations—Fractions **183**

Math-to-Math Connection

Arithmetic and Geometry In Unit 4, students will relate fractions to angle measures as they study the angles of circles. Each angle around the center of the circle is equal to a unit fraction of $\frac{1}{360}$ of the circle. As students practice multiplication of whole numbers by unit fractions, they are gaining the skills that they will use to calculate fractional parts of a circle using angle measures. When using circular fraction models in the classroom, use terminology that relates these models to geometry, including *angle*, *ray*, and *arc*.

Connect: Writing a mixed number or a fraction greater than 1 as a product of a whole number and a unit fraction Use this page to strengthen students' understanding of the relationship between an improper fraction and the product of a whole number and a unit fraction.

■ Explain that a mixed number needs to be written as a fraction greater than 1 in order to show it as a product of a unit fraction and a whole number. If necessary, review that the whole number 1 can be written as a fraction with any denominator, as long as the numerator is the same as the denominator. For example, $1 = \frac{2}{2} = \frac{3}{3} = \frac{4}{4}$.

■ Help students realize that $\frac{7}{5} = n \times \frac{1}{5} = 7 \times \frac{1}{5}$. Explain that the fraction $\frac{7}{5}$ is the product of the whole number 7 times the unit fraction with the same denominator, $\frac{1}{5}$.

■ You can help students see equivalent mixed numbers on the number line by drawing the number line on the board and marking each multiple greater than 1 as both a fraction greater than 1 and an equivalent mixed number.

▸ Ask students to work in pairs to draw an area model that shows adding the unit fractions. Students may prefer to use manipulatives. Ask students to share their models with the class. Point out that each model needs to show five equal parts in one whole and two additional equal parts. Remind students that the parts within each model must be the same size.

Guided Practice

Observational Assessment

Use pages 184–185 to assess whether students are able to write fractions as a product of a whole number and a unit fraction. Make sure students realize that the denominator of the product should match the denominator of the unit fraction. Remind students that as they write multiples of unit fractions on the number line, they should write them as fractions, including fractions greater than 1.

Guided Practice

Complete the equation to find each product. Color the model to show the product.

1. $2 \times \frac{1}{4} = \frac{1}{4} + \frac{1}{4} = \frac{2}{4}$

2. $3 \times \frac{1}{4} = \frac{1}{4} + \frac{1}{4} + \frac{1}{4} = \frac{3}{4}$

3. $4 \times \frac{1}{8} = \frac{4}{8}$

4. $5 \times \frac{1}{8} = \frac{5}{8}$

For exercises 5–10, write the multiple of $\frac{1}{3}$ that names each point on the number line.

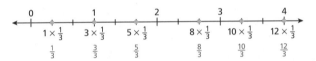

5. $1 \times \frac{1}{3} = \frac{1}{3}$

6. $3 \times \frac{1}{3} = \frac{3}{3}$

7. $5 \times \frac{1}{3} = \frac{5}{3}$

8. $8 \times \frac{1}{3} = \frac{8}{3}$

9. $10 \times \frac{1}{3} = \frac{10}{3}$

10. $12 \times \frac{1}{3} = \frac{12}{3}$

11. Write the missing fractions to count by thirds.

$\frac{1}{3}, \frac{2}{3}, \frac{3}{3}, \frac{4}{3}, \frac{5}{3}, \frac{6}{3}, \frac{7}{3}, \frac{8}{3}, \frac{9}{3}, \frac{10}{3}, \frac{11}{3}, \frac{12}{3}$

Math-to-Real World Connection

Buying in Bulk Students will encounter multiplication of a whole number and a unit fraction when buying products in bulk. Many products, such as mixed nuts, are sold in unit fractions of a pound.

Set up a station in the classroom where students can experiment with this type of problem. Use an inexpensive bulk item, such as kidney beans. Create a sign to identify the unit fraction to use to measure the item, such as, *Beans sold by the $\frac{1}{4}$ cup.* Allow students to practice measuring in $\frac{1}{4}$-cup increments and naming mixed number and fractional quantities greater than 1 cup.

Guided Practice

Solve the problems.

12. Complete the number pattern of multiples.
Rule: Start with $\frac{1}{2}$ and add $\frac{1}{2}$.

$\frac{1}{2}$, ____, $\frac{3}{2}$, ____, $\frac{5}{2}$, ____, $\frac{7}{2}$, ____, ...

$\frac{2}{2}$ $\frac{4}{2}$ $\frac{6}{2}$ $\frac{8}{2}$

13. Sam has 2 pounds of peanuts. He is going to make snack bags with $\frac{1}{4}$ pound of peanuts each. How many snack bags can Sam make? Explain your answer.
Possible explanation: Sam can make 8 small snack bags, because $2 = \frac{8}{4}$ so he has 8 fourths of a pound. $8 \times \frac{1}{4} = \frac{8}{4} = 2$

Write each fraction or mixed number as the product of a whole number and a unit fraction.

14. $\frac{2}{5} = 2 \times$ _____ $\frac{1}{5}$

15. $\frac{4}{6} =$ _____ $4 \times \frac{1}{6}$

16. $\frac{10}{8} =$ _____ $10 \times \frac{1}{8}$

17. $\frac{7}{10} =$ _____ $7 \times \frac{1}{10}$

18. $1\frac{2}{3} =$ _____ $5 \times \frac{1}{3}$
$1\frac{2}{3} = \frac{3}{3} + \frac{2}{3} = \frac{5}{3} = 5 \times \frac{1}{3}$

19. $2\frac{2}{5} =$ _____ $12 \times \frac{1}{5}$
$2\frac{2}{5} = \frac{5}{5} + \frac{5}{5} + \frac{2}{5} = \frac{12}{5} = 12 \times \frac{1}{5}$

Think · Pair · Share

MP3 20. Explain why the denominator stays the same when you multiply a unit fraction by a whole number.
Possible explanation: Multiplication is the same as adding the same number over and over. When you add fractions, you are adding the number of parts you are counting, so the numerator increases. But you can only add them because the parts are all the same size, and you do not change the size of the parts when you are joining more of them.

Unit 3 ■ Focus on Number and Operations—Fractions **185**

Think·Pair·Share

Peer Collaboration Ask students to work in pairs to share their explanations. Invite students to use examples to support their explanations. Suggest that students each choose a different unit fraction multiplied by the same whole number and compare the products. Ask:

- *What is the same about the numerators of your answers?*

- *What is different about the denominators of your answers?*

- *How can you create an addition problem that shows your answer?*

Return to the Essential Question

Reread the Lesson 21 Essential Question on page 182: *How is multiplying a unit fraction by a whole number like multiplying a whole number by a whole number?*

Ask volunteers to use what they learned in this lesson to answer this question. (Possible response: When I multiply two whole numbers, I repeatedly add equal groups to find how many in all. When I multiply a fraction by a whole number, I can repeatedly add equal fractional groups to find how many in all.)

Mathematical Practices

Mathematical Practice Standards underline the teaching and understanding of all concepts and skills presented. The emphasis of specific practices is noted throughout the guided and independent practice of this lesson.

MP3	**Construct viable arguments and critique the reasoning of others.**

Item 20: Students use previously established results in constructing arguments.

Concept Application

Students may work independently on these pages in the classroom or at home. They may refer to the first four pages of the lesson to revisit the instruction or to see a worked-out example.

Common Errors and **Teaching Tips** may help you support student learning either in the classroom or as a follow-up for work done at home.

Teaching Tips

Items 1–3

Point out that even though each of the models is a different size, each model represents one whole. If students are unsure, suggest that they count the number of parts in the whole and compare it to the denominator of the unit fraction.

Items 4–5

Remind students to use the number line models to represent the product. Tell students to record each fractional amount on the model, up to and including the answer.

Items 6–10

Explain to students that each problem has only one answer and some answers may not be used.

Independent Practice

Complete the equation to find each product. Color the model to support your answer.

1. $4 \times \frac{1}{5} = \frac{4}{5}$

2. $1 \times \frac{1}{6} = \frac{1}{6}$

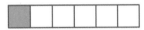

3. $10 \times \frac{1}{10} = \frac{10}{10}$

Complete the equation to find each product. Use the number line model to support your answer.

4. $3 \times \frac{1}{6} = \frac{3}{6}$

5. $5 \times \frac{1}{4} = \frac{5}{4}$

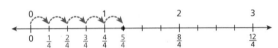

Draw lines to match.

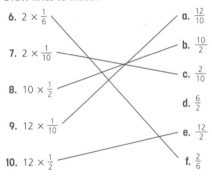

6. $2 \times \frac{1}{6}$

7. $2 \times \frac{1}{10}$

8. $10 \times \frac{1}{2}$

9. $12 \times \frac{1}{10}$

10. $12 \times \frac{1}{2}$

a. $\frac{12}{10}$

b. $\frac{10}{2}$

c. $\frac{2}{10}$

d. $\frac{6}{2}$

e. $\frac{12}{2}$

f. $\frac{2}{6}$

Writing About Math

■ · **Write an Informative Text** Ask students to write a paragraph defining unit fractions and explaining how to add and multiply them. Suggest that students give concrete examples and use mathematical vocabulary in their explanations. Look for terms such as *numerator, denominator,* and *equal groups.* Students should use good paragraph writing techniques, including introducing the topic early and providing a concluding statement.

Ask volunteers to read their paragraphs aloud. Invite a student to record any examples given in each paragraph and ask students to evaluate these examples for clarity and correctness.

Independent Practice

Write each fraction or mixed number as the product of a whole number and a unit fraction.

11. $\frac{5}{6} = 5 \times \underline{\quad \frac{1}{6} \quad}$

12. $\frac{4}{4} = \underline{\quad 4 \times \frac{1}{4} \quad}$

13. $\frac{7}{12} = \underline{\quad 7 \times \frac{1}{12} \quad}$

14. $\frac{20}{3} = \underline{\quad 20 \times \frac{1}{3} \quad}$

15. $1\frac{5}{10} = \underline{\quad 15 \times \frac{1}{10} \quad}$
$1\frac{5}{10} = \frac{10}{10} + \frac{5}{10} = \frac{15}{10} = 15 \times \frac{1}{10}$

16. $3\frac{1}{3} = \underline{\quad 10 \times \frac{1}{3} \quad}$
$3\frac{1}{3} = \frac{3}{3} + \frac{3}{3} + \frac{3}{3} + \frac{1}{3} = \frac{10}{3} = 10 \times \frac{1}{3}$

Solve.

17. Circle all the multiples of $\frac{1}{5}$.

(②/⑤) $\frac{1}{10}$ (③/⑤) $\frac{3}{4}$ $\frac{7}{6}$ (⑪/⑤)

   a. Write each multiple of $\frac{1}{5}$ as a product of a whole number and $\frac{1}{5}$.

   $\frac{2}{5} = 2 \times \frac{1}{5}$ $\frac{11}{5} = 11 \times \frac{1}{5}$

   $\frac{3}{5} = 3 \times \frac{1}{5}$

   b. Write each multiple of $\frac{1}{5}$ as a sum.

   $\frac{2}{5} = \frac{1}{5} + \frac{1}{5}; \frac{3}{5} = \frac{1}{5} + \frac{1}{5} + \frac{1}{5};$

   $\frac{11}{5} = \frac{1}{5} + \frac{1}{5} + \frac{1}{5} + \frac{1}{5} + \frac{1}{5} + \frac{1}{5} + \frac{1}{5} + \frac{1}{5} + \frac{1}{5} + \frac{1}{5} + \frac{1}{5}$

Circle the correct answer or answers.

18. Which of the sums are also multiples of $\frac{1}{3}$?

   a. $\frac{1}{1} + \frac{1}{2} + \frac{1}{3}$ **(b.)** $1 + \frac{1}{3}$

   c. $\frac{1}{2} + \frac{1}{1}$ **(d.)** $\frac{1}{3} + \frac{1}{3} + \frac{1}{3} + \frac{1}{3}$

19. Which fraction is a multiple of $\frac{1}{8}$ that equals 1?

   a. $\frac{1}{8}$ **(b.)** $\frac{8}{8}$

   c. $\frac{8}{1}$ **d.** $\frac{80}{10}$

Common Errors

Items 17–19

Students may incorrectly assume that they have solved the problem once they have found one answer. These problems may have more than one correct answer. Remind students to check each answer to determine whether it is correct.

Teaching Tips

Items 15–16

Remind students to write each mixed number as a fraction greater than 1 before trying to write it as a product of a whole number and a unit fraction.

Digital Connection

Random Number Generator Use a search engine to find an online fraction calculator that displays fractions. Use the calculator to multiply a unit fraction by a whole number and discuss the result given on the calculator. Ask students to explain any unexpected answers. For example, the calculator may reduce the fraction to lowest terms, so the denominator of the product may not match the unit fraction. Use this to generate a discussion about equivalent fractions.

Independent Practice

Common Errors

Items 22–23

Students will have an incomplete answer if they do not realize that they should reduce the fraction to solve the problem. Point out that students need to first multiply the unit fraction in each problem by the whole number. Then they need to determine the number of wholes in each product.

Teaching Tips

Item 20

If students have difficulty determining which explanation is correct, suggest students draw a model to show Eva's reasoning. If Eva's reasoning can be shown to be true, then Carrie's reasoning is false.

Item 21

Ask students to make a list of fractions that are equivalent to $\frac{1}{3}$. Have students circle each equivalent fraction with an even denominator. Invite a volunteer to explain how these equivalent fractions can be used to find a multiple of $\frac{1}{3}$.

Independent Practice

MP3 20. Carrie says that fractions can only have other fractions as multiples. Eva says that this is not true, because 2 is a multiple of $\frac{1}{2}$. Who is correct? Explain.

Possible explanation: Eva is correct, because a multiple of a number is just a number that you can get by multiplying that number by a whole number. $2 = \frac{2}{2} + \frac{2}{2} = \frac{4}{2} = 4 \times \frac{1}{2}$, so both 2 and $\frac{4}{2}$ are multiples of $\frac{1}{2}$.

MP3 21. Nicolas and Jun Ho are making up riddles for multiples of fractions. Nicolas says his number is a multiple of $\frac{1}{3}$ that has an even number as a denominator. Jun Ho says this is impossible. Can you guess Nicolas's number? Explain. Possible explanation: Nicolas's number could be any number that can be written as an equivalent fraction with a denominator of 3. For example, his number could be $\frac{4}{6}$ because $\frac{4}{6}$ is equivalent to $\frac{2}{3}$, or his number could be $\frac{12}{4}$, because $\frac{12}{4}$ is equivalent to 3 and 3 is equivalent to $\frac{9}{3}$, or his number could be $\frac{20}{6}$ because $\frac{20}{6}$ is equivalent to $\frac{10}{3}$.

Solve the problems.

MP1 22. A restaurant makes big hamburgers with $\frac{1}{4}$ pound of beef in each. If the restaurant makes 12 hamburgers in one hour, how many pounds of beef does the restaurant use?

▸ **Show your work.** Work may vary. Possible work:
$12 \times \frac{1}{4} = \frac{12}{4} = \frac{12 \div 4}{4 \div 4} = \frac{3}{1} = 3$

Answer The restaurant uses 3 pounds of beef.

MP4 23. Reagan's town has a clock tower with bells that ring once every $\frac{1}{2}$ hour. If the bells ring 6 times, how many hours have gone by?

▸ **Show your work.**
Work may vary. Possible work:

$6 \times \frac{1}{2} = \frac{6}{2} = 3$

Answer Three hours have gone by.

Mathematical Practices

MP1	**Make sense of problems and persevere in solving them.**
Item 22: Students analyze a problem and plan a solution.	
MP3	**Construct viable arguments and critique the reasoning of others.**
Item 20: Students analyze two arguments and determine which makes sense.	
Item 21: Students analyze a problem and explain a method to solve it.	
MP4	**Model with mathematics.**
Item 23: Students relate mathematics to everyday problems.	

Lesson 21

Independent Practice

MP5 **24.** The picture shows a ruler marked with some fractions of an inch. The markings are multiples of $\frac{1}{4}$ and $\frac{1}{2}$.

For each of these fractions, what is the greatest multiple less than 5 inches? To help you identify each multiple, write it as a product of the fraction and a whole number.

▶ **Show your work.** Work may vary. Possible work:

multiple of $\frac{1}{4}$: $4\frac{3}{4} = \frac{19}{4} = 19 \times \frac{1}{4}$

multiple of $\frac{1}{2}$: $4\frac{1}{2} = \frac{9}{2} = 9 \times \frac{1}{2}$

The greatest multiple of $\frac{1}{4}$ that is less than 5 is $\frac{19}{4}$, or $4\frac{3}{4}$.

Answer The greatest multiple of $\frac{1}{2}$ that is less than 5 is $\frac{9}{2}$, or $4\frac{1}{2}$.

MP4 **25.** Victoria says that $\frac{17}{6}$ is not a multiple of $\frac{1}{6}$. As proof, she says that $\frac{17}{6}$ equals $2\frac{5}{6}$ instead of a whole number. Is Victoria correct? Draw a model to justify your answer.

Answer No, Victoria is not correct. $\frac{17}{6}$ is a multiple of $\frac{1}{6}$.

▶ **Justify your answer using words, drawings, or numbers.** Possible justification:

A number does not have to be a whole number to be a multiple of a fraction. My number line shows that $\frac{17}{6}$ is 17 sixths, or $17 \times \frac{1}{6}$. It also shows that most multiples of fractions are not whole numbers, since all the tick marks in between the whole numbers are multiples of $\frac{1}{6}$ too.

MP8 **26.** Samir says that you can write any fraction as a product of a whole number and a unit fraction. Do you agree? Give an example to support your answer.

Answer I agree with Samir.

▶ **Justify your answer using words, drawings, or numbers.** Possible justification: A unit fraction is one part of the total parts named by the denominator. The numerator is the total number of those parts that are counted. So, to write a product, you can use the numerator of any fraction as one factor and the unit fraction as the other factor; for example: $\frac{8}{10} = 8 \times \frac{1}{10}$.

Unit 3 ■ Focus on Number and Operations—Fractions **189**

Teaching Tips

Item 24

Make sure students realize that this problem requires finding the greatest multiple less than 5 inches for multiples of $\frac{1}{4}$ and for multiples of $\frac{1}{2}$. If students have difficulty, encourage them to draw two number lines, dividing one number line into fourths and the other number line into halves. Have students solve the problem using the number lines and writing the products as fractions and as mixed numbers.

Item 26

Point out to students that for Samir's statement to be true, it must work for all examples. Suggest that they include more than one example to support their answers.

Mathematical Practices

MP4	**Model with mathematics.**
Item 25: Students use concrete tools to justify an answer.	
MP5	**Use appropriate tools strategically.**
Item 24: Students use given tools to answer a word problem.	
MP8	**Look for and express regularity in repeated reasoning.**
Item 26: Students look for a pattern and make generalizations about a situation.	

Common Core Focus:

4.NF.4b Understand a multiple of *a/b* as a multiple of 1/*b*, and use this understanding to multiply a fraction by a whole number.

OBJECTIVE
Multiply fractions by whole numbers.

ESSENTIAL QUESTION

Students have learned how to multiply a unit fraction by a whole number and how to write any fraction as a product of a whole number and a unit fraction. In this lesson students will use both of these skills to multiply a non-unit fraction by a whole number.

FLUENCY PRACTICE

Fluency practice is available at **sadlierconnect.com**.

Concept Development

Understand: Multiplication as repeated addition

■ This presentation extends students' understanding of multiplication as repeated addition and connects students' developed skills involving operations with fractions.

■ Be sure students understand that the multiplication $6 \times \frac{2}{3}$ can be interpreted as 6 groups of $\frac{2}{3}$ and written as repeated addition $\frac{2}{3} + \frac{2}{3} + \frac{2}{3} + \frac{2}{3} + \frac{2}{3} + \frac{2}{3}$ and that the repeated addition $\frac{2+2+2+2+2+2}{3}$ can be written as the multiplication $\frac{6 \times 2}{3}$.

✏ ▶ Remind students that to find a multiple of a fraction, multiply the fraction by a whole number. To find the first six multiples, multiply by 1, 2, 3, 4, 5, and 6. Students should be able to recognize the pattern where the denominator stays the same, but the numerators increase by 2.

Essential Question:
How can you multiply a fraction that is not a unit fraction by a whole number?
4.NF.4b

Guided Instruction

In this lesson you will learn how to multiply any fraction by a whole number.

Understand: Multiplication as repeated addition

Sabrina is making carrot muffins. Her muffin pan has 6 baking cups. Sabrina will put $\frac{2}{3}$ cup of batter in each baking cup. How much batter does she need for all 6 baking cups?

To find the total cups of batter, multiply $6 \times \frac{2}{3}$.

Draw a model for the 6 groups of $\frac{2}{3}$.
The model shows that $6 \times \frac{2}{3}$ is the same as $\frac{2}{3} + \frac{2}{3} + \frac{2}{3} + \frac{2}{3} + \frac{2}{3} + \frac{2}{3}$.

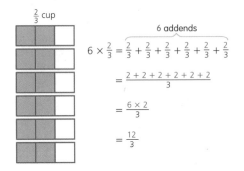

$\frac{2}{3}$ cup

6 addends

$$6 \times \frac{2}{3} = \frac{2}{3} + \frac{2}{3} + \frac{2}{3} + \frac{2}{3} + \frac{2}{3} + \frac{2}{3}$$
$$= \frac{2 + 2 + 2 + 2 + 2 + 2}{3}$$
$$= \frac{6 \times 2}{3}$$
$$= \frac{12}{3}$$

Write the product $\frac{12}{3}$ as a whole number. You can use the fact $12 = 4 \times 3$ to help you find the whole number.

$$\frac{12}{3} = \frac{4 \times 3}{3} = \frac{3}{3} + \frac{3}{3} + \frac{3}{3} + \frac{3}{3} = 4$$

▶ Sabrina needs 4 cups of batter for all 6 baking cups.

Remember!
You can break apart the numerator of a fraction in the same way as a whole number.

✏ ▶ Write the first six multiples of $\frac{2}{3}$.
$\frac{2}{3}, \frac{4}{3}, \frac{6}{3}, \frac{8}{3}, \frac{10}{3}, \frac{12}{3}$

Support English Language Learners

Review the terms *numerator*, *denominator*, and *product* to make sure students understand the solutions in the Guided Instruction. Sometimes students will skip over explanations that sound complicated or have a lot of mathematical terms.

Have students look at the explanation following the arrow on page 191: *To multiply any fraction by a whole number, you can multiply the numerator of the fraction by the whole number. Then write the product over the denominator.*

As students read through the explanation, have them identify the parts of the symbolic representation that correspond to the words. Using symbolic representations helps to give meaning to words and explanations.

Guided Instruction

Understand: Writing the fraction as a multiple of a unit fraction before multiplying

> How can you multiply a fraction by a whole number without using repeated addition?

You can solve Sabrina's muffin problem in a different way. To multiply $6 \times \frac{2}{3}$, you can think of $\frac{2}{3}$ as $2 \times \frac{1}{3}$ and then use the Associative Property of Multiplication.

$6 \times 2 = 12$ $\frac{2}{3}$ cup

2 thirds

$$6 \times \frac{2}{3} = 6 \times \left(2 \times \frac{1}{3}\right)$$
$$= (6 \times 2) \times \frac{1}{3}$$
$$= 12 \times \frac{1}{3}$$
$$= \frac{12}{3}$$
$$= 4$$

Remember!
The Associative Property of Multiplication states that you can change the grouping of the factors without changing the product.

The product is the same as with the repeated addition method.

➡ To multiply any fraction by a whole number, you can multiply the numerator of the fraction by the whole number. Then write the product over the denominator.

$$6 \times \frac{2}{3} = \frac{6 \times 2}{3} = \frac{12}{3} = 4$$

✏ Find the total cups of batter Sabrina will need for a pan with 9 baking cups instead of 6.

$9 \times \frac{2}{3} = \frac{9 \times 2}{3} = \frac{18}{3} = 6$; Sabrina will need 6 cups of batter.

Understand: Writing the fraction as a multiple of a unit fraction before multiplying

■ The Common Core State Standards for Mathematics expect that students understand that a fraction a/b is a multiple of its unit fraction $1/b$, and use this understanding to multiply a fraction by a whole number. From the previous lesson, students should understand that $\frac{2}{3}$ can be written as a multiple of a unit fraction, $2 \times \frac{1}{3}$. When you multiply $6 \times 2 \times \frac{1}{3}$, the result is another multiple of the unit fraction, $12 \times \frac{1}{3}$ or $\frac{12}{3}$.

■ This presentation should lead students to the understanding that $n \times \left(\frac{a}{b}\right) = \frac{(n \times a)}{b}$. Help students understand this concept by explaining how the model shows $6 \times \frac{2}{3}$.

✏ After students have completed the exercise, have volunteers share their reasoning. Suggest that students check their answer by drawing a model that shows 9 groups of $\frac{2}{3}$.

Math-to-Geometry Connection

Area Many formulas in geometry contain fractions. In later grades, students will multiply fractions to find the area of triangles and trapezoids. You can use the formula below to show students how to find the area of a triangle.

Area of Triangle

$A = \frac{1}{2}b \times h$, where b is the base and h is the height of the triangle.

Area of a triangle with a base of 6 inches and a height of 3 inches:

$A = \frac{1}{2} \times 6 \times 3 = 9$

The area of the triangle is 9 square inches.

Connect: Multiplying a mixed number by a whole number Use this page to help students apply what they have learned about multiplying a fraction by a whole number to the skill of multiplying a mixed number by a whole number.

■ Students should recognize that any operation with a mixed number begins with writing the mixed number as a fraction and then performing the operation in the same way as with fractions.

■ A common mistake students make when multiplying a whole number and a mixed number, is multiplying the whole number and the whole-number part of the mixed number, and leaving the fraction unchanged. You may want to use models to show students why this process will lead to an incorrect answer.

✏ Remind students how to write an equation using the Distributive Property. When they are finished, discuss any errors that were made and answers that did not agree. Students have now seen that the properties of operations for whole numbers also hold true for fractions and mixed numbers.

Connect: Multiplying a mixed number by a whole number

> Damian is teaching himself to play the guitar. This week, he plays his guitar for $1\frac{3}{4}$ hours on each of 4 days. For how many hours does Damian play his guitar this week?

To find how many hours Damian plays his guitar, multiply $4 \times 1\frac{3}{4}$. You can use an equivalent fraction for the mixed number.

Step 1

Rewrite $1\frac{3}{4}$ as a fraction greater than 1.

$$1\frac{3}{4} = 1 + \frac{3}{4}$$
$$= \frac{4}{4} + \frac{3}{4}$$
$$= \frac{7}{4}$$

So, rewrite the multiplication as $4 \times \frac{7}{4}$.

Step 2

Multiply 4 times the numerator in the fraction $\frac{7}{4}$.
Write the total number of fourths over the denominator.
$$4 \times \frac{7}{4} = \frac{4 \times 7}{4} = \frac{28}{4} = 7$$

To check, you can mark off 4 groups of $\frac{7}{4}$ on a number line.
The fourth multiple of $\frac{7}{4}$ is the product, $\frac{28}{4} = 7$.

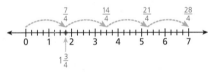

➡ Damian plays his guitar for 7 hours this week.

✏ Sarah says that you can also multiply $4 \times 1\frac{3}{4}$ by writing $4 \times (1 + \frac{3}{4})$ and then adding 4×1 and $4 \times \frac{3}{4}$. Do you agree?
Yes. Sarah is using the Distributive Property.

$$4 \times (1 + \frac{3}{4}) = (4 \times 1) + (4 \times \frac{3}{4})$$
$$= 4 + \frac{12}{4}$$
$$= 4 + 3 = 7$$

192 Unit 3 ■ Focus on Number and Operations—Fractions

Math-to-Art Connection

Scale Models A scale model is a smaller version of an actual object. To keep the dimensions proportional, the actual dimensions of an object are multiplied by a fraction to determine the dimensions of the smaller scale model.

Propose that the class will build a scale model of an Iroquois longhouse. Relate that a typical longhouse was about 80 feet long by 20 feet wide by 18 feet high. To find the dimensions of the scale model in inches, have students use a scale of 1 inch = 8 feet. Have students find the dimensions of the scale model in inches by multiplying the actual dimensions by $\frac{1}{8}$. Students should calculate the dimensions of the scale model to be 10 inches by $2\frac{1}{2}$ inches by $2\frac{1}{4}$ inches.

Guided Practice

Use the model or the number line to show that your product is correct.

1. $2 \times \frac{3}{5} = \frac{3}{5} + \frac{3}{5} = \frac{2 \times 3}{5} = \frac{6}{5} = 1\frac{1}{5}$

2. $3 \times \frac{4}{6} = \frac{4}{6} + \frac{4}{6} + \frac{4}{6} = \frac{3 \times 4}{6} = \frac{12}{6} = \underline{2}$

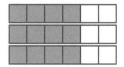

3. $3 \times \frac{5}{8} = \frac{3 \times 5}{8} = \frac{15}{8} = 1\frac{7}{8}$

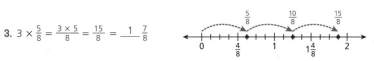

Complete the equation to multiply. If the product is greater than 1, write it as a whole or mixed number.

4. $7 \times \frac{3}{10} = \frac{7 \times 3}{10} = \frac{21}{10} = \underline{2}\ \frac{1}{10}$

5. $4 \times 2\frac{1}{2} = 4 \times \frac{5}{2} = \frac{4 \times 5}{2} = \frac{20}{2} = \underline{10}$

Think ∘ Pair ∘ Share

MP4 **6.** Compare the problem in exercise 2 to multiplying the whole numbers 3 × 4. How are the problems alike? How are they different?
Possible answer: If you think of the numerator 4 in $\frac{4}{6}$ as a whole number, like the number of items in a group instead of a number of fractional parts, then the problem is the same as multiplying 3 × 4. The only difference is in the last step, when you regroup the product 12 into sets of 6 sixths to make whole amounts.

Unit 3 ■ Focus on Number and Operations—Fractions **193**

Mathematical Practices

Mathematical Practice Standards underline the teaching and understanding of all concepts and skills presented. The emphasis of specific practices is noted throughout the guided and independent practice of this lesson.

| MP4 | **Model with mathematics.** |

Item 6: Students describe how a strategy used for multiplying two whole numbers can be applied to multiplying a whole number and a fraction.

Observational Assessment

Use page 193 to assess whether students are able to multiply a fraction or mixed number by a whole number. Watch for students who are not sure how to approach determining the solution once steps are no longer provided for them. Those students may benefit from a short list of written steps that they can follow for every exercise.

♕ Think∘Pair∘Share

Peer Collaboration After students have had a chance to work on their own, have them discuss their solution with a partner. Then, have students volunteer to share their work with the class. To facilitate the discussion, ask questions such as:

- *How would you represent 3 × 4 using repeated addition?*

- *How would you represent $3 \times \frac{4}{6}$ using repeated addition?*

- *How does the product of $3 \times \frac{4}{6}$ (written as a fraction) compare to the product of 3 × 4?*

To summarize, remind students that $3 \times 4 = 3 \times \frac{4}{1}$. The process of multiplying $3 \times \frac{4}{1}$ is the same as $3 \times \frac{4}{6}$, except the size of the denominator is different.

Return to the Essential Question

Reread the Lesson 22 Essential Question on page 190: *How can you multiply a fraction that is not a unit fraction by a whole number?*

Ask volunteers to use what they learned in this lesson to answer this question. (Possible response: I can write the multiplication using repeated addition or I can multiply the numerator of the fraction by the whole number and write the product over the denominator.)

Concept Application

Students may work independently on these pages in the classroom or at home. They may refer to the first four pages of the lesson to revisit the instruction on how to multiply a fraction that is not a unit fraction by a whole number or to see a worked-out example.

Common Errors and **Teaching Tips** may help you support student learning either in the classroom or as a follow-up for work done at home.

Common Errors

Item 4

Students may multiply the whole numbers, 4 × 1, and keep the fraction unchanged to get a product of $4\frac{3}{8}$. Remind students that they must multiply both parts of the mixed number by 4. One way to do this is to write the mixed number as an equivalent fraction greater than 1 before multiplying.

Teaching Tips

Item 3

Remind students that to find the first five multiples of a fraction, multiply the fraction by the whole numbers 1, 2, 3, 4, and 5.

Independent Practice

Use the model or the number line to show that your product is correct.

1. $2 \times \frac{7}{10} = \frac{2 \times 7}{10} = \frac{14}{10} = 1\frac{4}{10}$

2. $3 \times \frac{4}{5} = \frac{3 \times 4}{5} = \frac{12}{5} = \underline{\ 2\ }\ \frac{2}{5}$

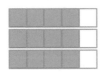

3. $5 \times \frac{3}{6} = \frac{5 \times 3}{6} = \frac{15}{6} = \underline{\ 2\ }\ \frac{3}{6}$

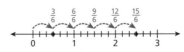

List the first five multiples of $\frac{3}{6}$. Use the model to help you.

$\frac{3}{6}, \frac{6}{6}, \frac{9}{6}, \frac{12}{6}, \frac{15}{6}$ _____

4. $4 \times 1\frac{3}{8} = 4 \times \frac{11}{8} = \frac{4 \times 11}{8} = \frac{44}{8} = 5\frac{4}{8}$

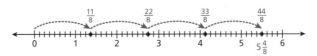

Writing About Math

▸ **Write an Opinion** Have students review the two different methods that were used on pages 190 and 191 to multiply a fraction by a whole number. Ask students to write an opinion about the lesson. Students may write about the method they liked best, or they may choose one method and write about whether the method was easy to understand. Remind students to include reasons to support their opinion.

When students have finished writing, ask for volunteers to share their opinions with the class. Tell students that an opinion is neither right nor wrong, and some students will have differing opinions.

For exercises 5–9, use the number line. The number line shows multiples of $\frac{3}{4}$. Write each multiple as a product of a whole number and a fraction.

Answers may vary.

5. $\frac{3}{4} =$ _____ $1 \times \frac{3}{4}, 3 \times \frac{1}{4}$

6. $\frac{6}{4} =$ _____ $2 \times \frac{3}{4}, 6 \times \frac{1}{4}$

7. $\frac{9}{4} =$ _____ $3 \times \frac{3}{4}, 9 \times \frac{1}{4}$

8. What are the next three multiples?

$\frac{12}{4}, \frac{15}{4}, \frac{18}{4}$

9. Are there any multiples of $\frac{3}{4}$ between $\frac{6}{4}$ and $\frac{9}{4}$? Explain.
   No, there are no multiples between those two fractions. Possible explanation: A multiple of $\frac{3}{4}$ is a product of $\frac{3}{4}$ and a whole number; $\frac{6}{4} = 2 \times \frac{3}{4}$ and $\frac{9}{4} = 3 \times \frac{3}{4}$, and there is no whole number between 2 and 3.

Multiply. If the product is greater than 1, write it as a whole or mixed number. You can use a model to help.

10. $5 \times \frac{2}{5} =$ _____ $\frac{10}{5} = 2$

11. $4 \times \frac{5}{6} =$ _____ $\frac{20}{6} = 3\frac{2}{6}$

12. $3 \times \frac{9}{12} =$ _____ $\frac{27}{12} = 2\frac{3}{12}$

13. $6 \times 2\frac{2}{10} =$ _____ $6 \times \frac{22}{10} = \frac{132}{10} = 13\frac{2}{10}$

Teaching Tips

Items 5-7
Remind students that the first multiple of a number has 1 as a factor; the second multiple of a number has 2 as a factor; and so on.

Item 12
Students may have difficulty writing the product as a mixed number. They should decompose the fraction greater than 1 into fractions equal to 1 with a denominator of 12. Guide them to write $\frac{27}{12}$ as $\frac{12}{12} + \frac{12}{12} + \frac{3}{12}$.

Digital Connection

Random Number Generator Use a search engine to find a random number generator Web site. Assign parameters for the random number generator to select two numbers between 1 and 8. Students should write a fraction using the lesser number as the numerator and the greater number as the denominator. Tell students to write the first 6 multiples of the fraction they created. Then have students identify if any of the multiples can be written as whole numbers.

Independent Practice

Teaching Tips

Item 14
Since the denominator is 3, students can write multiples of 3 until they find a number that is close to 14. Show that using the multiples 3, 6, 9, and 12 in the numerator result in whole numbers: $\frac{3}{3} = 1$, $\frac{6}{3} = 2$, $\frac{9}{3} = 3$, and $\frac{12}{3} = 4$.

Item 17
Challenge students by having them use the Distributive Property to multiply by a mixed number. Students should show that $9 \times \left(1 + \frac{6}{10}\right) = (9 \times 1) + \left(9 \times \frac{6}{10}\right)$ results in the same product as $9 \times \frac{16}{10}$.

Lesson 22 **Multiply Fractions by Whole Numbers**

Independent Practice

MP2 **14.** Brenda wants to write the product $\frac{14}{3}$ as a mixed number. How can Brenda use multiplication to help her rename the product?
Answers will vary. Possible answer: Brenda can use multiplication or division facts to make groups of 3 thirds from 14 thirds. Since 12 is close to 14, the fact $12 = 4 \times 3$ tells her there are 4 whole sets of 3 in $\frac{14}{3}$. $14 - 12 = 2$, so the fraction part of the mixed number is $\frac{2}{3}$.

MP1 **15.** How does drawing a model help you multiply a fraction by a whole number? Explain your opinion.
Possible explanation: A model gives you a picture of the product. It also reminds you that you are multiplying a fraction, and that the result of multiplying the whole number and the numerator is not the final answer.

Solve the problems.

MP1 **16.** Kristin is making soup. The recipe calls for $\frac{6}{8}$ pound of beef. Kristin wants to make 4 times the amount of soup in the recipe. How many pounds of beef does Kristin need?

▶ **Show your work.** Work may vary. Possible work:

$4 \times \frac{6}{8} = \frac{4 \times 6}{8} = \frac{24}{8} = 3$

Answer Kristin needs 3 pounds of beef.

MP6 **17.** Levi watched his favorite movie 9 times on DVD. The movie is $1\frac{6}{10}$ hours long. How many hours did it take Levi to watch the movie 9 times?

▶ **Show your work.** Work may vary. Possible work:

$9 \times 1\frac{6}{10} = 9 \times \frac{16}{10}$
$= \frac{9 \times 16}{10}$
$= \frac{144}{10} = \frac{140}{10} + \frac{4}{10} = 14 + \frac{4}{10}$
$= 14\frac{4}{10}$

Answer It took Levi $14\frac{4}{10}$ hours to watch the movie 9 times.

196 Unit 3 ■ Focus on Number and Operations—Fractions

Copyright © by William H. Sadlier, Inc. All rights reserved.

Mathematical Practices	
MP1	**Make sense of problems and persevere in solving them.**
Item 15: Students explain how a model helps make sense of a problem. **Item 16:** Students use multiplication to solve a problem.	
MP2	**Reason abstractly and quantitatively.**
Item 14: Students use number sense and multiplication to rename a fraction greater than 1 as a mixed number.	
MP6	**Attend to precision.**
Item 17: Students calculate with greater numbers.	

196 Unit 3 ■ Focus on Number and Operations—Fractions

Independent Practice

MP1 **18.** A gardener is moving some houseplants into bigger pots. She has 3 plastic pots that hold $4\frac{1}{12}$ quarts of soil each. She also has 4 clay pots that hold $3\frac{2}{5}$ quarts of soil each. Does the gardener need more soil for the plastic pots or the clay pots?

Show your work. Work may vary. Possible work:

plastic pots: $3 \times 4\frac{1}{12} = 3 \times (4 + \frac{1}{12}) = 12 + \frac{3}{12} = 12\frac{3}{12}$

clay pots: $4 \times 3\frac{2}{5} = 4 \times (3 + \frac{2}{5}) = 12 + \frac{8}{5} = 13\frac{3}{5}$

$13\frac{3}{5} > 12\frac{3}{12}$

Answer The gardener needs more soil for the clay pots.

MP1 **19.** Darius reads $\frac{2}{10}$ of his book in 3 days. He says that if he reads the rest of the book at the same speed, it should take him 15 more days to finish the book. Is Darius correct?

Answer No, Darius is not correct. It will take him less than 15 days.

Justify your answer using words, drawings, or numbers.
Possible justification:
3 days

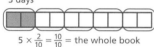

$5 \times \frac{2}{10} = \frac{10}{10} =$ the whole book

Darius is counting the 3 days it took him to read the first $\frac{2}{10}$ of the book. There are 4 more groups of $\frac{2}{10}$ left to read, and 4×3 days $= 12$ days to read the other $\frac{8}{10}$ of the book.

MP7 **20.** Jenny is helping to pack supplies for a school picnic. Each of three boxes of drinking straws are filled with only 50 out of 100 straws. Jenny says that she can multiply $3 \times \frac{1}{2}$ instead of $3 \times \frac{50}{100}$ to find the total number of full boxes. Is Jenny correct?

Answer Yes, Jenny is correct.

Justify your answer using words, drawings, or numbers.
Possible justification: $\frac{50}{100}$ and $\frac{1}{2}$ are equivalent fractions, and she wants to know the number of whole boxes, not the exact number of straws. $3 \times \frac{1}{2} = \frac{3}{2} = 1\frac{1}{2}$ boxes of straws. $3 \times \frac{50}{100} = \frac{150}{100} = \frac{100}{100} + \frac{50}{100} = 1\frac{1}{2}$ boxes. The two products are the same.

Unit 3 ■ Focus on Number and Operations—Fractions **197**

Common Errors

Item 19

Students may correctly calculate that it will take 15 days to read the book, but overlook what the problem is asking. Since Darius has already read part of the book, it will take him less than 15 days to finish the book.

Teaching Tips

Item 20

Students should reason that multiplying by equivalent fractions does not change the product. Suggest that students perform both multiplications to justify their reasoning.

Mathematical Practices

MP1	**Make sense of problems and persevere in solving them.**

Item 18: Students perform two multiplications and compare the products.

Item 19: Students must evaluate the real-world context of the problem to reach the correct conclusion.

MP7	**Look for and make use of structure.**

Item 20: Students use their understanding of equivalent fractions to justify their answer.

Common Core Focus:

4.NF.4c Solve word problems involving multiplication of a fraction by a whole number.

OBJECTIVE

Understand how to multiply fractions and mixed numbers by whole numbers to help solve real-world problems.

ESSENTIAL QUESTION

In this lesson, students will learn how to multiply fractions by whole numbers to solve word problems. This skill is often used when solving real-world problems, so it is important for students to gain a firm understanding of these multiplication concepts.

FLUENCY PRACTICE

Fluency practice is available at **sadlierconnect.com**.

Concept Development

Understand: Multiplying a fraction by a whole number and comparing two amounts

■ Students extend their understanding of multiplication of fractions and mixed numbers and apply that knowledge to solve real-world word problems.

■ Remind students that any whole number can be expressed as a fraction with 1 as the denominator.

■ When comparing a mixed number and a whole number, first compare the whole-number part of the mixed number to the whole number. If the whole numbers are different, it is not necessary to consider the fraction part.

✎ ➤ Suggest that students think about the number of fifths in one pound, and use multiplication to find the number of fifths in 5 pounds. The numerator is the total number of fifths, and the denominator is the number of fifths in one pack.

Guided Instruction

In this lesson you will learn how to multiply a fraction or a mixed number by a whole number to solve word problems.

Understand: Multiplying a fraction by a whole number and comparing two amounts

> Jordan is buying modeling clay to use for a project. He can buy six $\frac{3}{5}$-pound sticks of different colors. The store also sells a 5-pound pack of colors for the same price. Which should Jordan buy to get more clay?

To solve the problem, find the total weight of the 6 sticks and then compare it to 5 pounds.

Remember!
$$6 \times \frac{3}{5} = \frac{3}{5} + \frac{3}{5} + \frac{3}{5} + \frac{3}{5} + \frac{3}{5} + \frac{3}{5}$$

You can use a model to show 6 groups of $\frac{3}{5}$ pound.

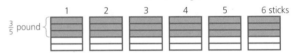

Find the total number of pounds in 6 sticks. You can count the shaded fifths in the model or you can write and solve an equation. Use w to represent the number of pounds of clay in 6 sticks.

$$w = 6 \times \frac{3}{5}$$
$$6 \times \frac{3}{5} = \frac{6 \times 3}{5} = \frac{18}{5} \text{ and } \frac{18}{5} = \frac{15}{5} + \frac{3}{5} = 3 + \frac{3}{5} = 3\frac{3}{5}$$
$$w = 3\frac{3}{5}$$

The total weight of the 6 sticks is $3\frac{3}{5}$ pounds.

Compare $3\frac{3}{5}$ to 5. Since $3 < 5$, the 5-pound pack has more clay. $3\frac{3}{5} < 5$

➤ Jordan should buy the 5-pound pack instead of six $\frac{3}{5}$-pound sticks to get more clay.

✎ ➤ How many fifths of a pound are in the 5-pound pack? How many more pounds are in the 5-pound pack than in six $\frac{3}{5}$-pound sticks? There are 25 fifths in the 5-pound pack. $\frac{25}{5} - \frac{18}{5} = \frac{7}{5} = 1\frac{2}{5}$. The 5-pound pack has $1\frac{2}{5}$ pounds more

than six $\frac{3}{5}$-pound sticks.

Support English Language Learners

Word problems can be challenging for English Language Learners because they require students to read and comprehend the text of the problem, to identify the question that needs to be answered, and to create the equation needed to solve the problem. For this lesson, it may be useful to help these students read over the problems several times. Another way to aid with comprehension is to break the problems into smaller segments. Finally, you could have students act out the word problems, use manipulatives, or make drawings or models to help them understand the problems.

Guided Instruction

Understand: Multiplying a fraction or mixed number greater than 1 by a whole number

> Jordan buys 3 different colors of paint. He needs $1\frac{1}{2}$ gallons of each color. How much paint does he buy?

Method 1

Solve the problem using visual models. Show 3 groups of $1\frac{1}{2}$.

The model shows that Jordan buys $\frac{9}{2}$ or $4\frac{1}{2}$ gallons of paint.

➡ Jordan buys $4\frac{1}{2}$ gallons of paint.

Method 2

Solve the problem using an equation. Let g represent the total number of gallons of paint Jordan buys.　　$g = 3 \times 1\frac{1}{2}$

One Way to Solve the Equation	Another Way to Solve the Equation
$g = 3 \times 1\frac{1}{2}$	$g = 3 \times 1\frac{1}{2}$
$g = 3 \times (1 + \frac{1}{2})$	$g = 3 \times (1 + \frac{1}{2})$
$g = 3 \times (\frac{2}{2} + \frac{1}{2})$	$g = (3 \times 1) + (3 \times \frac{1}{2})$
$g = 3 \times (\frac{3}{2})$	$g = 3 + \frac{3}{2}$
$g = \frac{3 \times 3}{2}$	$g = 3 + (\frac{2}{2} + \frac{1}{2})$
$g = \frac{9}{2}$	$g = 3 + (1 + \frac{1}{2})$
$g = \frac{8}{2} + \frac{1}{2}$	$g = 3 + 1\frac{1}{2}$
$g = 4 + \frac{1}{2}$	$g = 4\frac{1}{2}$
$g = 4\frac{1}{2}$	

Remember!
Multiplying a number by a sum is the same as multiplying the number by each addend of the sum and then adding the products.

➡ Jordan buys $4\frac{1}{2}$ gallons of paint.

✏ If Jordan can only buy gallon cans of paint, how many gallon cans must Jordan buy? Explain your reasoning.

Possible explanation: He must buy 6 gallons of paint. He needs $1\frac{1}{2}$ gallons of each color. $1\frac{1}{2}$ is between 1 and 2. So he must buy 2 gallons of each color.

Understand: Multiplying a fraction or mixed number greater than 1 by a whole number

■ Help students examine the different methods used to solve the problem. Then have them share with a partner which method they prefer and why. Explain to students that it is important to become familiar with both methods.

■ Encourage students to become comfortable using equations to solve these types of problems. As the values in the problems increase, it can become difficult to solve these problems by drawing models.

✏ After students have answered this question, ask a few volunteers to read their answers aloud and share which method they chose to solve the problem. Some students may round their answers to 5 gallons. Point out that in this situation, two halves cannot be combined to get one whole because each gallon of paint is a different color. Since Jordan needs $1\frac{1}{2}$ gallons of each color, 1 one-gallon can is not enough.

Math-to-Real World Connection

Exercise Multiplying fractions or mixed numbers by whole numbers has practical applications in the real world. Explain that Joe rides his bike $2\frac{3}{4}$ miles five times a week. Have students find the total distance Joe rides each week. Encourage students to draw a model and write an equation to solve the problem. When students are finished, have them share their methods and solutions in small groups.

Have students discuss how to find the total distance if Joe decides to increase his distance to $3\frac{1}{4}$ miles five times a week.

Connect: Solving a multi-step problem using equations and models Use this page to help students see how equations and models can be used when solving a multi-step problem.

■ Ask why this problem requires more than one step to solve. Lead students to see that the problem is asking for the greater of two total distances. Model how to break the problem into smaller steps. Each step represents one of the solutions needed to find the final solution.

■ In Step 1, remind students to decompose one of the factors into addends before applying the Distributive Property.

■ Ask students to discuss why it is a good idea to use different variables for the different equations. Although it would not be mathematically incorrect, make sure students understand that using the same variable can sometimes cause confusion. It is better to assign a unique variable for each unique value in each equation.

■ Students should understand that $6\frac{2}{4}$ is between the whole numbers 6 and 7, so $6\frac{2}{4} > 6$.

Lesson 23   Problem Solving: **Multiply Fractions by Whole Numbers**

Guided Instruction

Connect: Solving a multi-step problem using equations and models

Natalie and Rachel are hiking with their families. Natalie's family hikes a $3\frac{1}{4}$-mile trail to the end, and then hikes back on the same trail. Rachel's family hikes around a $\frac{3}{4}$-mile loop 8 times. Which family hikes more miles?

You can use equations and models to solve.

Step 1

Find the total distance Natalie's family hikes.

Use n for the number of miles Natalie's family hikes.

Solve $n = 2 \times 3\frac{1}{4}$.

$n = 2 \times 3\frac{1}{4} = 2 \times (3 + \frac{1}{4})$

$ = (2 \times 3) + (2 \times \frac{1}{4})$ ← Distributive Property

$ = 6 + \frac{2 \times 1}{4}$

$ = 6\frac{2}{4}$

So, $n = 6\frac{2}{4}$. Natalie's family hikes $6\frac{2}{4}$ miles.

> **Remember!**
> Estimate: $2 \times 3 = 6$

Step 2

Find the total distance Rachel's family hikes.

Use r for the number of miles Rachel's family hikes.

Solve $r = 8 \times \frac{3}{4}$.

$r = 8 \times \frac{3}{4} = \frac{8 \times 3}{4}$

$ = \frac{24}{4}$

$ = 6$

So, $r = 6$. Rachel's family hikes 6 miles.

Step 3

Compare the distances: $6\frac{2}{4} > 6$.

➡ Natalie's family hikes more miles than Rachel's family.

Math-to-Math Connection

Fractions and Mixed Numbers Write different mixed numbers or fractions greater than 1 on index cards. Label each card with a different letter. Give small groups of students one of the index cards and a large sheet of construction paper. Have each group plan and draw a model representing the number written on their index card. Gather the index cards and display them around the room. When all groups have finished drawing their models, collect the posters, number them consecutively, and display them around the classroom. Have students work with a partner to match each index card letter with the number on the corresponding poster.

Use the model to represent the word problem. Answer the questions below.

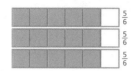

1. The class learns about 3 different subjects for $\frac{5}{6}$ hour each. What is the total amount of time the class spends on these 3 subjects?

   a. What do you need to find? <u>I need to find the total hours for the 3 subjects.</u>

   b. Color the model to show the given information.

   c. Write an equation you can use to solve the problem. Use h to represent the unknown number of hours. $\underline{h = 3 \times \frac{5}{6}}$

   d. Multiply to solve the equation. $h = 3 \times \frac{5}{6} = \frac{3 \times 5}{6} = \frac{15}{6}$

   Answer <u>The class spends $\frac{15}{6}$ hours on the 3 subjects or $2\frac{3}{6}$ hours.</u>

2. Lee needs 4 pieces of ribbon, each $1\frac{1}{3}$ yards long. How many yards of ribbon does she need in all?

   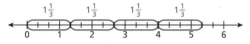

   a. What do you need to find? <u>I need to find the number of yards of ribbon Lee needs for the 4 pieces.</u>

   b. Draw and label <u>4</u> loops on the number line to represent the problem.

   c. Write an equation that you can use to solve the problem. Use r to represent the unknown. $\underline{r = 4 \times 1\frac{1}{3}}$

   d. Solve the equation. If the solution is equal to or greater than 1, write it as a whole or mixed number. $4 \times 1\frac{1}{3} = 4 \times (1 + \frac{1}{3}) = 4 \times (\frac{3}{3} + \frac{1}{3}) = 4 \times \frac{4}{3}$

   $r = \underline{5\frac{1}{3}}$ $= \frac{4 \times 4}{3} = \frac{16}{3} = \frac{15}{3} + \frac{1}{3} = 5 + \frac{1}{3} = 5\frac{1}{3}$

   Answer <u>Lee needs $5\frac{1}{3}$ yards of ribbon.</u>

Ⴤ Think·Pair·Share

MP2 3. Show a different way to multiply $4 \times 1\frac{1}{3}$. Which way do you prefer?
Possible answer: $4 \times 1\frac{1}{3} = 4 \times (1 + \frac{1}{3}) = (4 \times 1) + (4 \times \frac{1}{3})$
$= 4 + \frac{4}{3} = 4 + (\frac{3}{3} + \frac{1}{3}) = 4 + (1 + \frac{1}{3})$
$= 4 + (1\frac{1}{3}) = 5\frac{1}{3}$ Students' preferences will vary.

Observational Assessment

Use page 201 to assess whether students are able to multiply a fraction or mixed number by a whole number to solve a real-world word problem. Watch for students who mistakenly multiply the whole number by both the numerator and the denominator. Reinforce using equations, models, and the Distributive Property to solve these problems.

Ⴤ Think·Pair·Share

Peer Collaboration After students have had a chance to work on their own, have them find a partner and share their solutions. Then, have the class gather together to share some of the different solutions they found. Review the content of this lesson by using discussion questions such as these:

- *Which property of operations did we discuss in this lesson?*

- *How can the Distributive Property help you solve the problem?*

- *What are some important things to remember when multiplying a fraction or mixed number by a whole number?*

Return to the Essential Question

Reread the Lesson 23 Essential Question on page 198: *How can multiplying fractions by whole numbers help you to solve real-world problems?*

Ask volunteers to use what they learned in this lesson to answer this question. (Possible response: I can write equations or draw models to find the total when equal groups are being combined to solve real-world problems.)

Allow time for students to share and discuss their thoughts.

Mathematical Practices

Mathematical Practice Standards underline the teaching and understanding of all concepts and skills presented. The emphasis of specific practices is noted throughout the guided and independent practice of this lesson.

MP2	**Reason abstractly and quantitatively.**

Item 3: Students use properties of operations to solve a problem.

Concept Application

Students may work independently on these pages in the classroom or at home. They may refer to the first four pages of the lesson to revisit the instruction or to see a worked-out example.

Common Errors and **Teaching Tips** may help you support student learning either in the classroom or as a follow-up for work done at home.

Teaching Tips

Items 1–3

Encourage students to use a model to organize their thoughts and plan how to write the corresponding equation. Remind them there is more than one way to solve an equation and find the answer to a problem.

Independent Practice

For problems 1–3, identify what you need to find. Then use the model and an equation to solve the problem.

1. Alyssa has 4 snack bags of raisins. Each bag has $\frac{2}{3}$ cup of raisins. How many cups of raisins does Alyssa have altogether?

   4 bags

   Find I need to find the total number of cups of raisins.

   Equation $c = 4 \times \frac{2}{3}$ $4 \times \frac{2}{3} = \frac{4 \times 2}{3} = \frac{8}{3} = 2\frac{2}{3}$

   Answer Alyssa has $2\frac{2}{3}$ cups of raisins.

2. Luis mixes equal amounts of orange, cranberry, and grape juice to make a fruit punch. He uses $1\frac{1}{4}$ cups of each kind of juice. How many cups of punch does Luis make?

   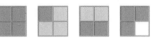

   Find I need to find the number of cups of punch Luis makes.

   Equation $c = 3 \times 1\frac{1}{4}$ $3 \times 1\frac{1}{4} = 3 \times (1 + \frac{1}{4}) = 3 \times (\frac{4}{4} + \frac{1}{4}) = 3 \times \frac{5}{4}$

   Answer Luis makes $3\frac{3}{4}$ cups of punch. $= \frac{15}{4} = \frac{12}{4} + \frac{3}{4} = 3 + \frac{3}{4} = 3\frac{3}{4}$

MP5 3. In Diana's class, $\frac{2}{5}$ of the students ride the Blue Bus to school. In Troy's class, 2 times as many students ride the Blue Bus as in Diana's class. If both classes have the same number of students, what fraction of Troy's class rides the Blue Bus?

   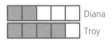
   Diana
   Troy

   Find I need to find the fraction that is twice as much as $\frac{2}{5}$.

   Equation $f = 2 \times \frac{2}{5}$ $2 \times \frac{2}{5} = \frac{2 \times 2}{5} = \frac{4}{5}$

   Answer In Troy's class, $\frac{4}{5}$ of the students ride the Blue Bus.

MP1 4. If 12 students in Diana's class ride the Blue Bus, how many students in Troy's class ride the Blue Bus? Use exercise 3 to solve.

   ▪▪▪▪ **Show your work.**
   Possible work: $2 \times 12 = 24$

   Answer Twenty-four students in Troy's class ride the Blue Bus to school.

202 Unit 3 ▪ Focus on Number and Operations—Fractions

Writing About Math

▪▪▪▪ · **Write an Opinion Text** Ask students to write a paragraph giving their opinion as to which method they prefer to use when multiplying fractions and mixed numbers by whole numbers. Have students organize their ideas; being sure to provide reasons that are supported by facts, use linking words such as *for instance* or *because*, and end their paragraph with a concluding statement.

Ask volunteers to read their paragraphs aloud. Remind students that these are opinion paragraphs, so there is no right or wrong answer. It is also acceptable for students to think that sometimes one method works better than another method, so their preference would depend on the real-world problem.

Independent Practice

**Circle the correct answer or answers to solve the problems.
You can use a model to help.**

MP6   **5.** Carrie uses fishing wire to make beaded necklaces. She uses $1\frac{3}{4}$ feet of wire to make one necklace. How much wire does Carrie need to make 5 necklaces?

    a. $3\frac{3}{4}$ feet   **b.** $6\frac{3}{4}$ feet

    c. $8\frac{3}{4}$ feet   **d.** 9 feet

MP4   **6.** About $\frac{6}{100}$ of the people in the United States are less than 5 years old. Four times as many people are less than 18 years old. What fraction of the people in the U.S. are less than 18 years old?

    a. $\frac{13}{100}$ **b.** $\frac{18}{100}$

    c. $\frac{20}{100}$ **d.** $\frac{24}{100}$

MP1   **7.** Andrew runs around a $\frac{1}{4}$-mile track 6 times. Which of the following do NOT describe the total number of miles Andrew runs?

    a. $1\frac{1}{4}$ miles   **b.** $1\frac{1}{2}$ miles

    c. between 1 and 2 miles   **d.** more than 2 miles

MP2   **8.** There are 4 quarts in 1 gallon. Marlon is trying to find out how many quarts of milk are in six $\frac{1}{2}$-gallon cartons. Which of the following does NOT represent the total number of quarts of milk?

    a. $6 \times \frac{1}{2}$ **b.** 4×3

    c. $4 \times (6 \times \frac{1}{2})$ **d.** $24 \times \frac{1}{2}$

Explain your answer.
Possible explanation: Answer a shows the number of gallons in 6 cartons. To find the number of quarts, multiply the number of gallons by 4. Answer c shows this. Answer b shows the value of the expression in answer c after you multiply $6 \times \frac{1}{2}$. Answer d shows the value of the expression in answer c if you change the way the factors are grouped and multiply 4×6 first.

Unit 3 ■ Focus on Number and Operations—Fractions   203

Teaching Tips

Items 5–8

Remind students that they may be able to eliminate one or more answer choices before they solve the problem. Help them reason why some answers are too small or large to be reasonable. This practice helps students learn to analyze problems to determine if their solutions makes sense.

Mathematical Practices

MP1	Make sense of problems and persevere in solving them.

Item 4: Students relate a solution to a similar problem.

Item 7: Students analyze a problem and plan a solution.

MP2	Reason abstractly and quantitatively.

Item 8: Students make sense of quantities and their relationships.

Item 9: Students understand the meaning of quantities.

MP4	Model with mathematics.

Item 6: Relate mathematics to everyday problems.

Item 10: Students use a model to write a multiplication word problem.

Independent Practice

Teaching Tips

Item 9

Suggest that students draw a model to see that $\frac{11}{12}$ of 6 is less than 1. They can use the drawing to help make generalizations about multiplying by a fraction less than 1 and multiplying by a fraction greater than 1.

Items 11–12

Some students might prefer to draw a model of the situation described in the problem. Help them use their models to write an equation they can use to solve the problem.

Independent Practice

MP2 **9.** Why is the product of 6 and $\frac{11}{12}$ less than 6? Is the product of a whole number and a fraction always less than the whole number?
Possible answer: The fraction $\frac{11}{12}$ is less than 1 whole. Since $6 \times 1 = 6$, 6 times an amount less than 1 will be less than 6. This is true for the product of any whole number and a fraction greater than 0 and less than 1. If the fraction is equal to 0, the product will be 0. If the fraction is equal to 1, the product will be the whole number. If the fraction is greater than 1, the product will be greater than the whole number.

MP4 **10.** What multiplication example does the model show? Write and solve a word problem that the model could represent.

Possible answer: The model shows $3 \times \frac{2}{3}$. Possible problem and solution: Sam cuts a piece of string into 3 pieces that are each $\frac{2}{3}$ foot long. How long was the piece of string Sam had in the beginning? Solution: The piece of string was 2 feet long in the beginning.

Solve the problems.

MP5 **11.** Daniella is using the length of her hand to measure the width of her desk. Her hand is $\frac{5}{12}$ feet long. The width of her desk is 7 lengths of her hand. How many feet wide is Daniella's desk?

Show your work. Work may vary. Possible work:

$$7 \times \frac{5}{12} = \frac{7 \times 5}{12} = \frac{35}{12}$$
$$= \frac{12}{12} + \frac{12}{12} + \frac{11}{12} = 2\frac{11}{12}$$

Answer _Daniella's desk is $2\frac{11}{12}$ feet wide._

MP6 **12.** Brad is making popcorn in the microwave. It takes $3\frac{3}{4}$ minutes to pop one bag of popcorn. How long will Brad take to pop 4 bags, one at a time?

Show your work. Work may vary. Possible work:

$$4 \times 3\frac{3}{4} = 4 \times (3 + \frac{3}{4}) = (4 \times 3) + \frac{4 \times 3}{4}$$
$$= 12 + \frac{12}{4} = 12 + 3 = 15$$

Answer _Brad will take 15 minutes to pop 4 bags of popcorn, one at a time._

204 Unit 3 ▪ Focus on Number and Operations—Fractions

Mathematical Practices

MP5	**Use appropriate tools strategically.**
Item 3: Students construct arguments using drawings and equations.	
Item 11: Students use tools carefully and strategically.	
MP6	**Attend to precision.**
Item 5: Students analyze and determine a solution to a problem.	
Item 12: Students accurately calculate a solution and explain their answer.	

Independent Practice

Teaching Tips

Item 13

Inform students that this is a multi-part problem. Students must find the weight of the cherries that Chelsea bought and the weight of the cherries that her sister bought and then compare the products.

Item 15

Students might need some help following how the Distributive Property is used in Kenny's work. He writes the mixed number as a sum of addends. He multiplies each addend by the whole number. Finally, he adds the partial products to get the final product.

MP1 **13.** Chelsea buys 3 bags of cherries that each weighs $\frac{3}{4}$ of a pound. Her sister buys 4 bags of cherries that each weighs $\frac{1}{2}$ of a pound. Who buys more pounds of cherries?

▐▬▬ **Show your work.**

$3 \times \frac{3}{4} = \frac{3 \times 3}{4} = \frac{9}{4}$ | $4 \times \frac{1}{2} = \frac{4}{2} = 2$

$= \frac{8}{4} + \frac{1}{4} = 2 + \frac{1}{4} = 2\frac{1}{4}$

$2\frac{1}{4} > 2$

Answer Chelsea buys more pounds of cherries.

MP4 **14.** Angela needs $\frac{3}{4}$ cup of milk for each batch of pancakes she makes. She draws the model below to find the amount of milk she needs to make 5 batches.

Is Angela's model correct?

Answer No, Angela's model is not correct.

▐▬▬ **Justify your answer using words, drawings, or numbers.**

Possible justification: The model shows $5 \times \frac{3}{5}$, not $5 \times \frac{3}{4}$.

MP8 **15.** Kenny knows that it takes him 13 minutes to walk 1 mile. His friend lives $2\frac{7}{8}$ miles away. Kenny writes the equation below to find out how long it will take to walk to his friend's house.

$13 \times 2\frac{7}{8} = 13 \times (2 + \frac{7}{8}) = (13 \times 2) + \frac{13 \times 7}{8}$

Can Kenny find the correct number of minutes with this method? Use Kenny's or a different method to solve the problem.

Answer Yes. It will take Kenny $37\frac{3}{8}$ minutes to walk to his friend's house.

▐▬▬ **Justify your answer using words, drawings, or numbers.**

Possible justification: Kenny is using the Distributive Property, so multiplying 13 times each addend in the sum $2 + \frac{7}{8}$ is the same as multiplying $13 \times 2\frac{7}{8}$.

$(13 \times 2) + (\frac{13 \times 7}{8}) = 26 + \frac{91}{8}$

$= 26 + \frac{80}{8} + \frac{8}{8} + \frac{3}{8}$

$= 26 + 10 + 1 + \frac{3}{8}$

$= 37\frac{3}{8}$

Unit 3 ■ Focus on Number and Operations—Fractions **205**

Mathematical Practices

MP1	**Make sense of problems and persevere in solving them.**
Item 13: Students analyze and plan a solution to a multi-step problem.	
MP4	**Model with mathematics.**
Item 14: Students relate mathematics to everyday problems.	
MP8	**Look for and express regularity in repeated reasoning.**
Item 15: Students evaluate the reasonableness of an answer.	

Common Core Focus:

4.NF.5 Express a fraction with denominator 10 as an equivalent fraction with denominator 100, and use this technique to add two fractions with respective denominators 10 and 100.

OBJECTIVE

Write equivalent fractions to add fractions with denominators of 10 and 100.

ESSENTIAL QUESTION

Students have written equivalent fractions and they have added fractions with like denominators. Ask students to explain the relationship between 10 and 100. In this lesson, students learn to add fractions with unlike denominators of 10 and 100 by writing equivalent fractions.

FLUENCY PRACTICE

Fluency practice is available at **sadlierconnect.com**.

Concept Development

Understand: Tenths and hundredths of a whole

■ In this presentation, students model a fraction with a denominator of 10 and a fraction with a denominator of 100. Fractions with denominators of 10 and 100 are called decimal fractions. This lesson lays the foundation for future work with decimals.

■ Dimes and pennies are used as familiar quantities to represent fractions of a dollar. Students should know that there are 10 dimes in one dollar and 100 pennies in one dollar. The models on the left side of the page show a whole as $\frac{10}{10} = 1$ and $\frac{100}{100} = 1$.

■ Point out that one row of 10 hundredths represents the same part on the model as one tenth. Ask students how this relates to the number of pennies that are equivalent to the value of one dime.

Lesson 24 Add Fractions: Denominators of 10 and 100

Essential Question:
How can you use the relationship between 10 and 100 to add tenths and hundredths?
4.NF.5

Words to Know:
tenth
hundredth

Guided Instruction

In this lesson you will learn how to write equivalent fractions so that you can add fractions with denominators of 10 and 100.

Understand: Tenths and hundredths of a whole

> One dollar equals 10 dimes or 100 pennies. If Carla has 6 dimes, how many tenths of a dollar does she have? If she has 6 pennies, how many hundredths of a dollar does she have?

To represent dimes and pennies as fractions of a dollar, you can use 10 and 100 as denominators.

First, model the 10 dimes in 1 dollar. Use 1 whole partitioned into 10 equal parts. Each part is 1 tenth, or $\frac{1}{10}$, of the whole.

$\frac{10}{10} = 1$

Six dimes is $\frac{6}{10}$ of a dollar.

To show 6 dimes, shade 6 tenths in the model.
Write the fraction for the shaded part.

$\frac{6}{10}$

Now model the 100 pennies in 1 dollar. Use 1 whole partitioned into 100 equal parts. Each part is 1 hundredth, or $\frac{1}{100}$, of the whole.

$\frac{100}{100} = 1$

Six pennies is $\frac{6}{100}$ of a dollar.

To show 6 pennies, shade 6 hundredths in the model.
Write the fraction for the shaded part.

$\frac{6}{100}$

➡ If Carla has 6 dimes, she has 6 tenths of a dollar. If Carla has 6 pennies, she has 6 hundredths of a dollar.

206 Unit 3 ■ Focus on Number and Operations—Fractions

Words to Know

tenth: Each part of a whole when the whole is partitioned into 10 equal parts.

$\frac{6}{10}$

hundredth: Each part of a whole when the whole is partitioned into 100 equal parts.

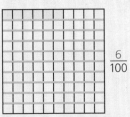

$\frac{6}{100}$

Glossary can be found on pp. 347-350.

MORE ONLINE | sadlierconnect.com   Lesson 24

Guided Instruction

Understand: Equivalent tenths and hundredths of dollars

Carla wants to exchange her 6 dimes for pennies. How many pennies will Carla get that equal 6 dimes?

You can rename tenths as hundredths the same way you write other equivalent fractions.
Look at the 6 tenths model below. Shade the same area of the hundredths model. How many hundredths did you shade? 60 hundredths
You can partition each tenth into 10 equal parts to make hundredths.
1 tenth equals 10 hundredths.

$$\frac{1}{10} = \frac{10 \times 1}{10 \times 10} = \frac{10}{100}$$

6 tenths equals 60 hundredths.

$$\frac{6}{10} = \frac{10 \times 6}{10 \times 10} = \frac{60}{100}$$

$\frac{6}{10}$ $\frac{60}{100}$

Since 1 hundredth dollar is 1 penny, 60 hundredths dollar is 60 pennies.
So, 6 dimes equal 60 pennies.

➡ Carla will get 60 pennies for 6 dimes.

Understand: Addition of tenths and hundredths when the whole is a dollar

One dollar equals 100 cents. Jason has $\frac{8}{10}$ dollar in dimes and $\frac{15}{100}$ dollar in pennies. How many cents does Jason have altogether?

To find the total number of cents, rename the tenths as hundredths and then add.
Model the 8 tenths of a dollar.
Write an equivalent fraction for $\frac{8}{10}$ using 100 as the denominator.

$$\frac{8}{10} = \frac{10 \times 8}{10 \times 10} = \frac{80}{100}$$

8 tenths equals 80 hundredths.

$\frac{8}{10}$ $\frac{80}{100}$

$\frac{80}{100}$ and $\frac{15}{100}$ have like denominators, so you can add the hundredths.

8 dimes 15 pennies

$$\frac{80}{100} + \frac{15}{100} = \frac{95}{100}$$

Remember!
To add fractions with like denominators, add the numerators.

One hundredth of a dollar is 1 cent, so 95 hundredths of a dollar is 95 cents.

➡ Jason has 95 cents altogether.

Understand: Equivalent tenths and hundredths of dollars

■ In this presentation, students use models to represent equivalent fractions with denominators of 10 and 100. Then they apply this technique to add two fractions with denominators of 10 and 100.

■ You may want to arrange 10 pennies in a row and then place a dime at the front of that row to show their equivalent values.

■ Remind students that they can skip count by tens to count columns of 10 that are completely shaded.

Understand: Addition of tenths and hundredths when the whole is a dollar

■ After working through this problem, have students discuss the steps they need to take when adding a fraction with a denominator of 10 and a fraction with a denominator of 100. Point out to students that they have already learned the skills in each step. Now they are putting the steps together to learn a new skill.

■ Encourage students to check their answers by shading an additional 15 hundredths on the model for 80 hundredths for a total of 95 shaded units, which represents the sum 95 hundredths.

Support English Language Learners

Since most other countries use the metric system, some English language learners may not make the connection between dimes and pennies to dollars. Use a meter stick to demonstrate the meaning of tenths and hundredths.

Follow the explanation on page 206, using a meter stick instead of a fraction model. Replace *dimes* with *decimeters* and replace *pennies* with *centimeters*. Explain that to represent decimeters and centimeters as fractions of a meter, you can use 10 and 100, respectively, as denominators. There are 10 decimeters in one meter. Show students how a meter is partitioned into 10 equal parts and each part (decimeter) is $\frac{1}{10}$ of a meter. There are 100 centimeters in one meter. Show students how a meter is partitioned into 100 equal parts and each part (centimeter) is $\frac{1}{100}$ of a meter.

Connect: Adding tenths and hundredths when the whole is not a dollar Use this page to help students strengthen their understanding of adding tenths and hundredths.

■ When using a fraction model, suggest that students show the hundredth fraction that is equivalent to tenths first because that fraction will fill complete columns. Since hundredths may only partially fill a column, it is easier to add the hundredths to the model after representing the fraction equivalent to tenths.

■ Students can use the fraction model to help express $\frac{2}{10}$ as an equivalent fraction in hundredths. The first two shaded columns show that $\frac{2}{10}$ and $\frac{20}{100}$ are the same amount.

■ Ask students if they are able to predict the number of units that will be shaded in the incomplete column just by looking at the fractions in the original problem. Remind them that the numerator 34 can be expressed as $30 + 4$.

✏ Students should understand that the entire model represents 1 whole, in this case, 1 mile. Have students explain how many units out of 100 would need to be shaded to represent $\frac{1}{2}$ mile.

Lesson 24 Add Fractions: Denominators of 10 and 100

Guided Instruction

Connect: Adding tenths and hundredths when the whole is not a dollar

Every school day, Maria walks to school in the morning and walks back home in the afternoon. When she walks to school in the morning, she takes a direct route which is $\frac{2}{10}$ mile. When she walks home, she takes a different route that goes along a jogging trail. That route is $\frac{34}{100}$ mile. How far does Maria walk each day during her trip to and from school?

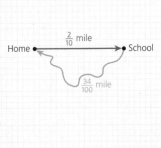

Home ● $\frac{2}{10}$ mile ● School $\frac{34}{100}$ mile

In this problem, the whole is 1 mile. You can add fractions of a mile just like you added fractions of a dollar.

Step 1

Rename $\frac{2}{10}$ as hundredths.
Write an equivalent fraction using 100 as the denominator.

$\frac{2}{10} = \frac{10 \times 2}{10 \times 10} = \frac{20}{100}$

$\frac{20}{100}$

Step 2

Now add $\frac{20}{100}$ and $\frac{34}{100}$.

$\frac{20}{100} + \frac{34}{100} = \frac{20 + 34}{100} = \frac{54}{100}$

$\frac{54}{100}$

➤ Maria walks $\frac{54}{100}$ mile during her trip to and from school.

✏ Does Maria walk more or less than $\frac{1}{2}$ mile during her trip to and from school? How did you decide?
She walks more than $\frac{1}{2}$ mile. Possible explanation: I looked at the model for $\frac{54}{100}$. $\frac{50}{100}$ is $\frac{1}{2}$ of the square, so $\frac{54}{100}$ is more than $\frac{1}{2}$.

Math-to-Money Connection

Mill In this lesson, students learned that a dime is $\frac{1}{10}$ of a dollar and a penny is $\frac{1}{100}$ of a dollar. However, the lowest value of money in the United States is the *mill* which has a value of $\frac{1}{1,000}$ of a dollar. At one time there was a half-cent coin worth 5 mills. Mills are still used today, but are usually described as $\frac{1}{10}$ of a cent. There are no mill coins. Students may have noticed gas prices displayed as \$3.25[9], which is *three dollars twenty-five and nine-tenths cents.* Mills are also used in property taxes. Many tax levies are referred to as mill levies. A 3-mill tax levy refers to the millage rate, and the tax is calculated by multiplying the value of a property by the millage rate, or $\frac{3}{1,000}$.

MORE ONLINE sadlierconnect.com

Lesson 24

Guided Practice

Color the model to show the tenths. Then rename the tenths as an equivalent number of hundredths.

1. 1 tenth

$$\frac{1}{10} = \frac{10 \times 1}{10 \times 10} = \frac{10}{100}$$

2. 5 tenths

$$\frac{5}{10} = \frac{10 \times 5}{10 \times 10} = \frac{50}{100}$$

Rename the tenths as an equivalent fraction with a denominator of 100. Add. Use the model to show the addition.

3. 3 tenths + 42 hundredths

$$\frac{3}{10} = \frac{30}{100}$$

$$\frac{30}{100} + \frac{42}{100} = \frac{72}{100}$$

3 tenths

4. 20 hundredths + 11 tenths

$$\frac{11}{10} = \frac{110}{100}$$

$$\frac{20}{100} + \frac{110}{100} = \frac{130}{100}$$

11 tenths

✿ Think • Pair • Share

MP7 **5.** Look at exercise 4 above. What is another way to write 11 tenths? What is another way to write 20 hundredths? Use your model to help you.
Possible answer: You can also write 11 tenths as the mixed number $1\frac{1}{10}$ or $1\frac{10}{100}$. Another name for 20 hundredths is 2 tenths.

Unit 3 ▪ Focus on Number and Operations—Fractions **209**

Mathematical Practices

Mathematical Practice Standards underline the teaching and understanding of all concepts and skills presented. The emphasis of specific practices is noted throughout the guided and independent practice of this lesson.

MP7	**Look for and make use of structure.**

Item 5: Students use models to evaluate the structure of equivalent fractions.

Observational Assessment

Use page 209 to assess whether students are able to rename tenths as equivalent fractions in hundredths and then find the sum of tenths and hundredths. Students should know that each column that is completely shaded in a model represents 10 hundredths or 1 tenth. Watch for students who have difficulty shading the models to represent the sum of two fractions with unlike denominators.

✿✿ Think•Pair•Share

Peer Collaboration Have students work with a partner to complete exercise 5. Students should be able to address these questions:

- *Can you decompose, or break apart, 11 tenths into a mixed number?*

- *Can you write 20 hundredths as a fraction with a denominator of 10? Explain.*

- *How many tenths does the model show altogether?*

To summarize, tell students they can use the model to add decimal fractions with like or unlike denominators. Each unit of one whole model represents one hundredth of one whole. Each column, or group of 10 units, represents one tenth of one whole.

Return to the Essential Question

Reread the Lesson 24 Essential Question on page 206: *How can you use the relationship between 10 and 100 to add tenths and hundredths?*

Ask volunteers to use what they learned in this lesson to answer this question. (Possible response: I can rename tenths as hundredths to write an equivalent fraction with a denominator of 100, and then add the numerators.)

Concept Application

Students may work independently on these pages in the classroom or at home. They may refer to the first four pages of the lesson to revisit the instruction or to see a worked-out example.

Common Errors and **Teaching Tips** may help you support student learning either in the classroom or as a follow-up for work done at home.

Teaching Tips

Items 1–2

To help students visualize the solution, suggest they draw lines to divide the columns into 10 equal rows.

Item 4

Remind students to check their answers. There are two complete shaded rows representing 2 tenths and there is one incomplete row with two shaded units representing 2 hundredths.

Item 8

Students may choose to find the sum of the fractions in answer choices c and d to help them determine if the expressions are equivalent to the fraction in the model.

Independent Practice

Look at the model. Name the fraction shown. Rename using equivalent fractions.

1.

$$\frac{4}{10} = \frac{10 \times 4}{10 \times 10} = \frac{40}{100}$$

2.

$$\frac{2}{10} = \frac{10 \times 2}{10 \times 10} = \frac{20}{100}$$

3.

$$\frac{140}{100} = \frac{14}{10}$$

4.

$$\frac{22}{100} = \frac{20}{100} + \frac{2}{100} = \frac{2}{10} + \frac{2}{100}$$

Rename the tenths as hundredths.

5. 7 tenths = ___70___ hundredths

$$\frac{7}{10} = \frac{70}{100}$$

6. 9 tenths = ___90___ hundredths

$$\frac{9}{10} = \frac{90}{100}$$

Circle the correct answer.

7. Which fraction is modeled below?

- (a.) $\frac{3}{100}$
- b. $\frac{30}{100}$
- c. $\frac{3}{10}$
- d. $\frac{30}{10}$

8. Which of the following is NOT equivalent to the fraction in the model?

- a. $\frac{75}{100}$
- (b.) $\frac{75}{10}$
- c. $\frac{5}{10} + \frac{25}{100}$
- d. $\frac{50}{100} + \frac{25}{100}$

Writing About Math

✏ · **Write an Explanatory Text** Have students write a paragraph that explains how to add a fraction that has a denominator of 10 to a fraction that has a denominator of 100. Students may a use step-by-step instructional format. Remind students to use precise mathematical language in their writing. Students should be aware of their audience and should assume that the reader has no knowledge of the content matter. Illustrations may be included to demonstrate students' understanding of the concepts.

When students are finished, have them exchange papers to read the instructions and decide whether the explanations were easy to follow and complete.

Use equivalent fractions to find each sum. Show your work.

9. $\frac{1}{10} + \frac{1}{100}$

$\frac{1}{10} = \frac{10}{100}$

$\frac{10}{100} + \frac{1}{100} = \frac{11}{100}$

Answer $\frac{11}{100}$ _____

10. $\frac{4}{10} + \frac{14}{100}$

$\frac{4}{10} = \frac{40}{100}$

$\frac{40}{100} + \frac{14}{100} = \frac{54}{100}$

Answer $\frac{54}{100}$ _____

11. $\frac{50}{100} + \frac{8}{10}$

$\frac{8}{10} = \frac{80}{100}$

$\frac{50}{100} + \frac{80}{100} = \frac{130}{100}$

Answer $\frac{130}{100}$ _____

12. $\frac{5}{10} + \frac{85}{100} + \frac{6}{10}$

$\frac{5}{10} = \frac{50}{100}, \frac{6}{10} = \frac{60}{100}$

$\frac{50}{100} + \frac{60}{100} + \frac{85}{100} = \frac{50}{100} + \frac{50}{100} + \frac{10}{100} + \frac{85}{100}$

$= \frac{195}{100}$

Answer $\frac{195}{100}$ _____

13. In exercises 9–12, which sums are greater than 1?

$\frac{130}{100}, \frac{195}{100}$ _____

Draw lines to match each addition exercise with the correct sum.

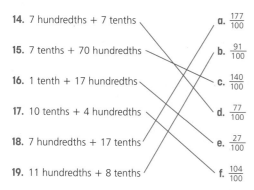

14. 7 hundredths + 7 tenths

15. 7 tenths + 70 hundredths

16. 1 tenth + 17 hundredths

17. 10 tenths + 4 hundredths

18. 7 hundredths + 17 tenths

19. 11 hundredths + 8 tenths

a. $\frac{177}{100}$

b. $\frac{91}{100}$

c. $\frac{140}{100}$

d. $\frac{77}{100}$

e. $\frac{27}{100}$

f. $\frac{104}{100}$

Unit 3 ■ Focus on Number and Operations—Fractions **211**

Common Errors
Items 9–12
Students may quickly add the numerators mentally and place the sum over 100. Tell them they must use equivalent fractions to rewrite the expressions and then show all of their work. This will help students avoid mistakes that can result from taking shortcuts.

Teaching Tips
Items 14–19
Students may find it helpful to write equivalent fractions for tenths fractions given in word form. For example, 7 tenths can be renamed as 70 hundredths. Then add the hundredths to identify the sum in the right-hand column.

Digital Connection
Have students use publishing software or a word processor to create their own game cards for a matching or concentration game with fractions. Students should create matching pairs that have equivalent values, such as $\frac{7}{10}$ and $\frac{70}{100}$ or $\frac{3}{10} + \frac{15}{100}$ and $\frac{45}{100}$. Then have students play a game with the cards they created.

Independent Practice

Teaching Tips

Item 21

Point out that the problem uses the word *only*. It is true that the model can be written as a sum of hundredths, but the shaded units in the incomplete columns represent an additional 10 units, or one tenth. Since each complete column is one tenth, the shaded amount can also be written as the sum of tenths.

Independent Practice

MP7 **20.** What is the relationship between tenths and hundredths? Discuss both the number of parts in 1 whole and the size of each part.
Answers will vary. Possible answer: One whole is equal to 10 tenths or 100 hundredths, so there are 10 times as many hundredths as tenths. If you divide 1 tenth into 10 equal parts, you get 10 hundredths, so each hundredth is also $\frac{1}{10}$ the size of each tenth.

MP4 **21.** Lily says that the amount modeled below can only be broken apart and written as a sum of hundredths. Do you agree with Lily? Write this amount as a sum of two addends.

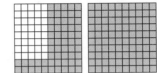

Possible answer: Lily is not right. The model on the left shows 6 groups of 10 squares, so it shows $\frac{6}{10}$. The model on the right shows 10 groups of 10 squares, or $\frac{10}{10}$. You can write the sum as $\frac{6}{10} + \frac{10}{10}$.

For problems 22 and 23, use the table at the right.

MP1 **22.** Curtis buys a book and gets pennies back in change. The pennies have the same value as 5 dimes. How many pennies does Curtis get?

▬▶ **Show your work.** Work may vary.
Possible work: 5 dimes is $\frac{5}{10}$ of a dollar.
$$\frac{5}{10} = \frac{50}{100}$$

Money Amounts	
Coin	Fraction of 1 Dollar
Dime	$\frac{1}{10}$
Penny	$\frac{1}{100}$

Answer Curtis gets 50 pennies.

MP6 **23.** A cashier at a store counts the change in the register drawer. She has 3 dimes and 12 pennies. What is the total fraction of a dollar for these coins?

▬▶ **Show your work.**
Work may vary. Possible work:

3 dimes $3 \times \frac{1}{10} = \frac{3}{10}$ and $\frac{3}{10} = \frac{10 \times 3}{10 \times 10} = \frac{30}{100}$

12 pennies $12 \times \frac{1}{100} = \frac{12}{100}$; $\frac{30}{100} + \frac{12}{100} = \frac{42}{100}$

Answer The total fraction of a dollar for the coins is $\frac{42}{100}$.

Mathematical Practices

MP1	**Make sense of problems and persevere in solving them.**
Item 22: Students relate a problem to a similar problem.	
MP4	**Model with mathematics.**
Item 21: Students use a model to explain operations.	
MP6	**Attend to precision.**
Item 23: Students use measurement units appropriately and communicate with precision.	
MP7	**Look for and make use of structure.**
Item 20: Students evaluate the structure of a problem.	

Lesson 24

Independent Practice

For problems 24–26, use the diagram at the right.

MP5 **24.** Tara is using wood to make a picture frame. The diagram shows the lengths of the pieces of wood she needs to make each side. She wants to know how much longer the bottom side of the picture frame is than the right side. She writes this equation to find the difference between the two lengths. $\frac{2}{10} + x = \frac{38}{100}$

$\frac{2}{10}$ meter

$\frac{38}{100}$ meter

What is the difference between the two lengths?

✏ **Show your work.** Work may vary. Possible work:

$\frac{2}{10} = \frac{20}{100}$; $\frac{20}{100} + x = \frac{38}{100}$; $\frac{38}{100} - \frac{20}{100} = \frac{18}{100}$

Answer The bottom side is $\frac{18}{100}$ meter longer than the right side.

MP1 **25.** Tara bought 1 meter of wood to make the picture frame. Does Tara have enough wood for all four sides of the picture frame?

Answer No, Tara does not have enough wood for all sides of the picture frame.

✏ **Justify your answer using words, drawings, or numbers.**

Possible justification: One whole meter is $\frac{100}{100}$. The total length for the left and right sides is $\frac{20}{100} + \frac{20}{100} = \frac{40}{100}$ meter. $\frac{100}{100} - \frac{40}{100} = \frac{60}{100}$, but the bottom side is more than half of $\frac{60}{100}$ meter. So Tara will not have enough wood left for the top side of the picture frame.

MP3 **26.** Geoffrey says that Tara should rename the lengths of the bottom and top of the picture frame as tenths instead of hundredths. He thinks this will make it easier to measure the correct lengths. Do you agree with Geoffrey? You can use the hundredths model below to explain.

Answer No, I do not agree with Geoffrey.

✏ **Justify your answer using words, drawings, or numbers.**

$\frac{38}{100}$

Possible justification: $\frac{38}{100}$ is greater than $\frac{3}{10}$ and less than $\frac{4}{10}$, so it is not a full number of tenths. It makes more sense to rename the length of the right and left sides of the picture frame as $\frac{20}{100}$.
Also, since hundredths are a smaller unit, Tara's measurements may be more exact if she uses hundredths instead of tenths.

Teaching Tips

Item 25

Students should identify the whole as 1 meter and rename it as $\frac{100}{100}$ meter. Students may use properties, the relationship between addition and subtraction, and reasoning to solve this problem.

Mathematical Practices

MP1	**Make sense of problems and persevere in solving them.**
	Item 25: Students analyze a problem and plan a solution.
MP3	**Construct viable arguments and critique the reasoning of others.**
	Item 26: Students respond to the arguments of others.
MP5	**Use appropriate tools strategically.**
	Item 24: Students use a model to solve a problem.

Common Core Focus:

4.NF.6 Use decimal notation for fractions with denominators 10 or 100; **4.NF.7** Compare two decimals to hundredths by reasoning about their size. Recognize that comparisons are valid only when the two decimals refer to the same whole. Record the results of comparisons with the symbols >, =, or <, and justify the conclusions.

OBJECTIVE

Write decimal numbers for tenths and hundredths and compare their magnitude.

ESSENTIAL QUESTION

Students now begin to connect fractions to decimals and to relate place value to denominators that are powers of 10. In this lesson, students work with fraction and decimal equivalents, eventually allowing them to work interchangeably with both forms.

FLUENCY PRACTICE

Fluency practice is available at **sadlierconnect.com**.

Concept Development

Understand: Equivalent decimals and fractions for tenths

■ Students see that fractions with denominators equal to 10 or 100 can be written using a decimal point.

■ Have students practice reading fraction and decimal forms of the same number. Students make the connection between fraction and decimal equivalents when they hear visually different forms of the numbers read the same way.

▪ Have students draw a place-value chart with 1 in the ones place and 7 in the tenths place. Ask students to explain how many equal parts are in the whole and how many more equal parts there are.

Lesson **25** **Write and Compare Decimal Fractions**

Essential Question:
How can you use place value to write and compare tenths and hundredths?
4.NF.6; 4.NF.7

Words to Know:
decimal
decimal point

Guided Instruction

In this lesson you will learn how to write and compare decimal numbers for tenths and hundredths.

Understand: Equivalent decimals and fractions for tenths

> Matt is making a cage for his hamster. The directions say to make the cage 0.7 meter long. Matt says this is the same as $\frac{7}{10}$ meter. Is Matt correct? Do 0.7 and $\frac{7}{10}$ name the same number?

A decimal fraction, or decimal, is a number that uses place value and a decimal point. You can also write a decimal as a fraction with a denominator of 10 or 100. The decimal point separates the whole-number part (which may be 0) and the part less than 1.

0.7
decimal point

You can use a fraction or a decimal to name the same number of tenths. Compare the model and the place-value chart.

The fraction $\frac{7}{10}$ names 7 tenths of the whole.

7 of the $\frac{1}{10}$-size parts are shaded.

tens	ones	.	tenths	hundredths
	0	.	7	

The decimal 0.7 also names 7 tenths, with the digit 7 in the tenths place. The tenths place is to the right of the ones and the decimal point.

You can use the same point on a number line diagram to represent $\frac{7}{10}$ and 0.7.

You can also read the numbers the same way.

seven tenths = 7 tenths = $\frac{7}{10}$ = 0.7

➡ Yes, Matt is correct. 0.7 and $\frac{7}{10}$ name the same number, seven tenths.

✏️ What do you think the number 1.7 means? Possible answer: 1 and 7 tenths or $1\frac{7}{10}$

214   Unit 3 ▪ Focus on Number and Operations—Fractions

Words to Know

decimal: A number that uses place value and a decimal point.

decimal point: Separates the whole-number part and the part that is less than 1 in a decimal.

Example: 0.7
decimal point

Glossary can be found on pp. 347-350.

Lesson 25

Guided Instruction

Understand: Equivalent decimals and fractions for hundredths

One side of Matt's hamster cage is too long. It measures 0.79 meter instead of 0.7 meter. What equivalent fraction represents the length 0.79 meter?

To understand the decimal 0.79, use place value to write an equivalent fraction and model the amount.

Remember!
The value of each place is $\frac{1}{10}$ the value of the place to the left.

Look at 0.79 in a place-value chart.

tens	ones	.	tenths	hundredths
	0	.	7	9

The 7 in the tenths place names 7 tenths, or 0.7.
The 9 in the hundredths place names 9 hundredths, or 0.09.

As with fractions, you can rename the decimal 7 tenths as 70 hundredths.

$0.7 = \frac{7}{10} = \frac{10 \times 7}{10 \times 10} = \frac{70}{100} = 0.70$

$\frac{70}{100} + \frac{9}{100}$
or
$0.70 + 0.09$

Now add 9 hundredths.
$0.70 + 0.09 = 0.79$

So altogether, 0.79 is equivalent to 79 hundredths, or *seventy-nine hundredths*. The equivalent fraction is $\frac{79}{100}$.

➡ The equivalent fraction that represents 0.79 meter is $\frac{79}{100}$ meter.

Look at the number line below. The decimal 0.79, or $\frac{79}{100}$, is just 1 hundredth less than $\frac{80}{100}$. This means it is a little to the left of $\frac{80}{100}$ on the number line.

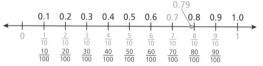

✏ Write both $\frac{79}{100}$ and 0.79 as sums of tenths and hundredths.

$\frac{79}{100} = \frac{7}{10} + \frac{9}{100}$; $0.79 = 0.7 + 0.09$

Unit 3 ■ Focus on Number and Operations—Fractions **215**

Support English Language Learners

Equivalent fractions and decimals can cause some confusion for English language learners because they are read exactly the same way. They are interpreted by context in much the same way homophones are interpreted in spoken language. To help students understand whether a word name refers to a fraction or decimal, reinforce each usage with a written representation. Write and read aloud the fraction or decimal on the board as it is used on the page. Ask students to point to the same fraction or decimal on the page and read the number aloud.

Understand: Equivalent decimals and fractions for hundredths

■ Remind students that they can count the number of parts in the whole to determine the denominator of the fraction represented in the model. In this case, there are 100 parts, so the model is divided into *hundredths*.

■ Help students make connections between the tenths model on the previous page and the hundredths model on this page. Point out that students already know that 7 shaded columns show $\frac{7}{10}$ of the model, which matches the previous example. Explain that each tenth now has 10 parts.

■ Explain that the number of digits to the right of the decimal point is the same as the number of zeros in the denominator of the equivalent fraction.

■ Review the pattern for multiplying by 10. Connect that pattern to writing tenths fractions as equivalent hundredths.

✏ After students have written their answers, ask them to use grid paper and two different colored pencils to shade a model showing the sum of tenths and hundredths. As students explain their sums, have them show how tenths and hundredths are represented in their models. Each tenth is a column of 10 units. Each hundredth is one unit.

Connect: **Comparing decimal tenths and hundredths** Use this page to help students strengthen their understanding of the magnitude of tenths and hundredths so they can compare decimals.

■ Be sure students understand that they can compare decimals by comparing their equivalent fractions with the same denominator.

■ Point out that both numbers have the same whole number amount, so students need to compare the fractional parts of the whole. Students should realize that if one of the amounts has a greater whole number, that amount will always have the greater value.

■ Just as it is easier to compare fractions with equal denominators, it is also easier to compare decimals that are shown to the same place value. Encourage students to write zeros at the end of any decimals so all numbers being compared are written to the same place value.

■ If students are struggling with the inequality symbols, review the meaning of < and >. Invite students to share their strategies for remembering which symbol to use.

■ Direct students back to the original question in the problem. Though they were comparing the numbers, the question really asked which route is shorter. Therefore, the answer is not the comparison itself, but the conclusion drawn from it.

✏ Have students share their solution processes with the class. Ask some students to explain the solution using decimals and others to explain using fractions.

Lesson 25 **Write and Compare Decimal Fractions**

Guided Instruction

Connect: **Comparing decimal tenths and hundredths**

> Carmen wants to find the shortest way to the museum. She calls for directions and someone at the museum says one route is about four and three tenths miles long. A map website shows a different route that is 4.05 miles long. Which route is shorter?

First write both numbers as decimals. Then make models and use equivalent fractions to help you compare the two decimals.

Step 1

Write "four and three tenths" as a decimal. The "and" tells you where to place the decimal point.

$$4.3 = 4\frac{3}{10}$$
four and three tenths
4.3

Step 2

Make sure the decimals name parts of the same unit or whole amount. In this problem, the unit, or whole amount, is 1 mile. 4.3 and 4.05 are both numbers of miles, so you can compare them.

Remember!
Tenths and hundredths are parts of a whole.

Step 3

Now compare the numbers. Both decimals have 4 as a whole number amount, so you can model just the tenths and hundredths.

$0.3 = \frac{3}{10} = \frac{30}{100}$; $0.05 = \frac{5}{100}$

$\frac{30}{100} > \frac{5}{100}$ and $0.3 > 0.05$

4.3 > 4.05

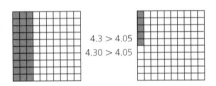
4.3 > 4.05
4.30 > 4.05

➡ The route from the map website is shorter.

You can also line up 4.3 and 4.05 by their decimal points and compare them as you compare whole numbers. Compare the values of the digits in the first place where they are different.

tens	ones	.	tenths	hundredths
	4	.	3	
	4	.	0	5

3 tenths > 0 tenths, so 4.3 > 4.05.

✏ How much shorter is the website's route? $\frac{30}{100} - \frac{5}{100} = \frac{25}{100}$, so the website route is 0.25 mile shorter.

Math-to-Real World Connection

Money Students are already familiar with using decimals in relationship to money. Have students write the decimal and fraction equivalents for monetary amounts less than $1. For example, 42 cents is written as 0.42 and $\frac{42}{100}$. Include amounts in pennies and dimes.

Guided Practice

Color the model to show each amount. Then write the amount as both a fraction and a decimal.

1. 6 tenths

$\frac{6}{10} = 0.\underline{6}$

2. 8 hundredths

$\frac{8}{100} = 0.\underline{08}$

Color the models to show the decimals. Then write <, =, or > to compare.

3. 0.52   0.9 $0.52 \underline{<} 0.9$

What is the first place where the digits are different?

_____tenths_____

Label points on the number line diagram to show the decimals. Then write <, =, or > to compare.

4. 0.21 and 0.29 $0.21 \underline{<} 0.29$

What is the first place where the digits are different?

_____hundredths_____

⚊ Think ⚊ Pair ⚊ Share

MP5   **5.** Look at exercise 3 above. Explain how the place values of the digits in 0.52 and 0.9 relate to the models, and show which decimal is greater. Discuss the number and values of the digits.
Possible explanation: 0.52 has more digits than 0.9, but the 5 in 0.52 shows that it has only 5 tenths, so about half the model is colored. 0.9 has a 9 in the tenths place, so its model has 9 tenths colored. The 2 hundredths in 0.52 are too small to make up for the larger-sized tenths in 0.9.

Mathematical Practices

Mathematical Practice Standards underline the teaching and understanding of all concepts and skills presented. The emphasis of specific practices is noted throughout the guided and independent practice of this lesson.

MP5	**Use appropriate tools strategically.**

Item 5: Students use models to compare decimals.

Observational Assessment

Use page 217 to assess whether students are able to compare fraction and decimal numbers to tenths and hundredths. Be sure students are using appropriate place values and comparing place values accurately using <, =, or >.

⚊⚊ Think▪Pair▪Share

Peer Collaboration Ask students to discuss their answers with a partner. Remind them to refer back to the models during their discussion. Suggest that students may find it easier to compare numbers with the same place values. Have students work together to rewrite the numbers in exercise 3 as decimals written with the same place values or as fractions with a denominator of 100. Have students consider the following discussion points:

- *Explain whether the number of digits in two different decimals can be used to compare their values.*

- *Explain whether it is useful to compare the digits in two different decimals without considering their place values.*

Return to the Essential Question

Reread the Lesson 25 Essential Question on page 214: *How can you use place value to write and compare tenths and hundredths?*

Ask volunteers to use what they learned in this lesson to answer this question. (Possible response: I can use decimal place value to name the number of tenths or hundredths. I can compare decimal tenths and hundredths by modeling the amounts or comparing the digits in each place value.)

As students describe how to compare decimal numbers, listen for explanations that include comparing place values from left to right.

Concept Application

Students may work independently on these pages in the classroom or at home. They may refer to the first four pages of the lesson to revisit the instruction or to see a worked-out example.

Common Errors and **Teaching Tips** may help you support student learning either in the classroom or as a follow-up for work done at home.

Teaching Tips

Items 5-6

To help students identify hundredths on the number line, suggest that they rewrite $\frac{5}{10}$ as hundredths. This will help them order the same units on the number line.

Item 8

If students are having difficulty comparing the numbers, suggest that they create a place-value chart and use it to order the numbers. They can also include the number line benchmark numbers in the place-value chart to help determine where to place the additional points on the number line.

Lesson 25 **Write and Compare Decimal Fractions**

Independent Practice

Identify the amount as a number of tenths or hundredths. Then write an equivalent fraction and decimal.

1.

2.

2 ___hundredths___

$\frac{2}{100} = 0.$ __02__

__2__ tenths

$\frac{2}{10} = 0.$ __2__

3.

4.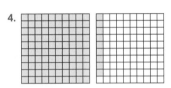

___55 hundredths___

$\frac{55}{100} =$ ___0.55___

1 and ___9 hundredths___

$1\frac{9}{100} =$ ___1.09___

Draw points on the number line diagram to represent the numbers. Label each point as a fraction and decimal.

5. 5 hundredths

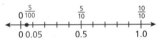

6. 68 hundredths

7. Compare the numbers in exercises 5 and 6 above. Which is the greater decimal? Explain.
The greater number is 0.68. Possible explanation: 0.05 < 0.68, because 0.68 is farther to the right on the number line and closer to 1. Five hundredths is very close to 0, so it is a shorter length and represents a lesser number.

8. 8 tenths, 91 hundredths, 1 and 38 hundredths

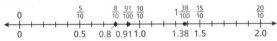

Writing About Math

• **Write a Narrative Text** Ask students to write a paragraph detailing an experience that they had using decimals or decimal fractions. If students cannot think of their own experience, suggest that they write about a time in the future when they expect to use decimals or decimal fractions. Ask students to be detailed in their description of the events and explain clearly which number form they used.

Ask volunteers to read their paragraphs aloud. Look for any common examples between students, such as decimal representation for money or fraction representation for numbers placed in order.

Independent Practice

Write each money amount as a sum of fractions. Then write the expanded decimal form. Use the table at the right to help.

Money Amounts	
Coin	Fraction of 1 Dollar
Dime	$\frac{1}{10}$
Penny	$\frac{1}{100}$

9. 5 dimes and 3 pennies

fraction: $\frac{53}{100}$ = $\frac{5}{10}$ or $\frac{50}{100}$ + $\frac{3}{100}$

decimal: $0.53 = \underline{0.5\ or\ 0.50} + \underline{0.03}$

10. 13 pennies and 2 dimes

fraction: $\frac{33}{100}$ = $\frac{13}{100}$ + $\frac{2}{10}$ or $\frac{20}{100}$

decimal: $0.33 = \underline{0.13} + \underline{0.2\ or\ 0.20}$

11. 1 dollar and 7 pennies

fraction: $1\frac{7}{100}$ = $\frac{100}{100}$ or $\frac{1}{1}$ + $\frac{7}{100}$

decimal: $1.07 = \underline{1} + \underline{0.07}$

12. 4 dollars and 9 dimes

fraction: $4\frac{9}{10}$ or $4\frac{90}{100}$ = $\frac{400}{100}$ or $\frac{4}{1}$ + $\frac{9}{10}$ or $\frac{90}{100}$

decimal: $4.90 = \underline{4} + \underline{0.9\ or\ 0.90}$

All of the fractions are for the same-size whole. Write the fractions as decimals. Use <, =, or > to compare. Use the place-value chart to help.

tens	ones	.	tenths	hundredths
		.		

13. $\frac{1}{10}$ and $\frac{8}{10}$

$\underline{0.1}\ <\ \underline{0.8}$

14. $\frac{15}{100}$ and $\frac{7}{100}$

$\underline{0.15}\ >\ \underline{0.07}$

15. $\frac{32}{100}$ and $\frac{9}{10}$

$\underline{0.32}\ <\ \underline{0.9}$

16. $\frac{6}{10}$ and $\frac{40}{100}$

$\underline{0.6}\ >\ \underline{0.4}$

17. $1\frac{18}{100}$ and $1\frac{2}{10}$

$\underline{1.18}\ <\ \underline{1.2}$

18. $2\frac{5}{10}$ and $2\frac{50}{100}$

$\underline{2.5}\ =\ \underline{2.5}$ or 2.5 = 2.50

Common Errors
Items 15–18
Students may have difficulty comparing correctly if they do not write decimals to the same place value. Suggest that students write all decimals to the hundredths place before comparing them.

Teaching Tips
Items 9–12
The addends for the decimal form should represent the same values as the corresponding fractions. For example, in exercise 9, the total is the sum of the fraction of a dollar represented by 5 dimes and the fraction of a dollar represented by 3 pennies.

Digital Connection

Spreadsheet Use a spreadsheet program to create an interactive hundredths model. Modify a 10 × 10 grid of cells so that each cell is square. Change the colors of the cells to show which cells are shaded. Ask students to name the decimal number and fraction represented in the model. Experiment with shading rows or columns of 10 at a time and ask students to describe the difference between shading $\frac{1}{10}$ and $\frac{1}{100}$. Expand the spreadsheet to include more than one whole to display mixed numbers and decimals greater than 1.

Independent Practice

Teaching Tips

Item 19

Students may find it helpful to write these fractions as decimals in a place value chart. Demonstrate how to extend the chart already used in this lesson to thousandths.

Item 22

The more decimal places included in the explanation, the more accurate the answer. For example, saying 0.45 is a little less than 0.5 is true, but not very precise. Encourage students to be as specific as possible, using two other decimals in their explanations.

Independent Practice

MP1 **19.** Use the patterns in the table to help you write decimals for fractions with a denominator of 1,000. What decimals are equivalent to $\frac{4}{1,000}$, $\frac{14}{1,000}$, and $\frac{345}{1,000}$?

Fraction	Decimal
$\frac{3}{10}$	0.3
$\frac{6}{100}$	0.06
$\frac{45}{100}$	0.45

0.004 is equivalent to $\frac{4}{1,000}$,

Answer 0.014 is equivalent to $\frac{14}{1,000}$, and 0.345 is equivalent to $\frac{345}{1,000}$.

Justify your answer using words, drawings, or numbers.
The number of zeros in the denominator of the fraction tells me how many places will be after the decimal point in the decimal.

MP7 **20.** Annika says that you can use this pattern to write a fraction or mixed number for a decimal: if a decimal has two places to the right of the decimal point, the denominator will be 100, so there will be two zeros in the denominator; if a decimal has one place to the right of the decimal point, the denominator will be 10, so there will be one zero in the denominator. Do you agree? Give examples.
Possible answer: I agree that Annika's pattern works. Examples: $0.23 = \frac{23}{100}$ and $2.03 = 2\frac{3}{100}$ (two decimal places and two zeros in the denominator), $0.3 = \frac{3}{10}$; $4.5 = 4\frac{5}{10}$ (one decimal place and one zero in the denominator)

MP3 **21.** Steven says that decimals are easier to compare than fractions. Do you agree? Use the amounts modeled below as an example.

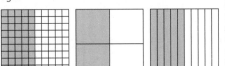

Possible answer: If you model the numbers, then they are equally easy to compare. But it is easier to compare decimals without models, because you can just use place value to compare the same-size parts. The tenths digit in 0.50 and 0.5 tells you the decimals are equal. To compare $\frac{50}{100}$, $\frac{2}{4}$, and $\frac{5}{10}$ without models, you need to recognize the halves or rewrite the fractions to have the same denominator or numerator.

MP6 **22.** Priya needs to measure a length of exactly 0.45 meter for science class. Where does 0.45 belong on a number line?

Show your work. Work may vary. Possible work:

$0.45 = 45$ hundredths $= \frac{45}{100}$

```
     0.42  0.44  0.46  0.48
  0.41 | 0.43    | 0.47 | 0.49
  <——+——+——+——+——+——+——+——+——>
  0.4           0.45          0.5
```

$\frac{40}{100} < 0.45 < \frac{50}{100}$

Answer On a number line, 0.45 is exactly halfway between 0.40 and 0.50.

Mathematical Practices

MP1	Make sense of problems and persevere in solving them.

Item 19: Students apply their understanding of decimal fractions.

MP3	Construct viable arguments and critique the reasoning of others.

Item 21: Students analyze a word problem and share their reasoning.

MP6	Attend to precision.

Item 22: Students express precise, appropriate numerical answers.

MP7	Look for and make use of structure.

Item 20: Students discern and explain a pattern.

MORE ONLINE sadlierconnect.com   Lesson 25

Independent Practice

MP1 23. One bottle has 1.25 pints of water. The other bottle has 1.4 pints of water. Which bottle has more water?

▸ **Show your work.** Work may vary.

Possible work:

1.②5
1.④
↓
2 tenths < 4 tenths
Also, 1.25 < 1.40.

Answer The bottle with 1.4 pints has more water.

MP7 24. Dennis thinks he may have a fever. In the morning, his temperature is 99.45 degrees. In the afternoon, the school nurse says his temperature is ninety-nine and 6 hundredths. Does Dennis's temperature go up or down by the afternoon?

▸ **Show your work.** Work may vary.

Possible work: $99.45 = 99\frac{45}{100}$

$99.06 = 99\frac{6}{100}$

$45 > 6$, so $99\frac{45}{100} > 99\frac{6}{100}$

Answer Dennis's temperature goes down by the afternoon.

MP2 25. Jacob says that 1.5 is not the same as 1.50 because 1 dollar and 5 dimes equal $1.50, not $1.5. Do you agree that 1.5 and 1.50 are not equivalent? You can use hundredths models to help support your answer.

Answer No, I do not agree; they are equivalent.

▸ **Justify your answer using words, drawings, or numbers.**

Possible justification: $\frac{5}{10} = 0.5$

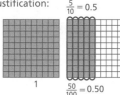

1          $\frac{50}{100} = 0.50$

0.5 and 0.50 are the same area on the model. We always use hundredths digits with money amounts because there are 100 cents in one dollar, so we write all cents as parts out of 100.

Unit 3 ▪ Focus on Number and Operations—Fractions   **221**

Teaching Tips

Item 23

Have students use grid paper to draw a model for each decimal. Students can align the models and use the shaded sections to represent the place values. All completely shaded hundredths grids represent whole numbers. All completely shaded columns represent tenths. All the remaining shaded units represent hundredths.

Item 24

Suggest that students read both decimal numbers aloud so they can hear the similarities between the place values.

Item 25

Remind students that a hundredths model can be used to represent tenths. Use the interactive whiteboard to show $\frac{5}{10}$ on a tenths model. Then overlay a hundredths grid on the shaded model.

Return to the

Remind students to return to the Progress Check self-assessment, page 123, to check off additional items they have mastered during the unit.

Mathematical Practices	
MP1	**Make sense of problems and persevere in solving them.**
Item 23: Students analyze the relationship between given values.	
MP2	**Reason abstractly and quantitatively.**
Item 25: Students attend to the meaning of quantities.	
MP7	**Look for and make use of structure.**
Item 24: Students discern the structure of numbers written in different forms.	

Unit 3 Common Core Review

The Common Core Review covers all the standards presented in the unit. Use it to assess your students' mastery of the unit's concepts and skills.

Depth of Knowledge

The depth of knowledge is a ranking of the content complexity of assessment items based on Webb's Depth of Knowledge (DOK) levels. The levels increase in complexity as shown below.

Level 1: Recall and Reproduction
Level 2: Basic Skills and Concepts
Level 3: Strategic Reasoning and Thinking
Level 4: Extended Thinking

Item	Standard	DOK
1	4.NF.3a	2
2	4.NF.3a	2
3	4.NF.3c	2
4	4.NF.3c	2
5	4.NF.2	1
6	4.NF.2	1
7	4.NF.2	1
8	4.NF.1	2
9	4.NF.1	2
10	4.NF.3b	3
11	4.NF.4a	2
12	4.NF.4b	2
13	4.NF.4b	2
14	4.NF.7	2
15	4.NF.6	2
16	4.NF.5	3
17	4.NF.3d	2
18	4.NF.2	4
19	4.NF.3b	3
20	4.NF.4c	3

Add or subtract.

1. $\frac{1}{5} + \frac{1}{5} =$ _____ $\frac{2}{5}$

2. $\frac{8}{6} - \frac{3}{6} =$ _____ $\frac{5}{6}$

3. $4\frac{1}{8} + \frac{7}{8} =$ _____ $\frac{40}{8}$

4. $3\frac{1}{4} - 1\frac{3}{4} =$ _____ $\frac{6}{4}$

Compare. Write <, =, or >.

5. $\frac{3}{4}$ $\boxed{=}$ $\frac{9}{12}$

6. $\frac{3}{3}$ $\boxed{>}$ $\frac{9}{10}$

7. $\frac{2}{5}$ $\boxed{<}$ $\frac{2}{3}$

Circle the correct answer.

8. Which fraction is equivalent to $\frac{1}{2}$?

   a. $\frac{10}{24}$

   (b.) $\frac{6}{12}$

   c. $\frac{2}{3}$

   d. $\frac{3}{4}$

9. Which fraction is equivalent to $\frac{40}{100}$?

   a. $\frac{10}{4}$

   b. $\frac{5}{10}$

   (c.) $\frac{2}{5}$

   d. $\frac{1}{5}$

10. Jaxon is writing a fraction as a sum of three addends. The fraction is represented by the point on the number line.

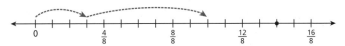

So far, Jaxon has two addends, $\frac{3}{8}$ and $\frac{7}{8}$. Which of the following can Jaxon use as the third addend?

   (a.) $\frac{4}{8}$

   b. $\frac{6}{8}$

   c. $\frac{10}{8}$

   d. $\frac{14}{8}$

11. Shade the model to show $7 \times \frac{1}{5}$. Then multiply.

   $7 \times \frac{1}{5} =$ _____ $\frac{7}{5}$

UNIT **3** **Common Core Review**

Write an equation to multiply. Write the product as a whole number or mixed number.

12. $2 \times \frac{4}{5}$

$2 \times \frac{4}{5} = \frac{(2 \times 4)}{5} = \frac{8}{5} = 1\frac{3}{5}$

13. $9 \times \frac{5}{9}$

$9 \times \frac{5}{9} = \frac{(9 \times 5)}{9} = \frac{45}{9} = 5$

14. Draw a model to show that $0.6 > 0.52$. Models may vary. Possible models shown.

0.6   0.52

15. Draw and label the point 0.67 on the number line.

0.67

0   0.1   0.2   0.3   0.4   0.5   0.6   0.7   0.8   0.9   1

Solve the problems.

16. Peyton surveyed 100 students about their transportation to school. Forty-three hundredths students reported riding bicycles to school and $\frac{3}{10}$ students said they walked. What fraction of the students surveyed rode bicycles or walked to school?

➤ **Show your work.** Possible answer:

bike to school $\frac{43}{100}$

walk to school $\frac{3}{10} = \frac{(10 \times 3)}{(10 \times 10)} = \frac{30}{100}$

total $\frac{43}{100} + \frac{30}{100} = \frac{73}{100}$

Answer Of the 100 students surveyed, $\frac{73}{100}$ rode bicycles or walked to school.

17. A pancake recipe calls for $\frac{2}{4}$ cup whole wheat flour, $\frac{2}{4}$ cup white flour, and $\frac{1}{4}$ cup corn flour. How many cups of flour does the recipe call for in all?

➤ **Show your work.**

Possible answer: $f = \frac{2}{4} + \frac{2}{4} + \frac{1}{4}$

$f = \frac{5}{4}$

Answer The recipe calls for $\frac{5}{4}$ cups of flour in all.

Unit 3 ▪ Focus on Number and Operations—Fractions **223**

This chart correlates the Common Core Review items with the lessons in which the concepts and skills are presented.

Item	Lesson
1	17
2	17
3	19
4	19
5	16
6	16
7	16
8	15
9	15
10	18
11	21
12	22
13	22
14	25
15	25
16	24
17	20
18	16
19	18
20	23

Writing About Math

✏️ ➤ Direct students to respond to the Unit 3 Essential Question. (This can also be found on student page 125.)

> **Essential Question:**
> How can writing fractions more than one way help you to compare and compute fractions?

Possible responses:

- When fractions are rewritten so that they have the same denominator, you can compare the numerators to determine the greater fraction.
- When adding or subtracting fractions with like denominators, it is only necessary to add or subtract the numerators. The denominators stay the same.
- Writing fractions as decimals can make it easier to compare and compute them, especially if you cannot write both fractions with the same denominator.

Unit Assessment

- Unit 3 Common Core Review, *pp. 222–224*
- Unit 3 Performance Task (ONLINE)

Additional Assessment Options

- Performance Task 1, *pp. 225–230* (ALSO ONLINE)

Optional Purchase:

- iProgress Monitor (ONLINE)
- Progress Monitor Student Benchmark Assessment Booklet

UNIT 3 Common Core Review

MP8 **18.** Liko used a 10 × 10 grid and Yuri used an 8 × 8 grid to represent the same whole unit. Each boy shaded grid squares to show $\frac{1}{4}$. How many grid squares did Liko shade? How many grid squares did Yuri shade?

Answer Liko shaded 25 grid squares and Yuri shaded 16 grid squares.

✏️ **Use fraction models. Show why Liko and Yuri had to shade a different number of squares to show $\frac{1}{4}$.**

Liko had to shade 25 squares because $\frac{1}{4}$ of 100 is 25. Yuri had to shade 16 squares because $\frac{1}{4}$ of 64 is 16.

Liko's grid   Yuri's grid

MP3 **19.** Samantha says that $\frac{3}{6} = \frac{2}{3} + \frac{1}{3}$. Describe Samantha's error and tell how to correct it.

✏️ **Justify your answer using words, drawings, or numbers.**

Possible justification: When you decompose a fraction into two or more parts, you should use the same denominator, so that the parts are the same size. Samantha decomposed the fraction into parts with a different denominator. To decompose $\frac{3}{6}$, Samantha should break apart only the number in the numerator. So, the correct answer is $\frac{3}{6} = \frac{2}{6} + \frac{1}{6}$.

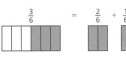

$$\frac{3}{6} = \frac{2}{6} + \frac{1}{6}$$

MP2 **20.** For a class party Ms. Vega estimates each student will eat $\frac{1}{6}$ pizza. There are 22 students. How many pizzas should Ms. Vega order? How much pizza will be left over?

Answer Ms. Vega should order 4 pizzas. There will be $\frac{2}{6}$ pizza left over.

✏️ **Justify your answer using words, drawings, or numbers.**

Possible justification: To find how many pizzas Ms. Vega needs, multiply the fraction of a pizza one student will eat by the number of students.

$$22 \times \frac{1}{6} = \frac{(22 \times 1)}{6} = \frac{22}{6} = 3\frac{4}{6}$$

So, Ms. Vega needs $3\frac{4}{6}$ pizzas. However, since she can only order whole pizzas, she must order 4 pizzas so that she has enough for all her students to have $\frac{1}{6}$ of a pizza.

To find how much pizza will be left over, subtract the amount of pizza needed from the 4 whole pizzas:

$$4 - 3\frac{4}{6} = \frac{24}{6} - \frac{22}{6} = \frac{2}{6}$$

So, there will be $\frac{2}{6}$ pizza left over.

224 Unit 3 ▪ Focus on Number and Operations—Fractions

Mathematical Practices

MP2	**Reason abstractly and quantitatively.**
Item 20: Students make sense of quantities and attend to the meaning of those quantities in problem solving.	
MP3	**Construct viable arguments and critique the reasoning of others.**
Item 19: Students construct an argument by using words, drawings, or numbers to justify their reasoning.	
MP8	**Look for and express regularity in repeated reasoning.**
Item 18: Students use reasoning to generate similar models.	

4.OA.1, 4.OA.2, 4.OA.3, 4.NBT.1, 4.NBT.2, 4.NF.3a, 4.NF.3d, 4.NF.4a, 4.NF.4c, 4.NF.6, 4.NF.7

Performance Tasks

Performance Tasks show your understanding of the Math that you have learned. You will be doing various Performance Tasks as you complete your work in this text, **Common Core Progress Mathematics**.

Beginning This Task

The next five pages provide you with the beginning of a Performance Task. You will be given 5 items to complete, and each item will have two or more parts. As you complete these items you will:

I   Demonstrate that you have mastered mathematical skills and concepts

II Reason through a problem to a solution, and explain your reasoning

III Use models and apply them to real-world situations.

Extending This Task

Your teacher may extend this Performance Task with additional items provided in our online resources at sadlierconnect.com.

Scoring This Task

Your response to each item will be assessed against a rubric, or scoring guide. Some items will be worth 1 or 2 points, and others will be worth more. In each item you will show your work or explain your reasoning.

Performance Task 1   225

ONLINE Customize Performance Task 1

Performance Task 1 in *Common Core Progress Mathematics* also provides students with additional practice. You can use the online items of Performance Task 1 to customize the amount and kind of performance task practice based on your ongoing evaluation of your students. You may choose to challenge some students, to give extra experience with a particular kind of task for other students, or to extend exposure to performance assessments for the entire class.

Go to **sadlierconnect.com** to download the following resources for Performance Task 1.

- Additional Items

- Additional Teacher Support

- Additional Scoring Rubrics

Performance Task 1 Overview

Performance Task 1 in *Common Core Progress Mathematics* provides students with practice for the types of items that may be found on standardized performance assessments.

Various item formats, including short- and extended-response items and technology-enhanced items, are included in the tasks. All items connect mathematical content correlated to the mathematical practices.

Items in Performance Task 1 are based on three primary types of tasks.

Type I   Mastery of mathematical concepts, skills and procedures

Type II Using and explaining mathematical reasoning

Type III Modeling problem situations in a real-world context

Performance Task 1 begins with a collection of five self-contained items in the Student Book and continues with additional items online at **sadlierconnect.com**.

Introduce Performance Task 1 Read student page 225 with the class. Explain that Performance Task 1 may cover any of the math they have learned in Units 1–3. Orient students to each item and communicate helpful reminders that will enable students to approach each item successfully. Once students have completed each item, go over the correct responses with them.

Recommended Pacing Administer Performance Task 1 on Student Book pages 226–230 over five 20-minute sessions.

Teacher Resources For each task, the teacher materials include:

- Item types and purposes

- Correlations to Common Core State Standards for Mathematical Content and Practice and Depth of Knowledge (DOK) levels

- Suggested Administration procedure

- Scoring Rubric

Item 1: A Visit to the Natural History Museum

Item	Type	Purpose
1.a.	III	Draw a diagram to represent a multiplication comparison.
1.b.	II	Explain how the diagram represents the multiplication comparison.
1.c.	III	Write an equation to represent the multiplication comparison.
1.d.	I	Solve to determine the solution of the multiplication comparison.

Item	CCSS	MP	DOK
1.a.	4.OA.2	7	Level 2
1.b.	4.OA.2	3	Level 3
1.c.	4.OA.1	4	Level 2
1.d.	4.OA.2	5	Level 1

Administering Item 1 (Pacing: 20 minutes)

Ask a volunteer to read the introductory paragraph. Have others describe the situation in their own words.

Item 1.a. (4 minutes)

Diagrams should accurately represent the numbers of children who voted for each exhibit.

Item 1.b. (6 minutes)

Diagrams may vary, but explanations should state that the diagram for Minerals Hall represents 3 times more votes than the diagram for Whale Exhibit.

Item 1.c. (4 minutes)

Remind students that there is more than one way to write the equation. They should be able to justify how their equation represents the diagram.

Item 1.d. (6 minutes)

Be sure students use the equation they wrote in item 1.c to solve. Their answer should be written in a sentence that relates to the problem.

A Visit to the Natural History Museum

1. The fourth-grade students go on a field trip to the Natural History Museum. They vote to decide where they will start their visit in the museum.

   a. Seven children vote to start at the Whale Exhibit. Three times as many children vote to start at the Minerals Hall. Draw a diagram to show the comparison.

   Whale Exhibit
   Minerals Hall

   b. Explain how your diagram shows the comparison.
   Possible explanation: Since 3 times as many children voted for the Minerals Hall than the Whale Exhibit, the tape for the Minerals Hall is 3 times as long as the tape for the Whale Exhibit.

   c. Write an equation to show the comparison.
   w = number of votes for the Whale Exhibit
   m = number of votes for the Minerals Hall
   Possible equations: $3 \times w = m$; $w = m \div 3$

   d. Use your equation and the information given in the problem to find the number of students who vote to start at the Minerals Hall.
   Possible solution:
   $$3 \times w = m$$
   $$3 \times 7 = m$$
   $$21 = m$$
   Twenty-one students vote to start at the Minerals Hall.

Scoring Rubric

Item	Points	Student Responses
1.a.	2	Correctly draws a diagram representing the comparison.
	1	Draws a diagram but does not correctly show the comparison.
	0	Does not draw a diagram.
1.b.	2	Demonstrates a clear understanding of multiplicative comparisons.
	1	Demonstrates some understanding of multiplicative comparisons.
	0	Demonstrates no understanding of multiplicative comparisons.
1.c.	2	Correctly writes the equation.
	1	Writes an incorrect equation.
	0	Does not write an equation.
1.d.	2	Correctly determines the answer.
	1	Solves the equation incorrectly.
	0	Does not solve the equation.

Performance Task 1

Deep-Sea Minerals

2. A scientist will talk about deep-sea minerals. Many students will listen to the scientists. Fifty-four students are already seated. The remaining 32 students are standing in line. The seats are arranged in rows. Each row has 9 seats.

a. Describe the steps you will take to find how many rows of seats are needed for all the students.

   Possible answer: To find the number of rows, first add the number of students seated to the number of students in line. Then divide that sum by the number of seats in each row.

b. Write an equation that shows how you can find the number of rows of seats the students will need. Use r to represent the unknown number of rows.

   Possible equation: $r = (54 + 32) \div 9$

c. Find the number of rows the students will need. Explain how you decided on the final answer.

   $(54 + 32) \div 9$
   $86 \div 9$
   $9 \text{ R}5$

   The students will need 10 rows of seats. Nine rows will be full, and 5 students will sit in the tenth row.

d. Check that your answer is reasonable. Use reasoning or mental math. Justify your reasoning.

   Possible answer: $54 + 32$ is about $50 + 30$ or 80.
   $80 \div 9$ is about $81 \div 9$ or 9.
   My answer, 10 rows of seats, is close to 9, so it is reasonable.

Scoring Rubric

Item	Points	Student Responses
2.a.	2	Shows clear understanding of how to solve multi-step problems.
	1	Shows some understanding of how to solve multi-step problems.
	0	Shows no understanding of how to solve multi-step problems.
2.b.	2	Correctly writes a multi-step equation to represent the problem.
	1	Incorrectly writes a multi-step equation to represent the problem.
	0	Does not write a multi-step equation.
2.c.	2	Correctly solves the equation.
	1	Solves the equation incorrectly.
	0	Does not solve the equation.
2.d.	2	Justifies solution appropriately.
	1	Justifies solution without correct strategies or reasoning.
	0	Provides no justification.

Item 2: Deep-Sea Minerals

Item	Type	Purpose
2.a.	II	Organize information and plan a solution path.
2.b.	III	Write a multi-step equation to represent the problem.
2.c.	II	Solve a multi-step equation and explain the answer in terms of the problem.
2.d.	II	Use estimation to determine the reasonableness of an answer.

Item	CCSS	MP	DOK
2.a.	4.OA.3	3	Level 2
2.b.	4.OA.3	4	Level 3
2.c.	4.OA.3	8	Level 3
2.d.	4.OA.3	3	Level 2

Administering Item 2 (Pacing: 20 minutes)

Ask a volunteer to read the introductory paragraph. Have others describe the situation in their own words.

Item 2.a. (7 minutes)

Students should first find the total number of students, and then divide by the number of rows.

Item 2.b. (3 minutes)

Students' equations should accurately reflect their explanations from part a.

Item 2.c. (5 minutes)

Have students solve their equation then explain their answer in terms of the problem. The remainder should be included in the explanation.

Item 2.d. (5 minutes)

Discuss different methods that can be used to justify an answer. Have students independently check their results.

Item 3: Ocean Giants

Item	Type	Purpose
3.a.	I	Write numbers in standard form.
3.b.	I	Compare numbers using place value.
3.c.	II	Explain how to use place value to compare numbers.
3.d.	I	Order numbers from least to greatest.

Item	CCSS	MP	DOK
3.a.	4.NBT.1	1	Level 1
3.b.	4.NBT.2	1	Level 1
3.c.	4.NBT.2	3	Level 3
3.d.	4.NBT.2	2	Level 1

Administering Item 3 (Pacing: 20 minutes)

Ask a volunteer to read the introductory paragraph. Have others describe the situation in their own words.

Item 3.a. (4 minutes)

Students should analyze the numbers in the table and discuss the different types of numbers shown. Remind them how to write a number in standard form.

Item 3.b. (4 minutes)

Encourage students to use the numbers they wrote in 3.a. to determine the greatest and least values.

Item 3.c. (8 minutes)

Students should explain how they compared numbers in standard form.

Item 3.d. (4 minutes)

Students should use the standard form of each number to order the whales by mass.

Ocean Giants

3. At the Whale Exhibit, the class sees whale fossils, whale skeletons, and whale models. The table shows the masses of different species of whales.

Whales	
Species	Mass (kg)
Orca	five thousand, seven hundred sixty-four
Blue	100,000 + 60,000 + 3000 + 70 + 2
Humpback	30,000 + 4000 + 200 + 90
Gray	thirty-three thousand, three hundred eight
Beluga	6000 + 100 + 70 + 8

a. Write the mass of each whale in standard form.
   Orca: 5764 kg
   Blue: 163,072 kg
   Humpback: 34,290 kg
   Gray: 33,308 kg
   Beluga: 6178 kg

b. Which whale has the greatest mass? Which whale has the least mass?
   The blue whale has the greatest mass; the orca has the least mass.

c. Explain how you found the whale with the greatest mass and the whale with the least mass.
   Possible explanation: I looked at the numbers in standard form. The blue whale was the only whale with a mass having more than five digits. So, it has to have the greatest mass. The least number of digits for any mass was four. Both the beluga and the orca had a mass with four digits, so I compared the thousands digits of the two numbers. Since 5 is less than 6, the orca has the least mass.

d. Write the names of the whales in order from least mass to greatest mass.
   Orca, Beluga, Gray, Humpback, Blue

Scoring Rubric

Item	Points	Student Responses
3.a.	2	Writes the numbers correctly.
	1	Writes some of the numbers correctly in standard form.
	0	Writes the numbers incorrectly.
3.b.	2	Correctly compares the numbers.
	1	Correctly identifies either the greatest or the least number.
	0	Does not identify either the greatest or the least number.
3.c.	2	Shows clear understanding of how to use place value to compare.
	1	Shows some understanding of how to use place value to compare.
	0	Shows no understanding of how to use place value to compare.
3.d.	2	Correctly orders the numbers.
	1	Correctly orders some numbers.
	0	Does not correctly order the numbers.

Performance Task 1

Dinosaur Tracks

4. A museum guide shows the fourth-grade class a model of dinosaur tracks found in Utah. Each step is $\frac{1}{3}$ meter long. The dinosaur took 7 steps.

a. Draw a model to show the total length of the 7 steps.
Possible model:

b. Write an addition equation that represents the length of the 7 steps. Use m to represent the total length.
Possible addition equations:
$\frac{1}{3}+\frac{1}{3}+\frac{1}{3}+\frac{1}{3}+\frac{1}{3}+\frac{1}{3}+\frac{1}{3} = m$
$\frac{3}{3}+\frac{3}{3}+\frac{1}{3} = m$

c. Write a multiplication expression that represents the length of the 7 steps. Use m to represent the total length.
$7 \times \frac{1}{3} = m$

d. Find the total length of the 7 steps. Explain your method and why you chose that method.
The total length of the 7 steps is $\frac{7}{3}$ meters or $2\frac{1}{3}$ meters.
Students' methods and explanations will vary. They may use the model, an addition equation, or the multiplication equation.

Performance Task 1 **229**

Item 4: Dinosaur Tracks

Item	Type	Purpose
4.a.	III	Draw and shade a model.
4.b.	III	Write an addition equation to represent the model.
4.c.	III	Write the addition equation as a multiplication equation.
4.d.	I	Solve the equations.

Item	CCSS	MP	DOK
4.a.	4.NF.3a, 4.NF.3d	5	Level 2
4.b.	4.NF.3a, 4.NF.3d	4	Level 1
4.c.	4.NF.4c	4	Level 1
4.d.	4.NF.3d, 4.NF.4c	3	Level 3

Administering Item 4 (Pacing: 20 minutes)

Ask a volunteer to read the introductory paragraph. Have others describe the situation in their own words.

Item 4.a. (5 minutes)
Ask students how many $\frac{1}{3}$ meters are in 1 meter. Remind them they should have whole meters drawn but only need to shade the appropriate parts.

Item 4.b. (5 minutes)
Encourage students to label their model and then use their labels to write the addition equation.

Item 4.c. (3 minutes)
Have students independently write their addition equation as a multiplication equation.

Item 4.d. (7 minutes)
Remind students that they can write their answer as a fraction greater than 1 or as a mixed number although a mixed number makes more sense in terms of the problem.

Scoring Rubric

Item	Points	Student Responses
4.a.	2	Correctly depicts a fraction model.
	1	Correctly draws the model but does not shade the model correctly.
	0	Does not draw or shade the model.
4.b.	2	Correctly writes the equation.
	1	Correctly writes the addition equation but does not use the variable correctly.
	0	Does not write an equation.
4.c.	2	Correctly writes the equation.
	1	Writes a multiplication equation but does not use the values or variable correctly.
	0	Does not write an equation.
4.d.	2	Finds the correct answer and justifies their reasoning.
	1	Finds the correct answer but does not justify their reasoning.
	0	Does not find the correct answer.

Item 5: Fossil Footprints

Item	Type	Purpose
5.a.	I	Use models to represent decimals and fractions.
5.b.	I	Label points to show fractions and decimals on a number line.
5.c.	II	Order fractions and decimals from least to greatest.

Item	CCSS	MP	DOK
5.a.	4.NF.6	6	Level 1
5.b.	4.NF.6	4	Level 1
5.c.	4.NF.7	5	Level 3

Administering Item 5 (Pacing: 20 minutes)

Ask a volunteer to read the introductory paragraph. Have others describe the situation in their own words.

Item 5.a. (5 minutes)

Remind students that each model represents 100. They may want to rewrite each fraction and decimal out of 100.

Item 5.b. (7 minutes)

Discuss methods that can be used to locate decimals and fractions on a number line. Encourage students to write all the footprints lengths as either fractions or decimals.

Item 5.c. (8 minutes)

Remind students to use the answers they got in parts **a.** and **b.** to help them order the fractions from least to greatest.

Fossil Footprints

5. The children see a display of five fossil dinosaur footprints. The data below shows the lengths of the footprints in meters.

Footprint Lengths (meter)

$\frac{2}{10}$	0.15	$\frac{6}{100}$	$\frac{42}{100}$	0.1

a. Each large square represents 1 whole. Color the models to show each fraction and decimal from the data.

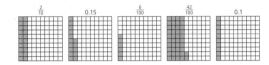

b. Label points on the number line to show each fraction and decimal from the data.

c. Order the lengths of the footprints from least to greatest. Explain the method you used and why you chose that method.

$\frac{6}{100}$, 0.1, 0.15, $\frac{2}{10}$, $\frac{42}{100}$

Explanations of methods will vary. Students may use the models, the number line, or place value.

Scoring Rubric

Item	Points	Student Responses
5.a.	2	Correctly shades all models.
	1	Correctly shades some models.
	0	Does not correctly shade the models.
5.b.	2	Correctly labels all points on the number line.
	1	Correctly labels some points on the number line.
	0	Does not correctly label the points on the number line.
5.c.	2	Correctly orders all numbers from least to greatest.
	1	Correctly orders some numbers from least to greatest.
	0	Does not correctly order the numbers.

Focus on Measurement and Data

Progress Check — Student Page 231

Progress Check

UNIT 4

Look at how the Common Core standards you have learned and will learn connect. It is very important for you to understand the standards from the prior grade level so that you will be able to develop an understanding of measurement and data in this unit and be prepared for next year. To practice your skills, go to sadlierconnect.com.

	GRADE 3		Before Unit 4	GRADE 4	After Unit 4	GRADE 5	
	I Can...			**Can I ?**		**I Will...**	
			☐	**4.MD.1** Express measurements in a larger unit in terms of a smaller unit within the same system	☐	**5.MD.1** Convert among different-sized measurement units within the same measurement system while solving problems	
	3.MD.2 Measure and estimate liquid volumes and masses Solve one-step problems involving masses or volumes	☐		**4.MD.2** Solve word problems involving distance, time, liquid volumes, masses, and money	☐		
	3.MD.7 Find the area of a rectangle **3.MD.8** Solve real-world and mathematical problems involving perimeter	☐		**4.MD.3** Solve real-world and mathematical problems using the area and perimeter formulas for rectangles	☐	**5.MD.5** Apply the volume formulas for rectangular prisms in real-world and mathematical problems	
	3.MD.4 Display a set of measurements in inches, half inches, and quarter inches on a line plot	☐		**4.MD.4** Make a line plot and use the data to solve problems	☐	**5.MD.2** Make a line plot and use the data to solve problems	
				4.MD.5 Understand angles and angle measurement	☐		
				4.MD.6 Measure angles using a protractor or sketch angles with a given number of degrees	☐		
				4.MD.7 Solve problems by using addition and subtraction to find unknown angle measures	☐		

Unit 4 ■ Focus on Measurement and Data

Student Page 231

Progress Check

Progress Check is a self-assessment tool that students can use to gauge their own progress. Research shows that when students take accountability for their learning, motivation increases.

Before students begin work in Unit 4, have them check any items they know they can do well. Explain that it is fine if they don't check any of the boxes; they will have the opportunity to learn and practice all the standards through the course of the unit.

Let them know that at the end of the unit they will review their checklists to check their progress. After students have completed the last lesson of the unit, before they begin Common Core Review, you will be prompted to have students revisit this page.

HOME ◆ CONNECT...

The Home Connect feature is a way to keep parents or other adult family members apprised of what their children are learning. The key learning objectives are listed, and some ideas for related activities and discussions are included.

Explain to students that they can share the Home Connect page at home with their families. Let students know there is an activity connected to their classroom learning that they can do with their families.

Encourage students and their parents to share their experiences using the suggestions on the Home Connect. You may wish to invite students to share this work with the class.

HOME ◆ CONNECT... — Student Page 232

In this unit your child will:

- Convert customary and metric measurement units.
- Solve problems involving measurement, area and perimeter formulas, and line plots.
- Use a protractor to measure angles.
- Find unknown angle measures.

NOTE: All of these learning goals for your child are based on the Grade 4 Common Core State Standards for Mathematics.

Ways to Help Your Child

Writing neatly and showing math work clearly is important. Your child's teacher will analyze math homework to better understand your child's progress and thought processes. During homework time, encourage neat drawing and writing.

The customary system of measurement is most commonly used in the United States of America. In other parts of the world, the metric system of measurement, which is based on 10, is more common. Units of measurement can be converted as equivalent measurements in smaller or larger units.

The meter is a basic metric unit of length. The table below shows the relationship between the sizes of units shorter than and greater than 1 meter.

Metric Unit of Length	Equivalent Lengths	
kilometer	1000 meters	10 hectometers
meter	1 meter	10 decimeters
centimeter	$\frac{1}{100}$ meter	10 millimeters
millimeter	$\frac{1}{1000}$ meter	

Conversation Starter: Make a game of naming units of metric or customary measurement that would most likely be used when measuring distances, liquid volumes, or weights. For example:

- The length of a caterpillar
- The weight of a dog
- The volume of a water bottle
- The volume of a swimming pool

ONLINE
For more Home Connect activities, continue online at sadlierconnect.com

232   Unit 4 ■ Focus on Measurement and Data

Student Page 232

UNIT PLANNER

	Lesson	Standard(s)	Objective
26	Convert Customary Measurement Units	4.MD.1	Understand customary units of measurement and how to convert measurements expressed in larger units as measurements in equivalent smaller units.
27	Convert Metric Measurement Units	4.MD.1	Learn about the relationship between larger and smaller metric units of measurement.
28	Problem Solving: Measurement	4.MD.2	Solve real-world problems using measurement.
29	Problem Solving: Apply Area and Perimeter Formulas	4.MD.3	Understand how you use area and perimeter formulas for rectangles to solve problems.
30	Problem Solving: Use Line Plots	4.MD.4	Use a line plot to display measurement data and draw conclusions from the displayed data.
31	Understand Angle Measures	4.MD.5a 4.MD.5b	Relate measures of angles to fractions of circles and use these fractions to determine the measure of an angle in degrees.
32	Use a Protractor to Measure Angles	4.MD.6	Understand how to categorize obtuse, acute, right, and straight angles and use a protractor to determine their measurement.
33	Problem Solving: Find Unknown Angle Measures	4.MD.7	Understand how to use the relationships between angles to find angle measures and solve problems.

Essential Question: How can measurement data be used to solve problems?

UNIT

Essential Question	Words to Know
How are larger and smaller customary units of measurement related?	customary units
How are larger and smaller metric units of measurement related?	metric units
How can you use what you know about whole numbers, fractions, and decimals to solve measurement problems?	
How can you use area and perimeter formulas for rectangles to solve problems?	length, width, formula
How can representing data on a line plot help you to better understand and interpret a set of measurements?	line plot, data
How is the measure of an angle related to a circle?	ray, point, endpoint, angle, vertex, degree (°), one-degree angle, right angle, straight angle
How can classifying angles and using a protractor help you measure angles?	acute angle, perpendicular, obtuse angle, protractor
How can you use known relationships between angle measures to solve problems?	supplementary angles, complementary angles

Unit Assessment

- Unit 4 Common Core Review, *pp. 298–300*
- Unit 4 Performance Task   ONLINE

Additional Assessment Options

Optional Purchase:

- iProgress Monitor   ONLINE
- Progress Monitor Student Benchmark Assessment Booklet

ONLINE Digital Resources

- Home Connect Activities
- Unit Performance Tasks
- Additional Practice
- Fluency Practice
- Teacher Resources
- iProgress Monitor (optional purchase)

Go to SadlierConnect.com to access your Digital Resources.

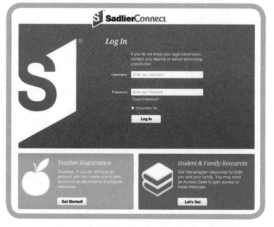

For more detailed instructions see page T3.

LEARNING PROGRESSIONS

This page provides more in-depth detail on the development of the standards across the grade levels. See also the unit Progress Check page in the Student Edition for a roadmap of the Learning Progressions.

Grade 3

- Students measure and estimate liquid volumes and masses using common metric units and solve one-step word problems involving masses or volumes. (3.MD.2)
- Students generate measurement data using rulers marked to halves and fourths of an inch and display the data on a line plot marked off in appropriate units. (3.MD.4)
- Students show that the area found by tiling a rectangle with unit squares may be found by multiplying the side lengths. (3.MD.7a, 3.MD.7b)
- Students use area models to represent the distributive property. They recognize area as additive and use this understanding to find the area of rectilinear figures by decomposing them into rectangles. (3.MD.7c, 3.MD.7d)
- Students solve problems involving perimeter, including finding an unknown side length. (3.MD.8)

Grade 4

- Conversion of larger measurement units to smaller units relates to multiplicative comparison. Students know the relative sizes of units within a measurement system and convert measurements from a larger unit to a smaller unit. (4.MD.1)
- Students solve word problems involving distance, time, liquid volumes, masses, and money. (4.MD.2)
- Students apply the area and perimeter formulas for rectangles to solve real world and mathematical problems, including finding a missing length or width. (4.MD.3)
- Students display a set of measurements in half, quarter, and eighth units on a line plot and solve problems based on displayed data using addition and subtraction. (4.MD.4)
- Students understand angles and angle measurement in degrees. They measure angles using a protractor, draw angles of given measure and add and subtract to solve problems involving unknown angle measures, including the use of an equation with a symbol for the unknown measure. (4.MD.5, 4.MD.6, 4.MD.7)

Grade 5

- Students convert among different-sized measurement units within the same measurement system while solving problems. (5.MD.1)
- Students make a line plot to display a set of measurements in half units, quarter units, and eighth units. They apply grade 5 fraction operations to solve problems involving data displayed on line plots. (5.MD.2)
- Students develop and apply formulas to find the volume of rectangular solids and figures composed of rectangular solids. (5.MD.5)

Focus on Measurement and Data

Essential Question:
How can measurement data be used to solve problems?

Unit 4   Focus on Measurement and Data   **233**

Essential Question:
How can measurement data be used to solve problems?

As students become involved with the Essential Question, they begin by completing conversions involving customary and metric units of measurement. They then use this knowledge to complete measurement problems with area, perimeter, angles, and organize data using line plots.

Conversation Starters

Have students discuss the photograph. Ask questions such as: *What is going on in this picture? What information can you gather about the pool from the picture? What information might the swimmers want to know about the pool?*

Ask students to think about any experience they may have had with swim races. This can include personal experiences or races such as the Olympics. *What two parts of the race are used to name a swim race?* (A swim race is named for the kind of stroke and the distance to swim in the race.)

Tell students the length of the pool is 50 meters and the width is 25 meters. *What is the perimeter of the pool? How did you determine your answers?* (The perimeter is 150 meters because $2(50 + 25) = 150$.)

Lead students to see that their understanding of measurement can be helpful in solving this problem.

Activity

Materials: grid paper, pencil, number line, race times as given
Marla's practice times for a 50-meter freestyle swim race are shown.

53.50	54.43	53.51	54.26	53.63
54.02	53.73	54.09	54.43	54.16
54.35	54.26	54.37	53.66	54.42

Encourage students to use a number line to organize the practice times. Ask: *What is Marla's fastest time? What is her slowest time? What time occurs most often in her practice times?*

Students should determine Marla's fastest time is 53.5 seconds and her slowest time is 54.43. She swam a time of both 54.26 and 54.43 twice so these times occur most often.

Common Core Focus:

4.MD.1 Know relative sizes of measurement units within one system of units including lb, oz.; hr, min, sec. Within a single system of measurement, express measurements in a larger unit in terms of a smaller unit. Record measurement equivalents in a two-column table.

OBJECTIVE

Understand customary units of measurement and how to convert measurements expressed in larger units as measurements in equivalent smaller units.

ESSENTIAL QUESTION

Ask students to tell what they know about the units of time. Have students form pairs and give each pair a stopwatch. One student will hop on one foot 10 times and then recite the ABCs while the other student records the time. Students should then switch roles. Let volunteers share their times with the class.

FLUENCY PRACTICE

Fluency practice is available at **sadlierconnect.com**.

Concept Development

Understand: Relative sizes of customary units of weight

■ Students will convert measurements within the customary system.

■ Explain to students how they can also use addition to complete the conversion table. Have students explain why they can add 16 to the previous number of ounces listed in the table.

■ Be sure students understand that the measurements in each row of the table are equivalent.

■ Have students explain how expressing 4 pounds as 64 ounces is expressing a larger unit of measurement in terms of a smaller unit of measurement.

Lesson
26 Convert Customary Measurement Units

Essential Question:
How are larger and smaller customary units of measurement related?
4.MD.1

Words to Know:
customary units

Guided Instruction

In this lesson you will learn about customary units of measurement and how to convert measurements expressed in larger units as measurements in equivalent smaller units.

Understand: Relative sizes of customary units of weight

> A restaurant serves 1 ounce of butter with each basket of bread.
> Will 4 pounds of butter be enough for 50 baskets of bread?

Customary units are the measurement units used in the United States customary system of measurement. A pound and an ounce are customary units of weight. 1 pound is heavier than 1 ounce, so 1 pound is a larger unit.

The model shows the relationship between 1 pound and 1 ounce of butter. The long bar represents 1 pound and the short bar represents 1 ounce.

Customary Units of Weight
1 pound (lb) = 16 ounces (oz)

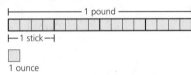

Complete this conversion table to express pounds as ounces.

Pounds	Ounces	
1	16	
2	32	← 2 × 16
3	48	← 3 × 16
4	64	← 4 × 16

Four pounds of butter is equivalent to 64 ounces. 64 > 50

▶ Four pounds of butter will be enough for 50 bread baskets.

Words to Know

customary units: the measurement units used in the United States customary system of measurement

Glossary can be found on pp. 347–350.

Lesson 26

Guided Instruction

Understand: Relative sizes of customary units of liquid volume

> Lisa's mother goes to the corner store to buy 3 gallons of milk. When she gets there, she sees that there are only quart containers of milk left. How many quarts of milk should she buy?

A gallon, a quart, a pint, and a cup are customary units of liquid volume. The picture shows how the units are related.

Customary Units of Liquid Volume
1 cup (c) = 8 fluid ounces (fl oz)
1 pint (pt) = 2 cups
1 quart (qt) = 2 pints
1 gallon (gal) = 4 quarts

Use the information above to complete the conversion table.

Gallons	Quarts	
1	4	
2	8	← 2 × 4
3	12	← 3 × 4

Three gallons of milk is the same amount as 12 quarts.

▶ Lisa's mother should buy 12 quarts of milk.

How many cups of milk can Lisa's mother pour from 3 gallons of milk? Explain.
Lisa's mother can pour 48 cups of milk from 3 gallons. Possible explanation: We know from the problem above that 3 gallons is 12 quarts. Each quart is 2 pints. So 12 quarts is 2 × 12 or 24 pints. Each pint is 2 cups. So, 24 pints is 2 × 24 or 48 cups. That means that 3 gallons is 48 cups.

Unit 4 ■ Focus on Measurement and Data **235**

Understand: Relative sizes of customary units of liquid volume

■ In this presentation, students convert customary units of liquid volume for the first time.

■ Explain to students that they can also use addition to complete the conversion table. Students can add 4 to the previous number of quarts listed in the table.

■ Be sure students understand the relationship between the two columns in the conversion table. Explain how these are equivalent measurements.

■ When expressing 3 gallons as 12 quarts, students are expressing a larger unit of measurement (gallons) in terms of a smaller unit of measurement (quarts).

✏ Lead a discussion about strategies that can be used to convert larger units of measurement to smaller units of measurement. Have students select one of the strategies and find the number cups. Have volunteers share their responses.

Support English Language Learners

Explore the term *customary units* with students. Ask students to identify any root words they may immediately see in the term. Write the word *custom* on the board and invite children to talk about customs in their homes or native countries. Explain that a custom is a tradition or widely accepted way of doing things. Explore with children how this definition can be applied to the customary units of measurement in the United States. Some English language learners may be accustomed to the metric system of measurement. Write some of the customary units on the board and have students relate what they know about the units.

Connect: Relating units and converting time measurements Use this page to help students strengthen their understanding of expressing larger units of measurements in terms of smaller units of measurements.

■ This lesson extends students' knowledge of units of time to include seconds. Students will also convert units of time for the first time.

■ Explain to students how they can also use addition to complete the conversion table. Students can add 60 to the previous number of seconds listed in the table.

■ Be sure students understand the relationship between the two columns. Explain that these are equivalent measurements.

■ Explain that when expressing 3 minutes as 180 seconds, students are expressing a larger unit of measurement in terms of a smaller unit of measurement.

✏ Lead a discussion about how the units of time are related. Make sure students connect seconds to minutes and minutes to hours. Then have students answer the question. Ask volunteers to share their responses.

Lesson 26   Convert Customary Measurement Units

Guided Instruction

Connect: Relating units and converting time measurements

> Kevin is helping his mother fold and put letters in envelopes. If it takes him 9 seconds for each envelope, how many envelopes can Kevin complete in 3 minutes?

An hour, a minute, and a second are units of time.

Units of Time
1 minute (min) = 60 seconds (s)
1 hour (h) = 60 minutes

The clock shows that there are 60 minutes in 1 hour. There are also 60 seconds in each minute.

The minute hand moves around the clock one complete turn (60 minutes) each hour.

The second hand moves around the clock one complete turn (60 seconds) each minute.

To solve the problem, first find how many seconds are in 3 minutes. Then find how many groups of 9 seconds are on that number of seconds.

Step 1

Complete the conversion table to find the number of seconds in 3 minutes.

Minutes	Seconds
1	60
2	120	← 2 × 60
3	180	← 3 × 60

Step 2

Find the number of envelopes Kevin can complete in 180 seconds.

To find how many groups of 9 seconds there are in 180 seconds, divide 180 by 9.
180 ÷ 9 = 20

➡ Kevin can complete 20 envelopes in 3 minutes.

✏ How many seconds are there in 1 hour? Explain. There are 3,600 seconds in 1 hour. Possible explanation: 1 hour is the same as 60 minutes. Since there are 60 seconds in 1 minute, there are 60 × 60 or 3,600 seconds in 1 hour.

236   Unit 4 ■ Focus on Measurement and Data

Math-to-Social Studies Connection

Olympic Records Have students find an Olympic record that is recorded in hours or minutes. Then have students rewrite the Olympic record in a smaller unit of measurement. Ask students to share both measurements.

Lesson 26

Guided Practice

Customary Units of Measurement	
Length	**Weight**
1 foot = 12 inches 1 yard = 3 feet	1 pound = 16 ounces 1 ton = 2,000 pounds
Liquid Volume	**Time**
1 cup = 8 fluid ounces 1 pint = 2 cups 1 quart = 2 pints 1 gallon = 4 quarts	1 minute = 60 seconds 1 hour = 60 minutes 1 day = 24 hours 1 week = 7 days

Complete the sentence to compare the sizes of the units.

1. The smallest customary unit of time is 1 __second__.

2. 1 yard is __3__ times as long as 1 foot.

3. 1 quart is 2 times as much as 1 __pint__.

4. 1 ton is __2,000__ times as heavy as 1 __pound__.

5. 1 quart is 4 times as much as 1 __cup__.

6. 1 yard is __36__ times as long as 1 inch.

Complete the conversion tables. Then use the pattern to complete the equations below.

7.

Cups	Fluid Ounces
1	8
2	16
3	24

4 cups = __32__ ounces

8.

Pounds	Ounces
1	16
2	32
3	48

6 pounds = __96__ ounces

⊻⊽ Think • Pair • Share

MP7 **9.** What equation can you use to convert 3 pounds to ounces directly, without a conversion table? Possible answer: Since there are 16 ounces in 1 pound, you can multiply 16 by 3 to find the total number of ounces in 3 pounds. 3 × 16 = 48.

Unit 4 ▪ Focus on Measurement and Data **237**

Mathematical Practices

Mathematical Practice Standards underline the teaching and understanding of all concepts and skills presented. The emphasis of specific practices is noted throughout the guided and independent practice of this lesson.

MP7 **Look for and make use of structure.**

Item 9: Students identify a pattern in converting larger measurements to smaller measurements.

Observational Assessment

Use page 237 to assess whether students know relative sizes of customary units of measurement and can express larger customary units of measurement in terms of smaller customary units of measurement.

⊻⊽ Think•Pair•Share

Peer Collaboration Have students work in pairs. If pairs struggle to complete the problem, ask:

- *What is the relationship between pounds and ounces?*

- *How many pounds are being converted?*

- *What operations can be used to find the number of ounces in 3 pounds?*

Return to the Essential Question

Reread the Lesson 26 Essential Question on page 234: *How are larger and smaller customary units of measurement related?*

Ask volunteers to use what they learned in this lesson to answer this question. (Possible response: You can multiply to express larger customary units of measurement as smaller customary units of measurement. The larger and smaller customary units of measurement are equivalent.)

Concept Application

Students may work independently on these pages in the classroom or at home. They may refer to the first four pages of the lesson to revisit the instruction or to see a worked-out example.

Common Errors and **Teaching Tips** may help you support student learning either in the classroom or as a follow-up for work done at home.

Common Errors

Items 1–4

Some students may confuse the *greater than* and *less than* symbols. Review the meaning of these symbols. Ask proficient students to explain how they remember the meaning of each symbol.

Teaching Tips

Items 7–10

Remind students that they can make a conversion table to find the equivalent measurement. They should also use the Customary Units of Measurement chart at the top of the page.

Lesson 26 Convert Customary Measurement Units

Independent Practice

Customary Units of Measurement	
Length	**Weight**
1 foot = 12 inches 1 yard = 3 feet	1 pound = 16 ounces 1 ton = 2,000 pounds
Liquid Volume	**Time**
1 cup = 8 fluid ounces 1 pint = 2 cups 1 quart = 2 pints 1 gallon = 4 quarts	1 minute = 60 seconds 1 hour = 60 minutes 1 day = 24 hours 1 week = 7 days

Write < or > to compare the sizes of the units. Then write a comparison using multiplication.

1. foot $>$ inch

   1 foot is 12 times as long as 1 inch.

2. second $<$ minute

   1 minute is 60 times as long as 1 second

3. fluid ounce $<$ cup

   1 cup is 8 times as much as 1 fluid ounce.

4. pint $>$ fluid ounce

   1 pint is 16 times as much as 1 fluid ounce.

Complete the conversion tables. Then use the pattern to complete the equations below.

5.

Feet	Inches
1	12
2	24
3	36
4	48

5 feet = 60 inches

6.

Pints	Cups
1	2
2	4
3	6
4	8

10 pints = 20 cups

Write the equivalent measurement.

7. 5 yards = 15 feet

8. 3 pounds = 48 ounces

9. 6 quarts = 12 pints

10. 1 day = 1,440 minutes

238 Unit 4 ■ Focus on Measurement and Data

Writing About Math

▸ **Write an Explanatory Text** Give students a larger customary unit of measurement to express as a smaller customary unit of measurement. Ask students to explain how to convert the measurement. Have students use precise language and vocabulary.

Ask volunteers to read their paragraphs aloud.

Independent Practice

Lesson 26

Convert the measurements. You can use the Customary Units of Measurement chart on page 238.

11. 3 yards = __9__ feet

12. 2 pounds = __32__ ounces

13. 4 gallons = __16__ quarts

14. 4 days = __96__ hours

15. 2 yards = __72__ inches

16. 5 quarts = __20__ cups

For exercises 17–22, circle the correct answer.

17. Claudia uses eye drops to help with her contact lenses. The bottle of eye drops is about the size of a thumb. Which unit is probably printed on the bottle?

a. pint **b.** fluid ounces
c. quart **d.** cup

18. Jerry is mailing 4 boxes of books. Which unit should Jerry use to measure the total weight of the 4 boxes?

a. ounces **b.** pounds
c. tons **d.** quarts

19. Each student has 5 minutes to explain his or her project to the class. How many seconds does each student have?

a. 50 seconds **b.** 60 seconds
c. 300 seconds **d.** 360 seconds

20. A restaurant offers a large order of chicken soup. If the large order is 3 pints of soup, how many fluid ounces (fl oz) do you get?

a. 6 fl oz **b.** 8 fl oz
c. 12 fl oz **d.** 48 fl oz

21. The tallest living man in the world is 8 feet and 3 inches tall. What is his height in inches?

a. 27 inches **b.** 96 inches
c. 99 inches **d.** 128 inches

22. One mile is 5,280 feet. How many yards equal 1 mile?

a. 440 yards **b.** 1,760 yards
c. 15,840 yards **d.** 63,360 yards

Common Errors

Items 17–22

Some students may select the first answer choice that seems correct without examining the other choices. Remind students that when answering a multiple-choice question, they need to examine all of the choices.

Teaching Tips

Items 11-16

If students are struggling, remind them that they can find the equivalent measurement by making a conversion table or by writing an equation.

Digital Connection

Internet Resources Use a search engine to find online customary units of measurement calculators. Create a list of acceptable websites for students to use. Have students convert different customary units of measurement. Have students record the conversion and have them present their conversions to the class. Students can use the calculator to check their work or for additional practice.

Independent Practice

Common Errors

Item 24

Some students may agree with Charlotte because they recognize ounces as the smallest unit of weight. Remind students that pounds can be converted to ounces.

Teaching Tips

Items 25-26

Remind students that these are multi-step problems, and after they convert the units of measurement, they still need to solve the problem.

Independent Practice

MP6 **23.** Michael says that if you convert a whole number of feet to inches, the number of inches must be a multiple of 12. Is Michael correct?
Answers will vary. Possible answer: Yes, Michael is correct because there are 12 inches in 1 foot. When you convert feet to inches, you multiply the number of feet by 12. So the number of inches will be a whole number times 12, which is the definition of a multiple of 12.

MP7 **24.** Charlotte's baby brother weighs 9 pounds 12 ounces when he is born. Charlotte says that this weight is already in the smallest units possible, because it includes ounces. Is Charlotte correct, or can you convert the weight to smaller units?
Answers will vary. Possible answer: Charlotte is not correct, because you can still convert the 9 pounds to ounces and then add the extra 12 ounces. The weight includes both pounds and ounces because the 12 ounces are not enough to make a whole pound. There are 16 ounces in one pound.

Solve the problems.

MP5 **25.** A clothing designer needs 4 yards of fabric to make a sample outfit. If the designer has 16 feet of the fabric, is there enough fabric to make one outfit?

> **Show your work.** Work may vary. Possible work:
> 1 yard = 3 feet
> $4 \times 3 = 12$ feet needed
> $12 < 16$

Answer Yes, there is enough fabric for one outfit.

MP6 **26.** Tammy drinks 2 pints of milk every day. Her doctor says that girls her age should drink 3 cups of milk every day to be healthy. How many extra cups of milk does Tammy drink in 1 week?

> **Show your work.** Work may vary. Possible work:
> 1 pint = 2 cups, so Tammy drinks $2 \times 2 = 4$ cups each day.
> $4 - 3 = 1$ extra cup each day
> 1 week = 7 days
> $1 \times 7 = 7$ extra cups each week

Answer Tammy drinks 7 extra cups of milk in 1 week.

240 Unit 4 ■ Focus on Measurement and Data

Mathematical Practices

MP5	**Use appropriate tools strategically.**
Item 25: Students use pencil and paper and/or models to solve a conversion problem.	
MP6	**Attend to precision.**
Item 23: Students communicate precisely to others using clear terminology and units of measure.	
Item 26: Students calculate accurately and efficiently.	
MP7	**Look for and make use of structure.**
Item 24: Students see complex measurements as single entities.	

MP1 **27.** Steve wants to paint his room light blue. He picks up 3 gallons of white paint at the store. He also buys 2 quarts of blue to mix with the white paint. How many quarts of paint does Steve buy altogether?

▮▶ **Show your work.** Work may vary. Possible work:
1 gallon = 4 quarts
3 gallons = 3 × 4 or 12 quarts
12 quarts + 2 quarts = 14 quarts.

Answer Steve buys 14 quarts of paint altogether.

MP3 **28.** Molly says that to convert 100 fluid ounces to cups, you can divide 100 by 8. Then any remainder will be a whole number of fluid ounces. Is Molly correct?

Answer Yes, Molly is correct.

▮▶ **Justify your answer using words, drawings, or numbers.**
Possible justification: $100 \div 8 = 12$ R4.

12 cups $\nearrow^{+\,4}$

0 8 16 24 32 40 48 56 64 72 80 88 96 104
fluid ounces

The remainder of 4 is 4 fluid ounces that are not enough to make a whole cup. They make $\frac{4}{8}$ of a cup, or $\frac{1}{2}$ cup, but they are still whole fluid ounces.

MP8 **29.** William makes the table below to convert fractions of an hour to minutes.

Hour	Minutes
$\frac{1}{4}$	25
$\frac{1}{2}$	50
$\frac{3}{4}$	75
1	100

Hour	Minutes
1	60
$\frac{3}{4}$	45
$\frac{1}{2}$	30
$\frac{1}{4}$	15

Did William convert the measurements correctly?

Answer No, William did not convert the measurements correctly.

▮▶ **Justify your answer using words, drawings, or numbers.**
Possible justification: One hour is 60 minutes, not 100 minutes, so all of the converted measurements are wrong. William should have started with 1 hour = 60 minutes. Then he could have converted the $\frac{1}{2}$ hour to minutes first and follow from there.

Unit 4 ▪ Focus on Measurement and Data **241**

Common Errors
Item 29
Some students may say that William's conversion is accurate because the table follows a pattern of adding 25 to the previous number of minutes. Remind students to pay attention to the meaning of the units. Students should recognize that there are not 100 minutes in an hour.

Mathematical Practices

MP1	**Make sense of problems and persevere in solving them.**

Item 27: Students use quantitative relationships to solve a problem.

MP3	**Construct viable arguments and critique the reasoning of others.**

Item 28: Students analyze a student's method to determine if the method results in a correct answer.

MP8	**Look for and express regularity in repeated reasoning.**

Item 29: Students analyze a process and determine that the results are not reasonable.

Common Core Focus:

4.MD.1 Know relative sizes of measurement units within one system of units including km, m, cm; kg, g; L, mL. Within a single system of measurement, express measurements in a larger unit in terms of a smaller unit. Record measurement equivalents in a two-column table.

OBJECTIVE

Learn about the relationship between larger and smaller metric units of measurement.

ESSENTIAL QUESTION

Students will learn about the relationship between smaller and larger units, and how to convert these measurements.

FLUENCY PRACTICE

Fluency practice is available at **sadlierconnect.com**.

Concept Development

Understand: Relative sizes of metric measurements of length

■ Expressing metric measurements as their equivalents in smaller metric units helps to reinforce place-value understanding.

■ It may be helpful for students to have access to the chart shown on this page while they work on the lesson. Reproduce a copy for each student. Note that the metric unit of length, *dekameter,* is also seen as *decameter.*

■ To help students understand the meter explain that it is a little longer than a yard.

✏️ Discuss the chart as a class. Students should explain how they determined which units in the chart are longer than 1 meter and which units are smaller than 1 meter.

Lesson 27   Convert Metric Measurement Units

Essential Question: How are larger and smaller metric units of measurement related?

4.MD.1

Words to Know: metric units

Guided Instruction

In this lesson you will learn about metric units of measurement and how to convert measurements expressed in larger units as equivalent measurements in smaller units.

Understand: Relative sizes of metric measurements of length

> What are the metric units of length and which units are used most often?

Metric units are the measurement units used in the metric system of measurement.
A meter is the basic unit of length in the metric system.

The chart shows how each metric unit of length compares to 1 meter. The units used most often are kilometer, meter, centimeter, and millimeter. These units are highlighted in the chart.

Like the base-ten number system, the metric system is also based on 10. Each unit is 10 times the length of the next smaller unit.

Metric Unit of Length	Equivalent Lengths	
kilometer	10 hectometers	1000 meters
hectometer	10 dekameters	100 meters
dekameter	10 meters	10 meters
meter	10 decimeters	1 meter
decimeter	10 centimeters	$\frac{1}{10}$ meter
centimeter	10 millimeters	$\frac{1}{100}$ meter
millimeter		$\frac{1}{1000}$ meter

Remember!
Each place value in whole and decimal numbers is 10 times the next place to the right.

➡️ The chart above shows the metric units of length. The highlighted rows show the units used most often.

✏️ Which units in the chart are longer than 1 meter? Which units are shorter than 1 meter? What is the longest unit in the chart? What is the shortest unit? Kilometer, hectometer, and dekameter are longer than 1 meter. Decimeter, centimeter, and millimeter are shorter than 1 meter. Kilometer is the longest unit; millimeter is the shortest unit.

Words to Know

metric units: the measurement units used in the metric system of measurement

Glossary can be found on pp. 347–350.

MORE ONLINE · sadlierconnect.com   Lesson 27

Guided Instruction

Understand: Converting metric units of length

> Lucy is running a 5K race. A 5K race is 5 kilometers long. She stops for a few seconds at the halfway point. How many meters does Lucy have left to run?

The chart shows how the most often used metric units of length are related.

Metric Units of Length
1 kilometer (km) = 1000 meters (m)
1 meter = 100 cm (cm)
1 centimeter = 10 millimeters (mm)

- **1 kilometer** is about the distance you walk if you walk around a football field 3 times.

- **1 meter** is about the distance from a door knob to the floor.

- **1 centimeter** is about the width of your finger.

- **1 millimeter** is about the thickness of a dime.

To solve the problem, find the number of meters in a 5K race.

The chart shows that 1 kilometer = 1000 meters.
Complete this conversion table.

Kilometers	Meters
1	1000
2	2000	← 2 × 1000
3	3000	← 3 × 1000
4	4000	← 4 × 1000
5	5000	← 5 × 1000

The race is 5000 meters long.

2500 is exactly between 0 and 5000 on the number line.

The halfway point is at 2500 meters. Lucy has run 2500 meters and has 2500 meters left to run.

➡ Lucy has 2500 meters left to run.

✏ Which is longer: a kilometer or a meter? A millimeter or a meter? Explain. A kilometer is longer than a meter. A meter is longer than a millimeter. Possible explanation. 1 kilometer is equal to 1000 meters, so 1 kilometer is longer than 1 meter. 1 meter = 1000 millimeters, so 1 meter is longer than 1 millimeter.

Unit 4 ■ Focus on Measurement and Data   **243**

Understand: Converting metric units of length

■ In this presentation, students convert metric units of length. Up until this point, students have learned about the relationship between units but have not actually converted measurements.

■ Have students identify which unit is the larger unit and which unit is the smaller unit. Once students identify that a meter is smaller than a kilometer, guide them to reason that the *number* of meters will be greater than the *number* of kilometers.

■ Review the real-world examples that are used for benchmarks for kilometer, meter, centimeter, and millimeter. Have students give other examples of objects that have about the same length as these units.

✏ Have small groups of students discuss their explanations. To make sure students have a solid understanding of the relationships between units, they should include terms like *equal to, shorter than,* and *longer than* in their explanations.

Support English Language Learners

Many metric measurement terms may be unfamiliar. Students need to have a solid understanding of these terms in order to understand the relationships between them.

Write the word *meter* on the board and explain that it is the standard unit of length in the metric system. Explain that all of the other metric units of length are based on the meter. On index cards, write the prefixes *kilo-, hecto-, deka-, deci-, centi-,* and *milli-*. Hold the prefix index cards up and pronounce each one independently and have the class repeat it back. Then, hold the card up to the word on the board and pronounce the word in its entirety and have the class repeat it back to you. If students are confident with their pronunciations, encourage a discussion on how the measurements are related mathematically.

Guided Instruction

Connect: Converting metric units of liquid volume and mass Use this page to help students deepen their understanding of metric units and the corresponding base-ten relationships.

■ Have students develop a plan before solving the first problem. Have students explain the multiple steps involved in solving the problem.

■ Remind students that in order to compare two measurements, they must have the same unit. Students should convert the larger unit to a smaller unit so they can use multiplication.

■ Remind students to include units with their solutions. They should refer to the question being asked in the problem to make sure they are finding the correct quantity. In the second problem students need to find the number of nickels in the pile.

Guided Instruction

Connect: Converting metric units of liquid volume and mass

Andrew buys 6 bottles of orange juice. Each has 355 milliliters of juice. Does Andrew buy more or less than 2 liters of juice?

The chart shows how the metric units of liquid volume are related.

Metric Units of Liquid Volume
1 liter (L) = 1000 milliliters (mL)

• **1 liter** is about the amount of 8 small juice boxes.
• **1 milliliter** is about 20 drops.

To solve the problem, first find the number of milliliters in 2 liters.

Liters	Milliliters
1	1000
2	2000

←— 2 × 1000   2 liters of juice is equivalent to 2000 milliliters.

Compare 2000 milliliters to the number of milliliters in the 6 bottles of juice.

6 × 355 = 2130   The 6 bottles have __2130__ milliliters.   2130 > 2000

➡ Andrew buys more than 2 liters of juice.

A nickel has a mass of 5 grams. How many nickels are in a pile of nickels that has a mass of 3 kilograms?

Metric Units of Mass
1 kilogram (kg) = 1000 grams (g)

• **1 kilogram** is about the mass of 10 apples.
• **1 gram** is about the mass of 1 paperclip.

To solve the problem, first find the number of grams in 3 kilograms.

Kilograms	Grams
1	1000
2	2000
3	3000

←— 2 × 1000
←— 3 × 1000   3 kg is equivalent to 3000 g.

Find the number of groups of 5 in 3000 grams. 3000 ÷ 5 = __600__

➡ There are 600 nickels in the pile.

Math-to-Science Connection

Standard Units of Measure The International System of Units, or SI, is the standard system of measurement used by many scientists. Using the same standards of measurement makes it easier for scientists around the world to communicate with one another. There are 7 base units of SI. All other units of measure can be derived from these base units.

meter (length)
kilogram (mass)
second (time)
ampere (electric current)

kelvin (temperature)
mole (amount of substance)
candela (luminous intensity)

Note that volume is not a base unit; it is a derived unit. The measurement for liter can be derived from a meter using the conversion 1 mL = 1 cm^3.

Metric Units of Measurement	
Length	**Liquid Volume**
1 kilometer = 1000 meters	1 liter = 1000 milliliters
1 meter = 100 cm	**Mass**
1 centimeter = 10 millimeters	1 kilogram = 1000 grams

Complete the sentences to compare the sizes of the units.

1. A _____kilogram_____ is 1000 times as heavy as a gram.

2. There are 1000 _____milliliters_____ in 1 liter.

3. A _____centimeter_____ is 10 times as long as 1 millimeter.

4. A meter is _____100_____ times as long as 1 centimeter.

5. A meter is _____1000_____ times as long as 1 millimeter.

Complete the conversion tables. Then use the pattern to complete the equations below.

6.

Liters	Milliliters
1	1000
2	2000
3	3000
4	4000

5 liters = _____5000_____ milliliters

7.

Kilograms	Grams
1	1000
2	2000
3	3000

6 kilograms = _____6000_____ grams

Think • Pair • Share

MP2 **8.** Discuss the basic metric units—meters, grams, and liters. Which of these units has the most surprising size? Can you think of a reason why this size is the one to which the others are compared? Possible answer: A gram is the mass of a paper clip. It is also the basic unit for mass. We think it would be more useful to have a larger unit as the basic unit. Instead of using hundreds of grams to measure a larger object, it would be better to use kilograms. The people who get the most use out of grams are probably scientists.

Unit 4 ■ Focus on Measurement and Data   **245**

Observational Assessment

Use page 245 to assess whether students have a grasp of the relationships among metric units of measurement. Make sure students understand the relationship between any pair of metric units of length, volume, or mass and the correct way to convert a metric measurement to its equivalent in terms of smaller metric units.

Think•Pair•Share

Peer Collaboration Ask pairs of students to work together, and then share their answers with the class. As student pairs share their responses, ask questions such as:

• *What basic unit did you choose?*

• *What does the basic unit you chose measure?*

• *Do you think it is easy to estimate measurements with this basic unit? Explain.*

Return to the Essential Question

Reread the Lesson 27 Essential Question on page 242: *How are larger and smaller metric units of measurement related?*

Ask volunteers to use what they learned in this lesson to answer this question. (Possible response: It takes several of the smaller units to equal one of the larger units. The metric system is based on 10. You can multiply to convert a measurement to its equivalent in terms of smaller units.)

Mathematical Practices

Mathematical Practice Standards underline the teaching and understanding of all concepts and skills presented. The emphasis of specific practices is noted throughout the guided and independent practice of this lesson.

MP2   Reason abstractly and quantitatively.

Item 8: Students discuss abstractly the relative sizes of metric units.

Concept Application

Students may work independently on these pages in the classroom or at home. They may refer to the first four pages of the lesson to revisit the instruction or to see a worked-out example.

Common Errors and **Teaching Tips** may help you support student learning either in the classroom or as a follow-up for work done at home.

Teaching Tips

Items 5–8

It may be helpful to review the inequality symbols with students before they do these items.

Items 9–10

Students should be aware that one mistake can throw off all their work on the rest of the chart. Ask students to double-check their first answer before moving on.

Independent Practice

Metric Units of Measurement		
Length	Liquid Volume	Mass
1 kilometer = 1000 meters 1 meter = 100 cm 1 centimeter = 10 millimeters	1 liter = 1000 milliliters	1 kilogram = 1000 grams

Draw lines to match each metric unit with what it measures.

1. meter — b. length or distance
   gram — a. mass
   liter — c. liquid volume

Write an example of something that could be measured with each metric unit. Answers will vary.

2. meter
   height of a building

3. gram
   a button

4. liter
   amount of water

Write < or > to compare the sizes of the units. Then write a comparison using multiplication.

5. meter $>$ centimeter
   1 meter is $100\ times$ as long as 1 centimeter.

6. milliliter $<$ liter
   1 liter is
   1000 times as much as 1 milliliter.

7. meter $<$ kilometer
   1 kilometer is
   1000 times as long as 1 meter

8. gram $<$ kilogram
   1 kilogram is
   1000 times as heavy as 1 gram

Complete the conversion tables. Then use the pattern to complete the equations below.

9.

Meters	Centimeters
1	100
2	200
3	300
4	400

5 meters = 500 centimeters

10.

Liters	Milliliters
1	1000
2	2000
3	3000
4	4000

8 liters = 8000 milliliters

246 Unit 4 ▪ Focus on Measurement and Data

Writing About Math

✏️ › **Write an Informative Text** Ask students to write a paragraph describing the metric units of measure. Their paragraph could include definitions of the units, examples of when to use the units of measure, and the relationships among the units.

Remind students that an informative text is meant to teach others so their paragraphs should be set up for someone who might not have any knowledge of the metric system.

Lesson 27

Independent Practice

Teaching Tips

Items 11-20
Remind students that they can use the chart on page 246 for reference.

Convert the measurements. You can use the Metric Units of Measurement chart on page 246.

11. 4 centimeters = __40__ millimeters

12. 6 kilometers = __6000__ meters

13. 5 meters = __500__ centimeters

14. 2 kilograms = __2000__ grams

15. 8 grams = __8000__ milligrams

16. 3 meters = __3000__ millimeters

For exercises 17–20, circle the correct answer.

17. Several rolls of yarn are needed to knit a pair of mittens. Which unit is best used to measure lengths of yarn?

    a. meter **b.** kilometer

    c. milliliter **d.** liter

18. Which of these units is most likely to be used to measure the mass of a comic book?

    a. kilograms **b.** grams

    c. centimeters **d.** liters

19. Josh uses a dropper to give medicine to his cat. Which is the best estimate for the total amount of medicine Josh gives his cat?

    a. 2 milliliters **b.** 2 millimeters

    c. 2 liters **d.** 2 meters

20. Amy jogs every day. Which of the following might be the distance she jogs each day?

    a. 6 millimeters **b.** 6 kilograms

    c. 6 kilometers **d.** 6 liters

Digital Connection

Internet Resources Find a game on the Internet that explores the metric system. The game can focus on conversions or on the units and their appropriate measures. It is not only important for students to understand how to convert between measures, but also for students to know what each type of unit is used to measure. Allow students to work in pairs to complete the activity and have them record their scores.

Independent Practice

Teaching Tips

Item 22

If students struggle to answer this question, ask them to think about how they might subtract a measurement such as 7 millimeters from 5 centimeters.

Independent Practice

MP5 **21.** In science class, the students are growing beans and measuring the roots. A meter stick is 1 meter long, and a metric ruler is about 30 centimeters long. Which tool is better for measuring the bean roots? Explain.
Answers will vary. Possible explanation: The roots are probably very small, so it would be easier to use a metric ruler than a meter stick. Even if the meter stick also has centimeter and millimeter marks on it, it would be awkward to use such a long measurement tool.

MP7 **22.** Allison says that 5 centimeters can also be written as 50 millimeters. Dave says that 50 millimeters is incorrect, since 50 millimeters can be written as a whole number of centimeters. Who do you agree with? Explain.
Answers will vary. Possible explanation: I agree with Allison, because using a greater number of smaller units is something we do all the time. For example, you may need to convert the 5 centimeters to 50 millimeters so that you can subtract a number of millimeters.

Solve the problems.

MP1 **23.** A school textbook has a mass of about 1 kilogram. Joel is taking 3 textbooks home from school. In grams, what is the combined mass of the books that Joel is taking?

▸ **Show your work.**
Work may vary. Possible work:
3 books have a mass of 3 kilograms.
$3 \times 1000 = 3000$ grams

Answer The combined mass of the books that Joel is taking is 3000 grams.

MP6 **24.** One milliliter of water has a mass of 1 gram. Trisha buys 5 liters of water. What is the mass of the water in kilograms?

▸ **Show your work.**
Work may vary. Possible work:
5 liters of water is 5000 milliliters. So, it has a mass of 5000 grams.
5000 grams is 5 kilograms.

Answer The mass of 5 liters of water is 5 kilograms.

Mathematical Practices

MP1	**Make sense of problems and persevere in solving them.**
Item 23: Students convert metric units to solve a word problem.	
MP5	**Use appropriate tools strategically.**
Item 21: Students decide which tool is better for metric measurement.	
MP6	**Attend to precision.**
Item 24: Students solve a word problem about metric measure.	
MP7	**Look for and make use of structure.**
Item 22: Students determine how two different units should be written to show that they are equivalent.	

MP3 **25.** Toni has a bottle of grape juice that is labeled 1893 milliliters. Oliver has a bottle of grape juice that is labeled 2 liters. Toni says that her bottle has more grape juice than Oliver's. Is Toni correct?

✎ **Show your work.**
Work may vary. Possible work:
Convert 2 liters to milliliters to compare.
2 × 1000 = 2000 milliliters.
2000 > 1893, so Oliver's bottle has more grape juice.

Answer <u>No, Toni is not correct.</u>

MP7 **26.** The produce section of a grocery store has a digital scale that customers can use. The scale shows that a bunch of bananas has a mass of 1.2 kilograms. If the bunch has 6 bananas that are about the same size, what could be the mass in grams of 1 banana?

Answer <u>Each banana will have a mass of about 200 grams.</u>

✎ **Justify your answer using words, drawings, or numbers.**
Possible justification:
1.2 kilograms is the same as 1200 grams.
1200 ÷ 6 = 200

MP8 **27.** A very small unit of mass is the milligram (mg). One gram is equivalent to 1000 milligrams. Raul learns that he should have at least 1 gram of calcium each day. A glass of milk has about 300 milligrams of calcium. If Raul drinks 4 glasses of milk, will that give him enough calcium for the day?

Answer <u>Yes. Four glasses of milk will give Raul enough calcium.</u>

✎ **Justify your answer using words, pictures, or numbers.**
Possible justification: 4 × 300 = 1200
3 glasses of milk will have 1200 milligrams of calcium.
1 gram = 1000 milligrams
1200 > 1000

Unit 4 ■ Focus on Measurement and Data **249**

Teaching Tips

Item 26

Some students may have trouble converting 1.2 kilograms to grams. Suggest that students who are struggling with this problem use the fractional equivalent of 1.2. They can then think of 1.2 kilograms as 1 kilogram plus $\frac{2}{10}$ kilogram. They know that 1 kilogram is 1000 grams. They need to find $\frac{2}{10}$ kilogram, or $\frac{2}{10}$ × 1000 grams, and add that amount to the 1000 grams. So 1.2 kilograms is equivalent to 1000 grams plus 200 grams, or 1200 grams.

Mathematical Practices

MP3	**Construct viable arguments and critique the reasoning of others.**
Item 25: Students critique the reasoning of other students to decide which student is correct.	
MP7	**Look for and make use of structure.**
Item 26: Students justify their answer using words, drawings, or numbers.	
MP8	**Look for and express regularity in repeated reasoning.**
Item 27: Students explain their reasoning in solving a word problem.	

Common Core Focus:

4.MD.2 Use the four operations to solve word problems involving distances, intervals of time, liquid volumes, masses of objects, and money, including problems involving simple fractions or decimals, and problems that require expressing measurements given in a larger unit in terms of a smaller unit. Represent measurement quantities using diagrams such as number line diagrams that feature a measurement scale.

OBJECTIVE
Solve real-world problems using measurement.

ESSENTIAL QUESTION
Ask students to list some measurement units. Encourage them to discuss occasions when they might need to compute with these units.

PREREQUISITE SKILLS
Use Item I on page 341 of the Foundational Skills Handbook, to help students understand how to measure time intervals and determine elapsed time.

FLUENCY PRACTICE
Fluency practice is available at **sadlierconnect.com**.

Concept Development

Understand: Using a diagram with a measurement scale to solve a problem

■ Be sure students understand that measurements must be in the same unit before operations can be performed with them.

■ Discuss the plan for finding the answer. Note that this is a multistep problem.

▸ Have small groups of students discuss other ways to solve the problem.

Lesson 28 — Problem Solving: Measurement

Essential Question:
How can you use what you know about whole numbers, fractions, and decimals to solve measurement problems?
4.MD.2

In this lesson you will learn how to use diagrams and what you know about measurement to solve real-world problems.

Understand: Using a diagram with a measurement scale to solve a problem

> Mrs. Norton buys 30 liters of fruit punch for the fourth grade end-of-year party. Does she buy enough punch so that each of the 114 students can have 250 milliliters of punch?

To find out if Mrs. Norton buys enough punch, find the number of 250-ml servings in 30 liters and compare that number to the number of students.

Draw a diagram to show 1 liter as milliliters.

Remember!
1 liter = 1000 milliliters

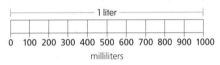

Color the diagram to find the number of servings in 1000 milliliters. Each serving is 250 milliliters.

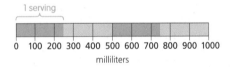

There are 4 servings in 1000 milliliters, or 1 liter.

So, there are 30 × 4, or 120 servings in 30 liters.

120 > 114

▸ Yes, Mrs. Norton buys enough punch.

▸ How could you use a calculator to solve the problem in a different way? Possible answer: I could multiply 250 by 114 and compare the product to 30,000, since 30 liters = 30,000 milliliters.

Support English Language Learners

In this lesson, the term *model* is used to refer to a number of different diagrams that illustrate the problems. Be sure that students understand that a model is meant to represent the conditions presented in the word problem. It should be used as a tool that helps students understand the information they are given and what they need to find. Have students compile a list of the diagrams that are used as models in this lesson. Suggest that their lists include examples of the models.

Lesson 28

Guided Instruction

Understand: Using models for units of time

> Cindy goes to see a movie. The movie starts at 2:30 P.M. and ends 2 hours and 45 minutes later. What time does the movie end?

To solve the problem, you can use a number line to model the time and the number of hours and minutes.

The clock at the right shows:

1 hour = 60 minutes

$\frac{1}{4}$ hour = 15 minutes

$\frac{1}{2}$ hour = 30 minutes

$\frac{3}{4}$ hour = 45 minutes

The number line shows the time in quarter hours starting at 2:30 P.M.

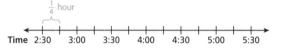

Remember!
A quarter hour is $\frac{1}{4}$ hour or 15 minutes.

Use the number line to count 2 hours 45 minutes ahead. Move 2 hours to the right. Then add $\frac{3}{4}$ hour.

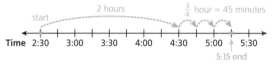

▶ The movie ends at 5:15 P.M.

✏ Cindy's mother picks her up $\frac{1}{2}$ hour after the movie ends. What time does Cindy's mother pick her up? Explain.
Cindy's mother picks her up at 5:45 P.M. A half hour is 30 minutes. 30 minutes after 5:15 P.M. is 5:45 P.M.

Unit 4 ■ Focus on Measurement and Data   **251**

Understand: Using models for units of time

■ In previous grades, students had experience telling time and solving problems involving elapsed time. In this grade, students solve problems with time intervals that span across several hours. Number lines are a useful tool to help students keep track of hours and minutes when performing operations with time.

■ Students may benefit from using a clock as they solve the problem. Actually manipulating the clock makes the passage of time seem more concrete.

■ Review fractional parts of an hour and how to write time as hours and minutes. Students will see time represented in both ways.

■ Discuss the time intervals on the number line provided in the presentation. Ask if other intervals could have been used and the advantages or disadvantages of using a different scale.

✏ Students can use the clock provided in the presentation if they need help determining the number of minutes in $\frac{1}{2}$ hour. After students have answered the question, ask volunteers to explain their answers using the clock and the number line diagram.

Math-to-Social Studies Connection

Time and Schedules Discuss with students how to use time intervals to describe their daily routines. Have students write down their daily school schedule. Then, have them figure out the time intervals. For example, if math class begins at 9:30 and lunch begins at 11:00, they could say that lunch begins an hour and a half after math class begins.

If time permits, students can write down their schedule for Saturday or Sunday. Have students then work in small groups to figure out how to describe those schedules using time intervals.

Connect: Modeling and converting customary units Use this page to help students strengthen their understanding of using measurement in problem solving.

■ Be sure students understand how to interpret the model in the presentation. The model shows dividing 6 yards into 4 equal parts. To demonstrate this, have students find half of the model. Then have them find half of each half by dividing each half into two equal parts. Explain that $\frac{1}{2}$ of $\frac{1}{2}$ is $\frac{1}{4}$. Students can check that the model is now divided into 4 equal sections. Using the scale, they can see that each section is $1\frac{1}{2}$ yards.

■ Students may ask about the step that shows $\frac{1}{2}$ yard = $1\frac{1}{2}$ feet. They will study this relationship in the question at the end of the presentation, but this conversion is necessary to solve the problem described in the presentation.

■ After you have worked through the presentation, ask students to review the diagrams that they have used so far in the lesson. Be sure students are comfortable creating, reading, and interpreting diagrams.

✏ ▸ If the scale on the model were labeled in feet rather than yards, then the 3 would represent 3 feet, which is equivalent to 1 yard. Point out to students that the model shows that half the distance from 0 to 3 is $1\frac{1}{2}$. So half of 1 yard is equal to $1\frac{1}{2}$ feet.

Connect: Modeling and converting customary units

> Zach is helping his parents plan their vegetable garden. The garden is 6 yards wide. Zach's family wants 4 sections of equal width to plant 4 different kinds of vegetables. How many feet wide should Zach's family make each section?

To solve the problem, you can work with yards and then convert your answer to feet.

Step 1

The model shows the width of the garden as 6 yards. Partition the model into 4 equal sections. First, mark half the area. Then split each half in half to make 4 equal sections, or fourths. Each section will be $1\frac{1}{2}$ yards wide.

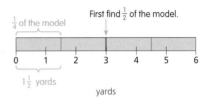

Step 2

Now convert $1\frac{1}{2}$ yards to feet.

$$1 \text{ yard} = 3 \text{ feet}$$
$$\frac{1}{2} \text{ yard} = 1\frac{1}{2} \text{ feet}$$
So, $1\frac{1}{2}$ yards = 3 feet + $1\frac{1}{2}$ feet
$$= 4\frac{1}{2} \text{ feet}$$

➡ Zach's family should make each section $4\frac{1}{2}$ feet wide.

✏ ▸ Explain how you could use the model in Step 1 to explain that $\frac{1}{2}$ yard is $1\frac{1}{2}$ feet.

The model shows that $1\frac{1}{2}$ is exactly between 0 and 3 on the number line, so $\frac{1}{2}$ of 3 feet must be $1\frac{1}{2}$ feet. The model shows yards, but it would look the same if you labeled it feet.

Math-to-Science Connection

Nonstandard Units of Measure In science, many formulas are standard throughout the world, but the units of measure for gathering and reporting data may vary. In 1958, Oliver R. Smoot created the nonstandard unit of measure to record the length of the Harvard Bridge in Boston. A "Smoot" was height of Oliver (five feet, seven inches). He used this to convert the length of the bridge from meters to "Smoots." Have students think of some non-standard units of measure such as their foot size or hand width to measure various object in the classroom. Make sure they can describe and name their non-standard unit of measure for other students.

MORE ONLINE sadlierconnect.com

Lesson 28

Guided Practice

Read the problem and answer the questions. Use the model to help you solve. Show your work.

1. Vicky buys 6 kilograms of potatoes. Each potato is about the same size and has a mass of 500 grams. How many potatoes does Vicky buy?

   a. What do you need to find?

   I need to find the number of potatoes Vicky buys.

   b. What units will you use?

   I will use grams and kilograms.

   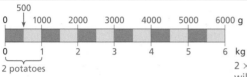

   1 kilogram = 1000 grams. Two potatoes will have a mass of 1 kilogram. So, 2 × 6 or 12 potatoes will have a mass of 6 kilograms.

   Answer Vicky buys 12 potatoes.

2. The directions on a bottle of plant food say to mix $\frac{2}{3}$ cup of plant food with 1 gallon of water. If there are $2\frac{1}{2}$ gallons of water in a watering can, how much plant food should you use?

   a. What do you need to find?

   I need to find the total cups of plant food for $2\frac{1}{2}$ gallons of water.

   b. What units will you use?

   I need to use cups and gallons, but the answer will be a number of cups.

   Answer I will use $1\frac{2}{3}$ cups of plant food. $\frac{2}{3} + \frac{2}{3} + \frac{1}{3} = \frac{5}{3} = 1\frac{2}{3}$

Think · Pair · Share

MP2 **3.** Why is it important to pay attention to the units of measurement in a word problem? Use the problems above to explain your answer.
Possible answer: The units can help you understand the problem. In problem 1, you need to convert kilograms to grams. In problem 2, if the scale on the model were not labeled as "gallons," it would have been confusing.

Unit 4 ■ Focus on Measurement and Data   **253**

Observational Assessment

Use page 253 to assess whether students are able to solve real-world problems using measurement. Take note of those students who struggle to model the word problems accurately. Be sure students are correctly using and converting the units of measurement.

Think·Pair·Share

Peer Collaboration Break the class into student pairs. Ask each pair to discuss their reasoning with their partner. Point out that there might be different explanations, as there are different ways to find the answers. Remind students to share the specific problems that they are describing in their answers. Ask for student pair volunteers to present their answers to the class. Have presenters answer the following questions:

- *What units of measure did you use? Why did you use these units of measure?*

- *What words in the word problems clued you into using the measurement units you used?*

- *What other units of measure can you think of?*

Return to the Essential Question

Reread the Lesson 28 Essential Question on page 250: *How can you use what you know about whole numbers, fractions, and decimals to solve measurement problems?*

Ask volunteers to use what they learned in this lesson to answer this question. (Possible response: You can convert measurements and use number operations to solve real-world problems. Use a model or a diagram to represent measurement quantities.)

Concept Application

Students may work independently on these pages in the classroom or at home. They may refer to the first four pages of the lesson to revisit the instruction or to see a worked-out example.

Common Errors and **Teaching Tips** may help you support student learning either in the classroom or as a follow-up for work done at home.

Teaching Tips

Items 1–2

Make sure students are using the correct units of measure. It may be necessary to check their units of measure before they finish solving the problem.

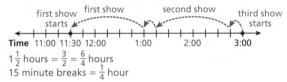

Independent Practice

Read the problem and answer the questions. Use the model to help you solve. Show your work.

1. The third showing of a movie starts at 3 P.M. The movie is $1\frac{1}{2}$ hours long. The theater workers spend 15 minutes cleaning the theater in between showings. At what time is the first showing of the movie?

   a. What do you need to find?

   I need to find the time the first show starts.

   b. What units will you use?

   I will use hours including $\frac{1}{2}$ hours and quarter hours.

   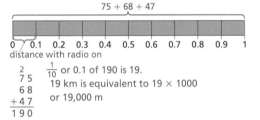

   first show starts   first show   second show   third show starts

   Time 11:00 11:30 12:00   1:00   2:00   3:00

   $1\frac{1}{2}$ hours $= \frac{3}{2} = \frac{6}{4}$ hours
   15 minute breaks $= \frac{1}{4}$ hour

   Answer The first showing of the movie starts at 11:30 A.M.

2. Three friends rent a car and take turns driving. Julia drives 75 kilometers, Imani drives 68 kilometers, and Kate drives 47 kilometers. They only used the car radio for 0.1 of the ride. How many meters did they travel with the radio on?

   a. What do you need to find?

   I need to find 0.1, or $\frac{1}{10}$, of the total distance, 75 + 68 + 47 kilometers.

   b. What units will you use?

   I need to use kilometers and then convert to meters.

   75 + 68 + 47

   0   0.1   0.2   0.3   0.4   0.5   0.6   0.7   0.8   0.9   1
   distance with radio on

   $\begin{array}{r} 2 \\ 75 \\ 68 \\ +47 \\ \hline 190 \end{array}$ $\frac{1}{10}$ or 0.1 of 190 is 19.
   19 km is equivalent to 19 × 1000
   or 19,000 m

   Answer They traveled 19,000 meters with the radio on.

Writing About Math

✏️ · **Write a Narrative Text** Ask students to pick one of the problems they have solved so far in this lesson and write a descriptive narrative about how they solved it. The narrative should include their methodology, specific details, and a sequence of how they solved the problem.

After students have written their paragraphs, have them exchange their paragraphs with a partner. Allow each partner to read the narrative text and see if the description can help the partner solve the same problem. If time allows, students could share how they would have solved the problem differently from their partner.

Lesson 28

Independent Practice

For exercises 3–5, circle the correct answer. You may use a model to help.

3. Marisa is decorating a room with streamers for a party. She uses 15 feet of red streamers and three times that length of blue streamers. How many yards of streamers does Marisa use altogether?

   a. 15 yards   **(b.)** 20 yards

   c. 45 yards   **d.** 60 yards

4. A worker at the grocery story cuts a 2-kilogram melon into 5 equal-sized pieces. What is the mass of each piece?

   a. 40 grams   **(b.)** 400 grams

   c. 40 kilograms   **d.** 400 kilograms

MP1 5. A DVD of a cartoon show has five 25-minute cartoons and one special cartoon that is longer. If the total length of the DVD is 3 hours, how long is the special cartoon?

   (a.) 55 minutes   **b.** 65 minutes

   c. 80 minutes   **d.** 125 minutes

MP5 6. Sunita and three friends share some frozen yogurt with extra topping. The yogurt costs $6.25 and the topping costs $3.75. If they split the cost equally, how much will each person pay?

   ▶ **Show your work.**
   Work may vary. Possible work:

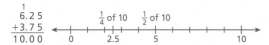

   $$\begin{array}{r} 1 \\ 6.2\,5 \\ +3.7\,5 \\ \hline 10.0\,0 \end{array}$$

   $\frac{1}{4}$ of 10 $\frac{1}{2}$ of 10

   Answer Each person will pay $2.50.

Common Errors

Item 6

Instead of adding the two costs together, students may mistakenly divide only the $6.25 or $3.75 into equal shares. Inform students that this is a multistep problem and discuss the steps needed to solve it.

Teaching Tips

Items 3-5

For multiple-choice answers, it can be helpful for students to cross out any answers that they know are incorrect or unreasonable. For example, in item 4, it is not reasonable to cut a 2-kilogram melon into 5 pieces and have each piece weigh 400 kilograms, so answer choice d cannot be correct.

Mathematical Practices

MP1	Make sense of problems and persevere in solving them.
Item 5: Students use time intervals to solve a word problem.	
MP5	Use appropriate tools strategically.
Item 6: Students create a model and solve a word problem.	

Teaching Tips

Items 7-9

The explanations for these questions are just as important as the correct answers. Be sure that student explanations include a conversion of the units of measure used in each problem.

Independent Practice

For problems 7 and 8, use the chart at the right.

MP7   **7.** Billy's school serves half-pint cartons of milk. Billy wants the school to let students pour their own milk from half-gallon containers. He says that this way, the school will recycle $\frac{1}{8}$ the number of milk cartons that it recycles now. Is Billy correct? Explain.

Yes, Billy is correct. Possible explanation: A half-pint is 1 cup, and there are 8 cups in a half-gallon carton. So the school can recycle 1 half-gallon carton instead of 8 half-pint cartons. One out of 8 is the fraction $\frac{1}{8}$.

Customary Units of Liquid Volume
1 cup (c) = 8 fluid ounces
1 pint (pt) = 2 cups
1 quart (qt) = 2 pints
1 gallon (gal) = 4 quarts

MP6   **8.** Mandy says that it is more difficult to convert customary units of weight than it is to convert metric units of mass. Do you agree? Why might Mandy think this is true? Explain.

Possible answer: I agree with Mandy. The customary units of weight are pounds and ounces. To convert pounds to ounces (larger unit to smaller unit), you multiply 16 by the number of pounds. The metric units of mass are kilograms and grams. To convert kilograms to grams (larger unit to smaller unit), you multiply 1000 by the number of kilograms. I think Mandy thinks it is easier to multiply with 1,000 as a factor than with 16 as a factor.

Solve the problems.

MP4   **9.** James takes swimming lessons at a large pool that is divided into lanes. Today, $\frac{1}{5}$ of the lanes are saved for slower swimmers to use. The combined width of the saved lanes is 5 meters. How wide is the whole pool? You can use the model below.

▭▬▶ **Show your work.** Work may vary. Possible work:

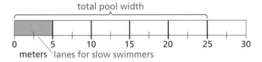

total pool width

0   5   10   15   20   25   30

meters   lanes for slow swimmers

Answer The whole pool is 25 meters wide.

Mathematical Practices

MP4	**Model with mathematics.**

Item 9: Students model the given information to solve a word problem.

MP6	**Attend to precision.**

Item 8: Students analyze two units of measure and determine a conclusion. They also justify their reasoning.

MP7	**Look for and make use of structure.**

Item 7: Students communicate their thought process to solve the problem.

Independent Practice

Solve the problems.

MP6 **10.** Curtis is shopping for a new fish tank. One is labeled as having a volume of 21 liters. He also likes two smaller tanks that have 9500 milliliter and 11,900 milliliter volumes. Which has a greater volume, the 21-liter tank or the two smaller tanks combined?

▭ · **Show your work.**
Work may vary. Possible work:
21 liters = 21,000 milliliters

$$\begin{array}{r} 1\,1 \\ 11{,}900 \\ +\ \ 9{,}500 \\ \hline 21{,}400 \end{array}$$ 21,400 > 21,000

Answer The two smaller tanks combined have a greater volume.

MP6 **11.** A baker is making loaves of cinnamon bread. He has 2 kilograms of flour. His recipe uses 385 grams of flour for each loaf. Does he have more or less flour than he needs to make 4 loaves? Tell how much more flour he needs or how much more he has than he needs.

▭ · **Show your work.**
Work may vary. Possible work:
The baker has 2 kilograms = 2000 grams

$$\begin{array}{r} 385 \\ \times\ \ 4 \\ \hline 20 \\ 320 \\ +1200 \\ \hline 1540 \end{array}\qquad \begin{array}{r} 2000 \\ -1540 \\ \hline 460 \end{array}$$

Answer The baker has more flour than he needs for 4 loaves. He has 460 more grams of flour than he needs.

MP1 **12.** Felix mixes cashews and pecans together to make a nut mixture. The weight of the pecans is three times the weight of the cashews. The mixture weighs 1 pound altogether. How many ounces do the cashews weigh?

Answer The cashews weigh 4 ounces.

▭ · **Justify your answer using words, drawings, or numbers.**
1 pound = 16 ounces.

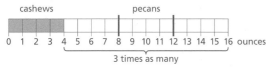

Common Errors

Items 10–12
Students may convert units of measure incorrectly. Have students check their conversions carefully before proceeding.

Mathematical Practices	
MP1	**Make sense of problems and persevere in solving them.**
Item 12: Students analyze a relationship and plan a solution.	
MP6	**Attend to precision.**
Item 10: Students calculate accurately while computing measurement units.	
Item 11: Students explain their reasoning using clear and precise language.	

Common Core Focus:

4.MD.3 Apply the area and perimeter formulas for rectangles in real world and mathematical problems.

OBJECTIVE

Understand how you use area and perimeter formulas for rectangles to solve problems.

ESSENTIAL QUESTION

Students will study the formulas for area and perimeter of a rectangle. Gaining this knowledge, students will be able to apply these formulas to real-world problems.

PREREQUISITE SKILLS

Use Item J on page 341 of the Foundational Skills Handbook, to help students understand how to find the area of a rectangle.

FLUENCY PRACTICE

Fluency practice is available at **sadlierconnect.com**.

Concept Development

Understand: Perimeter formulas for rectangles

■ Remind students that answers to measurement problems must be labeled with the correct measurement unit. The distance around the park is given in meters, so the answer must include the label *meters.*

■ Explain to students that *length* usually describes the longer sides of a rectangle while *width* is used to describe the shorter sides of a rectangle.

■ Have students try all three of the formulas to find the perimeter of one rectangle. In doing so, students see how all three formulas are related. Encourage students to choose one of the three formulas they prefer and to explain their formula preference.

Essential Question:
How can you use area and perimeter formulas for rectangles to solve problems?
4.MD.3

Words to Know:
length
width
formula

Guided Instruction

In this lesson you will learn how to apply area and perimeter formulas to different problem situations.

Understand: Perimeter formulas for rectangles

> The model at the right shows the distances of the park where Tate rides his scooter every Saturday. This Saturday Tate forgets to charge the battery for his electric scooter. He rides the scooter all the way around the park only once before the battery dies. How many meters is Tate able to ride the scooter?

To find out how far Tate rides, find the perimeter of the rectangular park. Perimeter is the total distance around a figure or shape.

One way to find the perimeter is to add the measures of all the sides. The measure of each side in one pair of opposite sides is called the length of the rectangle. The measure of each side in the other pair is called the width. Write an addition equation:

$$\text{Perimeter} = \underset{\text{length}}{10m} + \underset{\text{length}}{10m} + \underset{\text{width}}{8m} + \underset{\text{width}}{8m} = 36 \text{ meters}$$

Remember!
Opposite sides of a rectangle are sides that do not intersect.

➡ Tate rides his scooter 36 meters.

Since the opposite sides of a rectangle are the same length, you add the same length and width twice. This means you can also multiply to find the perimeter of a rectangle. You can:

Double the length and double the width. Then add. | or Use the Distributive Property. Add the length and width, and multiply the sum by 2.

$$\begin{aligned}\text{Perimeter} &= (2 \times \underset{\text{length}}{10}) + (2 \times \underset{\text{width}}{8}) \\ &= 20 + 16 \\ &= 36 \text{ meters}\end{aligned} \quad\Big|\quad \begin{aligned}\text{Perimeter} &= 2 \times (\underset{\text{length}}{10} + \underset{\text{width}}{8}) \\ &= 2 \times 18 \\ &= 36 \text{ meters}\end{aligned}$$

These methods work for all rectangles, so we describe each method with a formula. A formula is a rule that is written with symbols, such as ℓ for length and w for width. To find the perimeter you can use these formulas.

$$P = \ell + \ell + w + w \quad\quad P = (2 \times \ell) + (2 \times w) \quad\quad P = 2 \times (\ell + w)$$

258 Unit 4 ■ Focus on Measurement and Data

Words to Know

length: how long something is

Example: The measure of each side in the longer pair of opposite sides of a rectangle is called the length of the rectangle.

width: how wide something is

Example: The measure of each side in the shorter pair of opposite sides of a rectangle is called the width of the rectangle.

formula: a mathematical rule that is expressed with symbols

Example: $P = 2\ell + 2w$ is the formula for finding the perimeter of a rectangle.

Glossary can be found on pp. 347–350.

Lesson 29

Guided Instruction

Understand: Area formula for rectangles

Nicole is using a favorite photograph to cover a magnet she is making. The length and width of her photograph are shown at the right. Nicole glues the photo onto a magnetic sheet that is the same size as the photograph. How many square inches of a magnetic sheet does Nicole use to cover the whole back of the photo?

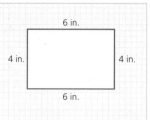

6 in.

4 in.   4 in.

6 in.

Since the photo is a rectangle, you can multiply its length and width to find its area.

$$Area = \overset{\text{length}}{6\text{in.}} \times \overset{\text{width}}{4\text{in.}}$$
$$= 24 \text{ square inches}$$

It takes 24 inch squares (1 inch on each side) to cover the rectangle. The area is 24 square inches.

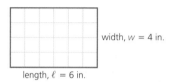

width, w = 4 in.

length, ℓ = 6 in.

➤ Nicole uses 24 square inches of a magnetic sheet.

The formula for the area of a rectangle is
$$A = \ell \times w.$$
You can use this formula to find the area of any rectangle, including squares.

If you know the area of a rectangle, you can also use the formula to find an unknown side length.
15 square inches = 3 × ?
15 ÷ 3 = 5

3 cm

?

 Write another factor pair for each area that you found above.
24 = 3 × 8, 15 = 1 × 15

Understand: Area formula for rectangles

■ In this presentation, students review how to find the area of a rectangle.

■ Lead students to see how the area formula leads to the same answer as covering the rectangle with one-inch unit squares. If students know the measure of the length and width, they can find the area using the area formula. Similarly, knowing the area and the length of one side allows students to find the missing side length.

■ Remind students that when they are given the area and a side length, they can write an unknown factor problem to find the length of the unknown side.

✏ After students have answered this question, ask a few volunteers to share their answers with the class. It may also be helpful to have students draw an example of what the new rectangles look like. Both rectangles would be longer, but not as wide.

Support English Language Learners

Students may have encountered the terms *area* and *perimeter* in earlier lessons, or in a previous grade. Take this opportunity to review these terms. Have students create vocabulary cards and connect each term with a drawing or model. For example, have students create a card with *perimeter* outlined in one color and the *area* shown in another color. Label each term on the card and then on the back list the *formulas* for each. Allow students to use these flash cards as they read the lesson.

Guided Instruction

Connect: Using formulas for perimeter and area Use this page to help students strengthen their understanding of how to find area and perimeter and how they are related.

- Students should understand that the information "30 feet of bricks" tells them the perimeter of the garden. They are also given the width of the garden. They need to find the length and area of the garden.

- Ask students which unknown they should find first based on the given information. Make the connection that once students solve to find the length, they have the information they need to find the area.

- Remind students to check their answers. An incorrect value for the length will give an incorrect answer for the area.

- After working through the page with students, extend the teaching by showing an area model (rectangle) with sides of 5 units and 12 units (partitioned into 10 + 2). Discuss the relationship between the model and the area of the rectangle: The model shows students how to use the Distributive Property to multiply 5 × 12, and the product is also the area of the rectangle.
$5 \times 12 = (5 \times 10) + (5 \times 2) = 50 + 10 = 60$
The area of the rectangle is 60 square units.

Lesson 29   Problem Solving: **Apply Area and Perimeter Formulas**

Guided Instruction

Connect: Using formulas for perimeter and area

A gardener has 30 feet of bricks that he can use to make the border of a rectangular garden. He will place bricks along each edge and place lights in the corners. The gardener wants to make the garden 5 feet wide. What is the greatest possible length for the garden? What will the area of a garden be with these measurements?

5 feet

You can use the formula for the perimeter of a rectangle to find the length of the garden, and then find its area.

Perimeter formulas
$P = \ell + \ell + w + w$
$P = (2 \times \ell) + (2 \times w)$
$P = 2 \times (\ell + w)$

Area formula
$A = \ell \times w$

Step 1

Identify the information given and what you need to find in the problem. The perimeter of the rectangle is 30 feet. The width of the rectangle is 5 feet.

You need to find the length of the largest rectangle that the gardener can make with 30 feet of bricks.

Step 2

Write an equation to represent the problem. You know that the perimeter is 2 times the sum of the length and the width. So, half of the perimeter equals the sum of the length and width. Half of the perimeter is 15.

Perimeter
$30 = 2 \times (\ell + 5)$,
so $15 = \ell + 5$.

Step 3

Solve the equation $15 = \ell + 5$ to find the unknown length.

$\ell = 10$

Check that the length ℓ of 10 feet will give you a perimeter of 30 feet.

$2 \times (10 + 5) = 2 \times 15 = 30$,
so 10 feet is correct.

Step 4

Now use the length of 10 feet to find the area of the garden.

length   width
Area = 10×5
= 50 square feet

➤ The greatest possible length for the garden is 10 feet. The garden will have an area of 50 square feet.

Math-to-Real-World Connection

Home Improvement Explain to students that owners of homes and office buildings often install or replace carpets. For this activity, tell students that they will have the opportunity to install carpet and a decorative border in a rectangular room. Provide all students with rectangle models with varying measurements. Have students find the area and perimeter of their rectangles. Then have them figure out how much carpet and border they need to decorate the room. Finally, you can have students decorate their rooms showing their new borders and carpet.

To extend the activity, have students research the cost of borders and carpet. Then, you can have students find the total cost to redecorate their rooms.

Guided Practice

Write an equation to find the area or perimeter of the rectangle. Outline the border or color the inside of the rectangle to represent your answer. Equations may vary.

1. Find the distance around all four sides of the rectangle.

   Equation __P = 4 × 10__   Perimeter __40 inches__

10 in.

10 in.

2. Find how many inch squares will cover the entire rectangle.

   Equation __A = 10 × 10__   Area __100 square inches__

10 in.

10 in.

For exercises 3 and 4, use the figure at the right. Write an equation to represent each. Then solve.

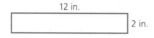

12 in.

2 in.

3. Peter is making bumper stickers for his baseball team. How much sticky paper does Peter need to make each sticker?

   Find the __area__ of the rectangle.

   Equation ___A = 12 × 2; A = 24 square inches___

   Answer __Peter needs 24 square inches of paper for each sticker.__

4. Peter decides to glue plastic string along the edge of each sticker. How much string will Peter need for all four sides?

   Find the __perimeter__ of the rectangle.

   Equation ___P = 2 × (12 + 2); P = 2 × 14 = 28___

   Answer __Peter will need 28 inches of string for all four sides.__

Think • Pair • Share

MP1 5. The area of a storage room floor is 36 square feet. Nancy knows that the length of the room is 9 feet long. She wants to buy shelves to fit all the way across the width of the room. What is the width of the room?

36 square feet ? ft

9 ft

   Find the __width__ of the rectangle.

   Equation ___36 = 9 × w; 36 ÷ 9 = w; w = 4___

   Answer __The width is 4 feet.__

Mathematical Practices

Mathematical Practice Standards underline the teaching and understanding of all concepts and skills presented. The emphasis of specific practices is noted throughout the guided and independent practice of this lesson.

MP1 **Make sense of problems and persevere in solving them.**

Item 5: Students use the formula for area and the model shown to find the value of an unknown side length.

Observational Assessment

Use page 261 to assess whether students are able to distinguish between area and perimeter and their ability to use the formulas for each to solve problems. Take note of those students who confuse the two. These students may need to review area and perimeter formulas before continuing on with the lesson.

Think•Pair•Share

Peer Collaboration Ask each student to find the width of the room. Then, have students divide into pairs and have each student explain how they found the unknown length. If some students struggle to determine the unknown side length, ask:

• *What information is given to you in the problem?*

• *What information are you trying to find?*

• *Which formula can you use to help you find the missing information?*

Return to the Essential Question

Reread the Lesson 29 Essential Question on page 258: *How can you use area and perimeter formulas for rectangles to solve problems?*

Ask volunteers to use what they learned in this lesson to answer this question. (Possible response: I can use the area formula to help me find the length, the width, or the area of different rectangles to help me solve problems. I can use perimeter formulas to help me find the length, the width, or the perimeter of different rectangles to help me solve problems.)

Invite as many volunteers as possible to express ideas about using area and perimeter formulas to find the length, the width, the area, or the perimeter of different rectangles in their own words.

Concept Application

Students may work independently on these pages in the classroom or at home. They may refer to the first four pages of the lesson to revisit the instruction or to see a worked-out example.

Common Errors and **Teaching Tips** may help you support student learning either in the classroom or as a follow-up for work done at home.

Teaching Tips

Items 4–5

Remind students there is more than one way to solve each of these items. Encourage them to use whichever formula or method they feel the most comfortable with.

Independent Practice

For exercises 1–3, find the area and perimeter of the rectangle at the right.

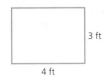

3 ft

4 ft

1. *Area = length × width*

   = __4__ × __3__ or 3 × 4

   = __12__

   The area of the rectangle is __12__ ___square___ feet.

2. *Perimeter = (2 × length) + (2 × width)*

   = (2 × __4__) + (2 × 3)

   = __8__ + __6__

   = __14__

   The perimeter of the rectangle is __14__ feet.

3. Use a different method to find the perimeter of the rectangle. Add the lengths of all four sides.

   4 + 4 + 3 + 3 = 8 + 6 = 14

Draw and label a model and then write an equation to represent the problem. Use *P* or *A* to represent what you need to find. Then solve the equation and answer the question. Equations and drawings may vary.

> **Perimeter formulas**
> $P = \ell + \ell + w + w$
> $P = (2 \times \ell) + (2 \times w)$
> $P = 2 \times (\ell + w)$
>
> **Area formula**
> $A = \ell \times w$

4. An architect is designing a wall of square windows. The wall is 20 feet wide and 10 feet high. How many squares of glass will fill the window if each square is 1 foot square?

   10 ft

   20 ft

   Equation ___$A = 20 \times 10$; $A = 200$ square feet___

   Answer ___Two hundred squares of glass will fill the window.___

5. Shelby wants to wrap a string of small lights around the border of her bedroom window. Her window is 2 feet wide and 4 feet tall. How many feet of stringed lights does Shelby need to go around the whole window?

   2 ft

   4 ft

   Equation ___$P = (2 \times 2) + (2 \times 4)$; $P = 4 + 8 = 12$ feet___

   Answer ___Shelby needs 12 feet of lights.___

Talking About Math

Defending a Position Divide students into small groups of three or four. Provide each group with a different problem involving either area or perimeter. Have each group determine which is needed to solve their problem. Then have the group share their problem situation and defend their decision to the class. Make sure students use appropriate facts and relevant details to support their decision. Students should also add a visual display of the rectangle to support their solution. Each student should be encouraged to take an active role in presenting their problem and solution to the class.

Lesson 29

Independent Practice

Find the perimeter of the rectangle or square. Write an equation and show your work. Equations may vary.

6.

12 cm

12 cm

12 + 12 + 12 + 12 =
Perimeter 48 cm

7.

3 m

18 m

(2 × 3) + (2 × 18) =
Perimeter 6 + 36 = 42 m

8. a rectangle 17 inches long and 11 inches wide

(2 × 17) + (2 × 11) =
Perimeter 34 + 22 = 56 inches

9. a square with side length 25 feet

Perimeter 4 × 25 = 100 feet

Find the area of the rectangle or square. Write an equation and show your work. Equations may vary.

10.

7 in.

2 in.

Area 2 × 7 = 14 square inches

11.

9 km + 10 km

6 km

6 × 19 = (6 × 10) + (6 × 9)
Area = 60 + 54 = 114 square km

12. a square with side length 15 miles

Area 225 square miles

```
   15
 ×15
   25
   50
   50
+100
  225
```

15 miles

15 miles

13. a rectangle 16 inches long and 5 inches wide

5 × 16 = (5 × 10) + (5 × 6)
Area = 50 + 30 = 80 square inches

Teaching Tips

Items 8-9
If students are having trouble finding the perimeter or area for these items, encourage them to draw a picture of the rectangle and label it before writing the equation.

Item 11
Tell students that this rectangle is set up to use the Distributive Property. Have students review the Distributive Property by defining it in their own words.

Item 12
Only the length of one side of a square is given. Ask students why only one side length is needed to determine the area of a square.

Digital Connection

Interactive Whiteboard Provide students with a specific number of squares on an interactive whiteboard. Have students take turns manipulating the squares into as many different rectangles as possible. For example, 6 squares can make a 1 × 6 rectangle or a 2 × 3 rectangle. Once all possible rectangles for a specific number of squares have been formed, have students take turns labeling the length and width of each rectangle. Next, have students take turns finding the area and perimeter for each rectangle. Continue with a different number of squares until all students have had at least one turn at the whiteboard.

Common Errors

Item 14

Students may be quick to agree with George because the area and the perimeter of a rectangle are rarely the same. Encourage students to draw all possible models to find the measurements for a perimeter of 16 inches and then all possible models to find the measurements for an area of 16 square inches. Then have students compare all of their drawings to see if any have the same measurements.

Teaching Tips

Item 15

Some students may not know where to begin to solve this problem. Have students look back through the lesson to see what the least amount of information needed to solve a problem is. Lead them to see that they need to know the measurement of at least one side and either the total area or perimeter of the rectangle.

Lesson 29   Problem Solving: **Apply Area and Perimeter Formulas**

Independent Practice

MP2 **14.** Ralph draws a square and writes the equations $P = 16$ inches and $A = 16$ square inches. George says that Ralph has made a mistake because the perimeter and the area can never have the same number. Do you agree or disagree with George?
Possible answer: I disagree with George. Usually, the perimeter and area of a rectangle or square have different numbers but, a square with side lengths of 4 inches is the exception. Ralph's square must be 4 inches on each side.

MP7 **15.** What is the least amount of information that you need to find an unknown length of a side in a given rectangle, such as the one shown at the right?
Answers will vary. Possible answer: You need to know the length of at least one side and the area or the perimeter of the rectangle.

Solve the problems.

MP5 **16.** The fourth graders are having a class party at school. To make one big rectangular table for everyone to sit at, they push two tables together. One table is 8 feet long and 5 feet wide and the other table is a square, 5 feet on each side. What is the perimeter of the combined table that the students make?

> **Show your work.** Work may vary. Possible work:
width = 5 ft
length = 8 + 5 = 13 ft
Perimeter = (2 × 5) + (2 × 13) = 10 + 26 = 36

Answer The perimeter of the combined table is 36 feet.

MP1 **17.** Lisa is choosing new carpet for her bedroom floor. Her bedroom is 12 feet long and 10 feet wide. If the carpet costs $5 per square foot, how much will a carpet to cover Lisa's whole bedroom floor cost?

> **Show your work.** Work may vary. Possible work:
100 + 20 = 120 square feet
120 × 5 = $600

Answer The carpet will cost $600.

264 Unit 4 ■ Focus on Measurement and Data

Mathematical Practices	
MP1	**Make sense of problems and persevere in solving them.**
Item 17: Students analyze the provided information to plan a solution.	
MP2	**Reason abstractly and quantitatively.**
Item 14: Students consider formulas in order to justify their reasoning.	
MP5	**Use appropriate tools strategically.**
Item 16: Students model a problem situation in order to find an answer.	
MP7	**Look for and make use of structure.**
Item 15: Students evaluate the structure of rectangles.	

Lesson 29

Independent Practice

MP5 **18.** The fabric store sells scrap pieces of fabric that are all 1 yard wide. A rectangular piece is labeled "9 square yards." How long is this piece of fabric? Sketch the rectangle to help you find the unknown side length.

▸ **Show your work.** Possible work:

9 yards

| 9 square yards | 1 yard

Answer The piece of fabric is 9 yards long.

MP4 **19.** A town is placing a wire fence around a rectangular field. The town orders 100 yards of fencing, which is the exact amount needed to surround the entire field. One end of the field is 30 yards long. What are the lengths of the other three sides of the field?

▸ **Show your work.**
Possible work: If one side is 30 yards, then the opposite side is 30 yards, too. $100 - 30 - 30 = 40$; 40 is the combined length of the other two opposite sides, so the length of each of these sides is $40 \div 2 = 20$.

Answer The lengths of the other three sides of the field are 30 yards, 20 yards, and 20 yards.

MP7 **20.** Gary's mother is replacing the tiles in a rectangular section of the bathroom floor. Each tile is square with an area of 4 square inches. Gary's mother uses 32 tiles (without cutting any tiles). Gary says that there is only one possible length and width for the rectangular section of the floor. His friend Angela says that there is more than one possible rectangular shape. Who is correct?

Answer Angela is correct.   Possible justification: A square tile with area 4 square inches will have a side length of 2 inches.

▸ **Justify your answer using words, drawings, or numbers.**
So, the length and width of the rectangular area will both be even numbers. The length and width must have a product of 32. There are exactly two pairs of even numbers with a product of 32: 2 and 16, and 4 and 8. So the length and width could be 2 inches and 16 inches, or 4 inches and 8 inches.

MP7 **21.** Tabitha is drawing models of rectangles that have a perimeter of 4 yards. Each side length is a whole number of feet. How many different models can Tabitha draw?

Answer Tabitha can draw 3 different models.

▸ **Justify your answer using words, drawings, or numbers.**
Possible justification: 4 yards = 4×3 or 12 feet. If the perimeter is 12 feet, the sum of the length and width will be 6 feet. The whole-number pairs with a sum of 6 are: 1 and 5, 2 and 4, and 3 and 3.

Unit 4 ■ Focus on Measurement and Data **265**

Teaching Tips

Item 20

Guide students to see that they must first find the side length of the square tile before they can answer the problem. It may also be helpful for students to realize they can only find lengths and widths that are even numbers as each tile has a side length of 2 inches, which is an even number.

Item 21

Help students figure out that they must first convert yards to feet in order to solve this problem.

Mathematical Practices

MP4	**Model with mathematics.**

Item 19: Students interpret the missing information by explaining the relationship of the given information and the formula for perimeter.

MP5	**Use appropriate tools strategically.**

Item 18: Students can use a model to solve the problem.

MP7	**Look for and make use of structure.**

Item 20: Students evaluate information to solve the problem.

Item 21: Students search for patterns in order to find the information necessary to solve the problem.

Common Core Focus:

4.MD.4 Make a line plot to display a data set of measurements in fractions of a unit (1/2, 1/4, 1/8). Solve problems involving addition and subtraction of fractions by using information presented in line plots.

OBJECTIVE

Use a line plot to display measurement data and draw conclusions from the displayed data.

ESSENTIAL QUESTION

Have students read the Essential Question and brainstorm a list of possible answers. In this lesson, students combine their prior knowledge and experience as they use number lines to display and interpret data.

PREREQUISITE SKILLS

Use Item K on page 342 of the Foundational Skills Handbook to review how to use a tally chart to make a line plot.

FLUENCY PRACTICE

Fluency practice is available at **sadlierconnect.com**.

Concept Development

Understand: Using number lines to display data

■ An important part of representing data is ensuring that students know how to properly label the number line. Point out that the line plot does not need to start at 0, as they can see in the presentation. The tick marks should be evenly spaced. The scale should be such that all data can be accurately recorded.

■ The goal of a line plot is to show data in an organized way. Ask students to explain why it is easier to see which length is most common from the line plot than it is from the original data display.

Lesson
30 Problem Solving:
Use Line Plots

Essential Question:
How can representing data on a line plot help you to better understand and interpret a set of measurements?
4.MD.4

Words to Know:
line plot
data

Guided Instruction

In this lesson you will learn how to display measurements on a line plot and make observations about the data.

Understand: Using number lines to display data

Debbie collects some red leaves from a maple tree. She is surprised to see that the leaves are different lengths, even though they are from the same tree. Debbie measures the leaves to the nearest eighth of an inch. How can you display her data in a more organized way?

Maple Leaf Lengths (to nearest $\frac{1}{8}$ inch)			
$2\frac{5}{8}$	$2\frac{2}{8}$	$2\frac{6}{8}$	$2\frac{4}{8}$
$2\frac{4}{8}$	$2\frac{4}{8}$	$2\frac{6}{8}$	2
3	$2\frac{1}{8}$	3	$2\frac{3}{8}$

You can organize and display data with a line plot. A line plot uses symbols or marks to show how many times each number, or measurement, appears in a set of data. The numbers or measurements are shown along a number line.

The least and greatest measurements in Debbie's data are 2 inches and 3 inches. Draw and label a number line to show these numbers. Use tick marks and labels to show all the $\frac{1}{8}$-units in between.

Now display the data. Draw an X above the location on the number line for each piece of data. If a piece of data appears more than once, draw an X above the previous X for each.

Maple Leaf Lengths

Title the line plot and label the number line with the units used.

➡ The line plot shows the data in a more organized way.

266 Unit 4 ■ Focus on Measurement and Data

Words to Know

line plot: a graph used to organize a set of data on a number line, with symbols to represent the data

data: facts or information

Glossary can be found on pp. 347-350.

MORE ONLINE ▸ sadlierconnect.com   Lesson 30

Guided Instruction

Understand: Reading and using line plots

What information can you learn from the line plot of Debbie's leaf data?

The line plot shows all 12 of Debbie's measurement data in order from least to greatest number of inches.

Maple Leaf Lengths

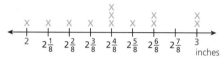

Maple Leaf Lengths (to nearest $\frac{1}{8}$ inch)			
$2\frac{5}{8}$	$2\frac{2}{8}$	$2\frac{6}{8}$	$2\frac{4}{8}$
$2\frac{4}{8}$	$2\frac{4}{8}$	$2\frac{6}{8}$	2
3	$2\frac{1}{8}$	3	$2\frac{3}{8}$

➡ Looking at the line plot, some of the things you can learn are:

• There are 12 Xs so there are 12 measurements altogether.

• All of the leaves are between 2 and 3 inches long.

• There are 2 leaves that are $2\frac{6}{8}$ inches long and 2 leaves that are 3 inches long.

• Three leaves are $2\frac{4}{8}$ inches long.

• No leaves are $2\frac{7}{8}$ inches long.

✏ Use the information in the line plot to answer these questions.

• Where would you draw the X for a leaf that measures $2\frac{1}{4}$ inches long? Explain.
I would draw the X above $2\frac{2}{8}$ because $2\frac{2}{8}$ and $2\frac{1}{4}$ are equivalent fractions.

• How many of Debbie's leaves are longer than $2\frac{1}{2}$ inches? How do you know?
Five of the Xs on the line plot are to the right of the location for $2\frac{4}{8}$. Since $2\frac{4}{8}$ is equivalent to $2\frac{1}{2}$, five of Debbie's leaves are longer than $2\frac{1}{2}$ inches.

• What is the difference between the longest leaf and the shortest leaf that Debbie measured?
The difference is $3 - 2$, or 1 inch.

Understand: Reading and using line plots

■ Invite students to share any other observations that they made based on the line plot.

■ Point out that even though no leaves are $2\frac{7}{8}$ inches long, that number is still included on the line plot. Have students explain why that tick mark must be there and why it might be confusing to leave a value off the line plot simply because it has no data. Leaving the tick mark unlabeled or off the number line completely would interfere with the accuracy of the number line.

✏ ▸ After students have answered each question, ask a few volunteers to read their answers aloud. Encourage students to relate their answers back to the line plot as they describe their reasoning. Explain that the line plot provides data that they can use to determine additional information about Debbie's maple leaves.

Support English Language Learners

To experience success with these skills, students need to understand key action words, such as *display* and *organize*. Review the meaning of *display* and help students see that the action of drawing Xs above the number line creates a display of the data. Show students the similarities between a line plot and the number lines with which they have already worked.

Help students understand the meaning of the term *organize* by using synonyms. Point out that students are organizing data so that it is placed in an orderly manner. Ask students to describe other real-world items that they see organized for easier use, such as books in a library or items in a grocery store. Explain that, like data on a line plot, these items are organized so they can easily be found and used.

Connect: Displaying and interpreting data

Use this page to help students strengthen their understanding of how to display and interpret data on a line plot.

■ If students have trouble finding the greatest and least data values, suggest that they rewrite the values, ordering them from least to greatest.

■ Point out that, just as on a number line, the value between the points on the line plot should remain equal. In this line plot, the points are $\frac{1}{4}$ hour apart.

■ Ask students to read the question at the end of the problem carefully. Look for key words that identify what type of computation they should use. The problem asks for the *difference*, so students should use subtraction.

Connect: Displaying and interpreting data

Devan asks some friends how much time they spend eating dinner. He asks them to give their answers to the nearest quarter hour. Devan records their answers in a line plot. What is the difference between the greatest amount of time and the least amount of time?

Time Eating Dinner (to nearest $\frac{1}{4}$ hour)

$\frac{3}{4}$	$\frac{1}{2}$	$\frac{1}{4}$
$\frac{1}{2}$	1	$\frac{3}{4}$
$\frac{3}{4}$	$\frac{3}{4}$	$\frac{1}{2}$

Time Eating Dinner

You can use the line plot to answer the question.

Step 1

Look at the number line used for the line plot.

The number with the least value is $\frac{1}{4}$, and the number 1 has the greatest value. All of the points on the line are the same distance apart, so, Devan used fourths as the scale.

Step 2

Use the number line on the line plot to find the difference between the greatest amount of time and the least amount of time.

$$\frac{4}{4} - \frac{1}{4} = \frac{3}{4}$$

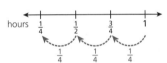

▶ The difference between the greatest amount of time spent eating and the least amount of time is $\frac{3}{4}$ hour.

Math-to-Science Connection

Experimental Data Recording and analyzing data are important skills when conducting experiments. As students conduct some of their own experiments, knowing how to organize and display data becomes critically important. When manipulating and using this data, students see that mathematics and science are interrelated.

Ask students to collect and display their own data. In small groups, have students collect leaves from trees that are located on school property. Then have them measure the leaves to the nearest $\frac{1}{4}$ inch. Ask each group to display their measurements on a line plot. Students should summarize the information about the leaves by using the data they collected.

MORE ONLINE sadlierconnect.com   Lesson 30

Guided Practice

For exercises 1–4, use the data shown at the right.

Amount of Rain for Rainy Days in May (in inches)			
$\frac{3}{4}$	$\frac{1}{8}$	$\frac{1}{4}$	$\frac{1}{2}$
$\frac{1}{8}$	$\frac{1}{4}$	$\frac{3}{4}$	$\frac{1}{8}$

1. Use the smallest unit to rename the amounts of rain as equivalent fractions.

   $\frac{1}{4}$ inch = $\frac{2}{8}$ inch

   $\frac{1}{2}$ inch = $\frac{4}{8}$ inch

   $\frac{3}{4}$ inch = $\frac{6}{8}$ inch

2. Find the least and greatest amounts of rain in the data.

   Least amount: $\frac{1}{8}$ inch   Greatest amount: $\frac{3}{4}$ inch

3. Label the number line below to show the $\frac{1}{8}$-inch units.

   inches $\frac{1}{8}$ $\frac{2}{8}$ $\frac{3}{8}$ $\frac{4}{8}$ $\frac{5}{8}$ $\frac{6}{8}$

4. Display the data. Then write a title for the line plot.

   Amount of Rain for Rainy Days in May

   ```
   X
   X       X               X
   X       X       X       X
   ```
   inches $\frac{1}{8}$ $\frac{2}{8}$ $\frac{3}{8}$ $\frac{4}{8}$ $\frac{5}{8}$ $\frac{6}{8}$

Use your line plot to solve the problems.

5. What is the total number of days that it rained in May?

   There are __8__ Xs on the line plot.   It rained on __8__ days.

6. What is the difference between the greatest and least amounts of rain?

   $\frac{6}{8} - \frac{1}{8} = \frac{5}{8}$ inch

⚊ **Think • Pair • Share**

MP1 7. Use the line plot to find the total amount of rain for rainy days in May. Explain your method.

   Possible answer: The total amount is $\frac{3}{8} + \frac{4}{8} + \frac{4}{8} + \frac{12}{8} = \frac{23}{8} = 2\frac{7}{8}$ inches of rain. My method was to multiply each fraction that had Xs by the number of Xs and then add the products.

Unit 4 ▪ Focus on Measurement and Data   **269**

Mathematical Practices

Mathematical Practice Standards underline the teaching and understanding of all concepts and skills presented. The emphasis of specific practices is noted throughout the guided and independent practice of this lesson.

MP1	**Make sense of problems and persevere in solving them.**

Item 7: Students analyze data and plan a solution.

Observational Assessment

Use page 269 to assess whether students are able to display and analyze data on a line plot. Watch for students to isolate the data with the greatest and least values and identify equivalent fractions with like denominators to properly label the line plot.

⚊ **Think•Pair•Share**

Peer Collaboration Suggest that students write equations to model their solutions. Have them work in small groups to share their equations. Ask groups to answer questions about their solutions:

- *How did you use the line plot to help determine your solution process?*

- *Which operation(s) did you use to find the total?*

- *How did your equation differ from others in your group?*

Return to the Essential Question

Reread the Lesson 30 Essential Question on page 266: *How can representing data on a line plot help you to better understand and interpret a set of measurements?*

Ask volunteers to use what they learned in this lesson to answer this question. (Possible response: I can see patterns in the data and use that information to answer questions about the data when it is organized into a line plot.)

Have volunteers explain why they think data is more useful when it is presented in an organized way.

Concept Application

Students may work independently on these pages in the classroom or at home. They may refer to the first four pages of the lesson to revisit the instruction or to see a worked-out example.

Common Errors and **Teaching Tips** may help you support student learning either in the classroom or as a follow-up for work done at home.

Common Errors

Item 1

Students may label the first three tick marks with the three weights listed in the table. Remind students that the number line represents a scale. The rate of change between each tick mark must be equivalent. Since the rate of change between the first and second tick marks is $\frac{1}{8}$, that rate of change must be used to determine the labels for the remaining tick marks.

Item 2

Students may think that they only need to write each weight once. Remind students to list the weight of each package, even if the weight is listed more than once.

Teaching Tips

Item 1

Point out that even though there are 6 sections in the table, there are only 5 pieces of data.

Item 5

Explain that even though there are two packages with the heaviest weight, the weight of the heaviest package is still $\frac{7}{8}$ pound.

Lesson 30   Problem Solving: **Use Line Plots**

Independent Practice

1. Complete the line plot to display the given data.

Weight of Packages of Cheese (in pounds)

$\frac{7}{8}$	$\frac{2}{8}$	$\frac{1}{8}$
$\frac{2}{8}$	$\frac{7}{8}$	

Weight of Packages of Cheese

pounds $\frac{1}{8}$ $\frac{2}{8}$ $\frac{3}{8}$ $\frac{4}{8}$ $\frac{5}{8}$ $\frac{6}{8}$ $\frac{7}{8}$

2. Write the weights of the packages of cheese in order from least to greatest.

$\underline{\frac{1}{8}, \frac{2}{8}, \frac{2}{8}, \frac{7}{8}, \frac{7}{8}}$

3. How many packages were weighed? __5__ packages

4. What is the weight of the lightest package? $\frac{1}{8}$ pound

5. What is the weight of the heaviest package? $\frac{7}{8}$ pound

6. What is the difference in the weights of the heaviest and lightest packages?

$\underline{\frac{7}{8}} - \underline{\frac{1}{8}} = \underline{\frac{6}{8}}$ pound   The difference in weights is $\frac{6}{8}$ pound.

Solve the problem.

MP5 7. Susie recorded the distances for her walks. The numbers of miles are shown at the right. To show this data on a line plot, what numbers should Susie use on the number line? Explain.

Distance Walked in One Week (in miles)

$1\frac{1}{2}$	$1\frac{1}{4}$	$1\frac{3}{4}$	$1\frac{1}{2}$
$1\frac{1}{4}$	$1\frac{3}{4}$	$1\frac{1}{2}$	$1\frac{1}{4}$

The first number should be $1\frac{1}{4}$ and the last number should be $1\frac{3}{4}$. The number scale should be fourths, since all of the numbers can be written as fourths. So, the number line will show $1\frac{1}{4}$, $1\frac{2}{4}$, and $1\frac{3}{4}$.

Writing About Math

◄▬ ▸ **Write an Informative Text** Ask students to write a paragraph that gives instructions on how to take a group of measurement data and display it on a line plot. Encourage students to describe the procedure for determining the scale and how to record multiple data points.

Ask volunteers to read their paragraphs aloud. While students are reading, ask other students to follow the stated process and see if it provides a complete explanation of how to create a line plot. If necessary, allow students to revise their paragraphs to add any missing instructions.

Independent Practice

MP2 **8.** Adam measured the lengths of the pencils in his desk. Make a line plot to display his data.

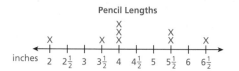

Pencil Lengths

			X						
			X		X				
X		X	X		X		X		
inches 2 $2\frac{1}{2}$ 3 $3\frac{1}{2}$ 4 $4\frac{1}{2}$ 5 $5\frac{1}{2}$ 6 $6\frac{1}{2}$

Pencil Lengths (in inches)

$3\frac{1}{2}$	4	$5\frac{1}{2}$	4
4	$5\frac{1}{2}$	2	$6\frac{1}{2}$

For exercises 9–14, use the line plot from exercise 8 to answer the questions.

9. How many pencils does Adam have altogether?

8 pencils

10. How many more 4-inch long pencils are there than 2-inch long pencils?

2 pencils

11. How much longer is Adam's longest pencil than his shortest pencil?

$4\frac{1}{2}$ inches

12. What is the total length of the pencils longer than 4 feet?

$(2 \times 5\frac{1}{2}) + 6\frac{1}{2} = 11 + 6\frac{1}{2} = 17\frac{1}{2}$ inches

13. What is the combined length of all of the pencils?

$2 + 3\frac{1}{2} + (3 \times 4) + 17\frac{1}{2} = 35$ inches

14. Adam finds another pencil that is $2\frac{2}{4}$ inches long in his backpack. Which of these best describes how Adam should change his line plot to include this data?

a. He should add another tick mark for $2\frac{2}{4}$ on the number line.

b. He should add another tick mark for $\frac{10}{4}$ on the number line.

c. He should add 1 X above $2\frac{1}{2}$ inches.

d. He should extend the number line and draw 2 Xs above $\frac{1}{2}$.

Teaching Tips

Items 10–12

Students will have difficulty answering these problems if they have created their line plot incorrectly. Check students' work and have them correct any errors in their line plots before allowing students to move on to these questions.

Item 13

Suggest that students use the solution to problem 12 when answering this problem.

Mathematical Practices

MP2	**Reason abstractly and quantitatively.**

Item 8: Students create an accurate representation of the problem.

MP5	**Use appropriate tools strategically.**

Item 7: Students analyze data to create an accurate graph.

Independent Practice

Common Errors

Item 18

Students may add each weight once when it is used on the line plot. Remind students that each X represents one apple. Suggest that students write an equation to find the total weight.

Teaching Tips

Item 15

If students have difficulty determining which number of tick marks is correct, suggest that students draw the line plot to support their answers.

Item 16

Remind students of the type of data they have been using in this lesson: measurement data.

Lesson 30   Problem Solving: Use Line Plots

Independent Practice

MP3 **15.** George is making a line plot to show the ages of children in a music group. He lists the ages in years: 13, $10\frac{1}{2}$, $13\frac{1}{2}$, 12, 14, 13, $10\frac{1}{2}$. He says that the number line on his line plot will have exactly 5 tick marks. Mandy says that the number line will show exactly 7 tick marks. Liz says that it must show at least 8 tick marks. Who is right? Explain. What numbers will the number line show?

Liz is right. Possible explanation: The line plot must show $10\frac{1}{2}$ and 14 and all the points between that represent halves, including whole numbers. The number line will show: $10\frac{1}{2}$, 11, $11\frac{1}{2}$, 12, $12\frac{1}{2}$, 13, $13\frac{1}{2}$, and 14.

MP6 **16.** Lisa is trying to choose a name for her new kitten. She writes her four top choices and then asks each of her 12 friends to choose one of the names. She places an X above the name that each friend chooses. Her friend Sandy says that Lisa is making a line plot. Lisa says that it is not really a line plot. Who is right?

Lisa is right. Possible answer: A line plot has to include a number line. There is no number line on Lisa's graph.

For exercises 17 and 18, use the line plot.

Weight of Apples in 1 Bag

MP1 **17.** How much heavier is the heaviest apple in the bag than the lightest apple?

Show your work. Work may vary. Possible work:
The heaviest apple weighs $\frac{7}{8}$ pound. The lightest apple weighs $\frac{1}{4}$ pound.
$\frac{1}{4} = \frac{2}{8}$
$\frac{7}{8} - \frac{2}{8} = \frac{5}{8}$

Answer ___The heaviest apple is $\frac{5}{8}$ pound heavier than the lightest apple.___

MP1 **18.** How much does the whole bag of apples weigh?

Show your work. Work may vary. Possible work:
$\frac{2}{8} + \frac{12}{8} + 1 + \frac{7}{8} = 1 + \frac{21}{8} = 1 + 2\frac{5}{8}$

Answer ___The whole bag of apples weighs $3\frac{5}{8}$ pounds.___

$\frac{1}{4} = \frac{2}{8}$	$\frac{2}{8}$	
$\frac{3}{8}$	$4 \times \frac{3}{8} = \frac{12}{8}$	
$\frac{1}{2} = \frac{4}{8}$	$2 \times \frac{4}{8} = \frac{8}{8}$	
$\frac{7}{8}$	$\frac{7}{8}$	

272   Unit 4 ■ Focus on Measurement and Data

Mathematical Practices

MP1	**Make sense of problems and persevere in solving them.**
Item 17: Students use a line plot to solve a problem.	
Item 18: Students analyze data and plan a solution.	
MP3	**Construct viable arguments and critique the reasoning of others.**
Item 15: Students analyze and respond to a problem solution.	
MP6	**Attend to precision.**
Item 16: Students carefully formulate full explanations.	

Lesson 30

Independent Practice

Teaching Tips

Item 21

Ask students to explain which distances they consider a good estimate for 3 feet. Have them explain the benefits and drawbacks to rounding. Discuss why precise measurements might be preferred.

For exercises 19–21, use the data below.
Michelle reads that 1 yard is about the distance from the tip of your nose to your fingertip, with your arm stretched out to your side. She measures this length for herself and some other people. The list below shows Michelle's data.

Distance from Nose to Fingertip (feet)

| $2\frac{4}{6}$ | $2\frac{1}{6}$ | $2\frac{4}{6}$ | $2\frac{2}{6}$ | $2\frac{2}{6}$ | 3 | $2\frac{3}{6}$ | $2\frac{4}{6}$ | 3 | $2\frac{2}{6}$ | 2 |

MP5 **19.** Make a line plot of Michelle's measurement data.

> **Show your work.**
Work may vary. Possible work:

Answer

Distance From Nose to Fingertip

```
                        X                 X
                        X                 X
        X       X       X       X    X    X           X
        X       X       X       X    X    X           X
  <--+---+---+---+---+---+---+--->
feet    2      2 1/6   2 2/6  2 3/6  2 4/6  2 5/6   3
```

MP4 **20.** Michelle makes a line plot for her data that starts at 2 feet and ends at 3 feet. Does the number line for Michelle's plot still represent the size of each measurement as a distance from 0 feet? Possible answer: Yes, the

Answer measurements labeled on the number line are still distances from 0. The full distance is not shown.
> **Justify your answer using words, drawings, or numbers.**
Possible justification: To really show the distance from 0, the number line could start at 0. But Michelle's number line will still show the measurements in order from least to greatest.

MP2 **21.** Based on Michelle's data, is the distance from your nose to your fingertip a good estimate of one yard?

Answer Possible answer: It is not a good estimate for about half of the people that Michelle measured.
> **Justify your answer using words, drawings, or numbers.**
Possible justification: One yard equals 3 feet. Six distances were equal to $2\frac{1}{2}$ feet or greater, so they could be rounded up to 3 feet or 1 yard. But five measurements were less than $2\frac{1}{2}$ feet, so they were not close to 1 yard.

Unit 4 ■ Focus on Measurement and Data **273**

Mathematical Practices

MP2	**Reason abstractly and quantitatively.**

Item 21: Students pay attention to all mathematical language.

MP4	**Model with mathematics.**

Item 20: Students interpret the solution in the context of a situation.

MP5	**Use appropriate tools strategically.**

Item 19: Students use tables and create graphs accurately.

Common Core Focus:

4.MD.5a An angle is measured with reference to a circle with its center at the common endpoint of the rays, by considering the fraction of the circular arc between the points where the two rays intersect the circle. An angle that turns through 1/360 of a circle is called a "one-degree angle," and can be used to measure angles; **4.MD.5b** An angle that turns through *n* one-degree angles is said to have an angle measure of *n* degrees.

OBJECTIVE

Relate measures of angles to fractions of circles and use these fractions to determine the measure of an angle in degrees.

ESSENTIAL QUESTION

Students are now building angles with measures greater than one by adding measures that are $\frac{1}{360}$ of a circle. Help students make this connection to a circle to give meaning to the size of 1 degree.

FLUENCY PRACTICE

Fluency practice is available at **sadlierconnect.com**.

Concept Development

Understand: Angles and parts of angles

■ Remind students that every circle has a center and each point on the circle is equidistant from the center.

■ It is important that students understand that you can extend the lengths of the sides of an angle without changing the angle measurement.

▪ Suggest that students try flipping the angles horizontally or rotating the angles to see if the angles are still the same size.

Understand Angle Measures

Guided Instruction

In this lesson you will learn about angles and angle measures.

Understand: Angles and parts of angles

The positions of the hands of a clock show the time. What geometric figure do the two hands of a clock form?

Essential Question:
How is the measure of an angle related to a circle?

4.MD.5a; 4.MD.5b

Words to Know:
 ray
 point
 endpoint
 angle
 vertex
 degree (°)
 one-degree angle
 right angle
 straight angle

To decide what geometric figure is formed by a clock's hand, you need to learn about rays and angles.

A ray starts at a point called an endpoint and goes on straight in one direction forever.

Two rays that share the same endpoint form an angle. The two rays of an angle are the sides of the angle. Their shared endpoint is the vertex of the angle.

The hour and minute hands of the clock are like two rays that begin at the same point. That point in the center of the clock is like the vertex of an angle.

➡ The two hands of a clock form an angle.

Changing the length of the sides of an angle does not change the angle measure.
The angles below are all the same size as the clock angle.

▪ Trace one of the angles. Then move the traced angle to match the vertex and rays of another angle. What do you notice?
The rays are different lengths, but the openings between the rays are the same.

Words to Know

ray: the part of a line that starts at an endpoint and goes on in one direction forever

point: an exact location in space

endpoint: the point at either end of a line segment or the starting point of a ray

angle: formed when two rays share the same endpoint

vertex: the shared endpoints of two rays that form an angle

Glossary can be found on pp. 347–350.

Guided Instruction

Understand: Angle measures and fractions of a circle

Carrie opens her laptop computer to the angle shown at the right. What is the measure of the angle of Carrie's open laptop?

To answer this question, you need to find an angle measure. The unit of measure for angles is the degree and its symbol is °.

Think of the vertex of an angle as the center of a circle. An angle forms as it turns through the circle. A circle measures 360 degrees, so a one-degree angle is $\frac{1}{360}$ of a circle. The measure of an angle is the number of one-degree angles it turns through.

A one-degree angle turns through just $\frac{1}{360}$ of a circle.

A 90° angle turns through $\frac{90}{360}$, or $\frac{1}{4}$, of a circle. This is a right angle.

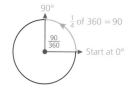

$\frac{1}{4}$ of 360 = 90

$\frac{90}{360}$

Start at 0°

A 180° angle, or straight angle, turns through $\frac{1}{2}$ of a circle. The rays of a straight angle form a line.

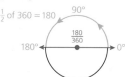

$\frac{1}{2}$ of 360 = 180

$\frac{180}{360}$

A 360° angle turns through a whole circle. One ray rests on top of the other.

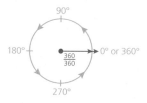

$\frac{360}{360}$

When Carrie opens her laptop, she turns the cover through 110 one-degree angles. The angle it forms measures 110°.

➤ The measure of the angle of Carrie's open laptop is 110°.

To name an angle, use the symbol ∠. Write the letter for a point on one ray and the letter for the vertex followed by the letter for a point on the other ray. This angle is ∠ABC or ∠CBA. A short form is ∠B.

Understand: Angle measures and fractions of a circle

■ Ensure that students have a good understanding of angles and all attributes in regard to angles. Students will learn how to measure angles and the unit of measure for angles (degrees).

■ Remind students that they are comparing angles to fractional parts of a circle. Though the first example shows only up to 90° of the circle, point out that if the arc is continued, it would complete a circle.

■ Though these examples all start with a horizontal line pointing to the right, remind students that an angle is formed by two rays, regardless of the orientation of each ray, just as long as the two rays share an endpoint.

■ Stress that when naming an angle, the middle letter must be the vertex. This concept must be understood for the students to succeed in this lesson and subsequent lessons. If necessary, you may want to give students additional practice naming angles.

Words to Know

degree (°): the unit of measure for angles

one-degree angle: an angle that turns through $\frac{1}{360}$ of a circle

right angle: an angle that turns through $\frac{90}{360}$, or $\frac{1}{4}$ of a circle. It measures 90°.

straight angle: An angle that turns through $\frac{180}{360}$, or $\frac{1}{2}$ of a circle. It measures 180°.

Connect: Identify angles and angle measures in degrees Use this page to help students strengthen their understanding of how the measure of an angle relates to its fractional part of a circle.

■ Remind students that fractions name equal parts of a whole. In this example, the whole is a circle with a total of 360°.

■ If students have difficulty identifying the shape of individual angles when they are all shown together, allow them to trace and label each individual angle on a piece of paper. Then they can compare their relative sizes.

■ Ask students to explain why they must use three letters to name each angle, instead of using the short form to name the angle ∠B. Point out that when there is more than one angle with the same vertex, they must use three points to name the angle.

Guided Instruction

Connect: Identify angles and angle measures in degrees

One of the angles in the figure at the right turns through $\frac{1}{6}$ of a circle. What is the size of this angle? What part of the figure shows this angle?

To identify the angle size and matching angle in the figure, use what you know about the degrees in a circle.

Step 1

Find the number of one-degree angles in $\frac{1}{6}$ of a circle. Think: One whole circle has 360 one-degree angles.

You can multiply to find $\frac{1}{6}$ of 360.

$$\frac{1}{6} \times 360 = \frac{1 \times 360}{6} = \frac{360}{6} = 60 \text{ one-degree angles}$$

Since each one-degree angle is 1°, 60 one-degree angles equal 60°.

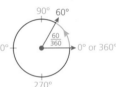

➡ The angle that turns through $\frac{1}{6}$ of a circle is a 60° angle.

Step 2

Identify which angle in the figure is the 60° angle. Use the points on the rays to name the angles.

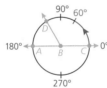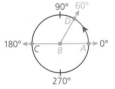

Angles *DBC* and *ABC* are both greater than 60°.

Angle *DBA* measures 60°.

➡ The part of the figure that shows the 60° angle is angle *DBA*.

276 Unit 4 ■ Focus on Measurement and Data

Support English Language Learners

This lesson uses several geometric terms that students need to know when describing and naming angles, such as *ray*, *endpoint*, and *vertex*. Many of these terms rely on pictorial representations to clarify their definitions. Review the terms and the visual representations with English language learners, helping students pronounce the terms and connect them with illustrations. Allow students to create a reference sheet with geometric terms and corresponding drawings that they can keep on their desks during this lesson. Having this sheet to refer to during the lesson will continually reinforce these definitions, and the act of creating the sheet will help solidify their understanding of these terms.

Lesson 31

Guided Practice

Name the measure of the angle for the fraction of a circle.

1.

$\frac{1}{4} = \frac{90}{360}$

Angle measure __90__°

2.

$\frac{1}{2} = \frac{180}{360}$

Angle measure __180__°

3.

$\frac{1}{6} = \frac{60}{360}$

Angle measure __60__°

Use the words at the right to complete the sentences. Then name an example in the figure at the right.

vertex
right angle
ray
straight angle

4. A __straight angle__ measures 180°.

   Example Possible answer: angle *ABD* or angle *EBC*

5. The point shared by two rays to form an angle is called the __vertex__.

   Example point *B*

6. A __ray__ is a line with one endpoint that goes on forever in one direction.

   Example Possible answers: rays *BA, BC, BD, BE*

7. Angle *ABC* has a greater measure than a __right angle__. Name another angle that turns through more than 90 one-degree angles.

   Possible answers: angle *EBD*, angle *ABD*, angle *CBE*

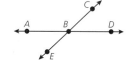

Think • Pair • Share

MP2

8. Shelly rides the Ferris wheel at the carnival. Her car moves $\frac{5}{8}$ of the way around the whole circle when the ride stops to let other people on. What is the measure of the angle between the starting and stopping point? Explain your solution. The measure of the angle is 225°. Possible explanation: A turn through $\frac{1}{8}$ of the circle is $\frac{1}{8} \times 360 = \frac{360}{8} = 45$ degrees. So a turn through 5 times as much of the circle is $5 \times 45 = 225$ degrees.

Unit 4 ■ Focus on Measurement and Data **277**

Mathematical Practices

Mathematical Practice Standards underline the teaching and understanding of all concepts and skills presented. The emphasis of specific practices is noted throughout the guided and independent practice of this lesson.

MP2 Reason abstractly and quantitatively.

Item 8: Students make sense of fractional parts of a circle and use its meaning to solve the problem.

Observational Assessment

Use page 277 to assess students' abilities to define and measure angles based on their relationship to a circle. Students should equate fractional parts of a circle to a fraction with a denominator of 360. Make note of those students who struggle with the terminology connected with this lesson, as these terms will be used in subsequent lessons.

Think•Pair•Share

Peer Collaboration Before solving the problem, ask students to estimate the size of the angle based on what they know about right angles and straight angles. Have students solve the problem and then explain their solution to a partner. Remind students to compare their solutions with their estimates to determine whether their solutions are reasonable. Ask:

- *Why is your answer greater than 90°?*

- *Why is your answer greater than 180°?*

- *How many $\frac{1}{8}$ parts of the circle are equal to a right angle? How many $\frac{1}{8}$ parts are equal to a straight angle?*

Return to the Essential Question

Reread the Lesson 31 Essential Question on page 274: *How is the measure of an angle related to a circle?*

Ask volunteers to use what they learned in this lesson to answer this question. (Possible response: An angle that turns $\frac{1}{360}$ of a circle is a one-degree angle. An angle's measure is equal to the number of one-degree angles that it turns through.)

Invite volunteers to explain the way an angle relates to a circle using mathematical vocabulary from this lesson.

Additional answers

Item 8: Another possible explanation: The circle is divided into 8 equal parts. $360 \div 8 = 45$; $5 \times 45 = 225$ degrees

Independent Practice

Concept Application

Students may work independently on these pages in the classroom or at home. They may refer to the first four pages of the lesson to revisit the instruction or to see a worked-out example.

Common Errors and **Teaching Tips** may help you support student learning either in the classroom or as a follow-up for work done at home.

Teaching Tips

Items 2-3

Refer students back to the first item to remind them that the fraction of a circle should have a denominator of 360.

Item 5

Students may wish to refer to an analog clock in the room when solving this problem. They should also be able to draw a sample clock on a piece of paper. Remind students to draw both the hour hand and the minute hand to see both rays for each angle.

Independent Practice

Name the measure of the angle for the fraction of a circle.

1.

2.

3.

$\frac{1}{3} = \frac{120}{360}$ $\frac{1}{8} = \frac{45}{360}$ $\frac{1}{5} = \frac{72}{360}$

Angle measure __120__°   Angle measure __45__°   Angle measure __72__°

4. Identify the parts of the angle below.

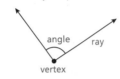

5. The table shows the angle between the hour and minute hand of a clock at different times of the day. Write the missing angle measures to complete the table.

Time	Angle
1:00	30°
2:00	60°
3:00	90°

6. Angles A and B represent a door opening into a room.

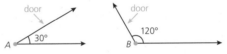

a. Compare the measures of the angles and the number of one-degree angles for each. Possible answer: Angle A is smaller than angle B. It only turns through 30 one-degree angles, but angle B turns through 120 one-degree angles so it opens wider.

b. Describe the relationship between the sizes of the angles. Possible answer: The measure of angle B is 4 times the measure of angle A.

Writing About Math

▸ **Write a Definition Paragraph** Ask students to write a definition paragraph of an *angle.* Be sure students include vocabulary terms when describing an angle and provide descriptions of common examples. Encourage students to rely on their explanations to define the word, rather than providing drawings or models.

Ask volunteers to read their paragraphs aloud while the rest of the class listens with their eyes closed. Encourage students to envision what they are hearing. Suggest that students provide feedback to their peers about whether or not they could picture an angle in their minds from the definition in the paragraph.

For exercises 7–9, use the figure.

Street Intersection

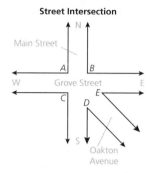

7. A car drives south along Main Street and makes a 90° turn onto Grove Street. Name two angles that can represent the corner where the car turns.

angle *A* and angle *B*

8. Which angles represent sharp turns that measure less than a right angle?

Possible answers include: angle *D* and angle *E*

9. A car drives through the intersection along a straight angle. Which street or streets is the car driving on?

The car is driving on Main Street or Grove Street.

Circle the correct answer.

10. A fin on a windmill moves from point *O* to point *A*. As it moves, it turns through $\frac{1}{10}$ of a circle. What is the measure of the angle?

   a. 10°

   b. 36°

   c. 90°

   d. 100°

Teaching Tips

Items 7–8

The letters that represent angles and the directional letters that represent North, South, East, and West might confuse students. Suggest that students give answers using the name of the vertex. Explain that in this diagram, each vertex only names one angle, so they can use the short form to name the angles.

Math-to-Real-World Connection

Piece of Pizza Students need not look any further than a pizza to see the concept of angle measurement as a fraction of a circle. When serving a pizza, it is usually cut into slices that pass through the center of the pizza. These slices have rays coming out from the vertex at the tip of the slice.

Ask students to experiment with paper circle "pizzas" that they need to cut into equal numbers of slices. Include circles of different diameters. Assign each group a number and ask them to use scissors to cut their circle into that number of equal slices. Do not use only even numbers. After the slices are divided, ask students to calculate the angle measures for their slices using what they know about the total number of degrees in a circle. Have groups compare the sizes of their slices with those of other groups, taking into account the size of the angle and the length of the rays of each slice.

Independent Practice

Common Errors

Item 12

Students may easily make the connection between the circle model and the answer $\frac{1}{3}$ without looking carefully at the size of the angles, leading them to choose answer a. Remind students that the total number of degrees in a circle is 360, so the measure of all angles together must equal that sum.

Teaching Tips

Item 11

Suggest that students draw a 90° angle and a 180° angle to use as references when solving this problem.

Item 13

Ask students to make connections between the size of the angle measure and the denominator of the fraction. As the denominator decreases, the angle measure increases.

Independent Practice

11. What is the measure of ∠XYZ?

    a. between 0° and 90°

    b. exactly 90°

    c. between 90° and 180°

    d. exactly 180°

12. The circle is divided into 3 equal sections. For each section, name the fraction of the circle and the measure of the angle.

    a. $\frac{1}{3}$, 60°

    b. $\frac{1}{3}$, 120°

    c. $\frac{1}{9}$, 40°

    d. $\frac{1}{9}$, 90°

Solve the problems.

MP7 13. The table below shows the relationship between angle measures and sections of a circle. Complete the table.

Angle Measure	Circle Section
40°	$\frac{1}{9}$
72°	$\frac{1}{5}$
90°	$\frac{1}{4}$
120°	$\frac{1}{3}$
180°	$\frac{1}{2}$

Show your work. Work may vary.
Possible work for first answer:
I know that angle measure times the denominator in the fraction equals 360.
$40 \times c = 360$; $c = 9$

Mathematical Practices

MP7	Look for and make use of structure.

Item 13: Students recognize the pattern between angle measures and sections of a circle to complete the table.

Lesson 31

Independent Practice

MP7 **14.** What is the measure of angle *MNP*?

Show your work. Work may vary. Possible work:
360 − 120 = 240
Angle *MNO* = 180 degrees
240 − 180 = 60

Answer The measure of angle *MNP* is 60 degrees.

MP3 **15.** Mark is taking leftover slices of pizza from different boxes and putting them into one box. The 5 leftover pizza slices are shown below in gold.

Are all the gold slices shown the same size?

Answer No, they are not the same size.

Justify your answer using words, drawings, or numbers.
Possible justification: The angle measures are not the same size. You can tell visually that the top 3 slices and the slice at the bottom left are the same size. They seem to have the same angle measure. The other piece appears to be bigger than the others.

MP1 **16.** Kendra's bicycle wheels cover a distance of about 6 feet with each full turn. She bikes two blocks and covers a distance of 420 feet. Kendra says that her wheels turned 2,520 times during her ride. Is Kendra right?

Answer No, Kendra is not right.

Justify your answer using words, drawings, or numbers.
Possible justification: Kendra is multiplying 6 × 420 instead of dividing 420 by 6; 420 feet ÷ 6 feet = 70 full turns of her wheels.

Teaching Tips

Item 14
Students do not need to use the whole circle to solve this problem. Remind them to use the definition of a straight angle and use what they know to find the unknown angle measure.

Item 16
If students have difficulty determining whether Kendra is right, ask them to use her information and work backwards to confirm the distance she would ride if her wheel turned 2,520 times.

Mathematical Practices	
MP1	**Make sense of problems and persevere in solving them.**
Item 16: Students deconstruct the meaning of distances given in the problem and use this information to determine the solution.	
MP3	**Construct viable arguments and critique the reasoning of others.**
Item 15: Students analyze a model and use it to determine a conclusion and justify their answers.	
MP7	**Look for and make use of structure.**
Item 14: Students use the known structure of a straight angle to determine the angle measurement.	

Common Core Focus:

4.MD.6 Measure angles in whole-number degrees using a protractor. Sketch angles of specified measure.

OBJECTIVE

Understand how to categorize obtuse, acute, right, and straight angles and use a protractor to determine their measurement.

ESSENTIAL QUESTION

Introduce the lesson by asking students what they know about angles and angle measures. Provide examples of angle types and the measurement of a circle.

FLUENCY PRACTICE

Fluency practice is available at **sadlierconnect.com**.

Concept Development

Understand: Classifying angles by size

■ Some students might not think of a straight angle as an angle type. Guide students to review the Remember! feature, and ask them to name the two rays and the common endpoint for straight angle *NOP*. Then, relate the acute and obtuse angles in the presentation to straight angle *NOP* and have them determine similarities between the three angles.

■ Since straight and right angles always have exact measurements and are easy to identify, classifying them will allow students to know their measurement without using a protractor.

■ Ensure that students use a right angle symbol to represent a right angle.

✎ · Right angles always have the exact measurement of 90°. Acute and obtuse angles are classified based on their relationship to a right angle.

Guided Instruction

In this lesson you will learn how to measure and draw angles using a protractor.

Understand: Classifying angles by size

> Meg says that there are only three types of angles: right angles, straight angles, and 360° angles. Is Meg's information correct?

You learned that angle measure is the number of one-degree angles that an angle turns through in a circle. You can classify or group angles by their angle measure.

- An acute angle measures between 0° and 90°. Angle *ABC* is an acute angle.

- A right angle is exactly 90°. Angle *DEF* shows the right angle symbol: a square at the vertex. Two rays that meet at a right angle are perpendicular, like the sides of a square or rectangle.

- An obtuse angle measures between 90° and 180°. Angle *GHJ* is an obtuse angle.

- A straight angle measures exactly 180°. Straight angle *NOP* is also a line.

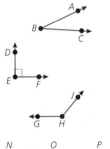

Remember!
Two rays that share the same endpoint form an angle.

> There are more than 3 types of angles, so Meg's information is not correct.

You can use benchmark angles such as right angles and straight angles to help you visualize angles in the problems that you work on.

✏ · Explain why there are acute angles with many different angle measures but there is only one angle measure for a right angle.
Possible answer: A right angle can only have 90°, but an acute angle can have angle measures between 0° and 90°, so for whole numbers of degrees that would be 89 different acute angles.

Essential Question:
How can classifying angles and using a protractor help you measure angles?
4.MD.6

Words to Know:
acute angle
perpendicular
obtuse angle
protractor

Words to Know

acute angle: an angle that measures between 0° and 90°

perpendicular: two lines, line segments, or rays that meet or intersect to form a 90° angle

Glossary can be found on pp. 347–350.

Understand: How to measure angles with a protractor

Tim says that the measure of ∠ABC is 50° and the measure of ∠DEF is 130°. Is Tim correct?

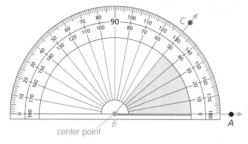

To find the exact measure of an angle, you can use a protractor. A protractor is a tool for measuring the number of degrees in an angle.

center point

On the protractor, find the center hole at the bottom. Place this directly over the vertex of the angle you are measuring. For ∠ABC, this is point B.

Line up one ray of the angle, such as ray BA, with the 0 on the inner number scale. On the inner scale, the degrees increase counterclockwise. When a ray is too short to reach the number scale, use the straight side of the protractor to extend the ray.

> A short way to write the measure of angle ABC is m∠ABC.

Look where the other ray of the angle crosses this scale. Ray BC goes through the tick mark for 50, so m∠ABC is 50°.

Now measure ∠DEF in the figure at the right. Place the center point of the protractor over vertex E and line up ray ED with 0 on the outer number scale. Ray EF goes through 50 on the outer number scale. The degrees increase clockwise. On the outer scale, m∠DEF is 50°, not 130°.

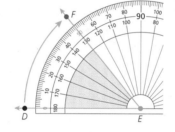

▶ Tim is correct about the measure of ∠ABC but not about the measure of ∠DEF. The angles have the same angle measure.

Unit 4 ■ Focus on Measurement and Data   **283**

Understand: How to measure angles with a protractor

■ Tim makes the common mistake of using the wrong scale on a protractor when measuring ∠DEF. Encourage students to think critically about an angle before measuring it. Suggest that students first classify the angle. If Tim had classified both angles as acute before measuring, he would have realized that ∠DEF could not have a measure greater than 90°.

■ Relate measuring angles to other types of measurements, such as finding length or area. Discuss the similarities shared by all types of measurement, such as being precise, using a tool, and identifying the unit of measure.

■ To extend the length of a ray, students need to use a ruler. Practice lining up the ruler at the beginning of the ray to ensure a straight line. If students place a ruler at the end of the ray, the extended line can be crooked.

■ There are two sets of measurements on a protractor because some angles face to the left and some to the right. Remind students to use the scale that starts with 0 and to stay on that scale throughout the measurement.

■ Challenge students to see if they can find a pattern between the top and bottom scales. Each pair of top and bottom numbers adds to 180°. Discuss this relationship of corresponding angles.

Words to Know

obtuse angle: an angle that measure between 90° and 180°

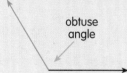

obtuse angle

protractor: a tool used to find the exact measure of an angle

Glossary can be found on pp. 347–350.

Connect: Use a protractor to draw an angle Use this page to help students strengthen their understanding of using a protractor to draw an angle.

■ This presentation shows how multiple angles interact with each other. ∠WEP and ∠PEG combine to create a straight angle. Ask students to classify ∠WEG. Thinking critically about this relationship will allow students to effectively find the measure of ∠WEG without using a protractor.

■ When drawing angles, students should focus on one ray at a time. Points are plotted first, and then straight lines connect the plotted points.

■ Students should practice drawing Janna's angles on a different sheet of paper. Model the step-by-step process on the board.

✏ Once students have drawn an angle, they can switch papers with a partner, who will measure the angle. Students can present their angle to the class and have others classify it as obtuse, acute, right, or straight.

Lesson 32 Use a Protractor to Measure Angles

Guided Instruction

Connect: Use a protractor to draw an angle

> Janna wants to put a peg on the wall to hang her jacket on. She starts to make a sketch of the peg's position. She wants the angle to be 135°. Help Janna draw an angle of 135°.

You can use a protractor to draw the angle.

Step 1

Put more information on Janna's sketch.
Name the angle PEG. Let line WEG represent the wall.

Step 2

Draw ray EG.
Use the straight edge of the protractor to draw ray EG.
Mark point E and draw a ray down from Point E. Label any point on the ray G.

Step 3

Draw ray EP.
Place the protractor over ray EG, with the center on E and ray EG lined up with 0.
Mark point P at 135° on the outer number scale.
Draw a ray connecting P and E.

➡ The three steps show how Janna can draw an angle of 135°.

What is the measure of angle PEW?
Straight angle WEG measures 180°.
180 − 135° = 45°, so angle PEW measures 45°.
Look at the inner number scale to check.

✏ Choose an angle measure between 0° and 180°. Use your protractor to draw the angle on another sheet of paper.
Drawings will vary. Check students' drawings.

Support English Language Learners

Some English language learners may struggle with using terms to classify angles such as *right angle*.

First, ask students to define *right* in their own words. Some students may relate *right* to behavior, such as the difference between *right and wrong*. Other students may relate *right* to directionality such as *right and left*. Write *right angle* on the board and provide an example of a right angle below the word. Then point to the right angle and say the sentence: *This is a right angle*. Encourage students to repeat the sentence. Repeat the process drawing right angles in various orientations reinforcing that right angles are classified as an angle that measures 90°. Ask students to describe the differences between a right angle and the other uses of right.

Lesson 32

Guided Practice

Match the angle with its description. Use angle benchmarks to help.

1. ∠AQC   a. acute angle

2. ∠BQD   b. right angle

3. ∠AQB   c. obtuse angle

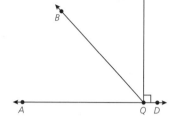

Use a protractor. Find the angle measure.

4. m∠AQC   __90__ °

5. m∠BQD   __132__ °

6. m∠AQB   __48__ °

Sketch an example of each type of angle. Sketches will vary. Possible angles shown.

7. acute   8. straight   9. obtuse

Use a protractor to draw an angle with the given measure.

10. 90°   11. 60°   12. 120°

Think • Pair • Share

MP5   13. On this drawing of angle *BEN*, draw two
angles: a 45° angle and a 135° angle.
Label your angles and explain your method.
How are the angles related?
Possible answer: To draw the 45° angle, I placed
the protractor over angle *BEN*, marked point *C*
at 45°, and then connected *E* and *C* with a ray.
I did the same for the 135° angle, except I used
a point *D* at 135°. Angle *CEN* is half the right angle,
and angle *DEN* is the right angle plus angle *CEN*.

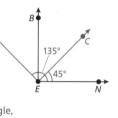

Unit 4 ■ Focus on Measurement and Data   **285**

Mathematical Practices

Mathematical Practice Standards underline the teaching and
understanding of all concepts and skills presented. The emphasis of
specific practices is noted throughout the guided and independent practice
of this lesson.

MP5   **Use appropriate tools strategically.**

Item 13: Students use a protractor and straightedge to draw an acute and
obtuse angle accurately.

Observational Assessment

Use page 285 to assess whether
students understand how to classify,
measure, and create angles. Take note of
those students who struggle to provide
an angle measure for ∠BQD due to the
length of ray *D*. These students may
need additional practice extending rays
to accurately measure angles.

Think•Pair•Share

Peer Collaboration Break the class
into student pairs. Ask each pair to share
their strategies with each other, and then
with the class. Ask these questions when
student pairs present to the class:

- *Can you reuse some of the rays
  already provided? Would ray BE or
  ray EN be easier to use? Why?*

- *How did you label the angle
  measurements?*

- *What is special about these two new
  angles? Do you see any patterns or
  relationships between them?*

To summarize, students should think
critically about how to effectively and
appropriately add angles to this drawing
of ∠BEN. Point out how curved lines
connecting each ray in an angle help
students label the angle. Some students
might reason about the relationship
between the ∠BEN and ∠CEN, such as
how a 45° angle is half of a right angle.

Return to the Essential Question

Reread the Lesson 32 Essential Question
on page 282: *How can classifying
angles and using a protractor help you
measure angles?*

Ask volunteers to use what they learned
in this lesson to answer this question.
(Possible response: Use an angle's size
compared to a right angle to determine
if it is obtuse or acute. This allows me
to make a strategic estimation about its
size. Using a protractor gives the exact
measurement, which should be within
the range of the estimated measure.)

Independent Practice

Concept Application

Students may work independently on these pages in the classroom or at home. They may refer to the first four pages of this lesson to revisit the instruction or to see a worked-out example.

Common Errors and **Teaching Tips** may help you support student learning either in the classroom or as a follow-up for work done at home.

Common Errors

Item 2

Students may make an error using the correct scale on the protractor since this angle opens to the left. Encourage students to determine the angle classification first, and then use the scale that starts with 0°.

Item 3

This angle is facing down. Remind students to pay attention to the curved line, which specifies which way the angle opens. If students struggle measuring it, they can turn their books upside down.

Teaching Tips

Items 1–4

The rays of all these angles will need to be extended in order to be measured. Students can extend the rays as much as needed to use a protractor. Model how to achieve a straight-line extension.

Independent Practice

Use a protractor. Find the angle measure of each. Then identify the type of angle.

1. measure __80°__
   type __acute__

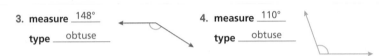

2. measure __25°__
   type __acute__

3. measure __148°__
   type __obtuse__

4. measure __110°__
   type __obtuse__

Use a protractor to draw an angle with the given measure.

5. 55°

6. 138°

7. 175°

Writing About Math

> **Write Explanatory Text** Have students write an explanation of how to create a geometric shape using various angle measures. Each student should draw a shape, such as a triangle or a square. Make sure students use their protractors to measure the angles and lengths of the sides. After creating and labeling their shape, they should describe it in words. For instance, a student with a square shape might write, "draw a right angle with each ray measuring 3 inches." Once students have written their directions, have them exchange the explanatory text with a partner and see if they can draw their partner's shape.

Independent Practice

For exercises 8–9, circle the correct answer.

8. What is the measure of ∠MNO?
Use a protractor.

a. 53° b. 120°

c. 127° d. 130°

9. What type of angle is ∠MNO?

a. acute b. obtuse

c. right d. straight

10. Use a protractor to measure angle ACD and angle ECB.

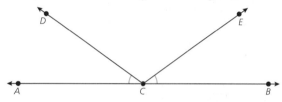

a. Write the angle measures.

m∠ACD __35°__   m∠ECB __35°__

b. Complete the sentence. Use *acute*, *right*, *obtuse*, or *straight*.

Angle ACB is a __straight__ angle.

c. Use your protractor to find the measure of angle DCE.

m∠DCE __110°__

d. Draw angle DCB. m∠DCB = 145°

Common Errors

Item 8

If students choose answer choice a, they probably used the wrong scale on the protractor. Encourage students to classify the angle first and then measure the angle.

Teaching Tips

Item 10

For part c, when finding the measure of ∠DCE, encourage students to reason about its size without using a protractor. Because ∠ACB is straight and ∠ACD and ∠ECB equal 35°, the equation 180 – 70 can be used to find the measure of ∠DCE.

For part d, the angle should look exactly like ∠DCB in the drawing given in the problem.

Math-to-Math Connection

Geography and Geometry A fun way to interest students in angles is to have them create a treasure map with a partner. Each pair of students will secretly choose a random item in the room and draw a map of how to get to the item from the classroom door. They should explain how many steps to take, what approximate angle to turn, and in what direction. Groups can trade maps and see if they can find the secret items. For an extra challenge, have student pairs place items in the gym or school yard and create a map using the same process described.

Independent Practice

Common Errors

Item 14

Students should read the question carefully. They may find the measure for the remaining three angles and not find the sum of the three angles, as required.

Teaching Tips

Item 11

Students do not need to actually measure this angle, only determine if it is acute, obtuse, right, or straight. Encourage students to read the problem in its entirety to ensure they provide the correct answer.

Item 12

Challenge students to determine if there are *any* examples where the measure of two acute angles would still result in an acute angle. For example, if two acute angles equal less than 90°, such as a 35° angle and a 10° angle, they would still create an acute angle.

Item 14

Thinking critically about the properties of angles will help students solve this problem. Discuss why making generalizations about angles is more effective than measuring every angle. Finding a straight angle will greatly reduce the amount of measuring needed because it will always be 180°.

Independent Practice

MP7   **11.** Classify the angle at the right. Use an angle benchmark to explain your reasoning.
Answers will vary. It is an acute angle.
Possible explanation: I see that the angle is less than a right angle, because it is smaller than a square corner. Since it is less than a right angle or 90°, it must be an acute angle.

MP3   **12.** Carrie says that if you combine the measures of two acute angles, the new angle is always acute. Do you agree? Give an example to explain your answer.
I do not agree. Possible explanation: An acute angle is any angle measuring less than 90 degrees. So two acute angles can be 80 degrees and 70 degrees, and 80 + 70 = 150 degrees, which is an obtuse angle.

Solve the problems.

MP5   **13.** On the line below, use a protractor to draw two angles. Use point A as the vertex for both angles. Write the measure of each angle below.

▭▷ **Show your work.** Drawings may vary. Possible angles:

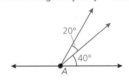

Angle measures _____ Answers will vary. Possible answers: 40° and 20°

MP2   **14.** The figure at the right shows the angles formed by two lines, line AC and line ED. Angle ABE measures 70°. What is the sum of the measures of angles DBC, CBE, and ABE?

▭▷ **Show your work.** Work may vary. Possible work:
Line DE is made up from angles DBC and CBE, so the sum of these two angle measures is 180°.
Angle ABE measures 70°.
180 + 70 = 250

Answer The sum of the measures of the angles is 250°.

288   Unit 4 ■ Focus on Measurement and Data

Mathematical Practices

MP2	**Reason abstractly and quantitatively.**
Item 14: Students use what they know about angles to determine the measure of multiple angles.	
MP3	**Construct viable arguments and critique the reasoning of others.**
Item 12: Students analyze and critique another student's reasoning.	
MP5	**Use appropriate tools strategically.**
Item 13: Students use a protractor to create two angles.	
MP7	**Look for and make use of structure.**
Item 11: Students evaluate the attributes of angles.	

MP5 **15.** Complete the table. Identify and then sketch each angle.

Angle Measure	Angle Type	Sketch
60° + 30°	right angle	
90° + 90°	straight angle	
30° + 30°	acute angle	
120° − 20°	obtuse angle	

MP4 **16.** George says that if you subtract 185° from an angle that measures 360°, the new angle is an obtuse angle. Is George's thinking correct? Use a protractor to draw a figure supporting your answer.

Answer Yes, George's thinking is correct.

▪ **Justify your answer using words, drawings, or numbers.**
Possible justification:
An obtuse angle is less than 180°
and more than 90°.
360 − 185 = 175°

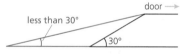

MP2 **17.** A store has a ramp up to its back door for deliveries. The ramp is angled at 30° up from the ground, as shown below.

less than 30°   door →

30°

The delivery person says that the ramp is too steep.
How can you change the ramp to make it less steep?
Draw your new design onto the drawing above.

Answer The angle of the ramp must be much less than 30°.

▪ **Justify your answer using words, drawings, or numbers.**
Possible justification: You must decrease the angle to make the ramp less steep and make the ramp longer so it still goes up to the door.

Unit 4 ▪ Focus on Measurement and Data **289**

Common Errors

Item 15

Students may add 120° and 20° instead of subtracting because the other examples in the chart use addition.

Teaching Tips

Item 16

Discuss what a 360° angle looks like and how it relates to angles less than 180°. An angle with 360° creates a circle and is the largest possible angle. Angles greater than 180° are not explored at this grade.

Item 17

Students may reason that the angle of the ramp needs to be less than 30°, but not know how to obtain it. Encourage them to collaborate and think critically about how a smaller angle would have to be placed to create an appropriate ramp. A protractor should be used to create the angle and place it correctly on the drawing.

Mathematical Practices	
MP2	**Reason abstractly and quantitatively.**
Item 17: Students represent problems and use angle properties to sketch approximate angle sizes.	
MP4	**Model with mathematics.**
Item 16: Students explain the relationship between the measures of obtuse angles and other angles to determine the size of an angle.	
MP5	**Use appropriate tools strategically.**
Item 15: Students reason about the classification of an angle and use a protractor to draw it.	

Common Core Focus:

4.MD.7 Recognize angle measure as additive. When an angle is decomposed into non-overlapping parts, the angle measure of the whole is the sum of the angle measures of the parts. Solve addition and subtraction problems to find unknown angles on a diagram in real world and mathematical problems.

OBJECTIVE

Understand how to use the relationships between angles to find angle measures and solve problems.

ESSENTIAL QUESTION

In Lesson 32, students learned how to measure angles. In this lesson, students will learn about and use angle relationships to find unknown angle measures in problems.

FLUENCY PRACTICE

Fluency practice is available at **sadlierconnect.com**.

Concept Development

Understand: Supplementary and complementary angles

■ Students will solve problems using a letter to represent an unknown angle measure on diagrams.

■ Make sure students understand how arcs are used to show angles in the first diagram. Identify the whole angle and the parts of the angle and how the three angles are related by addition and subtraction.

■ Be sure students understand that the second diagram on the page represents adding two more photos to the collage that Tobey is making.

✎ ▸ Ask students to write an equation that represents the relationship between the angle measures. Have them use a letter such as *m* or *p* as the measure of the corner angle of photo 4.

Lesson 33 — Problem Solving: Find Unknown Angle Measures

Essential Question: How can you use known relationships between angle measures to solve problems?
4.MD.7

Words to Know: supplementary angles complementary angles

Guided Instruction

In this lesson you will learn how to use the relationships between angles to find angle measures and solve problems.

Understand: Supplementary and complementary angles

Tobey is making a photo collage. The bottom right corner of photo 1 is cut at a 70° angle. Tobey wants to fit photo 1 next to photo 2 so that the corners do not overlap or have a gap in between them. At what angle should Tobey cut the bottom left corner of photo 2?

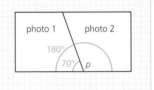

To find the angle measure Tobey needs for photo 2, you can use the relationship between supplementary angles.

Supplementary angles are two angles whose measures add to 180°. When supplementary angles have a side in common, they make a straight angle or line.

Remember!
A straight angle measures 180°.

For Tobey's two photos to fit together perfectly, the angles must be supplementary.

Write an equation that represents the relationship of the angle measures. Use *p* as the measure of the corner angle of photo 2.

sum of supplementary angles = sum of the two angle measures
$$180° = 70° + p$$
$$180° - 70° = p$$
$$110° = p$$

➡ Tobey should cut the bottom left corner of photo 2 at a 110° angle.

Complementary angles are two angles whose measures add to 90°. When complementary angles have a side in common, they make a right angle.

▰▭▸ Find the measure of the upper left corner angle for photo 4 in the collage.
$$90° - 30° = 60°$$

Words to Know

complementary angles: two angles whose measures add to 90°

supplementary angles: two angles whose measures add to 180°

Example:

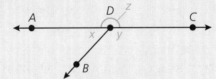

In the figure, angle *ADB* and angle *CDB* are supplementary angles.

Glossary can be found on pp. 347–350.

MORE ONLINE sadlierconnect.com | Lesson 33

Guided Instruction

Understand: Breaking apart and combining angles

A flower pattern in a quilt is made with identical hexagons. All of the angles in the hexagons have the same measure. What is the measure of each angle in the hexagons?

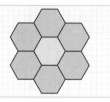

To find the measure of each angle, you can break apart, or decompose, a 360° angle about any point in the pattern. Then use the information given in the problem and what you know about angles to write and solve an equation.

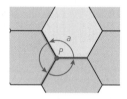

- The diagram shows that each point in the pattern is a vertex for three hexagons.

- The problem tells you that all of the angles in the hexagons have the same measure.

- A full circle is a 360° angle. At each point in the pattern, a circle is decomposed into 3 equal angles.

The three angles sharing a vertex at a point, *P*, have a combined measure of 360°. You can use *a* to represent the unknown measure of one angle.

Write and solve an equation that represents this problem.

$$360° = a + a + a$$
$$360° = 3a$$
$$360° \div 3 = a$$
$$120° = a$$

➡ The measure of each angle in the hexagons is 120°.

Unit 4 ■ Focus on Measurement and Data **291**

Understand: Breaking apart and combining angles

■ Students decompose a 360° angle to find the measure of one angle in a hexagon. An important part of this presentation is the understanding that a 360° angle turns through a whole circle. If students are struggling with this, review page 275 of Lesson 31.

■ Explain that since there are three non-overlapping angles that make up an angle that measures 360°, the sum of the three angles is 360°.

■ All of the angles in the hexagons have the same measure, so the same letter, *a,* can be used to represent the measure of each angle. If angles do not have equal measures, or you do not know the relationship between the angle measures, then a different letter should be used for each angle measure.

■ Students can check their answers by adding the measures of the three angles to make sure the sum is 360°.

Support English Language Learners

Students are introduced to two new terms in this lesson, *complementary* and *supplementary.* Write the word complement on the board. Explain that the term means to complete or make whole. Make sure students are not confusing complement with *compliment,* which is a polite expression of admiration or praise. Make the connection between an item complementing, or making a set complete, and complementary angles.

Next, write the word *supplement* on the board. Students may know that a *supplement* completes or enhances something else when added to it. Connect this idea to the idea of supplementary angles.

Guided Instruction

Connect: Using a drawing and an equation to represent a problem Use this page to help students strengthen their understanding of how to use relationships between angles to solve a problem.

■ Demonstrate how to sketch a drawing of the problem. Students need to represent the triangle and the angle measures accurately in a drawing. Explain why the 60° angle that the ladder makes with the floor is positioned inside the triangle instead of representing the exterior angle. Students should reason that the 60° angle represents the acute angle shown in the drawing.

■ Some students will find it easier to solve the problem in two steps. First, they can find the sum of the two given angle measures. Then, subtract that sum from 180.

■ You may wish to point out that the acute angles in a right triangle are always complementary, since 180 − 90 = 90. Using this fact, students can solve a simpler problem using the equation 90° = 60° + x, to find x = 30°.

✏ Have students draw an arc to represent the 180° angle on the diagram to verify that it is a straight line. Then have students identify the parts that make up the 180° angle and label the unknown measure. It is important to reinforce the concept of this lesson that angle measures are additive and that when an angle is decomposed into non-overlapping parts, the angle measure of the whole is the sum of the angle measures of the parts.

Connect: Using a drawing and an equation to represent a problem

> A ladder is leaning against a wall that forms a 90° angle with the floor. The bottom of the ladder makes a 60° angle with the floor. The ladder, wall, and floor form the three sides of a triangle. The combined measure of the angles in a triangle is 180°. What is the measure of the angle between the top of the ladder and the wall?

To find the unknown measure of the third angle, sketch a drawing to represent the problem and write an equation.

Step 1

- Use the given information to represent the problem.
- Sketch the triangle formed by the ladder, wall, and floor.
- Label each of the known angles with the given measures. Use x to represent the unknown angle measure.

To represent a problem situation, you do not need to draw the angles with exact measures.

Step 2

The sum of the measures of the three angles in a triangle is 180°. Write an equation for the sum.

$$180° = 60° + 90° + x$$
$$180° = 150° + x$$
$$180° − 150° = x$$
$$30° = x$$

➡ The angle between the top of the ladder and the wall measures 30°.

✏ What is the measure of the angle that is supplementary to the 60° angle from the floor?
$$180° − 60° = 120°$$

Math-to-Math Connection

Angles in Triangles In this lesson, students use the fact that "the sum of the three angles in a triangle is 180°." Let students verify this for themselves. Have students use a straight edge to draw a triangle on a sheet of paper and then cut out the triangle. Have them tear off the corners of the triangles and arrange the angles so the vertices meet at a common point and the rays do not overlap. Let students compare results. All results should be a straight line, or 180°, regardless of the size of the triangle.

Lesson 33

Guided Practice

Complete the equation to show the relationship between the angles. Then find the measure of the unknown angle.

1.

$a + 45° = \underline{180°}$

$a = \underline{180°} - 45°$

$a = \underline{135°}$

2.

$x + 50° = \underline{90°}$

$x = \underline{90°} - \underline{50°}$

$x = \underline{40°}$

Write an equation to represent the problem. Then solve.

3. Tanya is practicing her golf swing. Her first swing turns through 75° of a circle. For each of her next three tries, the angle of her swing increases by 10°. What is the angle of Tanya's last swing?

$75° + 3 \times \underline{10}° = s$
$75° + 30° = 105°$

Answer The angle of Tanya's last swing measures 105°.

4. Mallory has a triangular wedge of wood. The sum of the angles in the triangle equals 180°. What is the angle measure, x, of the third corner of the wedge?

$30° + 90° + x = 180°$
$120° + x = 180°$
$x = 180° - 120°$
$x = 60°$

Answer The angle of the third corner of the wedge measures 60°.

Think • Pair • Share

MP2 5. Draw two angles that share a side and whose measures have a sum of 90°. Explain why both angles are acute.
Possible answer:
Acute angles are angles with measures less than 90°. For the sum of two angle measures to equal 90°, both angles must be less than 90°.

Unit 4 ■ Focus on Measurement and Data **293**

Observational Assessment

Use page 293 to assess whether students are able to use diagrams and equations to find the unknown measure of an angle. Watch for students who are unable to recognize that the sum of the angle measures of the parts is equal to the angle measure of the whole.

Think•Pair•Share

Peer Collaboration Ask students to answer the question individually, and then divide them into pairs. Have pairs compare their answers. Extend students' thinking by asking:

* *What do we call the relationship between two angles whose measures have a sum of 90°?*

* *Can two acute angles be supplementary? Why or why not?*

Return to the Essential Question

Reread the Lesson 33 Essential Question on page 290: *How can you use known relationships between angle measures to solve problems?*

Ask volunteers to use what they learned in this lesson to answer this question. (Possible responses: Given the measure of one angle in a pair of supplementary or complementary angles, you can find the measure of the unknown second angle. You can use a diagram or write and solve an equation to find the measure of an unknown angle.)

Mathematical Practices

Mathematical Practice Standards underline the teaching and understanding of all concepts and skills presented. The emphasis of specific practices is noted throughout the guided and independent practice of this lesson.

| MP2 | **Reason abstractly and quantitatively.** |

Item 5: Given a problem about angle relationships, students draw a conclusion and provide an explanation.

Unit 4 ■ Focus on Measurement and Data **293**

Concept Application

Students may work independently on these pages in the classroom or at home. They may refer to the first four pages of the lesson to revisit the instruction or to see a worked-out example.

Common Errors and **Teaching Tips** may help you support student learning either in the classroom or as a follow-up for work done at home.

Teaching Tips

Items 2 and 4

If students have difficulty writing or understanding the angle names, remind them that the vertex is always the middle point in the name.

Item 4

Some students may have difficulty understanding the relationship between the two angles. Suggest they first draw and label a drawing of the two angles.

Independent Practice

Solve the problems.

1. Write an equation to find the complementary angle of 57°.

$x \underline{\;+\;} 57° = 90°$

$x = \underline{\;33°\;}$

2. The diagram shows three roads that meet at angles.

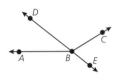

Name two pairs of supplementary angles.
Angles *ABD* and *ABE* are supplementary, and angles *DBC* and *CBE* are supplementary.

Write an equation to represent the problem. Then solve.

MP1 **3.** Jerome uses a telescope to look at stars at night. Each night, he increases the angle between the telescope and its stand by 5° to look at a different part of the sky. If this angle is 148° tonight, what was the angle 5 days ago?

telescope

148°

stand

$148° - \underline{\;5 \times 5\;}° = s$
$148° - 25° = 123°$

Answer The angle five nights ago was 123°.

MP3 **4.** Two angles, $\angle ROE$ and $\angle JOE$, share a common side and form a straight angle. The measure of $\angle ROE$ is three times that of $\angle JOE$. Find the measure of $\angle ROE$ and of $\angle JOE$.

Show your work. Possible work:
A straight angle is 180°.
$j + 3j = 180°$
$\quad 4j = 180°$
$\quad\; j = 45°$
$\quad 3j = 135°$

Answer The measure of $\angle ROE$ is 135° and the measure of $\angle JOE$ is 45°.

294   Unit 4 ■ Focus on Measurement and Data

Mathematical Practices	
MP1	**Make sense of problems and persevere in solving them.**
Item 3: Students analyze angle relationships to solve a problem.	
MP3	**Construct viable arguments and critique the reasoning of others.**
Item 4: Students use stated assumptions and definitions to construct an equation and solve a problem.	

Lesson 33

Independent Practice

For exercises 5–8, circle the correct answer.

5. Which angle measure is supplementary to a 25° angle?

   a. 25°

   b. 65°

   c. 90°

   (d.) 155°

6. Which of the following pairs of angle measures are not complementary?

   a. 45°, 45°

   b. 30°, 60°

   (c.) 20°, 90°

   d. 15°, 75°

7. The figure below shows two supplementary angles.

   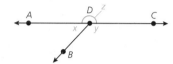

   Which of the following equations shows the relationship between the two angles?

   a. $x + z = 180°$

   (b.) $x + y = 180°$

   c. $z + y = 180°$

   d. $z - y = 180°$

8. Which of the following statements is true?

   a. Two angles whose measures add to 90° must share a side.

   b. Two angles whose measures add to 180° must share a side.

   (c.) Two angles formed by a straight angle always have measures that add to 180°.

   d. Two right angles always form complementary angles.

Unit 4 ■ Focus on Measurement and Data   295

Teaching Tips

Items 5–8

Some students may confuse the terms *supplementary* and *complementary*. Point out that alphabetically, complementary comes first and when counting, 90 comes before 180.

Writing About Math

▸ **Report on a Topic** Have students work in small groups. Tell students to prepare a presentation for the class about complementary and supplementary angles. Their presentations should include visual models and examples that demonstrate their knowledge about their topic. Have students present their reports and be prepared to answer questions.

Teaching Tips

Item 11

If students are confused trying to identify angle *B* in the drawing, have them label a point *A* on the vertical ray and a point *C* on the horizontal ray. Then refer to the right angle as angle *ABC*.

Item 12

Remind students that a 360° angle turns through a whole circle. Have students add the label for 360° next to the label for 0° on the drawing.

Independent Practice

MP2 **9.** A circle is divided into 4 equal parts. Any two angles formed in this circle are supplementary. Use this information to show that the circle has a total of 360 degrees. Answers will vary. Possible answer: In a circle that is divided into fourths, there are two pairs of angles that are supplementary. The sum of the measures of each pair of angles is 180°, so the sum of the measures of both pairs of angles is 360°.

MP6 **10.** Jeremy says that finding an unknown angle measure in a geometric figure is like finding the unknown side length of a rectangle. What do you think Jeremy means by this statement? Do you agree? Answers will vary. Possible answer: I think Jeremy means that in both cases, you can work backward from a known amount to find the unknown amount. I agree, because you can write and solve an equation to find the unknown amount for both cases.

Solve the problems.

MP2 **11.** If angle *B* below is a right angle, what is the value of *y*?

▭ **Show your work.**
$y = 90° - 27° = 63°$

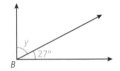

Answer The value of *y* is 63°.

MP7 **12.** A circle is divided into eight equal parts and labeled as shown below. Find the missing angle measures for the figure.

▭ **Show your work.** Work may vary.
Possible work:
Each angle equals 45°. The degrees increase moving counterclockwise, so you add 45° to each previous angle to find *x* and *y*.
$x = 90 + 45 = 135°$
$y = 225 + 45 = 270°$

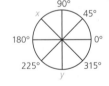

Answer The missing angle measures are $x = 135°$ and $y = 270°$.

Mathematical Practices

MP2	**Reason abstractly and quantitatively.**

Item 9: Students make sense of the supplementary angle relationship and apply it to angles in a circle.

Item 11: Students recognize that the sum of the parts of an angle is equal to the whole to find the missing angle measure.

MP6	**Attend to precision.**

Item 10: Students provide an explanation using appropriate terms.

MP7	**Look for and make use of structure.**

Item 12: Students use the information provided to determine the missing angle measures.

MP2 **13.** The equation $\frac{110}{360} + \frac{70}{360} = x$ represents fractions of a circle. Solve the equation. Then rewrite it with degree measures instead of fractions of circles. Describe the relationship between the two angles.

▸ **Show your work.** $\frac{110}{360} + \frac{70}{360} = \frac{180}{360}$ $110° + 70° = 180°$

Answer The two angles are supplementary.

MP5 **14.** Draw two angles that are complementary and do not share a side.

▸ **Show your work.**
Drawings will vary. Possible drawing:
$40° + 50° = 90°$

MP3 **15.** Tom builds an adjustable table with legs crossed, as shown at the right. Angles x and y are supplementary angles. As the height of the table is raised or lowered, angle x changes. As angle x changes, angle y changes too. Tom says that when the table is raised or lowered, the measures of angle y and angle x change in the same way. Is this true?

Answer No, it is not true. The measures of the angles change in opposite ways.

▸ **Justify your answer using words, drawings, or numbers.**
Possible justification: As the table is raised, x becomes smaller and y becomes bigger. The problem says the two angles are supplementary, so their sum always equals 180° and both their measures cannot increase.

MP4 **16.** The library has two identical entrance ramps that have an angle up from the ground of 9°. The diagram shows the two ramps set back-to-back. Sharon says that the sum $x + 9° = 90°$. Is that true?

Answer Yes, it is true.

▸ **Justify your answer using words, drawings, or numbers.**
Possible justification:
Since the two ramps are identical and have right angles, they can be halves of the same rectangle. Fitting them together to make a rectangle makes the two opposite corners of the triangle a right angle in the rectangle. So $x + 9° = 90°$.

Teaching Tips

Item 15
Caution students about drawing quick conclusions. Suggest students first make a drawing of the table raised and another of it lowered. Ask them to explain how angles x and y change in each of these situations.

Return to the

Progress Check

Remind students to return to the Progress Check self-assessment, page 231, to check off additional items they have mastered during the unit.

Mathematical Practices

MP2	**Reason abstractly and quantitatively.**

Item 13: Students demonstrate understanding that in a circle $\frac{1}{360} = 1°$ and use it to write a solution.

MP3	**Construct viable arguments and critique the reasoning of others.**

Item 15: Students express and support a conclusion.

MP4	**Model with mathematics.**

Item 16: Students apply their knowledge of angles to solve a problem.

MP5	**Use appropriate tools strategically.**

Item 14: Students use a protractor to draw angles.

The Common Core Review covers all the standards presented in the unit. Use it to assess your students' mastery of the unit's concepts and skills.

Depth of Knowledge

The depth of knowledge is a ranking of the content complexity of assessment items based on Webb's Depth of Knowledge (DOK) levels. The levels increase in complexity as shown below.

Level 1: Recall and Reproduction
Level 2: Basic Skills and Concepts
Level 3: Strategic Reasoning and Thinking
Level 4: Extended Thinking

Item	Standard	DOK
1	4.MD.7	2
2	4.MD.7	2
3	4.MD.1	1
4	4.MD.1	1
5	4.MD.4	2
6	4.MD.4	2
7	4.MD.4	2
8	4.MD.4	2
9	4.MD.4	2
10	4.MD.4	3
11	4.MD.1	1
12	4.MD.1	1
13	4.MD.6	2
14	4.MD.3	2
15	4.MD.5b	3
16	4.MD.6	2
17	4.MD.7	4
18	4.MD.2	3
19	4.MD.3	4
20	4.MD.2	4

UNIT **4** Common Core Review

In exercises 1 and 2, ray *BA* and ray *BC* are perpendicular. Find the missing angle.

1.

2.

$m = \underline{55°}$

$n = \underline{38°}$

3. Complete the conversion table.

Kilograms	Grams
1	1000
2	2000
3	3000
4	4000
5	5000

4. How many kilograms is 10,000 grams?

$\underline{\text{10 kilograms}}$

Ms. Kohl's gym class measured their standing long jumps to the nearest quarter foot. Their recorded data is shown at the right. Use the data for exercises 5–10.

Long Jumps (ft)

$5\frac{3}{4}$	$5\frac{2}{4}$	$6\frac{1}{4}$	$6\frac{1}{4}$	$6\frac{3}{4}$
7	$5\frac{3}{4}$	$6\frac{1}{4}$	$7\frac{1}{4}$	$6\frac{2}{4}$
$6\frac{2}{4}$	7	$7\frac{1}{4}$	$5\frac{3}{4}$	$6\frac{3}{4}$
$6\frac{3}{4}$	6	$6\frac{1}{4}$	$7\frac{1}{4}$	$7\frac{1}{4}$

MP6 5. Make a line plot of the long jump data. Give your line plot a title. Possible line plot shown.

Long Jumps (ft)

```
                    x
          x         x           x           x
          x         x    x    x    x    x    x
    x     x    x    x    x    x    x    x    x
◄───┼─────┼────┼────┼────┼────┼────┼────┼───►
   5²⁄₄  5³⁄₄   6   6¹⁄₄ 6²⁄₄ 6³⁄₄  7   7¹⁄₄  feet
```

6. How many students had a long jump of $5\frac{3}{4}$ feet? $\underline{\text{3 students}}$

7. What distance did the most students jump? $\underline{6\frac{1}{4}\text{ ft}}$

8. What was the longest jump? $\underline{7\frac{1}{4}\text{ ft}}$

   How many students jumped that far? $\underline{\text{4 students}}$

9. What was the shortest jump? $\underline{5\frac{2}{4}\text{ ft}}$

   How many students jumped that far? $\underline{\text{1 student}}$

10. What was the difference between the longest and shortest jumps?

   $\underline{1\frac{3}{4}\text{ ft}; 7\frac{1}{4} - 5\frac{2}{4} = \frac{29}{4} - \frac{22}{4} = \frac{7}{4} = 1\frac{3}{4}}$

Mathematical Practices

MP6	**Attend to precision.**

Item 5: Students carefully specify units of measure and display data.

UNIT 4 Common Core Review

Circle the correct answer.

11. How many inches are in 6 ft?

a. $\frac{1}{2}$ in.   b. 12 in.

c. 36 in.   (d.) 72 in.

12. How many ounces are in 2 pounds?

a. 40 oz.   (b.) 32 oz.

c. 20 oz.   d. 16 oz.

13. Use a protractor to draw a 60° angle on the line at the right. Write the measurement on the figure.

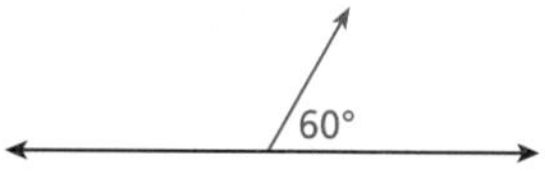

60°

14. What is the length of the rectangle?

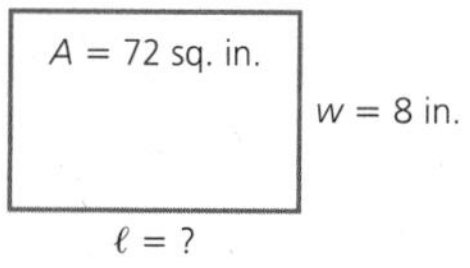

Show your work.
$A = \ell \times w$
$72 = \ell \times 8$
$72 = 9 \times 8$

$A = 72$ sq. in. $w = 8$ in. $\ell = ?$

Answer The length of the rectangle is 9 in.

15. A water sprinkler rotates one-degree turn at each interval. If the sprinkler rotates a total of 110°, how many one-degree turns has the sprinkler made?

The sprinkler has made 110 one-degree turns.

For exercises 16 and 17 use the figure at the right. The two angles form a straight angle.

MP5 16. Use a protractor to measure each angle. Write the measurements on the figure.

45° 135°

MP7 17. Amilah says that once you find the measure of one of the angles, you can calculate the measure of the other angle without using a protractor. Is she correct? Explain.

Answer Yes. The two angles form a straight angle, or 180° angle. Once you find the measure of one angle, you can subtract the measure you know from 180 to find the measure of the other angle. For example, 180° − 135° = 45°.

Unit 4 ▪ Focus on Measurement and Data **299**

This chart correlates the Common Core Review items with the lessons in which the concepts and skills are presented.

Item	Lesson
1	33
2	33
3	27
4	27
5	30
6	30
7	30
8	30
9	30
10	30
11	26
12	26
13	32
14	29
15	31
16	32
17	33
18	28
19	29
20	28

Mathematical Practices	
MP5	Use appropriate tools strategically.
Item 16: Students use a protractor to measure angles.	
MP7	Look for and make use of structure.
Item 17: Students use adjacent angles to explain how to find missing angle measures.	

Writing About Math

✏️ ▸ Direct students to respond to the Unit 4 Essential Question. (This can also be found on student page 233.)

> **Essential Question:**
> How can measurement data be used to solve problems?

Possible responses:

- Customary and metric measurement problems can be solved using measurement conversions. These problems can involve measurements of length, capacity, weight, and time.
- The length and width of a rectangle or square can be used to determine its area and perimeter.
- Measurement data can be organized on line plots that can be used to determine and verify answers.
- Angle measures can be determined by using a protractor or by using information given about the angles.

> ### Unit Assessment
>
> - Unit 4 Common Core Review, *pp. 298–300*
> - Unit 4 Performance Task ⬭ONLINE⬭
>
> ### Additional Assessment Options
>
> **Optional Purchase:**
>
> - iProgress Monitor ⬭ONLINE⬭
> - Progress Monitor Student Benchmark Assessment Booklet

Solve the problems.

MP4 **18.** The championship game is at 4:15 P.M. It takes the team bus 60 minutes to get to Central School where the game will be played. The coach wants the team to arrive at Central School 30 minutes before the game starts. What time should the team bus leave for the game?

Answer The team bus should leave for the game at 2:45 P.M.

✏️ ▸ **Justify your answer using words, drawings, or numbers.**
Possible justification shown.

```
              30 min          60 min
          ┌──────────┐ ┌────────────────────┐
    ◄──────┼─────┼─────┼─────┼─────┼─────┼─────┼──────►
         2:30  2:45  3:00  3:15  3:30  3:45  4:00  4:15
```

MP5 **19.** Joel is making a small rectangular blanket. He has 360 centimeters of fringe, which is the exact amount he needs to go around the edge of the blanket. One end of the blanket is 80 cm long. What are the lengths of the other three sides?

Answer The length of the opposite side is 80 cm, and the lengths of the other two sides are 100 cm and 100 cm.

✏️ ▸ **Show your work.**
Possible answer: This is a rectangle with opposite sides equal. If one side is 80 cm, then the opposite side is also 80 cm.
$360 - 80 - 80 = 200$ cm
200 cm is the combined length of the other pair of opposite sides, so the length of each of these sides is $200 \div 2 = 100$ cm.

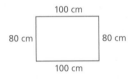

MP2 **20.** The supermarket sells 1 quart of milk for $1.89 or $\frac{1}{2}$ gallon for $3.00. Which is the better buy?

Answer The $\frac{1}{2}$ gallon of milk for $3.00 is the better buy.

✏️ ▸ **Justify your answer using words, drawings, or numbers.**
Possible justification:
There are 4 quarts in a gallon, so $\frac{1}{2}$ gallon = 2 quarts.
If you buy $\frac{1}{2}$ gallon for $3.00, you will pay $1.50 per quart.
If you buy 1 quart, you will pay $1.89 per quart.
$1.89 > $1.50, so the $\frac{1}{2}$ gallon is the better buy.

Mathematical Practices
MP2 **Reason abstractly and quantitatively.**
Item 20: Students make sense of quantities and their relationships in problem situations.
MP4 **Model with mathematics.**
Item 18: Students apply mathematical knowledge to solve problems in everyday life.
MP5 **Use appropriate tools strategically.**
Item 19: Students consider which tool would help them solve a mathematical problem.

Focus on Geometry

Progress Check

UNIT 5

Look at how the Common Core standards you have learned and will learn connect.

It is very important for you to understand the standards from the prior grade level so that you will be able to develop an understanding of geometry in this unit and be prepared for next year. To practice your skills, go to sadlierconnect.com.

GRADE 3	Before Unit 5	GRADE 4	After Unit 5	GRADE 5
I Can...		**Can I ?**		**I Will...**
		4.G.1 ☐ Draw points, lines, line segments, and rays	☐	**5.G.1** Understand the concept and representation of the coordinate plane
		☐ Draw right angles, acute angles, and obtuse angles	☐	
		☐ Draw parallel and perpendicular lines	☐	
		☐ Identify lines and angles in two-dimensional figures.	☐	
3.G.1 ☐ Explain that shapes in different categories may share attributes; for example, rectangles and squares both have four straight sides ☐ Classify quadrilaterals by their attributes		**4.G.2** ☐ Classify shapes by properties of their lines and angles ☐ Recognize right triangles as a category	☐ ☐	**5.G.3** Understand relationships among categories of figures; for example, all rectangles have four right angles and squares are rectangles, so all squares have four right angles **5.G.4** Classify two-dimensional figures [in a hierarchy] based on properties
		4.G.3 ☐ Identify and draw lines of symmetry ☐ Identify figures that have line symmetry	☐ ☐	

Unit 5 ▪ Focus on Geometry

Student Page 301

Progress Check

Progress Check is a self-assessment tool that students can use to gauge their own progress. Research shows that when students take accountability for their learning, motivation increases.

Before students begin work in Unit 5, have them check any items they know they can do well. Explain that it is fine if they don't check any of the boxes; they will have the opportunity to learn and practice all the standards through the course of the unit.

Let them know that at the end of the unit they will review their checklists to check their progress. After students have completed the last lesson of the unit, before they begin Common Core Review, you will be prompted to have students revisit this page.

HOME ◆ CONNECT...

The Home Connect feature is a way to keep parents or other adult family members apprised of what their children are learning. The key learning objectives are listed, and some ideas for related activities and discussions are included.

Explain to students that they can share the Home Connect page at home with their families. Let students know there is an activity connected to their classroom learning that they can do with their families.

Encourage students and their parents to share their experiences using the suggestions on the Home Connect. You may wish to invite students to share this work with the class.

HOME ◆ CONNECT...

Your child will use the language of geometry to analyze and classify angles and geometric figures. Support your child by using the following Math vocabulary:

- An **angle** is formed when two **rays** share the same endpoint, called the **vertex**.
- A **straight angle** forms a straight line. It measures 180°.
- A **right angle** measures 90° and is formed by the intersection of two perpendicular lines.
- An **acute angle** is less than a right angle, or measures between 0° and 90°.
- An **obtuse angle** is more than a right angle, or measures between 90° and 180°.

Activity: Plan a shape scavenger hunt for your child and some friends or siblings. Make a list of two-dimensional figures (such as right triangle, parallelogram, rectangle, pentagon), and ask the children to safely search around your home or other safe locale to find examples of each figure.

In this unit your child will:

- Draw and identify points, lines, and angles.
- Classify two-dimensional figures.
- Identify lines of symmetry.

NOTE: All of these learning goals for your child are based on the Grade 4 Common Core State Standards for Mathematics.

Ways to Help Your Child

Encourage your child to share math vocabulary words and their meanings with your family. Using the mathematical vocabulary will help your child to make connections, as well as to avoid misconceptions.

ONLINE
For more Home Connect activities, continue online at sadlierconnect.com

302 Unit 5 ▪ Focus on Geometry

Student Page 302

UNIT PLANNER

	Lesson	Standard(s)	Objective
34	Draw and Identify Points, Lines, and Angles	4.G.1	Use an understanding of geometric terms to analyze and classify geometric figures by locating and defining examples of such terms in a geometric figure.
35	Classify Two-Dimensional Figures	4.G.2	Classifying two-dimensional figures.
36	Identify Lines of Symmetry	4.G.3	Identify and draw lines of symmetry.

Essential Question: How does understanding lines and angles help you identify geometric shapes?

UNIT 5

303B

Essential Question	Words to Know
How do you draw and identify points, lines, and angles in geometric figures?	line, line segment, parallel lines, perpendicular lines
How do you classify two-dimensional figures?	parallelogram, adjacent, rectangle, trapezoid, right triangle, pentagon, hexagon
How do you identify and draw lines of symmetry?	line of symmetry

Unit Assessment

- Unit 5 Common Core Review, *pp. 328–330*
- Unit 5 Performance Task ONLINE

Additional Assessment Options

- Performance Task 2, *pp. 331–336*
  ALSO ONLINE

Optional Purchase:

- iProgress Monitor ONLINE
- Progress Monitor Student Benchmark Assessment Booklet

ONLINE Digital Resources

- Home Connect Activities
- Unit Performance Tasks
- Additional Practice
- Fluency Practice
- Teacher Resources
- iProgress Monitor (optional purchase)

Go to SadlierConnect.com to access your Digital Resources.

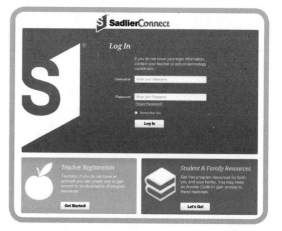

For more detailed instructions see page T3.

LEARNING PROGRESSIONS

This page provides more in-depth detail on the development of the standards across the grade levels. See also the unit Progress Check page in the Student Edition for a roadmap of the Learning Progressions.

Grade 3

- Students understand that shapes in different categories may share attributes and that the shared attributes may define a larger category. For example, rhombuses and rectangles have four sides, and having four sides defines the larger category of quadrilaterals. (3.G.1)
- Students recognize rhombuses, rectangles, and squares as types of quadrilaterals, and draw examples of quadrilaterals that do not belong to any of these subcategories. (3.G.1)

Grade 4

- Constructing a wide range of examples deepens understanding of geometric concepts; students draw points, lines, line segments, rays, angles (right, acute, obtuse), and perpendicular and parallel lines, and identify them in two-dimensional figures. (4.G.1)
- Students classify shapes by properties of their lines and angles. They identify right triangles and recognize them as a category. (4.G.2)
- Previous and continuing work with paper-folding activities supports recognition of a line of symmetry for a two-dimensional figure as a line across the figure along which the figure can be folded into matching parts. Students identify figures that have line symmetry and draw lines of symmetry. (4.G.3)

Grade 5

- Students build on previous work with number lines by using two perpendicular number lines to define a coordinate system to represent the coordinate plane. They use coordinates to identify and plot points in the first quadrant. (5.G.1)
- Students understand that attributes belonging to a category of figures are shared by all subcategories of the category. For example, all rectangles have four right angles and squares are rectangles, so all squares have four right angles. (5.G.3)
- Students classify two-dimensional figures in a hierarchy based on their properties. (5.G.4)

Focus on Geometry

Essential Question:
How does understanding lines and angles help you identify geometric shapes?

Essential Question:
How does understanding lines and angles help you identify geometric shapes?

As students become involved with the Essential Question, they develop their knowledge of points, lines, and angles. They will then use and apply this knowledge to identify shapes and characteristics of these shapes.

Conversation Starters

Have students discuss the photograph. Ask questions such as: *What shapes do you see in the design? Do you see any repeating shapes in the design? Can you look at larger shapes in such as way to see other shapes within them?*

Ask students to look at the 8-pointed star in the center of the design. Encourage students to draw lines to help them see the different shapes. *Look closely at the center of the design. How many triangles can you see? How many quadrilaterals? How many squares?* (Students should see at least 16 triangles, 8 quadrilaterals, and 1 square. If students see more of these shapes, ask them to justify their answers.)

Have students look at the purple and pink area of the design, the second circle out from the center. *How many shapes can you see in this area? They can be shapes with names you are familiar with or not.* (I can see triangles, quadrilaterals, parallelograms, and "arrows".)

Let students work in pairs to discover different shapes. They can draw the shapes they see if they are unable to name them. Encourage students to look at large shapes and shapes within the larger shapes.

Activity

Materials: paper, pencil, ruler

Have students begin by drawing a large shape they are familiar with such as a square or triangle. Have them use a ruler to draw lines through the shape to divide it into other shapes. Students can also color their design afterwards.

Students can then switch designs with another student. The other student should find and identify as many shapes as possible within the larger shape. They can draw any shapes they are unable to name.

Have a whole-class discussion to share the students' answers. Have students share all shapes they found and draw them on the board. Name the shapes based on the number of sides and keep these shapes available throughout the unit as a reference guide.

Common Core Focus:

4.G.1 Draw points, lines, line segments, rays, angles (right, acute, obtuse), and perpendicular and parallel lines. Identify these in two-dimensional figures.

OBJECTIVE

Use an understanding of geometric terms to analyze and classify geometric figures by locating and defining examples of such terms in a geometric figure.

ESSENTIAL QUESTION

An understanding of points, lines, and angles will allow students to classify angles, name figures, and locate examples in more complex geometric figures. Explain to students that an understanding of the Words to Know in this lesson will allow them to better understand later geometric concepts.

FLUENCY PRACTICE

Fluency practice is available at **sadlierconnect.com**.

Concept Development

Understand: Using and applying geometric terms

■ Students need to understand and be able to apply the geometric terms in this lesson. Students should also be able to locate and define these geometric terms within a figure. Some students may confuse lines with line segments. Give adequate time to understanding the differences between the two.

■ Make sure students can identify examples of each geometric term in the figure given in the problem.

■ Explain that intersecting perpendicular lines form 90° angles, or right angles. Ask students to identify other right angles formed by the intersecting perpendicular lines in the geometric figure.

Lesson 34 — Draw and Identify Points, Lines, and Angles

Essential Question:
How do you draw and identify points, lines, and angles in geometric figures?
4.G.1

Words to Know:
line
line segment
parallel lines
perpendicular lines

Guided Instruction

In this lesson you will learn how to use the language of geometry to analyze and classify geometric figures.

Understand: Using and applying geometric terms

> Using this geometric figure, what geometric terms can you define?

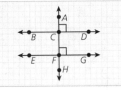

You learned that a point is an exact location in space. Points are named using capital letters. On this figure, points *A* through *H* identify locations.

A line is an endless collection of points along a straight path. To name a line, use any two points on the line. Look at lines *AH*, *BD*, and *EG*. Each line can also be named by any other two points on the line, for example, *CF* or *FH* also name line *AH*.

A line segment is part of a line that has two endpoints. Using the endpoints you can name line segments *AH*, *BD*, and *EG*. Some other line segments are line segments *AC*, *BC*, and *CF*.

A ray is a part of a line that has one endpoint and extends endlessly in the other direction. To name a ray, start with the endpoint and use any other point on the ray. For example, ray *AC* is the same ray as ray *AF* or ray *AH* since it starts at point *A* and extends endlessly along line *AH*. Some other rays are rays *CB*, *CA*, and *CD*.

Parallel lines are lines that will never meet, or intersect. Line *BD* is parallel to line *EG*.

Perpendicular lines are lines that meet, or intersect, to form a right angle. When you see a square in the corner it shows that a right angle is formed and thus the lines are perpendicular. Line *AH* is perpendicular to line *BD*. Line *AH* is also perpendicular to line *EG*.

> **Remember!**
> A right angle forms a square corner.

➡ You have defined points, lines, line segments, rays, parallel lines, and perpendicular lines.

Words to Know

line: an endless collection of points along a straight path

line segment: part of a line that has two endpoints

parallel lines: lines that will never meet, or intersect

perpendicular lines: lines that meet, or intersect, to form a right angle

Glossary can be found on pp. 347–350.

Understand: Identifying right, acute, obtuse, and straight angles

Identify the types of angles that are shown here.

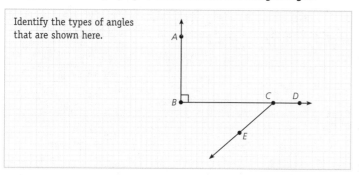

An angle is named by its vertex, the point from which the two sides of an angle begin. The angle at *B* is marked by the symbol (⌐) so it is a right angle and measures 90°. It can also be named as angle *ABC*, or angle *CBA*. The letter naming the vertex names the angle. In a three letter angle name, the vertex is the middle letter.

Remember!

An angle is formed when two rays share the same endpoint, called the vertex. The two rays form the sides of the angle.

An angle that is less than a right angle is an acute angle. It measures less than 90°. Angle *BCE* is an acute angle.

An angle that is greater than a right angle is an obtuse angle. It measures more than 90° and less than 180°. Angle *DCE* is an obtuse angle.

An angle that forms a straight line is a straight angle. It measures 180°. Angle *BCD* is a straight angle.

➡ Angle *ABC* is a right angle, angle *BCE* is an acute angle, angle *DCE* is an obtuse angle, and angle *BCD* is a straight angle.

✏ How can you check that angles *BCE* and *DCE* are not right angles? Possible answer: Use the square corner of a sheet of paper. If the angle is less, it is acute. If it is greater, it is obtuse.

Understand: Identifying right, acute, obtuse, and straight angles

■ In this presentation, students identify the types of angles that are shown in the figure. Students may be familiar with right, acute, obtuse, and straight angles from earlier lessons in Unit 4.

■ Remind students that angles are named according to the vertex and one point on each ray. It is also important to note that the vertex is the second point in the angle name.

■ Using the drawing, discuss the types of angles that are seen. You might show other visual examples of each type of angle. Additionally, you can allow students to draw examples of each type of angle.

✏ Have students share the methods they used to check that the angles are not right angles. Ask students to attempt each method shared.

Support English Language Learners

English language learners may have difficulty understanding some of the definitions in Words to Know. To help students better understand the definition of a *line,* explain or show what is meant by an *endless collection of points along a straight path.* Focus students on the words *endless* and *collection.* Ask students to define these terms in their own words, or show examples and provide the definitions. Make sure students understand that while there may appear to be gaps between a drawing of points, a line includes the points between the points, and it extends continuously in both directions.

Connect: What you know about the language of geometry and geometric shapes Use this page to help students strengthen their understanding of geometric terms and geometric figures.

■ Most triangles that students are familiar with probably have acute and right angles. It is necessary for students to understand what an obtuse angle is, in order to draw a triangle containing an obtuse angle.

■ Make the connection that the measure of an obtuse angle is greater than the measure of a right angle, but less than a straight angle.

✏ Have students classify the other two angles in the triangle. Tell students that the total measure of the angles in a triangle must be 180°. Therefore, the other two angles in this triangle must be acute.

Connect: What you know about the language of geometry and geometric shapes

> Pablo cuts a piece of blue glass to make a triangle that will be placed in a stained glass window. The triangle has one obtuse angle. Show what the triangle with one obtuse angle might look like.

Step 1

Understand what it means for an angle to be obtuse.
You know that it cannot be a right angle or measure 90°.

An obtuse angle must be ___greater___ than a right angle but
 greater or less
___less___ than a straight angle.
greater or less

Step 2

Now draw an obtuse angle: from the same vertex point draw one horizontal ray and then another ray that is between the two rays representing 90° and 180°.

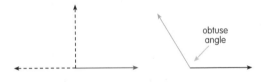

obtuse
angle

Step 3

Choose one point on each ray and connect the points to form a triangle with on obtuse angle.

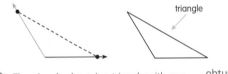

triangle

➡ The triangle above is a triangle with one ___obtuse___ angle.

✏ Name another angle or angles that you see in the triangle formed in Step 3. Possible answer: I see two acute angles

---

Math-to-Sports Connection

Athletic Fields and Courts A strong understanding of identifying points, lines, and angles in geometric figures will allow students to understand more complex geometric concepts. There are many examples of points, lines, and angles on athletic fields and courts. Show students pictures of football fields, baseball diamonds, soccer pitches, and basketball courts. Ask students to identify examples of points, lines, and angles in the pictures.

Lesson 34

Guided Practice

For exercises 1–4, draw and label an example.

1. line *JK*
Check students' drawings.

2. line segment *QR*
Check students' drawings.

3. acute angle *CDE*
Check students' drawings.

4. line *LM* parallel to line *ST*
Check students' drawings.

For exercises 5–9, use the figure at the right.

5. Name three line segments. Possible
answers: segments *PQ, NQ, MR*

6. Name two rays. Possible answers:
rays *QP, QS, QN, RM, RT*

7. Name an obtuse angle. Possible
answers: angle *PQS* or angle *QRT*

8. Name an acute angle. Possible
answers: angle *PQN* or angle *QRM*

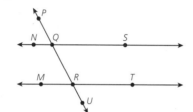

Solve the problem.

MP7 **9.** On a blueprint, a designer used two right angles to make a straight
angle. Draw an example to show how two right angles can make a
straight angle.
Drawings may vary. Possible drawing shown.

Think•Pair•Share

MP3 **10.** Describe something in your classroom that reminds you of parallel lines.
Explain why you think the lines are parallel.
Answers may vary.

Unit 5 ■ Focus on Geometry **307**

Mathematical Practices

Mathematical Practice Standards underline the teaching and understanding of all concepts and skills presented. The emphasis of specific practices is noted throughout the guided and independent practice of this lesson.

MP3	**Construct viable arguments and critique the reasoning of others.**

Item 10: Students share their reasoning about a connection between a classroom item and parallel lines.

MP7	**Look for and make use of structure.**

Item 9: Students create a drawing that matches the description given.

Observational Assessment

Use page 307 to assess whether students are able to correctly draw and identify points, lines, and angles in geometric figures.

Think•Pair•Share

Peer Collaboration Ask pairs of students to look for objects in the classroom that have lines resembling parallel lines and explain why the lines look parallel. Ask volunteers to share their responses with the class. Ask guiding questions, such as:

• *Did anyone else choose the same object as _____?*

• *Do you agree with _____? Explain why or why not.*

Return to the Essential Question

Reread the Lesson 34 Essential Question on page 304: *How do you draw and identify points, lines, and angles in geometric figures?*

Ask volunteers to use what they learned in this lesson to answer this question. (Possible response: I know a point is an exact location in space. Points are labeled with capital letters. I know a line is continuous through both points as well as any other points along a straight path. I know a ray begins at one point and passes through another point. I know perpendicular lines are ones that intersect making four right angles.)

Invite as many volunteers as possible to express ideas about drawing and identifying points, lines, and angles in geometric figures.

Concept Application

Students may work independently on these pages in the classroom or at home. They may refer to the first four pages of the lesson to revisit the instruction or to see a worked-out example.

Common Errors and **Teaching Tips** may help you support student learning either in the classroom or as a follow-up for work done at home.

Common Errors

Item 1

Students might reverse the order of points in a ray. Remind students that the starting point is named first and the point that the ray passes through is listed second.

Teaching Tips

Items 1–10

It is necessary for students to follow each specific direction to correctly draw and label examples. Encourage students to label their drawings according to the directions in each exercise.

Item 8

Remind students that parallel lines are always the same distance apart.

Lesson 34   Draw and Identify Points, Lines, and Angles

Independent Practice

For exercises 1–10, draw and label an example.

1. ray *CD*
   Check students' drawings.

2. line *XY*
   Check students' drawings.

3. right angle *JKL*
   Check students' drawings.

4. line segment *AB*
   Check students' drawings.

5. line *EF* perpendicular to line *GH*
   Check students' drawings.

6. acute angle *PQR*
   Check students' drawings.

7. obtuse angle *DEF*
   Check students' drawings.

8. line *QR* parallel to line *ST*
   Check students' drawings.

9. straight angle *LMN*
   Check students' drawings.

10. line *AB* perpendicular to line segment *CD*
    Check students' drawings.

308   Unit 5 ■ Focus on Geometry

Writing About Math

■ ▸ **Sequence of Events with Transitional Words** In order to manage the sequence of events in writing, students must effectively use transitional words such as *first, next, then, after that,* and *finally.* Transitional words are especially useful in writing directions.

Have students create a how-to book for a variety of geometric skills, such as drawing parallel lines, identifying angles, and labeling points. Encourage students to use transitional words when writing the steps within the how-to book.

Lesson 34

Independent Practice

Classify each angle as acute, right, obtuse, or straight.

11.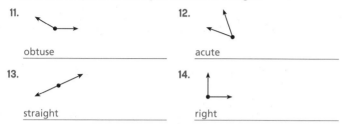

obtuse

12.

acute

13.

straight

14.

right

For exercises 15–23, use the figure.

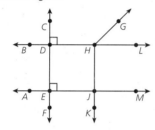

15. Name five points. Possible answers: A, B, C, D, E

16. Name four line segments. Possible answers: line segments EF, EJ, JK, JM, HJ

17. Name three lines. Possible answers: lines BL, AM, CF

18. Name four rays. Possible answers: rays EA, DC, EF, HG

19. Line segments DE and HJ have the same length. Name a pair of parallel lines. _____ lines BL and AM

20. Name a pair of perpendicular lines. lines BL and CF or lines AM and CF

21. Name a straight angle. Possible answer: angle CDE

22. Name an obtuse angle. Possible answer: angle DHG

23. Name an acute angle. _____ angle GHL

Teaching Tips

Items 15-23

Remind students of the order of the points in the names of rays and angles. In a ray, the point at which the ray starts is first and the point that the ray passes through is second. In the name of an angle, the vertex is named between the two other points.

Digital Connection

Interactive Whiteboard Use interactive whiteboard software to form line segments, rays, and lines. Students can create line segments, rays, and lines of many lengths. Encourage students to form and label examples of each. In addition, parallel lines, intersecting lines, perpendicular lines, and angles can also be created.

Independent Practice

Teaching Tips

Item 25

Some students may have difficulty determining parallel and intersecting line segments in the figure. Encourage students to use a straight edge to extend each side beyond the shape to determine whether the sides are parallel or perpendicular.

Independent Practice

24. Draw a triangle with one right angle.
Drawings will vary. Check students' drawings.

Classify the other two angles in your triangle as acute, right, obtuse, or straight. Explain how you classified the other two angles.
Both are acute. Possible explanation: The other two angles are both acute because they both measure less than 90°, a right angle.

Solve the problems.

MP6 **25.** The window above a door is in the shape shown at the right. How many acute, obtuse, and right angles are in the window? Do any of the pairs of line segments used in the shape of the window look parallel or perpendicular?
The window has 2 acute and 2 obtuse angles. There are no right angles. The top and bottom line segments look parallel. None look perpendicular.

MP4 **26.** Look at the stop sign at the right. How many acute, obtuse, and right angles are in the stop sign? Do any of the pairs of line segments used in the shape of the stop sign look parallel or perpendicular?
The stop sign has 8 obtuse angles. There are no acute angles and no right angles. Each pair of opposite line segments look parallel. None look perpendicular.

Mathematical Practices

MP4	**Model with mathematics.**

Item 26: Students relate mathematics to a real-world item by identifying angles and parallel sides in the object.

MP6	**Attend to precision.**

Item 25: Students accurately identify the number and type of angles and the number of parallel and perpendicular sides in a drawing.

Lesson 34

Independent Practice

MP4 **27.** The street my friend Craig lives on is parallel to the street Francie lives on. The street Francie lives on is parallel to the street Briana lives on. The street Briana lives on is parallel to the street Drew lives on. Describe the relationship between Craig's street and Drew's street.

Answer Craig's street is parallel to Drew's street.

▸ **Justify your answer using words, drawings, or numbers.**
Possible justification: Students' drawings may show four parallel lines labeled with names.

MP7 **28.** Taylor has two tiles shaped like the rectangle and the square shown below. She notices that some geometric characteristics of the tiles are the same and some are different.

What is something the same that Taylor might notice? What is something different? Possible answer: In both tiles, the opposite sides are parallel. In both tiles, the figures have 4 right angles. The 4 line
Answer segments that form the square look the same length. In the rectangle, each pair of line segments look a different length.
▸ **Justify your answer using words, drawings, or numbers.**
Possible justification: In both figures, the line segments that form the opposite sides are parallel because they would not intersect even if they were extended to go on forever. The angles of both figures form square corners so they are all right angles.

MP6 **29.** Travis draws a pair of lines on a sheet of paper. The lines he draws do not intersect. What can you say about the lines? Are they necessarily parallel, perpendicular, or neither? Explain.

Answer The lines may be parallel, they may be perpendicular, or they may be neither.
▸ **Justify your answer using words, drawings, or numbers.**
Possible justification: If the lines will never meet no matter how far they are extended, the lines are parallel. If the lines can be extended, so that they meet to form right angles, the lines are perpendicular. If the lines can be extended so that they meet to form acute and obtuse angles, the lines are neither parallel or perpendicular.

Unit 5 ■ Focus on Geometry **311**

Teaching Tips

Items 27-29
Each of the problems includes multiple steps and questions. Encourage students to think about one step of the problem at a time.

Mathematical Practices

MP4	**Model with mathematics.**

Item 27: Students identify a solution in the context of a real-world situation.

MP6	**Attend to precision.**

Item 29: Students carefully formulate a full explanation of the possible lines that could have been drawn.

MP7	**Look for and make use of structure.**

Item 28: Students discuss geometric shapes in terms of their similarities and differences.

Common Core Focus:

4.G.2 Classify two-dimensional figures based on the presence or absence of parallel or perpendicular lines, or the presence or absence of angles of a specified size. Recognize right triangles as a category, and identify right triangles.

OBJECTIVE
Classify two-dimensional figures.

ESSENTIAL QUESTION

In Grade 3, students learned that rhombuses, rectangles, and squares were examples of quadrilaterals and classified them by using properties such as sides and right angles. In Grade 4 the focus shifts to classifying figures based on the presence or absence of parallel or perpendicular lines, or the presence or absence of angles of a specified size.

PREREQUISITE SKILLS

Use Item L on page 342 of the Foundational Skills Handbook to review how to use angles and lengths of sides to identify special quadrilaterals.

FLUENCY PRACTICE

Fluency practice is available at **sadlierconnect.com**.

Concept Development

Understand: Using parallel or perpendicular lines to classify two-dimensional figures.

■ If students do not have a clear understanding of the terms *parallel, perpendicular,* or *adjacent,* they will have difficulty classifying shapes. Suggest they use index cards to record the new terms along with the definitions and examples.

■ To reinforce the Remember! concept, have students measure the distance between parallel lines at different points.

■ Using the figures shown, have students identify adjacent, parallel, and perpendicular sides.

Essential Question:
How do you classify two-dimensional figures?
4.G.2

Words to Know:
parallelogram
adjacent
rectangle
trapezoid
right triangle
pentagon
hexagon

Guided Instruction

In this lesson you will learn how to classify two-dimensional figures using angle measures and pairs of parallel or perpendicular sides.

Understand: Using parallel or perpendicular lines to classify two-dimensional figures

> Dawn makes dog collars. She stamps the collars with two-dimensional figures to create decorative patterns. Two of the figures she uses are shown. Classify or identify by attributes the figures that Dawn uses to create the decorative patterns.

The figures that Dawn uses are quadrilaterals.

You can use parallel lines and perpendicular lines to further classify the quadrilaterals.

Parallel sides are sides that are parts of parallel lines. In quadrilateral *ABCD*, side *AB* is parallel to side *DC*. Side *AD* is parallel to side *BC*. Both pairs of opposite sides are parallel. So quadrilateral *ABCD* is a parallelogram. In quadrilateral *QRST*, side *QR* is parallel to side *TS*. Side *QT* is parallel to side *RS*. Both pairs of opposite sides of the quadrilateral are parallel. Quadrilateral *QRST* is also a parallelogram.

Perpendicular sides are sides that are adjacent, or next to each other, and are parts of perpendicular lines. In parallelogram *QRST*, side *QT* is perpendicular to side *TS*. Side *RS* is perpendicular to side *TS*. A parallelogram with two pairs of perpendicular sides is a rectangle. So quadrilateral *QRST* can also be classified as a rectangle.

➡ Dawn uses parallelograms and rectangles to create the decorative patterns.

You learned that a parallelogram with all sides of equal length can be classified as a rhombus. There is another kind of quadrilateral that has at least one set of parallel sides. It is a trapezoid.

Remember!
Parallel lines never meet and are always the same distance apart. Perpendicular lines meet at right angles.

Words to Know

parallelogram: a quadrilateral in which both pairs of opposite sides are parallel

adjacent: sides of a polygon that are next to each other

rectangle: a parallelogram with two pairs of perpendicular sides

trapezoid: a quadrilateral that has at least one pair of parallel sides

Glossary can be found on pp. 347–350.

Lesson 35

Guided Instruction

Understand: Using angle measurement to classify two-dimensional figures

Dawn creates another pattern by stamping the same pair of two-dimensional figures several times. Classify the two-dimensional figures Dawn uses to create this new pattern for her dog collars.

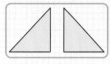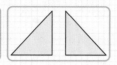

Each triangle has one pair of perpendicular sides. The perpendicular sides meet at right angles.

Each triangle has exactly one right angle. Notice that the other two angles in the triangle measure less than 90°, so they are acute angles. A triangle with one right angle is called a right triangle.

Remember!
A right angle measures 90° and forms a square corner.

➡ Dawn uses right triangles to create the new pattern for her dog collars.

✏ Draw an example of a triangle that is not a right triangle. How do you know it is not a right triangle?
Check students' drawings. Students should draw an acute or an obtuse triangle.
Possible answer: I know it is not a right triangle because none of the sides in the triangle form a right angle.

Unit 5 ■ Focus on Geometry **313**

Understand: Using angle measurement to classify two-dimensional figures

■ Students are expected to recognize right triangles as a category, and to identify right triangles. In this presentation, students examine the sides of the triangles to determine if they form right triangles. In order to do this, students must understand that perpendicular sides create a right angle where the sides meet. Review the term *perpendicular* if necessary.

■ Reinforce that right triangles have exactly one right angle and two acute angles. It is the right angle that defines a right triangle. There are many triangles that are not right triangles that also have two acute angles.

✏ Ask students to share their drawings and explain how they know that the figure they drew is not a right triangle. Ask if any students drew a triangle with an obtuse angle.

Words to Know

right triangle: a triangle with one right angle

pentagon: a polygon with 5 sides and 5 angles

hexagon: a polygon with 6 sides and 6 angles

Glossary can be found on pp. 347–350.

Connect: **What you know about classifying two-dimensional figures** Use this page to help students strengthen their understanding of how to classify two-dimensional figures.

■ This page focuses on the students' understanding of vocabulary necessary to classify the pentagons. It also strengthens students' understanding of the two-dimensional shape, pentagon. Math terms that should be emphasized on this page are *parallel, perpendicular,* and *right angles.*

■ Remind students that in order to determine if a figure has a right angle, they must look for sides that are perpendicular or for the symbol that indicates the angle measures 90°.

■ Point out that a regular pentagon has 5 equal side lengths and 5 equal angles. Ask students to determine if any of these pentagons are regular pentagons. Challenge them to identify a real-world example of a pentagon, such as a crosswalk sign they might see outside their school building.

Lesson 35 **Classify Two-Dimensional Figures**

Guided Instruction

Connect: **What you know about classifying two-dimensional figures**

Identify the polygons. Then identify any pairs of parallel or perpendicular sides.

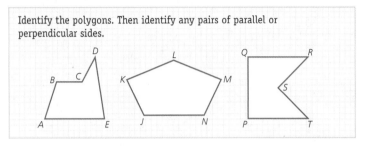

Each of the polygons is a pentagon.

A pentagon has __5__ straight sides and __5__ angles.

Do any pairs of sides of pentagon *ABCDE* form right angles? __No__

Are any pairs of sides of pentagon *ABCDE* perpendicular? __No__
In pentagon *ABCDE* side *AE* and side *BC* are always the same distance apart.

If the sides were extended, would the lines ever meet? __No__

Are any pairs of sides of pentagon *ABCDE* parallel? __Yes__

Which sides of pentagon *ABCDE* are parallel? ____side *AE* and side *BC*____

Do any pairs of sides of pentagon *JKLMN* form right angles? __No__

Are any pairs of sides of pentagon *JKLMN* parallel? __No__

Do any pairs of sides of pentagon *PQRST* form right angles? __Yes__
Which pairs of sides of pentagon *PQRST* are perpendicular?
_____side *TP* and side *QP*; side *RQ* and side *QP*_____

Are any pairs of sides of pentagon *PQRST* parallel? __Yes__

Which sides of pentagon *PQRST* are parallel? ____side *PT* and side *QR*____

▶ Polygons ____*ABCDE* and *PQRST*____ each have one pair of parallel sides

and polygon _____*PQRST*_____ has two pairs of perpendicular sides.

A hexagon is a polygon with 6 sides and 6 angles.

Support English Language Learners

One term that is used many times in this lesson is *right* when naming a 90° angle. English language learners may struggle with the term *right,* as they may already know *right* in different contexts. The most common uses of the word *right* are to describe a direction, or as being correct.

To help students remember the meaning of *right* in this context, pair a visual example with a definition. Draw a right angle and say, "This is a right angle. What is this?" and have students answer, "This is a right angle." Then draw examples of different types of angles, with one of them being a right angle. Have volunteers come up and identify which one is a right angle.

Lesson 35

Guided Practice

For questions 1–7, use polygons 1–5.

1. Which of the polygons have no right angles? ____1, 3, 5____

2. Which of the polygons have at least one pair of perpendicular sides?
   ____2, 4____

3. Which of the polygons seem to have at least one pair of parallel sides?
   ____3, 4, 5____

4. Which of the polygons is a right triangle? ____2____

5. Which of the polygons are quadrilateral? ____3, 4____

6. What is another way to classify each quadrilateral?
   3: parallelogram (or trapezoid); 4: trapezoid

7. Classify polygon 5. ____hexagon____

Solve the problem.

MP6 8. Julia says that she can draw a right triangle in which two sides have the same length. Is Julia correct? Draw an example to justify your answer.
Yes, Julia is correct. Possible drawing:

Think•Pair•Share

MP5 9. Draw a hexagon with exactly two right angles. Explain how you drew the hexagon. Does your hexagon have any pairs of parallel or perpendicular sides?
Possible explanation: I started with the right angles. Then I added the other sides to create a hexagon. The hexagon has one pair of parallel sides and two pairs of perpendicular sides.
Possible drawing:

Unit 5 ■ Focus on Geometry **315**

Mathematical Practices

Mathematical Practice Standards underline the teaching and understanding of all concepts and skills presented. The emphasis of specific practices is noted throughout the guided and independent practice of this lesson.

MP5	Use appropriate tools strategically.
Item 9: Students decide on appropriate tools to use to solve a problem.	
MP6	Attend to precision.
Item 8: Students use measurement tools appropriately.	

Observational Assessment

Use page 315 to assess whether students are able to identify properties of two-dimensional figures and accurately classify the figures.

Think•Pair•Share

Peer Collaboration After completing their drawings, have students share their work with a partner and discuss questions such as:

- *How many sides must the hexagon have?*

- *Must each drawing include perpendicular lines? How do you know?*

- *Must each drawing include parallel lines? How do you know?*

After students discuss these questions, lead a class discussion to determine whether students understand that they must have perpendicular lines to form right angles, but that they do not necessarily need parallel lines.

Return to the Essential Question

Reread the Lesson 35 Essential Question on page 312: *How do you classify two-dimensional figures?*

Ask volunteers to use what they learned in this lesson to answer this question. (Possible responses: If I see that lines are perpendicular, then I know that the figure includes a right angle. If the figure contains lines that are always the same distance apart, then I know that those sides are parallel. I can count the number of sides or the number of angles of a figure to name it. I can also use the general term *polygon* to name any of the two-dimensional figures in this lesson.)

You can record the accurate statements on chart paper for students to copy and use as a study guide.

Independent Practice

Concept Application

Students may work independently on these pages in the classroom or at home. They may refer to the first four pages of the lesson to revisit the instruction or to see a worked-out example.

Common Errors and **Teaching Tips** may help you support student learning either in the classroom or as a follow-up for work done at home.

Teaching Tips

Items 1–8

Make sure students recognize the right-angle symbol. Remind students that in order to be classified as a quadrilateral, the only requirement is that the figure has four sides.

Independent Practice

For questions 1–8, use polygons 1–5.

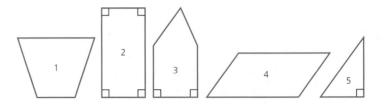

1. Which of the polygons have no right angles? ___1, 4___

2. Which of the polygons have at least one pair of perpendicular sides?
   ___2, 3, 5___

3. Which of the polygons seem to have at least one pair of parallel sides?
   ___1, 2, 3, 4___

4. Which of the polygons is a right triangle? ___5___

5. Which of the polygons are quadrilaterals? ___1, 2, 4___

6. Classify the quadrilaterals.
   ___1: trapezoid; 2: rectangle (or parallelogram); 4: parallelogram; (2 and 4 may___
   be classified as trapezoids)

7. Classify polygon 3. ___pentagon___

MP7   8. Choose two of the polygons. Tell how they are alike. Then tell how they are different.
   Answers will vary.

Mathematical Practices

MP7	**Look for and make use of structure.**

Item 8: Students use the structure of polygons to discuss similarities and differences.

Independent Practice

For exercises 9–15, draw an example of each. Then classify the polygon you drew.

9. A triangle with a pair of perpendicular sides <u>right triangle</u>
Check students' drawings.

10. A polygon with 3 sides and no right angles <u>triangle</u>
Check students' drawings.

11. A rhombus with at least one right angle <u>square</u>
Check students' drawings.

12. A parallelogram with at least one pair of perpendicular sides
<u>rectangle or square</u>
Check students' drawings.

13. A quadrilateral with no right angles and at least one pair of opposite sides that are parallel <u>parallelogram,</u> rhombus, or trapezoid
Check students' drawings.

14. A polygon with 5 sides, one pair of parallel sides, and at least one pair of perpendicular sides <u>pentagon</u>
Check students' drawings.

15. A polygon with 6 sides and two pairs of parallel sides <u>hexagon</u>
Check students' drawings.

Common Errors

Item 13

Students may incorrectly name the shape in item 13 as a rectangle. Help students to understand that a rectangle always has four right angles and the shape indicated here does not.

Teaching Tips

Items 9-12

Make sure students are able to distinguish between lines that are parallel and lines that are perpendicular. It is important that students make the connection that perpendicular sides form a right angle. Some students may benefit from the use of the vocabulary cards they made earlier in the lesson.

Math-to-Math Connection

Geometry A strong understanding of the math terms in this lesson and the properties used to classify two-dimensional shapes is important in geometry. In later grades students must be able to determine whether lines are parallel when the lines are cut by a transversal so they can determine missing angle measures without using a protractor.

Students will also need to be able to recognize properties that will help them make predictions when solving geometric problems. For example, when students determine the interior angles of a right triangle, they will already understand that one of the angles must equal 90° and that the other two must be acute. This will help them avoid errors in calculations.

Independent Practice

Teaching Tips

Item 16

Make sure students read the Venn diagram labels carefully and understand that shapes that have only one of the two attributes are placed in sections A or C. Shapes that contain both attributes are listed in section B where sections A and C overlap.

Independent Practice

For exercises 16–20, use polygons 1–6 and the Venn diagram.

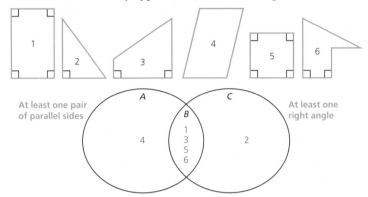

16. Write the numbers of the polygons in the correct parts of the Venn diagram (A, B, or C).

17. In which part did you place polygon 2 in the Venn diagram? Explain why.
Possible explanation: I placed it in part C because it has one right angle and no parallel sides.

18. In which part did you place polygon 3 in the Venn diagram? Explain why.
Possible explanation: I placed it in part B because it has one pair of parallel sides and two right angles.

19. In which part did you place polygon 4 in the Venn diagram? Explain why.
Possible explanation: I placed it in part A because it has no right angles and it has two pairs of parallel sides.

MP3 20. Explain why you placed some of the polygons in the overlapping part of the diagram.
Possible explanation: Some of the polygons have both attributes: at least one pair of parallel sides and at least one right angle, so these polygons must go in the overlapping part of the diagram.

Writing About Math

▸ **Write an Informative Text** Ask students to choose one figure from the top of the page and write a paragraph describing all of the geometric properties they can use to classify it. Then have students use that information to support and explain all of the ways they could name their shape. For example, figure 2 is a polygon because it is a two-dimensional closed figure; it is a triangle because it has three sides and three angles; it is a right triangle because it has two perpendicular sides that form a right angle.

When finished, ask students to trade papers and mark math terms that are *properly* used. When students receive their paper back, have them edit their text to provide proper usage of improperly used math terms.

Lesson 35

Independent Practice

MP7 **21.** Xavier says that he can draw a parallelogram with exactly one right angle. Is Xavier correct? If the statement is incorrect, how can you change it to make it correct?

Answer No, Xavier is not correct. Xavier can draw a parallelogram with four right angles.

▸ **Justify your answer using words, drawings, or numbers.**

Possible justification: When you draw one right angle and try to draw a parallelogram the other sides must also be perpendicular to make the quadrilateral a parallelogram.

MP8 **22.** Antoine says that every square is a rhombus. Is Antoine correct? If the statement is incorrect, how can you change it to make it correct?

Answer Yes, Antoine is correct.

▸ **Justify your answer using words, drawings, or numbers.**

Possible justification: In a rhombus, opposite sides are parallel and all sides are the same length. This is also true for every square.

MP3 **23.** Marisol says that every quadrilateral must be a parallelogram or a trapezoid. Is Marisol correct? If the statement is incorrect, how can you change it to make it correct? No, Marisol is not correct. Every quadrilateral does not have to be a parallelogram or a trapezoid. Parallelograms

Answer and trapezoids have at least one pair of parallel sides.

▸ **Justify your answer using words, drawings, or numbers.**

Possible justification: Students may draw any quadrilateral with no pair of parallel sides.

Unit 5 ▪ Focus on Geometry **319**

Teaching Tips

Item 22

Encourage students to use multiple methods to justify their reasoning.

Ask volunteers to share correct explanations to model how to justify an answer in various ways.

Mathematical Practices

MP3	**Construct viable arguments and critique the reasoning of others.**

Item 20: Students share their reasoning with others.

Item 23: Students construct arguments by using drawings.

MP7	**Look for and make use of structure.**

Item 21: Students evaluate the structure of a figure.

MP8	**Look for and express regularity in repeated reasoning.**

Item 22: Students look for patterns in shapes to express reasonableness of a solution.

Common Core Focus:

4.G.3 Recognize a line of symmetry for a two-dimensional figure as a line across the figure such that the figure can be folded along the line into matching parts. Identify line-symmetric figures and draw lines of symmetry.

OBJECTIVE
Identify and draw lines of symmetry.

ESSENTIAL QUESTION
Read the Essential Question to students and ask if they know the meaning of *symmetry.* Provide examples of symmetry from within the classroom. Show an example of a two-dimensional figure with multiple lines of symmetry.

FLUENCY PRACTICE
Fluency practice is available at **sadlierconnect.com**.

Concept Development

Understand: Identifying lines of symmetry

■ The Common Core State Standards for Mathematics expect that students are able to partition shapes into parts with equal areas. They should also be able to express the area of each part as a unit fraction of the whole. The shift in this lesson is to divide the shape into identical halves.

■ In this presentation, students should make a connection between a fold line and the math term *line of symmetry.* Students use the fold line to determine if the two parts are symmetrical or match exactly.

Lesson 36 — Identify Lines of Symmetry

Essential Question: How do you identify and draw lines of symmetry?

4.G.3

Words to Know: line of symmetry

Guided Instruction

In this lesson you will learn how to recognize and draw lines of symmetry for a two-dimensional figure.

Understand: Identifying lines of symmetry

Theresa has a triangular piece of paper that she wants to fold so that the two parts will match. Which drawings show ways that Theresa can fold the triangular piece of paper so that the two parts match exactly?

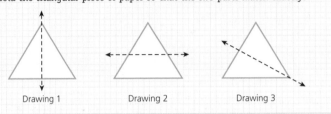

| Drawing 1 | Drawing 2 | Drawing 3 |

A two-dimensional figure has line symmetry if it can be folded along a line so that the two parts match exactly.

The line that represents the fold is called a line of symmetry. A two-dimensional figure can have one or more lines of symmetry. It can also have no lines of symmetry.

The dashed lines show different ways Theresa can fold the triangle. She must decide which of the dashed lines are lines of symmetry.

If Theresa folds the triangle along the dashed line shown in Drawing 1, both parts will match up exactly. The dashed line in Drawing 1 is a line of symmetry.

If Theresa folds the triangle along the dashed line shown in Drawing 2, both parts will not match up exactly. The dashed line in Drawing 2 is not a line of symmetry for the triangle.

If Theresa folds the triangle along the dashed line shown in Drawing 3, both parts will match up exactly. The dashed line in Drawing 3 is a line of symmetry.

➡ The two parts will match exactly if Theresa folds the triangular piece of paper along either of the lines of symmetry shown in Drawings 1 and 3.

Words to Know

line of symmetry: the line that is formed when a figure is folded into two parts that match exactly

Glossary can be found on pp. 347–350.

Lesson 36

Guided Instruction

Understand: Drawing lines of symmetry

Eric draws a pentagon. Each side of the pentagon is the same length. He wants to find all the lines of symmetry of the pentagon. How many lines of symmetry does his pentagon have?

To draw a line of symmetry, decide where to fold the figure so that the parts match up exactly. If the pentagon is folded along the line from the top vertex to the center of the opposite side of the pentagon, the parts will fold over one another exactly. The dashed line shows a line of symmetry.

All of the sides of this pentagon are the same length. If the figure is folded along the line from any vertex to the middle of the opposite side, the parts will match. The drawing shows two more lines of symmetry.

You can draw two more lines in the same way. Each line of symmetry goes through one of the vertices to the center of the opposite side. The drawing shows all the lines of symmetry of the pentagon.

▶ The pentagon that Eric draws has five lines of symmetry.

✏ Will every pentagon have five lines of symmetry? Explain your thinking. Draw a diagram to support your answer.
Possible answer: No, not every pentagon will have five lines of symmetry. Not every pentagon will have 5 sides that are the same length like Eric's pentagon.
Check students' diagrams.

Understand: Drawing lines of symmetry

■ In this presentation, students explore multiple lines of symmetry in a figure. The easiest fold line for students to see is commonly the vertical line. If students have difficulty recognizing the other fold lines as lines of symmetry, suggest they rotate their books so that each different vertex is at the top of the figure in each rotation.

✏ Challenge students to draw a pentagon that does not have five lines of symmetry. Ask students to consider whether the number of lines of symmetry corresponds to the numbers of sides and angles. Students may realize that only regular pentagons have five lines of symmetry.

Support English Language Learners

English language learners may need additional support understanding the term *symmetry* and how it relates to two-dimensional figures. Use cutouts of symmetrical figures. Show how symmetrical figures can be folded in half and both parts line up exactly with each other. With each model tell the students that a *line of symmetry* means both parts *match exactly.* Point out that some figures have one line of symmetry while others have more than one.

Provide students with a variety of two-dimensional figures that are and are not symmetrical. Challenge students to fold the shapes to find the line(s) of symmetry. For each figure, have students say whether the figure does or does not have a line of symmetry because the parts do or do not match exactly.

Guided Instruction

Connect: What you know about lines of symmetry Use this page to help students strengthen their understanding of line-symmetric figures by using the line of symmetry to draw the matching half of a given figure.

■ Remind students that when a line of symmetry exists, the parts on both sides of the line must be identical and match exactly when the figure is folded along the line of symmetry. The matching part is also referred to in the lesson as a mirror image.

■ Remind students that the specific properties, such as the length of line segments and the angle measures, must also be identical on both sides of the line of symmetry.

■ Note that the method described for creating the mirror image is to draw the picture from left to right. However, students may choose to draw from right to left if that works better for them.

Guided Instruction

Connect: What you know about lines of symmetry

Isabel is creating a design for a poster. The dashed line is a line of symmetry for the design. Draw the other half of Isabel's design.

Step 1

The dashed line is a line of symmetry. When the top part of the design is folded over the line of symmetry, the bottom part will match it exactly. This means the part below the line is a mirror image of the part above the line.

There are 4 line segments above the line of symmetry. How many line segments will be in the other half of Isabel's design?

_ 4 _

Step 2

Draw the part of the design that will be below the line of symmetry.

Start with the leftmost line segment. Below the line of symmetry draw a line segment that looks like a mirror image of that line segment.

Continue to draw the line segments in order from left to right.

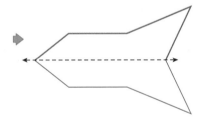

If you fold your completed design along the line of symmetry the parts match up.

Math-to-Science Connection

Symmetry Many living organisms exhibit symmetry. In science, an organism can exhibit bilateral symmetry, radial symmetry, or spherical symmetry. Have students work in groups to create a chart or poster that shows examples of plants and animals that exhibit symmetry. Students should be able to identify lines of symmetry for each organism.

Guided Practice

Draw all the lines of symmetry for each figure.

1.

2.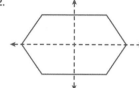

3.

4.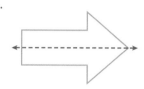

Solve the problem.

MP1 **5.** Blake designs a circular invitation that shows a happy face when it is opened. Draw the line of symmetry along which Blake folds his invitation.

 Think•Pair•Share

MP5 **6.** Use the dashed line below as a line of symmetry. Draw three sides of a polygon above this line of symmetry. Then draw the other half of the polygon below the line of symmetry. Explain why the completed polygon has line symmetry.
Drawings will vary. Check students' drawings.

←---------------------------------------→

Possible explanation: The completed polygon has line symmetry because if the figure is folded, the parts will match.

Observational Assessment

Use page 323 to assess whether students are able to identify and draw accurate lines of symmetry. Watch for students who draw just one line of symmetry for shapes that have multiple lines of symmetry.

Think•Pair•Share

Peer Collaboration Have students share their drawings with a partner and discuss how the figure demonstrates symmetry. Encourage students to answer questions such as:

- *Are the shapes symmetrical? How do you know?*

- *What strategies did you use to create a shape that has line symmetry?*

- *Do any of the shapes have multiple lines of symmetry?*

Return to the Essential Question

Reread the Lesson 36 Essential Question on page 320: *How do you identify and draw lines of symmetry?*

Ask volunteers to use what they learned in this lesson to answer this question. (Possible response: I can use my pencil as a line and move it around the figure until both parts of the figure on each side of the pencil are equal. Then draw a line on the shape and examine the halves to see if they are mirror images. I can fold the shape in half to see if both parts match exactly.)

Invite as many volunteers as possible to express ideas about strategies they use for identifying and drawing lines of symmetry.

Mathematical Practices

Mathematical Practice Standards underline the teaching and understanding of all concepts and skills presented. The emphasis of specific practices is noted throughout the guided and independent practice of this lesson.

MP1	**Make sense of problems and persevere in solving them.**

Item 5: Students analyze a problem and plan a solution.

MP5	**Use appropriate tools strategically.**

Item 6: Students use the appropriate tool for the situation.

Concept Application

Students may work independently on these pages in the classroom or at home. They may refer to the first four pages of the lesson to revisit the instruction or to see a worked-out example.

Common Errors and **Teaching Tips** may help you support student learning either in the classroom or as a follow-up for work done at home.

Teaching Tips

Item 6

Remind students that some shapes have multiple lines of symmetry and they should be sure to include all possible lines of symmetry.

Independent Practice

Is the dashed line on each figure a line of symmetry? Write *Yes* or *No*.

1.

_____Yes_____

2.

_____No_____

3.

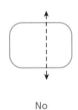

_____No_____

4.

_____Yes_____

Does the figure have line symmetry? If Yes, draw the line or lines of symmetry. If No, write *No*.

5.

_____No_____

6.

_____

7.

_____

8.

_____No_____

Writing About Math

✏ › **Write an Informative Text** Ask students to write a paragraph informing the reader what it means for a two-dimensional figure to have line symmetry. Tell students to include math vocabulary, details, and examples that support their explanation. Ask students to include real-world examples that would show the reader where they can see line symmetry in their surroundings.

Have students trade their paper with a classmate and check for any missing details or grammatical errors. Finally, have students revise their paragraphs if needed.

Draw all the lines of symmetry for each figure.

9.

10.

11.

12.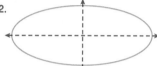

13.

14.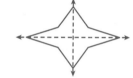

15.

16.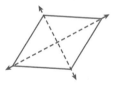

Unit 5 ■ Focus on Geometry **325**

Common Errors

Items 13–14, and 16

Some students may think these items have two additional lines of symmetry. Remind students that the line of symmetry is a line where the two-dimensional shape can be *folded* to create two parts that match exactly, not where the halves are cut apart and manipulated to match.

Digital Connection

Interactive Whiteboard Use the Internet or whiteboard software to create slides with pictures of items that students are familiar with or may see daily. Include as many pictures as you can find that have line symmetry. If possible, include pictures of items that have multiple lines of symmetry. Have students take turns using the dashed line tool or the interactive marker to draw lines of symmetry. Be sure to include some pictures that do not have line symmetry.

Independent Practice

Teaching Tips

Item 17

Students may recognize several lines of symmetry, but may not make the connection that a circle actually has an infinite number of lines of symmetry. It may be helpful to draw a circle on the board and demonstrate. Each student could take a turn drawing a line of symmetry and there would still be an infinite number left to draw.

Item 19

Students may not have noticed that the flower has multiple lines of symmetry because they were only required to find one. The flower has four more lines of symmetry through the middle of each petal. Look for students who drew more than one line of symmetry and ask them to share their drawings.

Independent Practice

17. Look at the circle. Does a circle have line symmetry? If so, how many lines of symmetry does a circle have? Explain your answer.
Possible answer: Yes, a circle has an infinite number of lines of symmetry. You can fold a circle into equal parts along any line through the center of the circle.

Solve the problems.

MP5 18. The logo for Zany's company is shown at the right. Does the logo have a line of symmetry? If so draw the line of symmetry.
Yes, the logo has a line of symmetry.

MP4 19. Alev drew these pictures of a shamrock, a leaf, and a flower that she saw while hiking. Do any of the shapes have line symmetry? If so, draw at least one line of symmetry on each shape.

Yes, each of the three shapes has line symmetry.

Mathematical Practices	
MP4	**Model with mathematics.**
Item 19: Students analyze relationships and draw conclusions.	
MP5	**Use appropriate tools strategically.**
Item 18: Students use tools to solve a problem.	

Lesson 36

Independent Practice

MP3 **20.** Jake says that the lines shown are lines of symmetry for the parallelogram. Is Jake correct?

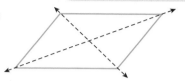

Answer No, Jake is not correct.

▸ **Justify your answer using words, drawings, or numbers.**
Possible justification: If you fold the parallelogram along either of the lines, the sides will not match up exactly. A parallelogram does not have any lines of symmetry.

MP7 **21.** Think of the capital letters of the alphabet. Name three letters that do not have a line of symmetry. Name three letters that have exactly one line of symmetry. Name three letters that have more than one line of symmetry.

Answer Possible answers: No line of symmetry: Q, R, P, F, G, J, L, Z, N; one line of symmetry: W, E, T, Y, U, A, D, K, V, B, M, I; more than one line of
▸ **Justify your answer using words, drawings, or numbers.** symmetry:
Students should draw the letters and show the lines of H, X, O
symmetry for the letters they chose.

MP8 **22.** Each of the polygons below has sides that are the same length. Describe the pattern between the number of sides and the number of lines of symmetry for each figure. Use the pattern to predict the number of lines of symmetry for a polygon with 10 sides of equal length.

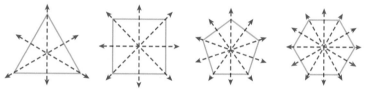

Answer Triangle: 3; square: 4; pentagon: 5; hexagon: 6. Each figure has the same number of lines of symmetry as the number of sides of equal length. A polygon with 10 equal side lengths will have 10 lines of
▸ **Justify your answer using words, drawings, or numbers.** symmetry.
Answers should include showing all the lines of symmetry of the polygons shown.

Common Errors
Item 20
Students may incorrectly think that this parallelogram has lines of symmetry. Previously, students identified lines of symmetry for a parallelogram that was also a rhombus. The rhombus and the square are two parallelograms that have symmetry, but when the side lengths of the parallelogram are not equivalent, the figure does not have any lines of symmetry. Allow students to use a piece of paper to draw a parallelogram with unequal pairs of sides and then fold the figure diagonally. They will see that the sides do not match up exactly.

Teaching Tips
Item 22
Point out that regular polygons have multiple lines of symmetry because all the sides lengths and angle measures are the same.

Return to the

Remind students to return to the Progress Check self-assessment, page 301, to check off additional items they have mastered during the unit.

Mathematical Practices

MP3	**Construct viable arguments and critique the reasoning of others.**

Item 20: Students analyze a problem situation and share their reasoning with others.

MP7	**Look for and make use of structure.**

Item 21: Students apply the rules of symmetry.

MP8	**Look for and express regularity in repeated reasoning.**

Item 22: Students look for patterns with regular shapes.

The Common Core Review covers all the standards presented in the unit. Use it to assess your students' mastery of the unit's concepts and skills.

Depth of Knowledge

The depth of knowledge is a ranking of the content complexity of assessment items based on Webb's Depth of Knowledge (DOK) levels. The levels increase in complexity as shown below.

Level 1: Recall and Reproduction
Level 2: Basic Skills and Concepts
Level 3: Strategic Reasoning and Thinking
Level 4: Extended Thinking

Item	Standard	DOK
1	4.G.1	1
2	4.G.1	1
3	4.G.1	1
4	4.G.1	1
5	4.G.1	1
6	4.G.1	1
7	4.G.3	1
8	4.G.3	2
9	4.G.2	3
10	4.G.1	1
11	4.G.2	1
12	4.G.2	1
13	4.G.2	1
14	4.G.2	1
15	4.G.2	3
16	4.G.2	3
17	4.G.3	4
18	4.G.1	3
19	4.G.3	4
20	4.G.2	4

Draw and label an example of each of the following. Check students' drawings.

1. line segment *AB*

2. line *CD* perpendicular to line *EF*

3. acute angle *GHI*

4. obtuse angle *JKL*

5. line *MN* parallel to line *OP*

6. ray *QR*

Circle the correct answer.

7. Which figure has a line of symmetry?

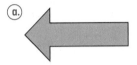
a.

b.

c.

d.

8. This triangle has all sides the same length. How many lines of symmetry does it have?

  a. 0   b. 1

  c. 2   d. 3

9. Draw a right triangle. Explain why your triangle is a right triangle.
Students should draw a triangle with a 90° angle.
Possible explanation: My triangle is a right triangle because it has one square corner/one right angle/one 90° angle.

UNIT 5 Common Core Review

10. What three kinds of angles can you find in the traffic sign? Label them.

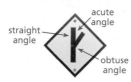

straight angle — acute angle — obtuse angle

For exercises 11–14, draw an example of each. Then classify the polygon you drew. Check students' drawings.

11. A polygon with 6 sides and 6 angles

_____hexagon_____

12. A triangle with a right angle

_____right triangle_____

13. A quadrilateral with at least one pair of parallel sides

_____trapezoid_____

14. A parallelogram with 4 right angles and all sides the same length

_____square_____

For exercises 15 and 16, one shape does not belong. Circle it. Tell why the shape does not belong.

MP7 15.

The shape I circled does not belong because

all the other shapes have at least one right angle.

MP7 16.

The shape I circled does not belong because

all the other shapes have at least two pairs of parallel sides.

Unit 5 ■ Focus on Geometry **329**

This chart correlates the Common Core Review items with the lessons in which the concepts and skills are presented.

Item	Lesson
1	34
2	34
3	34
4	34
5	34
6	34
7	36
8	36
9	35
10	34
11	35
12	35
13	35
14	35
15	35
16	35
17	36
18	34
19	36
20	35

Mathematical Practices

MP7	**Look for and make use of structure.**

Items 15-16: Students compare geometric shapes in terms of their similarities and differences.

Writing About Math

✏️ ▶ Direct students to respond to the Unit 5 Essential Question. (This can also be found on student page 303.)

Essential Question:
How does understanding lines and angles help you identify geometric shapes?

Possible responses:
- All lines are made of points, and all angles are made of lines. All polygons are made of combinations of lines and angles.
- A polygon is named by the number of sides and angles it has.

Unit Assessment

- Unit 5 Common Core Review, *pp. 328–330*
- Unit 5 Performance Task (ONLINE)

Additional Assessment Options

- Performance Task 2, *pp. 331–336*
  (ALSO ONLINE)

Optional Purchase:

- iProgress Monitor (ONLINE)
- Progress Monitor Student Benchmark Assessment Booklet

UNIT **5** Common Core Review

Solve the problems.

MP6 **17.** The dashed line is a line of symmetry. Draw the other half of the shape to make a symmetrical figure. What shape did you make?

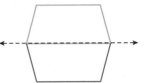

Answer <u>I made a hexagon.</u>

MP4 **18.** A bathroom tile is in the shape shown at the right. What kind of angles does the tile have—acute, right, or obtuse? Does the tile have any pairs of parallel or perpendicular sides?

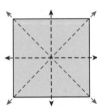

Answer <u>The tile has 8 obtuse angles.</u>

<u>The tile has 4 pairs of parallel sides.</u>

MP3 **19.** Autumn drew the figure at the right to prove that a square has only 2 lines of symmetry. Is Autumn correct?

Answer <u>No, Autumn is not correct. A square has 4 lines of symmetry.</u>

✏️ ▶ **Justify your answer using words, drawings, or numbers.**

Possible justification: If you fold a square along the diagonals, the two halves match exactly. So, a square has 4 lines of symmetry.

MP6 **20.** Dominic says that every rhombus is a square. Is Dominic correct?

Answer <u>No. Dominic is not correct. Some rhombuses are not squares.</u>

✏️ ▶ **Justify your answer using words, drawings, or numbers.**
Possible justification: In a rhombus and in a square, the opposite sides are parallel and all sides are the same length. However, I can draw a rhombus that is not a square because it does not have 4 right angles.

For example:

Mathematical Practices

MP3	**Construct viable arguments and critique the reasoning of others.**

Item 19: Students analyze a problem situation and share their reasoning.

MP4	**Model with mathematics.**

Item 18: Students analyze relationships and draw conclusions.

MP6	**Attend to precision.**

Item 17: Students apply their understanding of symmetry.

Item 20: Students analyze given information and communicate precisely to others.

Performance Task 2

4.OA.4, 4.NF.1, 4.NF.3a, 4.MD.1, 4.MD.2, 4.MD.3, 4.MD.4, 4.MD.6, 4.MD.7, 4.G.1, 4.G.2, 4.G.3

Performance Tasks

Performance Tasks show your understanding of the Math that you have learned. You will be doing various Performance Tasks as you complete your work in this text, *Common Core Progress Mathematics*.

Beginning This Task

The next five pages provide you with the beginning of a Performance Task. You will be given 5 items to complete, and each item will have two or more parts. As you complete these items you will:

I Demonstrate that you have mastered mathematical skills and concepts

II Reason through a problem to a solution, and explain your reasoning

III Use models and apply them to real-world situations.

Extending This Task

Your teacher may extend this Performance Task with additional items provided in our online resources at sadlierconnect.com.

Scoring This Task

Your response to each item will be assessed against a rubric, or scoring guide. Some items will be worth 1 or 2 points, and others will be worth more. In each item you will show your work or explain your reasoning.

Performance Task 2 **331**

ONLINE Customize Performance Task 2

Performance Task 2 in *Common Core Progress Mathematics* also provides students with additional practice. You can use the online items of Performance Task 2 to customize the amount and kind of performance task practice based on your ongoing evaluation of your students. You may choose to challenge some students, to give extra experience with a particular kind of task for other students, or to extend exposure to performance assessments for the entire class.

Go to **sadlierconnect.com** to download the following resources for Performance Task 2.

- Additional Items
- Additional Teacher Support
- Additional Scoring Rubrics

Performance Task 2 Overview

Performance Task 2 in *Common Core Progress Mathematics* provides students with practice for the types of items that may be found on standardized performance assessments.

Various item formats, including short- and extended-response items and technology-enhanced items, are included in the tasks. All items connect mathematical content correlated to the mathematical practices.

Items in Performance Task 2 are based on three primary types of tasks.

Type I   Mastery of mathematical concepts, skills and procedures

Type II   Using and explaining mathematical reasoning

Type III Modeling problem situations in a real-world context

Performance Task 2 begins with a collection of five self-contained items in the Student Book and continues with additional items online at **sadlierconnect.com**.

Introduce Performance Task 2 Read student page 331 with the class. Explain that Performance Task 2 may cover any of the math they have learned in Units 1–5. Orient students to each item and communicate helpful reminders that will enable students to approach each item successfully. Once students have completed each item, go over the correct responses with them.

Recommended Pacing Administer Performance Task 2 on Student Book pages 332–336 over five 20-minute sessions.

Teacher Resources For each task, the teacher materials include:

- Item types and purposes
- Correlations to Common Core State Standards for Mathematical Content and Practice and Depth of Knowledge (DOK) levels
- Suggested Administration procedure
- Scoring Rubric

Item 1: Building a Neighborhood Playground

Item	Type	Purpose
1.a.	I	Label a time on a number line.
1.b.	III	Use the number line in item 1.a. to determine an elapsed time.
1.c.	III	Use the number line item 1.a. and the answer in item 1.b. to determine an elapsed time.
1.d.	II	Determine the total amount of elapsed time and justify.

Item	CCSS	MP	DOK
1.a.	4.MD.1, 4.MD.2	4	Level 1
1.b.	4.MD.1, 4.MD.2	2	Level 2
1.c.	4.MD.1, 4.MD.2	2	Level 2
1.d.	4.MD.1, 4.MD.2	3	Level 3

Administering Item 1 (Pacing: 20 minutes)

Ask a volunteer to read the introductory paragraph. Have others describe the situation in their own words.

Item 1.a. (3 minutes)

Be sure students carefully analyze the number line prior to placing their label.

Item 1.b. (5 minutes)

Have a class discussion around how many minutes is $\frac{3}{4}$ of an hour. Then allow students to determine the new time independently.

Item 1.c. (5 minutes)

Remind students to use the number line in item 1.a. to help determine and justify their answer.

Item 1.d. (7 minutes)

If students write their answer in hours and minutes, have a class discussion around how to convert that to total minutes.

Performance Task 2

Building a Neighborhood Playground

1. The children and adults who live in Dan's neighborhood are building a playground. A team of children works together to tear down an old fence and take the boards away to a recycling bin.

   a. The team begins work at 3:30 P.M. Draw a point on the number line to show 3:30 P.M.

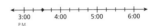

   b. The team spends $\frac{3}{4}$ hour tearing down the fence. What time does the team finish tearing down the fence? Show how to use the number line above to find what time the team finishes the task.

   The team finishes the task at 4:15 P.M. Modeling may vary. Students might draw curved arrows showing jumps from 3:30 to 3:45, from 3:45 to 4:00, and from 4:00 to 4:15, with each jump labeled "15 minutes" or "$\frac{1}{4}$ hour."

   c. Next, the team works $1\frac{1}{2}$ hours taking away the boards to a recycling bin. What time does the team finish taking away the boards? Show how to use the number line above to find what time the team finishes this task.

   The team finishes the task at 5:45 P.M.
   Modeling may vary. Students might draw a curved arrow from 4:15 to 5:15 and label it "1 hour." Then they might draw a curved arrow from 5:15 to 5:45, and label it "30 minutes" or "$\frac{1}{2}$ hour."

   d. How many minutes does the team spend altogether on the two tasks? Explain the method you used to find your answer.

   The team spends 135 minutes on the two tasks altogether. Methods will vary. Possible explanation of method: I knew the distance between points on the number line was 15 minutes. So, I counted intervals of 15 minutes between the start time, 3:30 P.M., and the end time, 5:45 P.M. There were 9 intervals. 9 × 15 = 135.

332   Performance Task 2

Scoring Rubric

Item	Points	Student Responses
1.a.	2	Labels time on a number line.
	0	Incorrectly labels time on a number line.
1.b.	2	Correctly determines the time using the number line.
	0	Incorrectly uses the number line to determine the time.
1.c.	2	Correctly determines the time using the number line.
	0	Does not use the number line correctly to determine the time.
1.d.	2	Understands how to find elapsed time on a number line.
	1	Demonstrates some understanding of finding elapsed time on a number line.
	0	Demonstrates no understanding of elapsed time.

A Lawn Area at the Playground

2. Rhonda is planning a lawn for a playground. The lawn will be a rectangle with an area of 60 square meters. The length of each side will be a whole number of meters.

   a. Explain how Rhonda can find possible side lengths for the lawn.

   Possible explanation: She can use the area formula, $A = \ell \times w$. Since the area of the lawn is 60 square meters, she needs to find factor pairs for 60.

   b. Find all possible pairs of side lengths for the lawn.

   Possible side lengths in meters: 1 and 60; 2 and 30; 3 and 20; 4 and 15; 5 and 12; 6 and 10

   c. How do you know that you found all possible pairs of side lengths?

   Possible answer: I began with side length 1 meter and continued listing pairs in order. There were no factor pairs that included 7, 8, or 9 because those numbers are not factors of 60. When I got to 10, I realized that the pair 6 and 10 was already on the list. I knew I had all the pairs because I saw a pattern: Any pair with a side length longer than 10 meters would be paired with a side length less than 6 meters.

   d. Find the side lengths for the lawn that would have the least perimeter. What is the least perimeter? Explain your reasoning.

   A rectangle with side lengths 6 meters and 10 meters would have the least perimeter. The perimeter would be 2 times the sum of 6 + 10, or 32 meters.

   Possible explanation: I looked at my ordered list and I added the side lengths in each pair. The least sum would result in the least perimeter. The sums followed a pattern: The first sum is 61 (the greatest sum) and the last sum is 16 (the least sum).

Scoring Rubric

Item	Points	Student Responses
2.a.	2	Understands how to use the area formula to solve.
	1	Shows some understanding of how to use the area formula to solve.
	0	Does not know how to use the area formula to solve.
2.b.	2	Determines all length pairs.
	1	Determines some length pairs.
	0	Does not determine any length pairs.
2.c.	2	Correctly justifies all length pairs.
	1	Correctly justifies one or more length pairs.
	0	Does not justify any length pairs.
2.d.	2	Determines the least perimeter.
	1	Correctly determines the perimeter, but not the least perimeter.
	0	Does not determine the perimeter.

Item 2: A Lawn Area at the Playground

Item	Type	Purpose
2.a.	II	Explain how to use the area formula to determine an unknown length.
2.b.	I	Use the area formula to determine all unknown lengths.
2.c.	II	Justify the answer in item 2.b.
2.d.	II	Determine perimeter using the answers in item 2.b.

Item	CCSS	MP	DOK
2.a.	4.OA.4, 4.MD.3	1	Level 4
2.b.	4.OA.4	2	Level 2
2.c.	4.OA.4	7	Level 4
2.d.	4.OA.3	8	Level 2

Administering Item 2 (Pacing: 20 minutes)

Ask a volunteer to read the introductory paragraph. Have others describe the situation in their own words.

Item 2.a. (5 minutes)

Students should see that they are working with the area formula.

Item 2.b. (5 minutes)

Remind students that there will be more than one correct answer. Drawing models may help students determine all answers.

Item 2.c. (5 minutes)

Be sure students explain that all their combinations are correct, as well as why there are no other possible combinations.

Item 2.d. (5 minutes)

Discuss how perimeter differs from area. If necessary, students can determine the perimeter for all their measurements in item 2.b. then identify the least perimeter.

Item 3: Future Shade

Item	Type	Purpose
3.a.	III	Use given data to create a line plot.
3.b.	I	Interpret the line plot in item 3.a.
3.c.	I	Convert feet to inches.
3.d.	III	Subtract mixed numbers with like denominators.

Item	CCSS	MP	DOK
3.a.	4.MD.4	4	Level 1
3.b.	4.NF.1	3	Level 3
3.c.	4.MD.1	1	Level 1
3.d.	4.NF.3c, 4.MD.4	2	Level 2

Administering Item 3 (Pacing: 20 minutes)

Ask a volunteer to read the introductory paragraph. Have others describe the situation in their own words.

Item 3.a. (10 minutes)

Students should determine their intervals and then draw the line plot.

Item 3.b. (3 minutes)

If students do not connect $2\frac{2}{4}$ to $2\frac{1}{2}$ remind them that fractions can be written in different, but equivalent ways.

Item 3.c. (2 minutes)

Encourage students to think about a ruler if they forgot how many inches are in a foot.

Item 3.d. (5 minutes)

Be sure students see the key word *difference* in the problem. Remind students that they may need to rewrite the fractions prior to solving.

Future Shade

3. A tree nursery donates some trees for a new playground. Carlos and Nikki measure the heights of the trees and record the data.

a. Use their data to make a line plot.

Heights of Trees (ft)

$1\frac{2}{4}$	$1\frac{3}{4}$	$2\frac{1}{4}$	2	$1\frac{3}{4}$
$2\frac{2}{4}$	2	$2\frac{3}{4}$	$1\frac{2}{4}$	$2\frac{1}{4}$
$1\frac{3}{4}$	$2\frac{1}{4}$	$1\frac{1}{4}$	$2\frac{2}{4}$	$1\frac{3}{4}$

Heights of Trees

b. Which Xs on the line plot represent trees that are $2\frac{1}{2}$ feet tall?

The two Xs above $2\frac{2}{4}$ represent trees that are $2\frac{1}{2}$ feet tall. $2\frac{1}{2}$ is equivalent to $2\frac{2}{4}$.

c. How many inches tall is a tree that is 2 feet tall?

A tree that is 2 feet tall is 24 inches tall.

d. What is the difference in height between the tallest tree and the shortest tree? Use the line plot.

The difference in height is $1\frac{1}{2}$ feet.

Possible solution: $2\frac{3}{4} - 1\frac{1}{4}$

Rename $2\frac{3}{4}$: $2\frac{3}{4} = \frac{8}{4} + \frac{3}{4}$
$= \frac{11}{4}$

Rename $1\frac{1}{4}$: $1\frac{1}{4} = \frac{4}{4} + \frac{1}{4}$
$= \frac{5}{4}$

$\frac{11}{4} - \frac{5}{4} = \frac{6}{4} = 1\frac{1}{2}$

Scoring Rubric

Item	Points	Student Responses
3.a.	2	Correctly creates the line plot.
	1	Correctly draws the line plot, but incorrectly labels some points.
	0	Does not create the line plot.
3.b.	2	Correctly interprets the line plot.
	1	Correctly interprets the line plot but makes mistake in explanation.
	0	Does not interpret the line plot.
3.c.	2	Correctly converts feet to inches.
	0	Does not convert feet to inches.
3.d.	2	Determines the difference in the height.
	1	Correctly sets up the subtraction, but does not determine the height.
	0	Does not correctly set up or solve the subtraction.

Performance Task 2

A Gate for the Playground

4. Bernard works on a gate for a playground. The diagram shows that the gate should open to ∠ABC, but it only opens to ∠DBC.

a. Use a protractor. Find the measure of ∠ABC and the measure of ∠DBC.
The measure of ∠ABC is 145° and the measure of ∠DBC is 80°.

b. Explain two ways to find the measure of ∠ABD.
Method 1: Use a protractor to measure the angle.
Method 2: Subtract 80° from 145°

c. Find the measure of ∠ABD using both of your methods.
Possible answer:
Method 1: Using a protractor, the measure of ∠ABD is 65°.
Method 2:
∠ABD = x
145° − 80° = x
65° = x
The measure of ∠ABD is 65°.

d. Which method do you prefer? Explain.
Students' answers and explanations will vary. Possible response:
I prefer subtraction because I find it faster than using a protractor.

Performance Task 2 335

Scoring Rubric

Item	Points	Student Responses
4.a.	2	Correctly measures both angles.
	1	Correctly measures one angle.
	0	Incorrectly measures both angles.
4.b.	2	Correctly identifies two methods.
	1	Correctly identifies one method.
	0	Does not identify either method.
4.c.	2	Correctly determines angle measure using both methods.
	1	Correctly determines angle measure using one method.
	0	Does not determine angle measure.
4.d.	2	Identifies and justifies a preferred method.
	1	Identifies but does not justify a preferred method.
	0	Does not identify a preferred method.

Item 4: A Gate for the Playground

Item	Type	Purpose
4.a.	I	Use a protractor to measure angles.
4.b.	II	Identify two ways to measure angles.
4.c.	I	Use the two ways given in item 4.b. to determine an angle measure.
4.d.	II	Explain method preference for measuring angles.

Item	CCSS	MP	DOK
4.a.	4.MD.6	5	Level 2
4.b.	4.MD.6, 4.MD.7	5	Level 3
4.c.	4.MD.6, 4.MD.7	5	Level 2
4.d.	4.MD.6, 4.MD.7	3	Level 3

Introducing Item 4 (Pacing: 20 minutes)

Ask a volunteer to read the introductory paragraph. Have others describe the situation in their own words.

Item 4.a. (3 minutes)
Encourage a class discussion on how to use a protractor. Then allow students to measure the angles independently.

Item 4.b. (5 minutes)
Remind students that they already used one method in item 4.a.

Item 4.c. (7 minutes)
Be sure students understand that they should get the same answer using both methods. If they do not, they should check their work.

Item 4.d. (5 minutes)
Remind students that there is no correct answer here as long as they can appropriately explain their preference.

Item 5: A Playground Game

Item	Type	Purpose
5.a.	I	Draw a rectangle that is not a square.
5.b.	II	Identify a parallelogram.
5.c.	III	Draw perpendicular lines and lines of symmetry.
5.d.	II	Identifying possible lines of symmetry by analyzing other's work.

Item	CCSS	MP	DOK
5.a.	4.G.1, 4.G.2	6	Level 2
5.b.	4.G.2	6	Level 2
5.c.	4.G.1, 4.G.3	1	Level 2
5.d.	4.G.3	6	Level 3

Administering Item 5 (Pacing: 20 minutes)

Ask a volunteer to read the introductory paragraph. Have others describe the situation in their own words.

Item 5.a. (3 minutes)

Be sure students carefully read the description of the figure they are drawing.

Item 5.b. (5 minutes)

If students have trouble answering this question, encourage a discussion about the properties of parallelograms.

Item 5.c. (4 minutes)

Review the words *perpendicular* and *symmetry* before students begin this question. After they are finished, have them check that their lines fit the description.

Item 5.d. (8 minutes)

Encourage students to draw a picture representing Derron's idea. This picture can be used to justify their answer.

A Playground Game

5. Pedro and Derron are designing a playground game.

a. Pedro begins by drawing a rectangle that is not a square. Draw a rectangle that could be Pedro's.

Students' drawings should show a rectangle with two different side lengths.

b. Is the figure you drew a parallelogram? Explain.

Yes. The figure is a parallelogram. Possible explanation: Any rectangle is also a parallelogram because all rectangles have opposite sides that are parallel.

c. Next Pedro draws two line segments inside the rectangle. The line segments are perpendicular and are parts of two lines of symmetry of the rectangle. Draw those two line segments in your rectangle.

Students' drawings should show a horizontal line segment that divides the rectangle into two equal parts and a vertical line segment that divides the rectangle into two equal parts. The segments will be both perpendicular and parts of lines of symmetry.

d. Derron says that Pedro can draw two more line segments that are also parts of lines of symmetry of the rectangle. Is Derron correct? Explain why or why not.

Derron is not correct. Possible explanation: A rectangle that is not a square has only two lines of symmetry. If you fold a rectangle (that is not a square) along a diagonal, the two parts will not match up.

Scoring Rubric

Item	Points	Student Responses
5.a.	2	Correctly draws a rectangle that is not a square.
	1	Correctly draws a quadrilateral, but it does not fit the description.
	0	Does not draw a quadrilateral.
5.b.	2	Understands the properties of parallelograms.
	1	Shows some understanding of the properties of parallelograms.
	0	Does not identify the parallelogram.
5.c.	2	Correctly draws two perpendicular lines that are lines of symmetry.
	0	Does not draw lines of symmetry.
5.d	2	Understands lines of symmetry.
	1	Shows some understanding of lines of symmetry.
	0	Shows no understanding of lines of symmetry.

Foundational Skills Handbook

A review of prerequisite mathematics needed to understand the concepts and skills of Grade 4.

A. Understand: The meaning of a product

A product is the result of multiplication.

The product of 4 × 5 is 20.

4 cards
5 dots on each card
4 fives equals 20.

factors ⟶ 4 × 5 = 20 ⟵ product

B. Understand: Use multiplication to solve division

You can use related multiplication facts to solve division problems. Knowing the fact family can help.

$$16 \div 2 = \blacksquare$$

number in all · number in each group · number of groups

Think: What number times 2 makes 16?

$$\blacksquare \times 2 = 16$$

number of groups · number in each group · number in all

Use the fact family for 2, 8, and 16 to help solve the problem.
2 × 8 = 16   16 ÷ 8 = 2
8 × 2 = 16   16 ÷ 2 = 8

Find the unknown factor in the multiplication: ■ × 2 = 16
Use the unknown factor to complete the related division: 16 ÷ 2 = 8

Foundational Skills Handbook Contents

The Foundational Skills Handbook:
Use to provide review of prerequisite content and skills needed for Grade 4.

Item A.

Understand: The meaning of a product

■ Explain that there are 4 groups with 5 objects in each group. The total number of objects in all the groups is the product.

■ Point out that the numbers being multiplied are called factors while the answer is called the product.

■ Ask students what would happen if the order of the factors were changed. Have them recall the Commutative Property of Multiplication.

Item B.

Understand: Use multiplication to solve division

■ Explain that the process of dividing is the reverse of the process of multiplying.

■ Remind students that a division problem can be written as unknown-factor multiplication problem. Knowing multiplication facts fluently can help students solve related divisions.

■ Point out the repeated use of the same numbers in the example. All four equations use the same numbers, but in a different order. The ability to manipulate numbers in this way can make solving more efficient.

Foundational Skills Handbook

Item C.

Understand: Round numbers to the nearest hundred

■ A number line diagram can be used to visualize the rounding process.

■ Remind students to first identify the digit in the place to which they are rounding. They may wish to underline the number.

■ Point out the rounding rules. Encourage students to come up with a unique way to remember the rules.

■ As a check, tell students that when rounding to the nearest hundred, their answer should always end in two zeros. If it does not, they did not round correctly.

Item D.

Understand: Multiplication Strategies

■ Remind students than an array is an organized group of objects arranged into rows and columns.

■ To use the array properly for multiplication, there must be an equal number of objects in each row and an equal number of objects in each column.

■ Be sure students understand how the multiplication relates to the array. They should be able to identify the number of rows as one factor and the number of columns as the other factor.

■ Have students explain the Commutative Property of Multiplication and how it pertains to this example.

■ Ask students to identify the similarities and differences between the two arrays shown. They should see that rotating the array 90° still results in the same two factors and the same product.

C. **Understand: Round numbers to the nearest hundred**

You can use a number line to round numbers to the nearest hundred.

Round 126 to the nearest hundred.
126 is closer to 100 than 200.
126 rounds to 100.

Round 271 to the nearest hundred.
271 is closer to 300 than to 200.
271 rounds to 300.

You can also use these rules to round three-digit numbers.
If the tens digit is 1, 2, 3, or 4, round to the lesser 100.
If the tens digit is 5 or greater, round to the greater 100.

Round 325 using the rules.
325 is between 300 and 400.
The tens digit is 2, so round to the lesser 100.
325 rounds to 300.

D. **Understand: Multiplication Strategies**

There are many ways to find a product. Here are two strategies you can use to find the product of 4 x 5.

You can draw an array.

The array at the left shows 4 equal groups of 5.
You can write $4 \times 5 = 20$.
You can also write
$$\begin{array}{r} 4 \\ \times\ 5 \\ \hline 20 \end{array}$$

You can also use the Commutative Property.

The array at the left shows that $5 \times 4 = 20$.

If you know that $5 \times 4 = 20$, then you know that $4 \times 5 = 20$.

E. **Understand:** Division Strategies

The result of a division problem is a quotient. Here are two strategies to find the quotient of 20 ÷ 5.

You can draw an array.

The array shows that 20 can be divided into 4 equal groups of 5.

You can write 20 ÷ 4 = 5.

You can also write $4\overline{)20}^{\,5}$

You can also use a related multiplication fact.

If you know that 4 × 5 = 20, then you know that 20 ÷ 5 = 4.

F. **Understand:** Find equivalent fractions on a number line

You can use number lines to find fractions that have different names but are at the same point on the number line. These are called equivalent fractions.

How many sixths are equivalent to $\frac{1}{3}$?

Find $\frac{1}{3}$ on the number line. Find the equivalent fraction in sixths directly below it on the number line on the bottom.

$\frac{1}{3}$ is equivalent to $\frac{2}{6}$.

$\frac{1}{3} = \frac{2}{6}$

Item E.

Understand: Division Strategies

■ Have students describe the characteristics of an array.

■ After they study the array and the related division, have students explain the parts of the division in terms of the array. For example, the dividend (20) tells the total number of objects in the array; the divisor (5) tells how many objects are in each row. The quotient (4) is the number of groups.

■ Point out that students can also use a related multiplication to solve the division.

■ Ask students to describe how an array for the equation 20 ÷ 4 = 5 differs from an array for the equation 20 ÷ 5 = 4.

Item F.

Understand: Find equivalent fractions on a number line

■ Point out to students that the prefix of the word *equivalent* is *equi-* which means "equal." Students may also notice that *equivalent* and *equal* start with the same three letters. This may help them remember that equivalent means equal.

■ Be sure students understand the layout of the number lines. Note that the 0 and 1 on each number line are lined up. Ask them why the bottom number line is split into more parts than the top number line.

■ Ask students if there are any other equivalent fractions shown on the number line. They should state that $\frac{2}{3}$ is equal to $\frac{4}{6}$.

Item G.

Understand: Compare fractions on a number line

■ Be sure students understand how to use the > and < symbols. Remind them that the wide part of the symbol should face the greater number.

■ Once students see the comparison on the number line, ask them if there is another way they can tell which is greater without using the number line. Students should see that since the denominators are the same, they can just compare the numerators.

■ Provide additional practice problems if students seem to have trouble understanding the objective.

Item H.

Understand: The meaning of a unit fraction

■ Be sure students have a firm understanding of the terms *numerator* and *denominator*. Practice writing fractions with different numerators and denominators to ensure understanding.

■ Remind students that all unit fractions have a 1 as the numerator.

■ Ask students to explain why the three fraction models shown all represent unit fractions. They should be able to explain that they are unit fractions because each model has only one piece shaded.

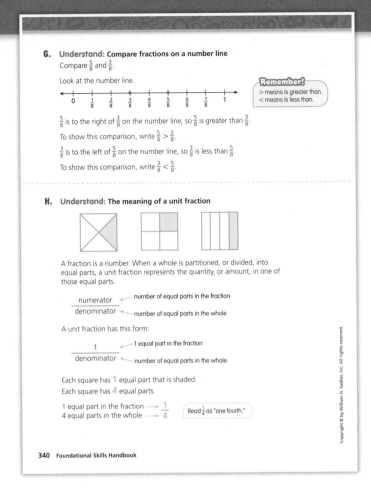

G. Understand: Compare fractions on a number line

Compare $\frac{5}{8}$ and $\frac{3}{8}$.

Look at the number line.

Remember!
> means is greater than.
< means is less than.

$\frac{5}{8}$ is to the right of $\frac{3}{8}$ on the number line, so $\frac{5}{8}$ is greater than $\frac{3}{8}$.

To show this comparison, write $\frac{5}{8} > \frac{3}{8}$.

$\frac{3}{8}$ is to the left of $\frac{5}{8}$ on the number line, so $\frac{3}{8}$ is less than $\frac{5}{8}$.

To show this comparison, write $\frac{3}{8} < \frac{5}{8}$.

H. Understand: The meaning of a unit fraction

A fraction is a number. When a whole is partitioned, or divided, into equal parts, a unit fraction represents the quantity, or amount, in one of those equal parts.

$\frac{numerator}{denominator}$ — number of equal parts in the fraction / number of equal parts in the whole

A unit fraction has this form:

$\frac{1}{denominator}$ — 1 equal part in the fraction / number of equal parts in the whole

Each square has 1 equal part that is shaded.
Each square has 4 equal parts.

1 equal part in the fraction → 1
4 equal parts in the whole → 4

Read $\frac{1}{4}$ as "one fourth."

I. Understand: How to measure time intervals

The difference from one time to another time is called elapsed time.

Aaron swam from 8:45 A.M. to 9:35 A.M.
How long did Aaron swim?

Look at the minute hand on the clock.
Count time intervals of 10 minutes.
10 + 10 + 10 + 10 + 10 = 50

Aaron swam for 50 minutes.

Practice for the school play was from 3:00 P.M. to 4:30 P.M.
How long was play practice?

Use a number line. Count time intervals of 30 minutes.

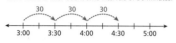

Remember!
60 minutes is 1 hour.

Play practice was 90 minutes, or 1 hour 30 minutes.

J. Understand: Multiply to find the area of rectangles

You can use different methods to find the area
of a rectangle.

Method 1

Tile the rectangle.
Count the unit squares that will cover the rectangle.
The sides are measured in feet, so the area will be in square feet.

8 unit squares cover the rectangle.
The area of the rectangle is 8 square feet.

Method 2

Each unit square has an area of 1 square foot. There are 2 rows
of unit squares.

Each row has an area of 4 square feet.

Multiply the side lengths of the rectangle.
2 × 4 = 8
The area of the rectangle is 8 square feet.

Foundational Skills Handbook **341**

Item I.

Understand: How to measure time intervals

■ Be sure students understand that the word *difference* in the problem means to compare the start time and the end time. Finding the difference doesn't always mean that subtraction is the best method to solve. Explain that because time is based on 60 minutes, subtraction strategies don't always work.

■ Ask students to explain how the clock and the number line relate to the problems shown.

■ Have students show their work to describe how 90 minutes is converted to 1 hour 30 minutes.

Item J.

Understand: Multiply to find the area of rectangles

■ Remind students that the area of a rectangle describes the flat surface of the rectangle.

■ The area of a rectangle can be found by covering the rectangle with unit squares and counting to find the total number of unit squares. The area can also be found using multiplication.

■ Ask students to explain how Method 1 relates to Method 2.

■ Explain to students that while Method 1 can be used, it is often difficult to draw unit squares that are equal in length and width. Multiplication is usually the more efficient method to solve.

Item K.

Understand: How to draw line plots

■ Ask students to explain what the information in the tally chart means. Be sure they mention that the chart lists the length of carrots in inches. Students should explain that the tally marks in each row represent the number of carrots of that length.

■ Have students explain how the information on the line plot represents the information in the tally chart. Be sure they understand where the Xs come from and why each measurement has the number of Xs it has.

■ Ask students why they think line plots are used when looking at data. They should see that the line plot is more organized and easier to understand than the tally chart.

Item L.

Understand: Use lengths of sides and angles to identify special quadrilaterals

■ Explain to students that *quad* means "four." Ask students to identify other words beginning with *quad* that mean 4, such as *quadruplets, quad bike, quadruple,* and *quadriceps.*

■ Ask students to compare and contrast the three shapes shown. They should identify that all three shapes have 4 sides, but that their side lengths and angle measures are different.

■ Point out that a square is also a rectangle and a rhombus because a square has the same attributes as the other two shapes. However, a rectangle or a rhombus cannot be named a square.

K. **Understand: How to draw line plots**

The tally chart shows lengths of carrots from Anya's garden.

Lengths of Carrots	
Length (in.)	Tally
6	II
$6\frac{1}{2}$	I
7	III
$7\frac{1}{2}$	IIII
8	I

Use the tally chart to make a line plot of the measurement data.

Lengths of Carrots (in.)

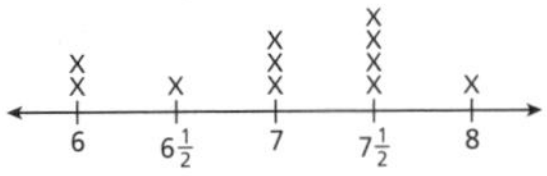

L. **Understand: Use lengths of sides and angles to identify special quadrilaterals**

To identify a quadrilateral, look at the sides and the angles.

rectangle
opposite sides the same length
4 right angles

rhombus
all 4 sides the same length

square
all 4 sides the same length
4 right angles

A square has the attributes of both a rhombus and a rectangle.

Problem-Solving Model

You can use this model to solve problems.

Read

Read the problem.
Focus on the facts and the questions.

- What facts do you know?
- What do you need to find out?

Plan

Outline a plan.
Plan how to solve the problem.

- What operation will you use?
- Do I need to use 1 step or 2 steps?
- Will you draw a picture?
- How have you solved similar problems?

Solve

Follow your plan to solve the problem.

- Did you answer the question?
- Did you label your answer?

Check

Test that the solution is reasonable.

- Does your answer make sense? If not, review and revise your plan.
- How can you solve the problem a different way? Is the answer the same?
- How can you estimate to check your answer?

Introducing the Problem-Solving Model

You can use the Problem-Solving Model pages to encourage students to think problems through and solve them successfully.

The Problem-Solving Model is just one way to help students master the art of problem solving. Many students intuitively see alternative methods or solutions. Their intuitive grasp of the problem/situation should not be impeded or slowed by having to use the model. Students should be asked only to demonstrate that they solved a problem using some logical plan, and not necessarily this specific model. Students should be able to explain the method they have used.

An Envelope Problem

When solving problems, students should not merely look for key words and phrases that suggest the correct operation. If students understand the meanings of the different operations, they should apply operation sense to determine what they need to do to solve a given problem.

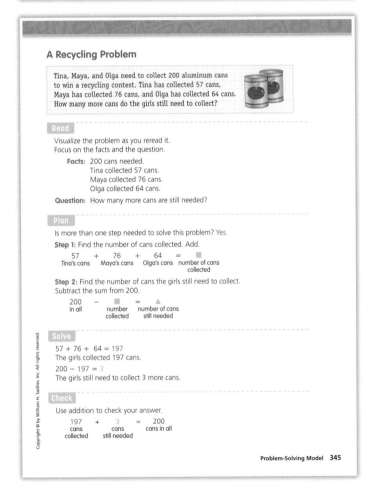

An Envelope Problem

Remember!

When you:	Use:
• Join like groups or quantities	$\square + \square = \square$
• Separate, or take away, from a group. • Compare two groups or quantities. • Find part of a group. • Find how many more are needed.	$\square - \square = \square$
• Join equal groups or quantities.	$\square \times \square = \square$
• Partition into equal shares. • Share a group equally.	$\square \div \square = \square$

Meg paints pictures and then puts them into envelopes. She puts 7 pictures into each envelope. How many envelopes does Meg need for 42 pictures?

Read

Visualize the problem as you reread it.
Focus on the facts and the question.

Facts: 7 pictures in each envelope
42 pictures

Question: How many envelopes does Meg need?

Plan

You are partitioning into equal groups.
The number of equal groups is unknown.
Divide: $42 \div 7 = \blacksquare$
Think: $\blacksquare \times 7 = 42$

Solve

$42 \div 7 = 6$

▷ Meg needs 6 envelopes.

Check

Multiply to check division.
$6 \times 7 = 42$

A Recycling Problem

To solve multistep problems, such as A Recycling Problem, students must be able to perceive and understand the interrelatedness of the multiple parts. By using the problem-solving model, students can analyze the problem and not only choose the correct operations, but plan the correct sequence in which to do each operation.

A Recycling Problem

Tina, Maya, and Olga need to collect 200 aluminum cans to win a recycling contest. Tina has collected 57 cans, Maya has collected 76 cans, and Olga has collected 64 cans. How many more cans do the girls still need to collect?

Read

Visualize the problem as you reread it.
Focus on the facts and the question.

Facts: 200 cans needed.
Tina collected 57 cans.
Maya collected 76 cans.
Olga collected 64 cans.

Question: How many more cans are still needed?

Plan

Is more than one step needed to solve this problem? Yes.

Step 1: Find the number of cans collected. Add.

$$\underset{\text{Tina's cans}}{57} + \underset{\text{Maya's cans}}{76} + \underset{\text{Olga's cans}}{64} = \underset{\substack{\text{number of cans} \\ \text{collected}}}{\blacksquare}$$

Step 2: Find the number of cans the girls still need to collect. Subtract the sum from 200.

$$\underset{\text{in all}}{200} - \underset{\substack{\text{number} \\ \text{collected}}}{\blacksquare} = \underset{\substack{\text{number of cans} \\ \text{still needed}}}{\blacktriangle}$$

Solve

$57 + 76 + 64 = 197$
The girls collected 197 cans.
$200 - 197 = 3$
The girls still need to collect 3 more cans.

Check

Use addition to check your answer.

$$\underset{\substack{\text{cans} \\ \text{collected}}}{197} + \underset{\substack{\text{cans} \\ \text{still needed}}}{3} = \underset{\substack{\text{cans in all}}}{200}$$

The Standards for Mathematical Practice, identified here, are an important part of learning mathematics. They are covered in every lesson in this book.

MP1	**Make sense of problems and persevere in solving them.**

- Analyze and plan a solution
- Relate to a similar problem
- Assess progress
- Use concrete objects or pictures
- Check solutions

MP2	**Reason abstractly and quantitatively.**

- Pay attention to all mathematical language
- Represent problems using symbols
- Consider units in problem solving
- Use properties of operations and objects

MP3	**Construct viable arguments and critique the reasoning of others.**

- Analyze a problem situation
- Share reasoning with others
- Explain an approach to a problem
- Construct arguments by using drawings or concrete objects

MP4	**Model with mathematics.**

- Relate mathematics to everyday problems
- Make assumptions and estimations
- Explain the relationship of quantities
- Use concrete tools to explain operations
- Interpret the solution in the context of a situation

MP5	**Use appropriate tools strategically.**

- Consider the range of available tools (e.g., place-value charts, graphs, clocks, etc.)
- Decide on appropriate tools to use for each situation
- Use tools carefully and strategically

MP6	**Attend to precision.**

- Communicate with precision
- Identify the meaning of symbols
- Use measurement units appropriately
- Calculate accurately
- Carefully formulate full explanations

MP7	**Look for and make use of structure.**

- Search for patterns or structure
- Evaluate the structure or design of a problem
- Discuss geometric shapes in terms of their similarities and differences

MP8	**Look for and express regularity in repeated reasoning.**

- Make generalizations in computation
- Obtain fluency using patterns
- Look for patterns with shapes and designs
- Use patterns to relate operations
- Evaluate reasonableness of answers

Key: MP = Mathematical Practice

A

acute angle An angle that measures between 0° and 90°.

Angle *ABC* is an acute angle.

adjacent Sides of a polygon that are next to each other.

angle Formed when two rays share the same endpoint.

B

benchmark A known amount that can be used to compare or estimate other amounts.

C

compatible numbers Numbers that are easy to compute mentally.

complementary angles Two angles whose measures add to 90°.

composite number A number greater than 1 that has more than two factors.

For example, number 12.
The factors for 12 are 1, 2, 3, 4, 6, and 12.

customary units The measurement units used in the United States customary system of measurement.

D

data Facts or information.

decimal A number that uses place value and a decimal point.

decimal point Separates the whole-number part and the part that is less than 1 in a decimal.

0.7
↑
decimal point

decompose Breaking apart a fraction by writing it as a sum of other fractions with the same denominator.

degree (°) The unit of measure for angles.

dividend The number being divided.

divisor The number by which the dividend is divided.

E

endpoint The point at either end of a line segment or the starting point of a ray.

equivalent fractions Fractions that have different names, but are at the same point on the number line.

For example, $\frac{1}{4} = \frac{2}{8}$

expanded form A number expressed in a way that shows the value of each digit.

For example,

2	9	,	0	3	5
↓	↓		↓	↓	↓
20,000	9,000		0	30	5

$29,035 = 20,000 + 9,000 + 30 + 5$

F

factor One of the two or more numbers that are multiplied to form a product.

factor pair Two numbers that multiply to give a product.

formula A mathematical rule that is expressed with symbols.

For example, $P = 2\ell + 2w$ is the formula for finding the perimeter of a rectangle.

fraction A number that names part of a whole, an area, or a group. It can be expressed in the form $\frac{a}{b}$.

H

hexagon A polygon with 6 sides and 6 angles.

hundredth Each part of a whole when the whole is partitioned into 100 equal parts.

The figure shows $\frac{6}{100}$.

L

length How long something is.

For example, the measure of each side in the longer pair of opposite sides of a rectangle, is called the length of the rectangle.

like denominators The denominators of two or more fractions that are the same.

For example, in $\frac{3}{8} + \frac{1}{8} = \frac{4}{8}$ the fractions have like denominators.

line An endless collection of points along a straight path.

line of symmetry The line that is formed when a figure is folded into two parts that match exactly.

line plot A graph used to organize a set of data on a number line, with symbols to represent the data.

Maple Leaf Lengths

$$2 \quad 2\frac{1}{8} \quad 2\frac{2}{8} \quad 2\frac{3}{8} \quad 2\frac{4}{8} \quad 2\frac{5}{8} \quad 2\frac{6}{8} \quad 2\frac{7}{8} \quad 3$$
inches

line segment Part of a line that has two endpoints.

M

metric units The measurement units used in the metric system of measurement.

mixed number A number that shows the sum of a whole number and a fraction but does not have a + sign.

For example, $4\frac{1}{2}$

multiple The product of a given whole number and another whole number.

N

number pattern An ordered list of numbers that follow a rule and repeat or change in some way.

O

obtuse angle An angle that measures between 90° and 180°.

obtuse angle

one-degree angle An angle that turns through $\frac{1}{360}$ of a circle.

P

parallel lines Lines that will never meet, or intersect.

parallelogram A quadrilateral in which both pairs of opposite sides are parallel.

partial products Numbers that are formed by multiplying the value of each digit by a factor.

pattern rule Tells the term to start with and how to find the next term in a number or shape pattern.

pentagon A polygon with 5 straight sides and 5 angles.

period A group of 3 places.

This place-value chart shows the Thousands period and the Ones period.

Thousands			Ones		
hundreds	tens	ones	hundreds	tens	ones
	2	9	0	3	5

perpendicular Two lines, line segments, or rays that meet or intersect to form a 90° angle.

In the figure, rays ED and EF are perpendicular.

perpendicular lines Lines that meet, or intersect, to form a right angle.

In the figure, lines AH and BD are perpendicular lines.

point An exact location in space.

prime number A number greater than 1 with only two factors, 1 and the number itself.

For example, 7 and 13 are prime numbers.

protractor A tool used to find the exact measure of an angle.

Q

quotient The result when two numbers are divided.

R

ray The part of a line that starts at an endpoint and goes on in one direction forever.

ray
endpoint

rectangle A parallelogram with two pairs of perpendicular sides.

remainder The amount left over after dividing.

For example, 52 ÷ 6 = 8 R4
"52 divided by 6 equals 8 remainder 4."
The amount left over after dividing is 4.

right angle An angle that turns through $\frac{90}{360}$, or $\frac{1}{4}$, of a circle. It measures 90°.

right triangle A triangle with one right angle and two acute angles.

S

shape pattern An ordered sequence of shapes that follow a rule.

straight angle An angle that turns through $\frac{180}{360}$, or $\frac{1}{2}$, of a circle. It measures 180°.

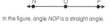

In the figure, angle NOP is a straight angle.

supplementary angles Two angles whose measures add to 180°.

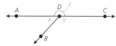

In the figure, angle ADB and angle CDB are supplementary angles.

T

tenth Each part of a whole when the whole is partitioned into 10 equal parts.

The figure shows $\frac{6}{10}$.

term Each number or shape in a number or shape pattern.

trapezoid A quadrilateral that has at least one pair of parallel sides.

U

unit fraction Represents the quantity, or amount, in one of the equal parts of a whole when the whole is partitioned, or divided.

V

vertex The shared endpoints of two rays that form an angle.

angle
side   side
vertex

W

width How wide something is.

For example, the measure of each side in the shorter pair of opposite sides of a rectangle, is called the width of the rectangle.

Notes